No BULLSHIT guide to MATH & PHYSICS

Ivan Savov

May 27, 2018

No bullshit guide to math and physics
by Ivan Savov

Published by MINIREFERENCE CO.
Montréal, Québec, Canada
minireference.com | @minireference | fb.me/noBSguide
For inquiries, contact the author at ivan@minireference.com

Mathematics Subject Classifications (2010): 00A09, 70-01, 97I40, 97I50.

Library and Archives Canada Cataloguing in Publication

Savov, Ivan, 1982-, author
No bullshit guide to math & physics / Ivan Savov. — Fifth edition.

ISBN 978-0-9920010-0-1 (pbk.)

1. Mathematics–Textbooks. 2. Calculus–Textbooks.
3. Mechanics–Textbooks. I. Title. II. Title: No bullshit guide to math and physics.

QA39.3.S28 2014 511′.07 C2014-905298-7

Fifth edition
v5.3 git commit 806:ab7d670

Previous editions: v1.0 2010, v2.0 2011, v3.0 2012, v4.0 2013, v5.0 2014.

ISBN 978-0-9920010-0-1

10 9 8 7 6 5 4 3

Contents

Preface vii

Introduction 1

1 Math fundamentals 3
- 1.1 Solving equations . . . 4
- 1.2 Numbers . . . 6
- 1.3 Number representations . . . 11
- 1.4 Variables . . . 24
- 1.5 Functions and their inverses . . . 26
- 1.6 Basic rules of algebra . . . 29
- 1.7 Solving quadratic equations . . . 34
- 1.8 Exponents . . . 39
- 1.9 Logarithms . . . 44
- 1.10 The Cartesian plane . . . 48
- 1.11 Functions . . . 51
- 1.12 Functions reference . . . 58
  - Line . . . 58
  - Square . . . 60
  - Square root . . . 61
  - Absolute value . . . 62
  - Polynomials . . . 63
  - Solving polynomial equations . . . 64
  - Sine . . . 67
  - Cosine . . . 69
  - Tangent . . . 70
  - Exponential . . . 71
  - Natural logarithm . . . 72
- 1.13 Function transformations . . . 73
- 1.14 Geometry . . . 79
- 1.15 Trigonometry . . . 83
- 1.16 Trigonometric identities . . . 89
- 1.17 Circle . . . 92

1.18 Ellipse . . . 95
1.19 Hyperbola . . . 99
1.20 Solving systems of linear equations . . . 104
1.21 Compound interest . . . 107
1.22 Set notation . . . 110
1.23 Math problems . . . 123

2 Introduction to physics **133**
2.1 Introduction . . . 133
2.2 Kinematics . . . 136
2.3 Introduction to calculus . . . 143
2.4 Kinematics with calculus . . . 148
2.5 Kinematics problems . . . 153

3 Vectors **159**
3.1 Great outdoors . . . 160
3.2 Vectors . . . 162
3.3 Basis . . . 172
3.4 Vector products . . . 173
3.5 Complex numbers . . . 176
3.6 Vectors problems . . . 182

4 Mechanics **185**
4.1 Introduction . . . 185
4.2 Projectile motion . . . 189
4.3 Forces . . . 199
4.4 Force diagrams . . . 202
4.5 Momentum . . . 214
4.6 Energy . . . 219
4.7 Uniform circular motion . . . 229
4.8 Angular motion . . . 238
4.9 Simple harmonic motion . . . 248
4.10 Conclusion . . . 263
4.11 Mechanics problems . . . 264

5 Calculus **275**
5.1 Introduction . . . 275
5.2 Overview . . . 277
5.3 Infinity . . . 288
5.4 Limits . . . 293
5.5 Limit formulas . . . 300
5.6 Derivatives . . . 305
5.7 Derivative formulas . . . 308
5.8 Derivative rules . . . 309
5.9 Higher derivatives . . . 316

5.10 Optimization algorithm 321
5.11 Implicit differentiation 326
5.12 Integrals 332
5.13 Riemann sums 343
5.14 The fundamental theorem of calculus 349
5.15 Techniques of integration 355
5.16 Applications of integration 376
5.17 Improper integrals 386
5.18 Sequences 387
5.19 Series 390
5.20 Conclusion 402
5.21 Calculus problems 403

End matter **419**
Conclusion 419
Acknowledgments 419
Further reading 420

A Answers and solutions **427**

B Notation **447**
Math notation 447
Set notation 448
Complex numbers notation 448
Vectors notation 449
Mechanics notation 449
Calculus notation 450

C Constants, units, and conversion ratios **451**
Fundamental constants of Nature 451
Units 452
Other units and conversions 453

D SymPy tutorial **455**

E Formulas **481**
Calculus formulas 481
Mechanics formulas 484

Index **485**

Placement exam

The answers[1] to this placement exam will tell you where to start reading.

1. What is the derivative of $\sin(x)$?

2. What is the second derivative of $A\sin(\omega x)$?

3. What is the value of x ?

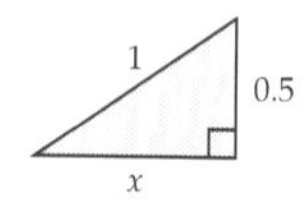

4. What is the magnitude of the gravitational force between two planets of mass M and mass m separated by a distance r?

5. Calculate $\displaystyle\lim_{x\to 3^-} \frac{1}{x-3}$.

6. Solve for t in:

$$7(3+4t) = 11(6t-4).$$

7. What is the component of the weight $\vec{W}$ acting in the x-direction?

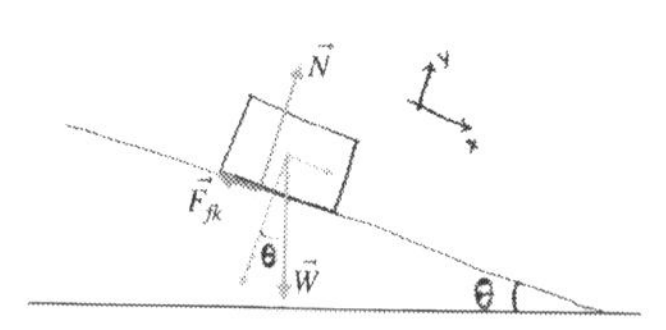

8. A mass-spring system is undergoing simple harmonic motion. Its position function is $x(t) = A\sin(\omega t)$. What is its maximum acceleration?

---

[1] Ans: 1. $\cos(x)$, 2. $-A\omega^2\sin(\omega x)$, 3. $\frac{\sqrt{3}}{2}$, 4. $\|\vec{F}_g\| = \frac{GMm}{r^2}$, 5. $-\infty$, 6. $\frac{65}{38}$, 7. $+mg\sin\theta$, 8. $A\omega^2$.
Key: If you didn't get Q3, Q6 right, you should read the book starting from Chapter 1. If you are mystified by Q1, Q2, Q5, read Chapter 5. If you want to learn how to solve Q4, Q7 and Q8, read Chapter 4.

Concept map

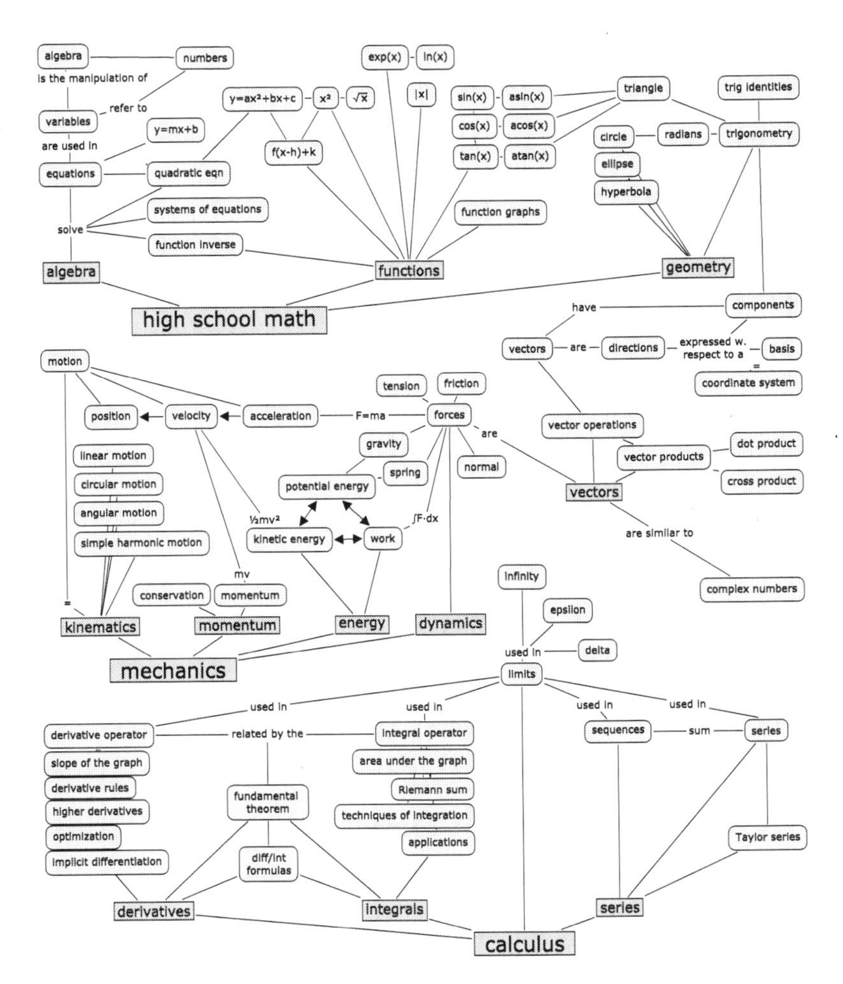

Figure 1: This diagram shows the connections between the concepts, topics, and subjects covered in the book. Seeing the connections between concepts is key to understanding math and physics. Consult the index on page 485 to find the exact location in the book where each concept is defined.

Preface

This book contains lessons on topics in math and physics, written in a style that is jargon-free and to the point. Each lesson covers one concept at the depth required for a first-year university-level course. The main focus of this book is to highlight the intricate connections between the concepts of math and physics. Seeing the similarities and parallels between the concepts is the key to understanding.

Why?

The genesis of this book dates back to my student days when I was required to purchase expensive textbooks for my courses. Not only are these textbooks expensive, they are also tedious to read. Who has the energy to go through thousands of pages of explanations? I began to wonder, "What's the deal with these thick books?" Later, I realized mainstream textbooks are long because the textbook industry wants to make more profits. You don't need to read 1000 pages to learn calculus; the numerous full-page colour pictures and the repetitive text that are used to "pad" calculus textbooks are there to make the $200 price seem reasonable.

Looking at this situation, I said to myself, "Something must be done," and I sat down and wrote a modern textbook to explain math and physics clearly, concisely, and affordably. There was no way I was going to let mainstream publishers ruin the learning experience of these beautiful subjects for the next generation of students.

How?

The sections in this book are **self-contained tutorials**. Each section covers the definitions, formulas, and explanations associated with a single topic. You can therefore read the sections in any order you find logical. Along the way, you will learn about the *connections* between the concepts of calculus and mechanics. Understanding mechanics is much easier if you know the ideas of calculus. At the same time, the ideas behind calculus are best illustrated through concrete physics examples. Learning the two subjects simultaneously is the best approach.

In order to make the study of mechanics and calculus accessible for all readers, we'll begin with a review chapter on numbers, algebra, equations, functions, and other prerequisite concepts. If you feel a little rusty on those concepts, be sure to check out Chapter 1.

Each chapter ends with a section of **practice problems** designed to test your understanding of the concepts developed in that chapter. Make sure you spend plenty of time on these problems to practice what you've learned. Figuring out how to use an equation on your own in the process of solving a problem is a much more valuable experience than simply memorizing the equation.

For optimal learning efficiency, I recommend that you spend as much time working through the practice problems as you will spend reading the lessons. The problems you find difficult to solve will tell you which sections of the chapter you need to revisit. An additional benefit of testing your skills on the practice problems is that you'll be prepared in case a teacher ever tries to test you.

Throughout the book, I've included **links to internet resources** like animations, demonstrations, and webpages with further reading material. Once you understand the basics, you'll be able to understand far more internet resources. The links provided are a starting point for further exploration.

Is this book for you?

My aim is to make learning calculus and mechanics more accessible. Anyone should be able to open this book and become proficient in calculus and mechanics, regardless of their mathematical background.

The book's primary intended audience is students. Students taking a mechanics class can read the chapters sequentially until Chapter 4, and optionally read Chapter 5 for bonus points. Taking a calculus course? Skip ahead directly to the calculus chapter (Chapter 5). High school students or university students taking a precalculus class will benefit from reading Chapter 1, which is a concise but thorough review of fundamental math concepts like numbers, equations, functions, and trigonometry.

MECH CLASS	CALC CLASS	PRECALC CLASS
Ch. 1	Ch. 1	Ch. 1
Ch. 2	Ch. 2	Ch. 2†
Ch. 3		
Ch. 4		
Ch. 5†	Ch. 5	

† = optional reading.

Non-students, don't worry: you don't

need to be taking a class in order to learn math. Independent learners interested in learning university-level material will find this book very useful. Many university graduates read this book to remember the calculus they learned back in their university days.

In general, anyone interested in rekindling their relationship with mathematics should consider this book as an opportunity to repair the broken connection. Math is good stuff; you shouldn't miss out on it. People who think they absolutely *hate* math should read Chapter 1 as therapy.

About the author

I have been teaching math and physics for more than 15 years as a private tutor. My tutoring experience has taught me how to explain concepts that people find difficult to understand. I've had the chance to experiment with different approaches for explaining challenging material. Fundamentally, I've learned from teaching that understanding connections between concepts is much more important than memorizing facts. It's not about how many equations you know, but about knowing how to get from one equation to another.

I completed my undergraduate studies at McGill University in electrical engineering, then did a M.Sc. in physics, and recently completed a Ph.D. in computer science. In my career as a researcher, I've been fortunate to learn from very inspirational teachers, who had the ability to distill the essential ideas and explain things in simple language. With my writing, I want to recreate the same learning experience for you. I founded the `Minireference Co.` to revolutionize the textbook industry. We make textbooks that don't suck.

Ivan Savov
Montreal, 2014

Introduction

The last two centuries have been marked by tremendous technological advances. Every sector of the economy has been transformed by the use of computers and the advent of the internet. There is no doubt technology's importance will continue to grow in the coming years.

The best part is that you don't need to know how technology works to use it. You need not understand how internet protocols operate to check your email and find original pirate material. You don't need to be a programmer to tell a computer to automate repetitive tasks and increase your productivity. However, when it comes to building *new* things, understanding becomes important. One particularly useful skill is the ability to create mathematical models of real-world situations. The techniques of mechanics and calculus are powerful building blocks for understanding the world around us. This is why these courses are taught in the first year of university studies: they contain keys that unlock the rest of science and engineering.

Calculus and mechanics can be difficult subjects. Understanding the material isn't hard *per se*, but it takes patience and practice. Calculus and mechanics become much easier to absorb when you break down the material into manageable chunks. It is most important you learn the *connections* between concepts.

Before we start with the equations, it's worthwhile to preview the material covered in this book. After all, you should know what kind of trouble you're getting yourself into.

Chapter 1 is a comprehensive review of math fundamentals including algebra, equation solving, and functions. The exposition of each topic is brief to make for easy reading. This chapter is highly recommended for readers who haven't looked at math recently; if you need a refresher on math, Chapter 1 is for you. It is extremely important to firmly grasp the basics. What is $\sin(0)$? What is $\sin(\pi/4)$? What does the graph of $\sin(x)$ look like? Arts students interested in enriching their cultural insight with knowledge that is 2000+ years old can read this chapter as therapy to recover from any damaging educational experiences they may have encountered in high school.

In Chapter 2, we'll look at how techniques of high school math can be used to describe and model the world. We'll learn about the basic laws that govern the motion of objects in one dimension and the mathematical equations that describe the motion. By the end of this chapter, you'll be able to predict the flight time of a ball thrown in the air.

In Chapter 3, we'll learn about vectors. Vectors describe directional quantities like forces and velocities. We need vectors to properly understand the laws of physics. Vectors are used in many areas of science and technology, so becoming comfortable with vector calculations will pay dividends when learning other subjects.

Chapter 4 is all about mechanics. We'll study the motion of objects, predict their future trajectories, and learn how to use abstract concepts like momentum and energy. Science students who "hate" physics can study this chapter to learn how to use the 20 main equations and laws of physics. You'll see physics is actually quite simple.

Chapter 5 covers topics from differential calculus and integral calculus. We'll study limits, derivatives, integrals, sequences, and series. You'll find that 120 pages are enough to cover all the concepts in calculus, as well as illustrate them with examples and practice exercises.

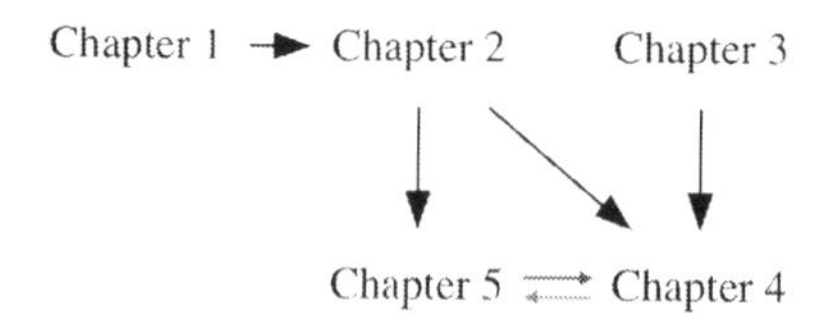

Figure 2: The prerequisite structure for the chapters in this book.

Calculus and mechanics are often taught as separate subjects. It shouldn't be like that! If you learn calculus without mechanics, it will be boring. If you learn physics without calculus, you won't truly understand. The exposition in this book covers both subjects in an integrated manner and aims to highlight the connections between them. Let's dig in.

Chapter 1

Math fundamentals

In this chapter we'll review the fundamental ideas of mathematics, including numbers, equations, and functions. To understand college-level textbooks, you need to be comfortable with mathematical calculations. Many people have trouble with math, however. Some people say they *hate* math, or could never learn it. It's not uncommon for children who score poorly on their school math exams to develop math complexes in their grown lives. If you are carrying any such emotional baggage, you can drop it right here and right now.

Do NOT worry about math! You are an adult, and you can learn math much more easily than when you were a kid. We'll review *everything* you need to know about high school math, and by the end of this chapter, you'll see that math is nothing to worry about.

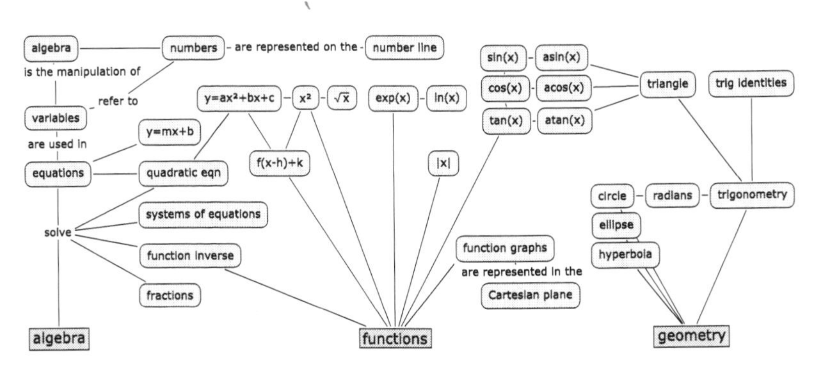

Figure 1.1: A concept map showing the mathematical topics that we will cover in this chapter. We'll learn how to solve equations using algebra, how to model the world using functions, and how to think geometrically. The material in this chapter is required for your understanding of the more advanced topics in this book.

1.1 Solving equations

Most math skills boil down to being able to manipulate and solve equations. Solving an equation means finding the value of the unknown in the equation.

Check this shit out:

$$x^2 - 4 = 45.$$

To solve the above equation is to answer the question "What is x?" More precisely, we want to find the number that can take the place of x in the equation so that the equality holds. In other words, we're asking,

"Which number times itself minus four gives 45?"

That is quite a mouthful, don't you think? To remedy this verbosity, mathematicians often use specialized symbols to describe math operations. The problem is that these specialized symbols can be very confusing. Sometimes even the simplest math concepts are inaccessible if you don't know what the symbols mean.

What are your feelings about math, dear reader? Are you afraid of it? Do you have anxiety attacks because you think it will be too difficult for you? Chill! Relax, my brothers and sisters. There's nothing to it. Nobody can magically guess the solution to an equation immediately. To find the solution, you must break the problem into simpler steps. Let's walk through this one together.

To find x, we can manipulate the original equation, transforming it into a different equation (as true as the first) that looks like this:

$$x = \text{only numbers}.$$

That's what it means to *solve* an equation: the equation is solved because the unknown is isolated on one side, while the constants are grouped on the other side. You can type the numbers on the right-hand side into a calculator and obtain the numerical value of x.

By the way, before we continue our discussion, let it be noted: the equality symbol ($=$) means that all that is to the left of $=$ is equal to all that is to the right of $=$. To keep this equality statement true, **for every change you apply to the left side of the equation, you must apply the same change to the right side of the equation**.

To find x, we need to manipulate the original equation into its final form, simplifying it step by step until it can't be simplified any further. The only requirement is that the manipulations we make transform one true equation into another true equation.

In this example, the first simplifying step is to add the number four to both sides of the equation:

$$x^2 - 4 + 4 = 45 + 4,$$

which simplifies to

$$x^2 = 49.$$

Now the expression looks simpler, yes? How did I know to perform this operation? I wanted to "undo" the effects of the operation -4. We undo an operation by applying its *inverse*. In the case where the operation is the subtraction of some amount, the inverse operation is the addition of the same amount. We'll learn more about function inverses in Section 1.5 (page 26).

We're getting closer to our goal of *isolating* x on one side of the equation, leaving only numbers on the other side. The next step is to undo the square x^2 operation. The inverse operation of squaring a number x^2 is to take its square root $\sqrt{\ }$, so that's what we'll do next. We obtain

$$\sqrt{x^2} = \sqrt{49}.$$

Notice how we applied the square root to both sides of the equation? If we don't apply the same operation to both sides, we'll break the equality!

The equation $\sqrt{x^2} = \sqrt{49}$ simplifies to

$$|x| = 7.$$

What's up with the vertical bars around x? The notation $|x|$ stands for the *absolute value* of x, which is the same as x except we ignore the sign that indicates whether x is positive or negative. For example $|5| = 5$ and $|-5| = 5$, too. The equation $|x| = 7$ indicates that both $x = 7$ and $x = -7$ satisfy the equation $x^2 = 49$. Seven squared is 49, $7^2 = 49$, and negative seven squared is also 49, $(-7)^2 = 49$, because the two negative signs cancel each other out.

The final solutions to the equation $x^2 - 4 = 45$ are

$$x = 7 \qquad \text{and} \qquad x = -7.$$

Yes, there are *two* possible answers. You can check that both of the above values of x satisfy the initial equation $x^2 - 4 = 45$.

If you are comfortable with all the notions of high school math and you feel you could have solved the equation $x^2 - 4 = 45$ on your own, then you can skim through this chapter quickly. If on the other hand you are wondering how the squiggle killed the power two, then this chapter is for you! In the following sections we will review all the essential concepts from high school math that you will need to power through the rest of this book. First, let me tell you about the different kinds of numbers.

1.2 Numbers

In the beginning, we must define the main players in the world of math: numbers.

Definitions

Numbers are the basic objects we use to count, measure, quantify, and calculate things. Mathematicians like to classify the different kinds of number-like objects into categories called *sets*:

- The natural numbers: $\mathbb{N} = \{0, 1, 2, 3, 4, 5, 6, 7, \ldots\}$
- The integers: $\mathbb{Z} = \{\ldots, -3, -2, -1, 0, 1, 2, 3, \ldots\}$
- The rational numbers: $\mathbb{Q} = \{\frac{5}{3}, \frac{22}{7}, 1.5, 0.125, -7, \ldots\}$
- The real numbers: $\mathbb{R} = \{-1, 0, 1, \sqrt{2}, e, \pi, \ 4.94\ldots, \ \ldots\}$
- The complex numbers: $\mathbb{C} = \{-1, 0, 1, i, 1+i, 2+3i, \ldots\}$

These categories of numbers should be somewhat familiar to you. Think of them as neat classification labels for everything that you would normally call a number. Each group in the above list is a *set*. A set is a collection of items of the same kind. Each collection has a name and a precise definition for which items belong in that collection. Note also that each of the sets in the list contains all the sets above it, as illustrated in Figure 1.2. For now, we don't need to go into the details of sets and set notation (page 110), but we do need to be aware of the different sets of numbers.

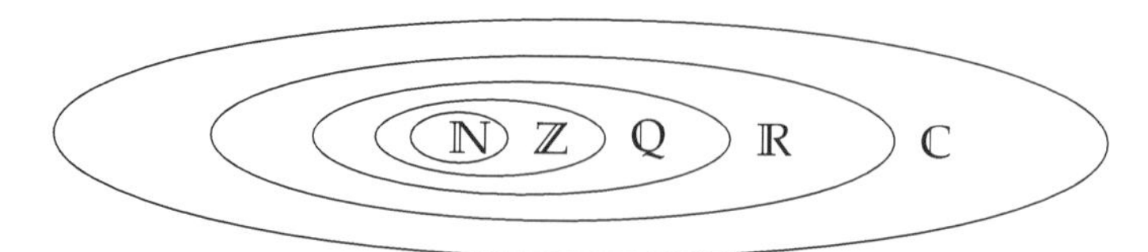

Figure 1.2: An illustration of the nested containment structure of the different number sets. The set of natural numbers is contained in the set of integers, which in turn is contained in the set of rational numbers. The set of rational numbers is contained in the set of real numbers, which is contained in the set of complex numbers.

Why do we need so many different sets of numbers? The answer is partly historical and partly mathematical. Each set of numbers is associated with more and more advanced mathematical problems.

The simplest numbers are the natural numbers $\mathbb{N}$, which are sufficient for all your math needs if all you're going to do is *count* things. How many goats? Five goats here and six goats there so the total is

11 goats. The sum of any two natural numbers is also a natural number.

As soon as you start using *subtraction* (the inverse operation of addition), you start running into negative numbers, which are numbers outside the set of natural numbers. If the only mathematical operations you will ever use are *addition* and *subtraction*, then the set of integers $\mathbb{Z} = \{\ldots, -2, -1, 0, 1, 2, \ldots\}$ will be sufficient. Think about it. Any integer plus or minus any other integer is still an integer.

You can do a lot of interesting math with integers. There is an entire field in math called *number theory* that deals with integers. However, to restrict yourself solely to integers is somewhat limiting. You can't use the notion of 2.5 goats for example. The menu at Rotisserie Romados, which offers $\frac{1}{4}$ of a chicken, would be completely confusing.

If you want to use division in your mathematical calculations, you'll need the rationals $\mathbb{Q}$. The rationals are the set of *fractions* of integers:

$$\mathbb{Q} = \left\{ \text{all } z \text{ such that } z = \frac{x}{y} \text{ where } x \text{ and } y \text{ are in } \mathbb{Z}, \text{ and } y \neq 0 \right\}.$$

You can add, subtract, multiply, and divide rational numbers, and the result will always be a rational number. However, even the rationals are not enough for all of math!

In geometry, we can obtain *irrational* quantities like $\sqrt{2}$ (the diagonal of a square with side 1) and π (the ratio between a circle's circumference and its diameter). There are no integers x and y such that $\sqrt{2} = \frac{x}{y}$. Therefore, $\sqrt{2}$ is not part of the set $\mathbb{Q}$, and we say that $\sqrt{2}$ is *irrational*. An irrational number has an infinitely long decimal expansion that doesn't repeat. For example, $\pi = 3.141592653589793\ldots$ where the dots indicate that the decimal expansion of π continues all the way to infinity.

Combining the irrational numbers with the rationals gives us all the useful numbers, which we call the set of real numbers $\mathbb{R}$. The set $\mathbb{R}$ contains the integers, the fractions $\mathbb{Q}$, as well as irrational numbers like $\sqrt{2} = 1.4142135\ldots$. By using the reals you can compute pretty much anything you want. From here on in the text, when I say *number*, I mean an element of the set of real numbers $\mathbb{R}$.

The only thing you can't do with the reals is to take the square root of a negative number—you need the complex numbers $\mathbb{C}$ for that. We defer the discussion on $\mathbb{C}$ until the end of Chapter 3.

Operations on numbers

Addition

You can add and subtract numbers. I will assume you are familiar with this kind of stuff:

$$2+3=5, \;\; 45+56=101, \;\; 65-66=-1, \;\; 9\,999+1=10\,000.$$

You can visualize numbers as sticks of different length. Adding numbers is like adding sticks together: the resulting stick has a length equal to the sum of the lengths of the constituent sticks, as illustrated in Figure 1.3.

Figure 1.3: The addition of numbers corresponds to adding lengths.

Addition is *commutative*, which means that $a+b = b+a$. It is also *associative*, which means that if you have a long summation like $a+b+c$ you can compute it in any order $(a+b)+c$ or $a+(b+c)$ and you'll get the same answer.

Subtraction is the inverse operation of addition.

Multiplication

You can also multiply numbers together:

$$ab = \underbrace{a+a+\cdots+a}_{b\text{ times}} = \underbrace{b+b+\cdots+b}_{a\text{ times}}.$$

Note that multiplication can be defined in terms of repeated addition.

The visual way to think about multiplication is as an area calculation. The area of a rectangle of width a and height b is equal to ab. A rectangle with a height equal to its width is a square, and this is why we call $aa = a^2$ "a squared."

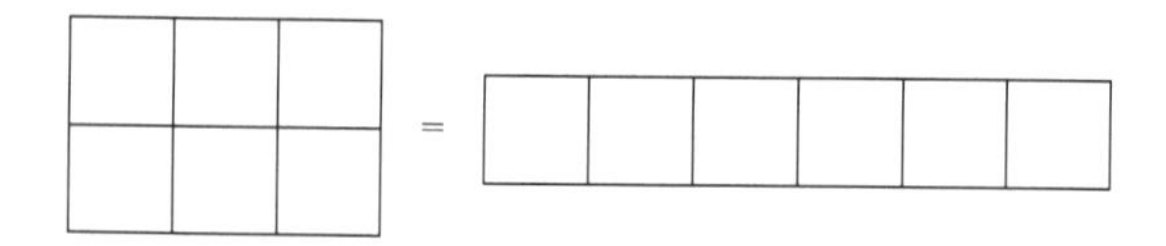

Figure 1.4: The area of a rectangle with width 3 m and height 2 m is equal to 6 m^2, which is equivalent to six squares with area 1 m^2 each.

Multiplication of numbers is also commutative, $ab = ba$; and associative, $abc = (ab)c = a(bc)$. In modern notation, no special symbol is used to denote multiplication; we simply put the two factors next to each other and say the multiplication is *implicit*. Some other ways to denote multiplication are $a \cdot b$, $a \times b$, and, on computer systems, $a * b$.

Division

Division is the inverse operation of multiplication.

$$a/b \;=\; \frac{a}{b} \;= a \div b = \; \text{one } b^{\text{th}} \text{ of } a.$$

Whatever a is, you need to divide it into b equal parts and take one such part.

Note that you cannot divide by 0. Try it on your calculator or computer. It will say "`error divide by zero`" because this action simply doesn't make sense. After all, what would it mean to divide something into zero equal parts?

Exponentiation

The act of multiplying a number by itself many times is called *exponentiation*. We denote "a exponent n" using a superscript, where n is the number of times the base a is multiplied by itself:

$$a^n \;=\; \underbrace{aaa \cdots a}_{n \text{ times}}.$$

In words, we say "a raised to the power of n."

To visualize how exponents work, we can draw a connection between the value of exponents and the dimensions of geometric objects. Figure 1.5 illustrates how the same length 2 corresponds to different geometric objects when raised to different exponents. The number 2 corresponds to a line segment of length two, which is a geometric object in a one-dimensional space. If we add a line segment of length two in a second dimension, we obtain a square with area 2^2 in a two-dimensional space. Adding a third dimension, we obtain a cube with volume 2^3 in a three-dimensional space. Indeed, raising a base a to the exponent 2 is commonly called "a squared," and raising a to the power of 3 is called "a cubed."

The geometrical analogy about one-dimensional quantities as lengths, two dimensional quantities as areas, and three dimensional quantities as volumes is good to keep in mind.

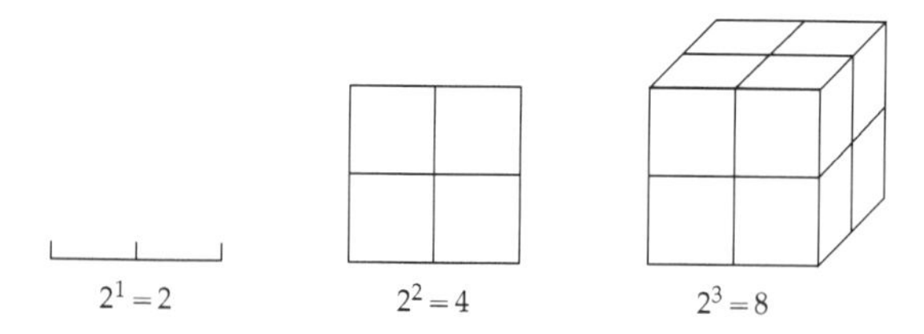

Figure 1.5: Geometric interpretation for exponents 1, 2, and 3. A length raised to exponent 2 corresponds to the area of a square. The same length raised to exponent 3 corresponds to the volume of a cube.

Our visual intuition works very well up to three dimensions, but we can use other means of visualizing higher exponents, as demonstrated in Figure 1.6.

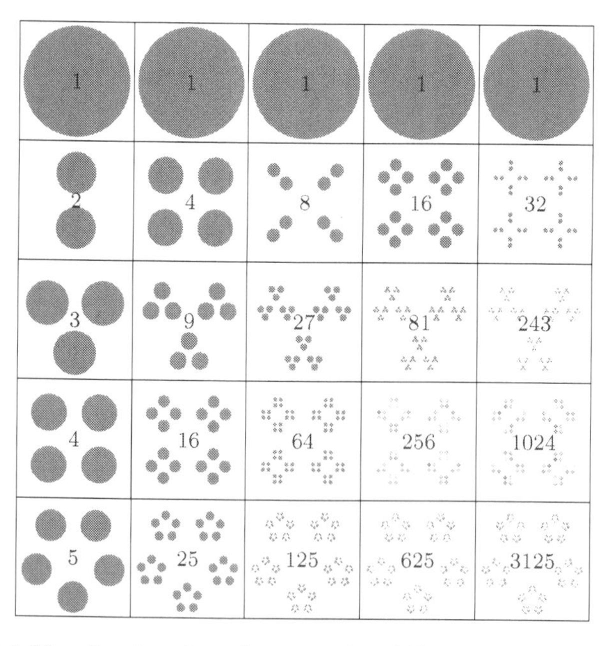

Figure 1.6: Visualization of numbers raised to different exponents. Each box in this grid contains a^n dots, where the base a varies from one through five, and the exponent n varies from one through five. In the first row we see that the number $a = 1$ raised to any exponent is equal to itself. The second row corresponds to the base $a = 2$ so the number of dots doubles each time we increase the exponent by one. Starting from $2^1 = 2$ in the first column, we end up with $2^5 = 32$ in the last column. The rest of the rows show how exponentiation works for different bases.

Operator precedence

There is a standard convention for the order in which mathematical operations must be performed. The basic algebra operations have the following precedence:

1. Parentheses
2. Exponents
3. Multiplication and Division
4. Addition and Subtraction

If you're seeing this list for the first time, the acronym PEMDAS and the associated mnemonic "Please Excuse My Dear Aunt Sally," might help you remember the order of operations.

For instance, the expression $5 \cdot 3^2 + 13$ is interpreted as "First find the square of 3, then multiply it by 5, and then add 13." Parentheses are needed to carry out the operations in a different order: to multiply 5 times 3 first and *then* take the square, the equation should read $(5 \cdot 3)^2 + 13$, where parentheses indicate that the square acts on $(5 \cdot 3)$ as a whole and not on 3 alone.

Exercises

E1.1 Solve for the unknown x in the following equations:

a) $3x + 2 - 5 = 4 + 2$ **b)** $\frac{1}{2}x - 3 = \sqrt{3} + 12 - \sqrt{3}$

c) $\frac{7x-4}{2} + 1 = 8 - 2$ **d)** $5x - 2 + 3 = 3x - 5$

E1.2 Indicate all the number sets the following numbers belong to.

a) -2 **b)** $\sqrt{-3}$ **c)** $8^{\frac{1}{3}}$ **d)** $\frac{5}{3}$ **e)** $\frac{\pi}{2}$

E1.3 Calculate the values of the following expressions:

a) $2^3 3 - 3$ **b)** $2^3(3 - 3)$ **c)** $\frac{4-2}{3^3}(6 \cdot 7 - 41)$

1.3 Number representations

We use the letters "a, b, c, ..." to write words. In a similar fashion, we use the digits $0, 1, 2, 3, 4, 5, 6, 7, 8$, and 9 to write numbers in the language of math. You can think of the digits 0 through 9 as the "letters" used to write numbers. For example, the number 334 consists of the digits 3, 3, and 4. Note that the same digit 3 denotes two different quantities depending on its position within the number. The first digit 3 corresponds to the value three hundred, while the second digit 3 corresponds to the value thirty.

Concepts

In this section, we'll review three important number representations:

- The *decimal notation* for integers, rationals, and real numbers consists of an integer part and a fractional part separated by a *decimal point*. For example, the decimal 32.17 consists of the integer 32 and the fractional part 0.17.
- The *fraction notation* for integers and rational numbers consists of a numerator divided by a denominator. Here are some sample math expressions with fractions: $\frac{1}{2}$, $\frac{3}{4}$, $\frac{3}{2} = 1\frac{1}{2}$, and $\frac{17}{100}$.
- The *number line* is a graphical representation for numbers that allows us to visualize numbers as geometric points on a line.

The same number a can be represented in multiple equivalent ways. It is often convenient to convert from one representation to another depending on the calculations we need to perform. For example, the number three can be expressed as the numeral 3, the decimal 3.0, the fraction $\frac{3}{1}$, or as the point that lies three units to the right of the origin on the number line. All these representations refer to the same quantity, but each representation is useful in different contexts.

The goal of this section is to get you comfortable working with all the number representations. The decimal representation for numbers is very common in everyday life; you're likely already familiar with decimals, so we won't spend too much time on them. Instead we'll focus on reviewing fractions, as well as fraction operations like addition and multiplication. It's important to understand fractions because many math concepts like ratios, percents, and proportionality are best described in the language of fractions.

Positional notation for numbers

The Hindu–Arabic numeral system is the most widely used system for writing numbers today. It is a *decimal positional* system. The term *decimal* refers to the fact that it uses 10 unique symbols (the digits 0 through 9) to represent numbers. The system is *positional* because the value of each digit depends on its position within the number. Positional number systems are also called *place-value* systems.

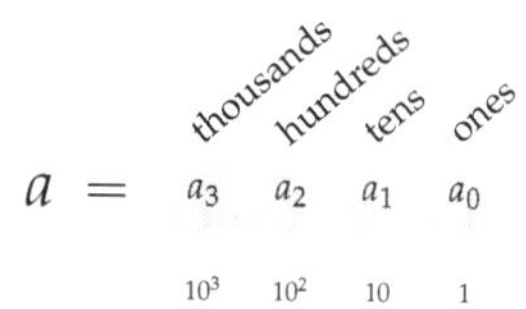

thousands hundreds tens ones

$$a = a_3 \quad a_2 \quad a_1 \quad a_0$$

10^3 10^2 10 1

Figure 1.7: The place-value representation of the number $a = a_3a_2a_1a_0$.

Note the terminology used to refer to the individual digits of the numeral: we call a_3 the thousands, a_2 the hundreds, a_1 the tens, and a_0 the units.

Any natural number $a \in \mathbb{N}$, no matter how large, can be written as a sequence of digits:

$$\begin{aligned} a &\equiv a_n \cdots a_2 a_1 a_0 \\ &= a_n \cdot 10^n + \cdots + a_2 \cdot 10^2 + a_1 \cdot 10 + a_0 \cdot 1, \end{aligned}$$

where the digits $a_0, a_1, \ldots$ come from the set $\{0, 1, 2, 3, 4, 5, 6, 7, 8, 9\}$.

For example, the numeral 4235 corresponds to this calculation:

$$\begin{aligned} 4235 &= 4 \cdot 10^3 \quad + 2 \cdot 10^2 + 3 \cdot 10 + 5 \cdot 1 \\ &= 4 \cdot 1000 + 2 \cdot 100 + 3 \cdot 10 + 5 \cdot 1 \\ &= 4000 + 200 + 30 + 5. \end{aligned}$$

Note how the English pronunciation of the number, "four thousand, two hundred and thirty-five," literally walks you through the calculation.

When reading the digits of a number from left to right, each "step" we take to the right brings us to a digit that has a place value 10 times smaller than the previous digit. In the next section we'll learn how to extend this pattern one step further to the right in order to describe numbers smaller than one.

Decimal representation

We can use *decimal notation* to represent integers, rationals, and approximations to real numbers. The *decimal point* indicates the beginning of the fractional part of a number. The place values of digits to the right of the decimal point correspond to different decimal fractions. For example $0.7 = \frac{7}{10^1} = 7 \times 10^{-1}$, $0.07 = \frac{7}{100} = 7 \times 10^{-2}$, and $0.007 = \frac{7}{1000} = 7 \times 10^{-3}$. Note the positional logic used for decimals is the same as the positional logic used for integers: the place value of each digit decreases by a factor of 10 each time we take a "step" to the right.

Any number a less than one can be written using a decimal point followed by a sequence of digits, as illustrated in Figure 1.8.

$$\begin{aligned} a &= 0\,.\,a_{-1} a_{-2} a_{-3} \cdots \\ &= 0 + \frac{a_{-1}}{10^1} + \frac{a_{-2}}{10^2} + \frac{a_{-3}}{10^3} + \cdots . \end{aligned}$$

The first digit to the right of the decimal point a_{-1} represents the *tenths*, the second digit a_{-2} represents the *hundredths*, the third the

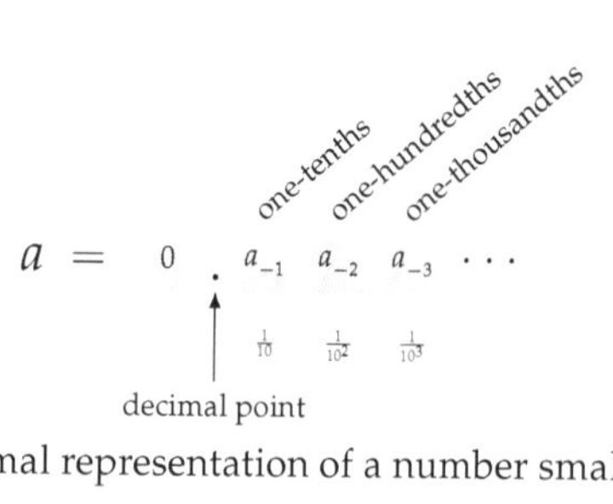

Figure 1.8: The decimal representation of a number smaller than one.

thousandths, and so on. We can use decimal notation to describe fractions like one-half (0.5), one-quarter (0.25), and three-quarters (0.75).

In general, a number written in decimal notation has an integer part and a fractional part:

$$\begin{aligned} a &= a_n \cdots a_2 a_1 a_0 . a_{-1} a_{-2} a_{-3} \cdots \\ &= a_n \cdot 10^n + \cdots + a_2 \cdot 10^2 + a_1 \cdot 10 + a_0 + \frac{a_{-1}}{10^1} + \frac{a_{-2}}{10^2} + \frac{a_{-3}}{10^3} + \cdots \end{aligned}$$

The decimal point appears in the middle of the digits and acts as a separator. The digits to the left of the decimal point, $a_n \cdots a_2 a_1 a_0$, correspond to the integer part of the number, while the digits to the right of the decimal, $0.a_{-1}a_{-2}a_{-3}\cdots$, correspond to the fractional part of the number.

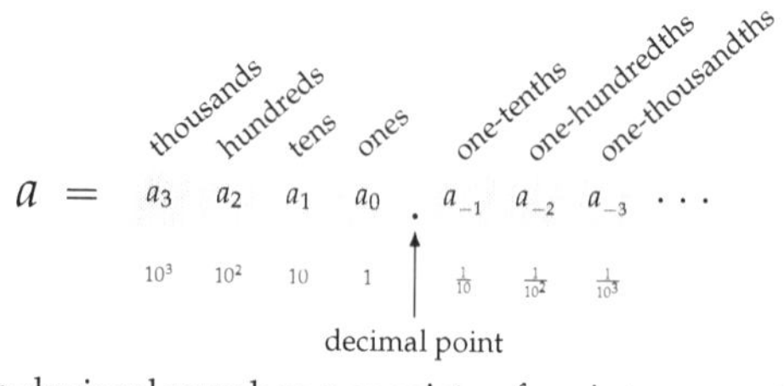

Figure 1.9: The decimal number a consists of an integer part $a_3a_2a_1a_0$ and a fractional part $0.a_{-1}a_{-2}\cdots$ separated by the decimal point.

Note the names for the different digits in the fractional part of the decimal in Figure 1.9. These names are used when we describe the fractional part of a decimal in words:

- "1.4" is read "one and four tenths," or you could informally describe the decimal as you see it written: "one point four."
- "45.37" is read "forty-five and thirty-seven hundredths," or sometimes "forty-five point three seven."
- A length measurement like "0.345[in]" is read "three-hundred forty-five thousandths of an inch."

We can write approximations for irrational numbers using decimal notation. For example, the irrational number $\sqrt{2}$ (the diagonal of a square with length one) is approximatively equal to 1.41421. We say the approximation 1.41421 is "accurate to five decimals," because this is how many digits there are in its fractional part.

So far we've discussed number representations that you are familiar with from your everyday life. Perhaps you're starting to think that math isn't so bad after all? Some of you must be saying, "Wonderful, I'm becoming friends with numbers while avoiding uncomfortable topics like fractions." Sorry, but you're not getting off so easily because this is exactly what's coming up next. That's right, we're about to make friends with fractions, too.

Fractions

First let's review the definition of the set of rational numbers $\mathbb{Q}$. Every rational number can be written as a *fraction* of two integers:

$$\mathbb{Q} \equiv \left\{ \frac{m}{n} \,\middle|\, m \text{ and } n \text{ are in } \mathbb{Z} \text{ and } n \neq 0 \right\},$$

where $\mathbb{Z}$ denotes the set of integers $\mathbb{Z} \equiv \{\ldots, -3, -2, -1, 0, 1, 2, 3, \ldots\}$.

Fractions describe what happens when a *whole* is cut into n equal parts and we are given m of those parts. For example, the fraction $\frac{3}{8}$ describes having three parts out of a whole cut into eight parts, hence the name "three-eighths."

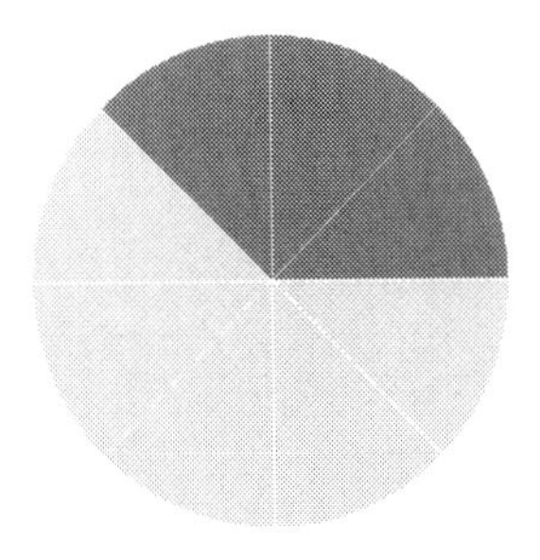

Figure 1.10: The fraction $\frac{3}{8}$ can be visualized as three slices from a pizza that has been cut into eight equal slices.

Definitions

The fraction "a over b" can be written three different ways:

$$a/b \equiv a \div b \equiv \frac{a}{b}.$$

The top and bottom parts of a fraction have special names:

- b is called the *denominator* of the fraction. It tells us how many parts make up the whole.
- a is called the *numerator*. It tells us the number of parts we have.

Fractions are the most natural way to represent rational numbers. Why natural? Check out these simple fractions:

$$\begin{aligned}
\tfrac{1}{1} &= 1.0\\
\tfrac{1}{2} &= 0.5\\
\tfrac{1}{3} &= 0.33333\ldots = 0.\overline{3}\\
\tfrac{1}{4} &= 0.25\\
\tfrac{1}{5} &= 0.2\\
\tfrac{1}{6} &= 0.166666\ldots = 0.1\overline{6}\\
\tfrac{1}{7} &= 0.142857142857142 85\ldots = 0.\overline{142857}
\end{aligned}$$

Note that a line above some numbers means the digits underneath the line are repeated infinitely many times. The fractional notation on the left is preferable because it shows the underlying *structure* of the number while avoiding the need to write infinitely long decimals.

Fractions allow us to carry out precise mathematical calculations easily with pen and paper, without the need for a calculator.

Example Calculate the sum of $\frac{1}{7}$ and $\frac{1}{3}$.

Let's say we decide, for reasons unknown, that it's a great day for decimal notation—we'd have to write our calculation as

$$\begin{aligned}
\text{ans} &= 0.\overline{142857} + 0.\overline{3}\\
&= 0.142\,857\,142\,857\ldots + 0.333\,333\,333\,333\ldots\\
&= 0.476\,190\,476\,190\,476\ldots\\
&= 0.\overline{476190}.
\end{aligned}$$

Wow that was complicated! This calculation is much simpler if we use fractions:

$$\frac{1}{7}+\frac{1}{3} = \frac{3\times 1}{3\times 7}+\frac{1\times 7}{3\times 7} = \frac{3}{21}+\frac{7}{21} = \frac{3+7}{21} = \frac{10}{21}.$$

Want to know how we did that? We multiplied the first term by $\frac{3}{3}=1$ and the second term by $\frac{7}{7}=1$ in order to obtain two equivalent fractions with the same denominator. This is one of the standard strategies when performing fraction addition: rewriting them as equivalent fractions that have the same denominator. Let's look at the procedure for adding fractions in more detail.

Adding fractions

Suppose we are asked to find the sum of the two fractions $\frac{a}{b}$ and $\frac{c}{d}$. If the denominators are the same, then we can add just the top parts: $\frac{1}{5}+\frac{2}{5}=\frac{3}{5}$. It makes sense to add the numerators since they refer to parts of the *same* whole.

However, if the denominators are different, we cannot add the numerators directly since they refer to parts of different wholes. Before we can add the numerators, we must rewrite the fractions so they have the same denominator, called a *common denominator*. We can obtain a common denominator by multiplying the first fraction by $\frac{d}{d}=1$ and the second fraction by $\frac{b}{b}=1$ in order to make the denominator of both fractions the same:

$$\frac{a}{b}+\frac{c}{d} = \frac{a}{b}\left(\frac{d}{d}\right)+\frac{c}{d}\left(\frac{b}{b}\right) = \frac{ad}{bd}+\frac{bc}{bd}.$$

Now that we have fractions with the same denominator, we can add their numerators. Note it's okay to change the denominator of a fraction as long as we also change the numerator in the same way. Multiplying the tops and bottoms of the fractions by the same number (in this case $\frac{d}{d}$ or $\frac{b}{b}$) is the same as multiplying by 1. So while the numbers of the fractions change, their equivalency is preserved:

$$\frac{a}{b}+\frac{c}{d} = \frac{ad}{bd}+\frac{bc}{bd} = \frac{ad+bc}{bd}.$$

Finding the least common denominator To add fractions they must share a common denominator. If you play around with the math, you'll quickly realize that two fractions can share many possible common denominators. Although any common denominator will do, generally you can make your life simpler by using the *least common denominator*—the smallest possible common denominator.

The least common denominator of two fractions is the *least common multiple* of the two denominators $\text{LCM}(b,d)$. The LCM of two numbers can be obtained using this formula:

$$\text{LCM}(b,d) = \frac{bd}{\text{GCD}(b,d)},$$

where $\text{GCD}(b,d)$ is the *greatest common divisor* of b and d—the largest number that divides both b and d.

Example To add $\frac{1}{6}$ and $\frac{1}{15}$, we could use the product of the two denominators as the common denominator: $6 \times 15 = 90$. Or, we could find the *least* common denominator by breaking each denominator into its smallest factors $6 = 3 \times 2$ and $15 = 3 \times 5$; then recognizing that 3 is the greatest common divisor of 6 and 15. We find the least common multiple is $\text{LCM}(6,15) = \frac{6 \times 15}{3} = 30$, then use common denominator 30 when performing the addition:

$$\frac{1}{6} + \frac{1}{15} = \frac{5 \times 1}{5 \times 6} + \frac{1 \times 2}{15 \times 2} = \frac{5}{30} + \frac{2}{30} = \frac{7}{30}.$$

Note that using the least common denominator is not *required*—but it is the most efficient way to add fractions without having to deal with excessively large numbers. If you skip all this GCD and LCM business and use the larger common denominator $6 \times 15 = 90$, you'll arrive at the same answer after simplifying the result:

$$\frac{1}{6} + \frac{1}{15} = \frac{15 \times 1}{15 \times 6} + \frac{1 \times 6}{15 \times 6} = \frac{15}{90} + \frac{6}{90} = \frac{21}{90} = \frac{7}{30}.$$

Multiplying fractions

Fraction multiplication involves multiplying the numerators together and multiplying the denominators together:

$$\frac{a}{b} \times \frac{c}{d} = \frac{a \times c}{b \times d} = \frac{ac}{bd}.$$

Yes, it's that simple!

Dividing fractions

To divide two fractions, compute the product of the first fraction times the second fraction "flipped" upside down:

$$\frac{a/b}{c/d} = \frac{a}{b} \div \frac{c}{d} = \frac{a}{b} \times \frac{d}{c} = \frac{a \times d}{b \times c} = \frac{ad}{bc}.$$

How the heck did we turn a division problem into a multiplication problem? The "flip and multiply" rule for dividing fractions works because multiplication by the fraction $\frac{d}{c}$ is the same as division by $\frac{c}{d}$.

Let's look at this *flip* thing more closely. For any number y, division by a number y is the same as multiplication by the *reciprocal* number $\frac{1}{y}$, read "one over y." Another way to denote the reciprocal is $y^{-1} = \frac{1}{y^1} = \frac{1}{y}$, where the negative sign in the exponent tells us y appears in the denominator of a fraction. We'll discuss negative exponents in Section 1.8. For now, you can think of the -1 exponent as a convenient notation for writing fractions on a single line: $\frac{x}{y} = xy^{-1}$.

Whole-and-fraction notation

A fraction greater than 1 like $\frac{5}{3}$ can also be denoted $1\frac{2}{3}$, which is read as "one and two-thirds." Similarly, $\frac{22}{7} = 3\frac{1}{7}$.

There is nothing wrong with writing fractions like $\frac{5}{3}$ and $\frac{22}{7}$. However, some teachers call these fractions *improper* and demand that all fractions are written in the whole-and-fraction way, as in $1\frac{2}{3}$ and $3\frac{1}{7}$. At the end of the day, both notations are correct.

Repeating decimals

When written as decimal numbers, certain fractions have infinitely long decimal expansions. We use the overline notation to indicate the digit(s) that repeat infinitely in the decimal:

$$\frac{1}{3} = 0.\bar{3} = 0.333\ldots; \qquad \frac{1}{7} = 0.\overline{142857} = 0.14285714285714\ldots.$$

Exercises

E1.4 Compute the value of the following expressions:

a) $\frac{1}{2} + \frac{1}{3}$ **b)** $\frac{1}{2} + \frac{1}{3} + \frac{1}{4}$ **c)** $3\frac{1}{2} + 2 - \frac{1}{3}$

Number line

The *number line* is a very useful visual representation for numbers. Every number from the sets $\mathbb{N}$, $\mathbb{Z}$, $\mathbb{Q}$, and $\mathbb{R}$ corresponds to some point on the number line. Developing a visual representation for numbers allows us to instantly compare the numbers' sizes based on their positions on the number line.

Figure 1.11 shows the natural numbers $\mathbb{N} = \{0, 1, 2, 3, 4, 5, 6, \ldots\}$ represented as equally spaced notches on the number line. We can construct the entire set of natural numbers by starting from 0 and taking steps of length one to the right on the number line. That's what counting is—we just keep adding one.

Note that natural numbers never end. We can always keep adding one to every number and obtain a larger number. The number line therefore extends to the right to infinity.

Figure 1.11: The natural numbers $\mathbb{N}$.

The integers $\mathbb{Z} = \{\ldots, -3, -2, -1, 0, 1, 2, 3, \ldots\}$ are similar to the naturals, but they also extend to the left of zero. Numbers to the left of zero are negative, while numbers to the right of zero are positive. The number line extends indefinitely on both sides, going to negative infinity on the left side and positive infinity on the right side.

Figure 1.12: The integers $\mathbb{Z}$.

The set of integers corresponds to a discrete set of points on the number line. Observe there are gaps of empty space between each integer. The rational numbers $\mathbb{Q}$ and the real numbers $\mathbb{R}$ fill these gaps.

Recall that the set of rational numbers $\mathbb{Q}$ consists of all numbers that can be written as a fraction of two integers. Rational numbers allow us to refer to points between the integers. To find the location of the rational number $a\frac{m}{n}$ on the number line, go to the integer a and then continue $\left(\frac{m}{n}\right)^{\text{th}}$ of the way to the next integer. For example, the rational number $\frac{-3}{2} = -1.5 = -1\frac{1}{2}$ corresponds to going to the point -1, then continuing halfway of the distance to the integer -2.

It is instructive to study the rational numbers in the interval between 0 and 1, which correspond to the fractions $\frac{m}{n}$ where $m \leqslant n$. There are infinitely many rational numbers between 0 and 1. The number line is packed with them! For example, the infinite sequence of fractions $\frac{1}{2}, \frac{1}{3}, \frac{1}{4}, \frac{1}{5}, \ldots$ consists of distinct rational numbers that all live in the interval between 0 and 1. The rational numbers $\frac{1}{n}$ get closer and closer to 0 as n becomes larger and larger. The numbers of this sequence are densely packed next to each other, filling all the space near 0.

The rational numbers have the same structure everywhere on the number line. No matter which interval of the number line you look at, you'll find it densely packed with rational numbers. In order to represent this density of numbers visually, we use a thick line to fill in the entire number line as illustrated in Figure 1.13. Basically, the rationals are represented by points everywhere!

Figure 1.13: The rationals $\mathbb{Q}$ and the reals $\mathbb{R}$ densely fill the number line.

The set of real numbers $\mathbb{R}$ includes all the rationals $\mathbb{Q}$ and also irrational numbers like $\sqrt{2} = 1.414213562\ldots$, $e = 2.7182818\ldots$, and $\pi = 3.14159265\ldots$. The visual representation for the reals is identical to the rationals: they also fill the entire number line.

Discussion

Since we're still on the topic of number representations, I want to add some footnotes with "bonus material" related to the ideas we've covered in this section. Feel free to skip to the next section if you're in a hurry, because this is definitely not going to be on the exam!

Integers and divisibility

Recall the concepts of *greatest common divisor* (GCD) and *least common multiple* (LCM) we used to add fractions. The GCD and LCM are related to the notion of *divisibility* for natural numbers. For example, 3 divides 12 since $12/3 = 4$ and 4 is an integer, but 3 does not divide 7 since $7/3$ is not an integer. We say "b divides a" whenever a/b is an integer. In other words, if b divides a, then $a = kb$ for some integer k. If a/b is not an integer, we say "b does not divide a."

The *divisors* of the number x is the set of numbers that divide x. Every number can be written as a product of its divisors. For example, $12 = 3 \times 4$ since 3 and 4 are divisors of 12. The number 4 can be subdivided further as 2×2, so another expression for 12 in terms of its divisors is $12 = 3 \times 2 \times 2$. This procedure of splitting a number into smaller and smaller divisors terminates when we write the number in terms of its prime divisors. The set of *prime numbers* is the set of numbers that cannot be subdivided any further:

$$\{2, 3, 5, 7, 11, 13, 17, 19, 23, 29, 31, 37, \ldots\}$$

A number p is *prime* if it has no divisors other than 1 and itself. All other numbers are called *composite numbers,* meaning they can be written as a product of prime numbers.

The *greatest common divisor* of a and b, denoted $\text{GCD}(a, b)$, is the largest number that divides both a and b. For example, let's calculate $\text{GCD}(12, 20)$. Writing 12 as a product of its divisors, we find $12 = 3 \times 2 \times 2$. Similarly, $20 = 5 \times 2 \times 2$. By comparing the two expressions, we see that 2×2 is common to both expressions, so $\text{GCD}(12, 20) = 4$.

The *least common multiple* of two numbers, denoted $\text{LCM}(a, b)$, represents the smallest integer that has both a and b as divisors. We can calculate the $\text{LCM}(a, b)$ using the following formula:

$$\text{LCM}(a, b) = \frac{ab}{\text{GCD}(a, b)}.$$

Continuing the above example, we find $\text{LCM}(12, 20) = \frac{12 \times 20}{\text{GCD}(12,20)} = \frac{240}{4} = 60$. Observe that 12 divides 60 and also 20 divides 60.

Elementary arithmetic procedures

The four basic arithmetic operations are addition, subtraction, multiplication, and division. We can perform these operations for numerals a and b of any size using only pen and paper. It is sufficient to follow one of the well-defined procedures (called algorithms) for manipulating the individual digits that make up the numbers. The Wikipedia articles on elementary arithmetic and long division offer an excellent discussion of these procedures.

[Algorithms for performing elementary arithmetic]
`https://en.wikipedia.org/wiki/Elementary_arithmetic`
`https://en.wikipedia.org/wiki/Long_division`

Computer representations

Whenever you want to store a number on a computer, you must choose an appropriate computer representation for this number. The two most commonly used types of numbers in the computer world are integers (`int`) and floating point numbers (`float`). Computer integers can accurately describe the set of mathematical integers $\mathbb{Z}$, but there are limitations on the maximum size of numbers that computers can store. We can use floating point numbers to store decimals with up to 15 digits of precision. The `int` and `float` numbers that computers provide are sufficient for most practical computations, and you probably shouldn't worry about the limited precision of computer number representations. Still, I want you to be aware of the distinction between the abstract mathematical concept of a number and its computer representation. The real number $\sqrt{2}$ is irrational and has an infinite number of digits in its decimal expansion. On a computer, $\sqrt{2}$ is represented as the approximation 1.41421356237310 (a `float`). For most purposes the approximation is okay, but sometimes the limited precision can show up in calculations. For example, `float(sqrt(2))*float(sqrt(2)) = 2.0000000000000004` $\neq 2$ and `float(0.1)+float(0.2) = 0.30000000000000004` $\neq 0.3$. The result of the computer's calculation is only accurate up to the 15th digit. That's pretty good if you ask me.

Scientific notation

In science we often work with very large numbers like *the speed of light* ($c = 299\,792\,458$[m/s]), and very small numbers like *the permeability of free space* ($\mu_0 = 0.000001256637\ldots$[N/A^2]). It can be difficult to judge the magnitude of such numbers and to carry out calculations on them using the usual decimal notation.

Dealing with such numbers is much easier if we use *scientific notation.* For example, the speed of light can be written as $c = 2.99792458 \times 10^8$[m/s], and the permeability of free space is denoted as $\mu_0 = 1.256637 \times 10^{-6}$[N/A^2]. In both cases, we express the number as a decimal number between 1.0 and 9.9999... followed by the number 10 raised to some power. The effect of multiplying by 10^8 is to move the decimal point eight steps to the right, making the number bigger. Multiplying by 10^{-6} has the opposite effect, moving the decimal point to the left by six steps and making the number smaller. Scientific notation is useful because it allows us to clearly see the *size* of numbers: 1.23×10^6 is 1 230 000 whereas 1.23×10^{-10} is 0.000 000 000 123. With scientific notation you don't need to count the zeros!

The number of decimal places we use when specifying a certain physical quantity is usually an indicator of the *precision* with which we are able to measure this quantity. Taking into account the precision of the measurements we make is an important aspect of all quantitative research. Since elaborating further would be a digression, we won't go into a full discussion about the topic of *significant figures* here. Feel free to read the Wikipedia article on the subject to learn more.

Computer systems represent numbers using scientific notation, too. When entering a floating point number into the computer, separate the decimal part from the exponent by the character `e`, which stands for "exponent." For example, the speed of light is written as `2.99792458e8` and the permeability of free space is `1.256637e-6`.

Links

Numbers and number representations are fascinating topics connected to hundreds of other topics in math. I encourage you to check the Wikipedia links provided below for interesting historical context.

[History of the Hindu–Arabic system for representing numbers]
`https://en.wikipedia.org/wiki/Hindu-Arabic_numeral_system`

[Positional number representation systems]
`https://en.wikipedia.org/wiki/Positional_notation`

[Decimal representation]
`https://en.wikipedia.org/wiki/Decimal_representation`

[More general number representation systems]
`https://en.wikipedia.org/wiki/Numeral_system`

1.4 Variables

In math we use a lot of *variables* and *constants*, which are placeholder names for *any* number or unknown. Variables allow us to perform calculations without knowing all the details.

Example You're having tacos for lunch today and wondering how many you can eat without going over your caloric budget. Your goal is to eat 800 calories for lunch and you want to do the calculation before getting to the restaurant because you fear your math abilities might be affected in the presence of tacos. You're not sure how many calories each taco contains, so you invent the variable c to denote this unknown. You also define the variable x to represent the number of tacos you will eat, and come up with the equation $800 = cx$ to represent the total number of calories of your lunch. Solving for x, you find the total number of tacos you should order is $x = \frac{800}{c}$. If the restaurant serves tacos that contain $c = 200$ calories each, then you should order $x = \frac{800}{200} = 4$ of them. If the restaurant serves only giant tacos worth $c = 400$ calories each, then you can only eat $x = \frac{800}{400} = 2$ of them. Observe we were able to solve for x even before knowing the value of c.

Variable names

There are common naming patterns for variables:

- x: general name for the unknown in equations (also used to denote a function's input, as well as an object's position in physics)
- v: velocity in physics problems
- x_i, x_f: denote an object's initial and final positions in physics
- i, j, k, m, n: common names for integer variables
- a, b, c, d: letters near the beginning of the alphabet are often used to denote constants (fixed quantities that do not change)
- θ, ϕ: the Greek letters *theta* and *phi* are used to denote angles
- C: costs in business along with P for profit and R for revenue
- X: a random variable in probability theory

Variable substitution

We can often *change variables* and replace one unknown variable with another to simplify an equation. For example, say you don't feel comfortable around square roots. Every time you see a square root, you freak out until one day you find yourself taking an exam trying to solve for x in the following equation:

$$\frac{6}{5-\sqrt{x}} = \sqrt{x}.$$

Don't freak out! In crucial moments like this, substitution can help with your root phobia. Just write, "Let $u = \sqrt{x}$" on your exam, and voila, you can rewrite the equation in terms of the variable u:

$$\frac{6}{5-u} = u,$$

which contains no square roots.

The next step to solve for u is to undo the division operation. Multiply both sides of the equation by $(5-u)$ to obtain

$$\frac{6}{5-u}(5-u) = u(5-u),$$

which simplifies to

$$6 = 5u - u^2.$$

This can be rewritten the equation $u^2 - 5u + 6 = 0$, which in tern can be rewritten as $(u-2)(u-3) = 0$. We now see that $u_1 = 2$ and $u_2 = 3$ are the solutions. The last step is to convert our u-answers into x-answers by using $u = \sqrt{x}$, which is equivalent to $x = u^2$. The final answers are $x_1 = 2^2 = 4$ and $x_2 = 3^2 = 9$. Try plugging these x values into the original square root equation to verify that they satisfy it.

Compact notation

Symbolic manipulation is a powerful tool because it allows us to manage complexity. Say you're solving a physics problem in which you're told the mass of an object is $m = 140$ kg. If there are many steps in the calculation, would you rather use the number 140 kg in each step, or the shorter symbol m? It's much easier in the long run to use m throughout your calculation, and wait until the last step to substitute the value 140 kg when computing the final numerical answer.

1.5 Functions and their inverses

As we saw in the section on solving equations, the ability to "undo" functions is a key skill for solving equations.

Example Suppose we're solving for x in the equation

$$f(x) = c,$$

where f is some function and c is some constant. We're looking for the unknown x such that $f(x)$ equals c. Our goal is to isolate x on one side of the equation, but the function f stands in our way.

By using the inverse function (denoted f^{-1}) we "undo" the effects of f. We apply the inverse function f^{-1} to both sides of the equation to obtain

$$f^{-1}(f(x)) = x = f^{-1}(c).$$

By definition, the inverse function f^{-1} performs the opposite action of the function f, so together the two functions cancel each other out. We have $f^{-1}(f(x)) = x$ for any number x.

Provided everything is kosher (the function f^{-1} must be defined for the input c), the manipulation we made above is valid and we have obtained the answer $x = f^{-1}(c)$.

The above example introduces the notation f^{-1} for denoting the function's *inverse*. This notation is borrowed from the notion of inverse numbers: multiplication by the number a^{-1} is the inverse operation of multiplication by the number a: $a^{-1}ax = 1x = x$. In the case of functions, however, the negative-one exponent does not refer to "one over-$f(x)$" as in $\frac{1}{f(x)} = (f(x))^{-1}$; rather, it refers to the function's inverse. In other words, the number $f^{-1}(y)$ is equal to the number x such that $f(x) = y$.

Be careful: sometimes applying the inverse leads to multiple solutions. For example, the function $f(x) = x^2$ maps two input values (x and $-x$) to the same output value $x^2 = f(x) = f(-x)$. The inverse function of $f(x) = x^2$ is $f^{-1}(x) = \sqrt{x}$, but both $x = +\sqrt{c}$ and $x = -\sqrt{c}$ are solutions to the equation $x^2 = c$. In this case, this equation's solutions can be indicated in shorthand notation as $x = \pm\sqrt{c}$.

Formulas

Here is a list of common functions and their inverses:

$$
\begin{array}{rcl}
\text{function } f(x) & \Leftrightarrow & \text{inverse } f^{-1}(x) \\
x+2 & \Leftrightarrow & x-2 \\
2x & \Leftrightarrow & \frac{1}{2}x \\
-1x & \Leftrightarrow & -1x \\
x^2 & \Leftrightarrow & \pm\sqrt{x} \\
2^x & \Leftrightarrow & \log_2(x) \\
3x+5 & \Leftrightarrow & \frac{1}{3}(x-5) \\
a^x & \Leftrightarrow & \log_a(x) \\
\exp(x) \equiv e^x & \Leftrightarrow & \ln(x) \equiv \log_e(x) \\
\sin(x) & \Leftrightarrow & \sin^{-1}(x) \equiv \arcsin(x) \\
\cos(x) & \Leftrightarrow & \cos^{-1}(x) \equiv \arccos(x)
\end{array}
$$

The function-inverse relationship is *symmetric*—if you see a function on one side of the above table (pick a side, any side), you'll find its inverse on the opposite side.

Example

Let's say your teacher doesn't like you and right away, on the first day of class, he gives you a serious equation and tells you to find x:

$$\log_5\left(3 + \sqrt{6\sqrt{x} - 7}\right) = 34 + \sin(5.5) - \Psi(1).$$

See what I mean when I say the teacher doesn't like you?

First, note that it doesn't matter what Ψ (the capital Greek letter *psi*) is, since x is on the other side of the equation. You can keep copying $\Psi(1)$ from line to line, until the end, when you throw the ball back to the teacher. "My answer is in terms of *your* variables, dude. *You* go figure out what the hell Ψ is since you brought it up in the first place!" By the way, it's not actually recommended to quote me verbatim should a situation like this arise. The same goes with sin(5.5). If you don't have a calculator handy, don't worry about it. Keep the expression sin(5.5) instead of trying to find its numerical value. In general, try to work with variables as much as possible and leave the numerical computations for the last step.

Okay, enough beating about the bush. Let's just find x and get it over with! On the right-hand side of the equation, we have the sum of a bunch of terms with no x in them, so we'll leave them as they are. On the left-hand side, the outermost function is a logarithm base 5. Cool. Looking at the table of inverse functions, we find the exponential function is the inverse of the logarithm: $a^x \Leftrightarrow \log_a(x)$. To get rid of $\log_5$, we must apply the exponential function base 5 to both sides:

$$5^{\log_5\left(3+\sqrt{6\sqrt{x}-7}\right)} = 5^{34+\sin(5.5)-\Psi(1)},$$

which simplifies to

$$3+\sqrt{6\sqrt{x}-7} = 5^{34+\sin(5.5)-\Psi(1)},$$

since 5^x cancels $\log_5 x$.

From here on, it is going to be as if Bruce Lee walked into a place with lots of bad guys. Addition of 3 is undone by subtracting 3 on both sides:

$$\sqrt{6\sqrt{x}-7} = 5^{34+\sin(5.5)-\Psi(1)} - 3.$$

To undo a square root we take the square:

$$6\sqrt{x}-7 = \left(5^{34+\sin(5.5)-\Psi(1)} - 3\right)^2.$$

Add 7 to both sides,

$$6\sqrt{x} = \left(5^{34+\sin(5.5)-\Psi(1)} - 3\right)^2 + 7,$$

divide by 6

$$\sqrt{x} = \frac{1}{6}\left(\left(5^{34+\sin(5.5)-\Psi(1)} - 3\right)^2 + 7\right),$$

and square again to find the final answer:

$$x = \left[\frac{1}{6}\left(\left(5^{34+\sin(5.5)-\Psi(1)} - 3\right)^2 + 7\right)\right]^2.$$

Did you see what I was doing in each step? Next time a function stands in your way, hit it with its inverse so it knows not to challenge you ever again.

Discussion

The recipe I have outlined above is not universally applicable. Sometimes x isn't alone on one side. Sometimes x appears in several places in the same equation. In these cases, you can't effortlessly work your way, Bruce Lee-style, clearing bad guys and digging toward x—you need other techniques.

The bad news is there's no general formula for solving complicated equations. The good news is the above technique of "digging toward the x" is sufficient for 80% of what you are going to be doing. You can get another 15% if you learn how to solve the quadratic equation:

$$ax^2 + bx + c = 0.$$

Solving third-degree polynomial equations like $ax^3 + bx^2 + cx + d = 0$ with pen and paper is also possible, but at this point you might as well start using a computer to solve for the unknowns.

There are all kinds of other equations you can learn how to solve: equations with multiple variables, equations with logarithms, equations with exponentials, and equations with trigonometric functions. The principle of "digging" toward the unknown by applying inverse functions is the key for solving all these types of equations, so be sure to practice using it.

Exercises

E1.5 Solve for x in the following equations:

a) $3x = 6$ **b)** $\log_5(x) = 2$ **c)** $\log_{10}(\sqrt{x}) = 1$

E1.6 Find the function inverse and use it to solve the problems.

a) Solve the equation $f(x) = 4$, where $f(x) \equiv \sqrt{x}$.

b) Solve for x in the equation $g(x) = 1$, given $g(x) \equiv e^{-2x}$.

1.6 Basic rules of algebra

It's important that you know the general rules for manipulating numbers and variables, a process otherwise known as—you guessed it—*algebra*. This little refresher will cover these concepts to make sure you're comfortable on the algebra front. We'll also review some important algebraic tricks, like *factoring* and *completing the square*, which are useful when solving equations.

Let's define some terminology for referring to different parts of math expressions. When an expression contains multiple things added together, we call those things *terms*. Furthermore, terms are usually composed of many things multiplied together. When a number x is obtained as the product of other numbers like $x = abc$, we say "x factors into a, b, and c." We call a, b, and c the *factors* of x.

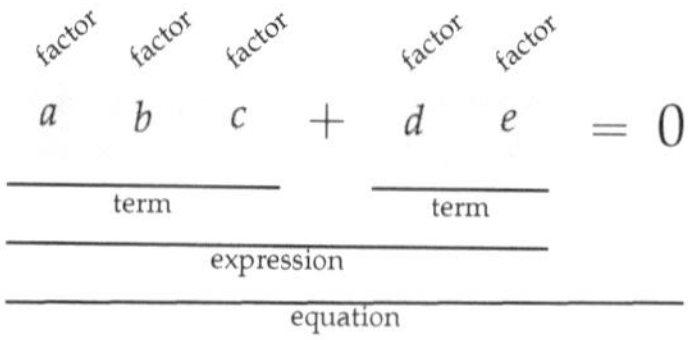

factor factor factor factor factor

$$a \quad b \quad c \; + \; d \quad e \; = 0$$

term term

expression

equation

Figure 1.14: Diagram showing the names used to describe the different parts of the equation $abc + de = 0$.

Given any four numbers a, b, c, and d, we can apply the following algebraic properties:

1. Associative property: $a + b + c = (a + b) + c = a + (b + c)$ and $abc = (ab)c = a(bc)$
2. Commutative property: $a + b = b + a$ and $ab = ba$
3. Distributive property: $a(b + c) = ab + ac$

We use the distributive property every time we *expand* brackets. For example $a(b + c + d) = ab + ac + ad$. The brackets, also known as parentheses, indicate the expression $(b + c + d)$ must be treated as a whole; as a factor consisting of three terms. Multiplying this expression by a is the same as multiplying each term by a.

The opposite operation of expanding is called *factoring*, which consists of rewriting the expression with the common parts taken out in front of a bracket: $ab + ac = a(b + c)$. In this section, we'll discuss both of these operations and illustrate what they're capable of.

Expanding brackets

The distributive property is useful when dealing with polynomials. For instance,

$$(x + 3)(x + 2) = x(x + 2) + 3(x + 2) = x^2 + x2 + 3x + 6.$$

We can use the commutative property on the second term $x2 = 2x$, then combine the two x terms into a single term to obtain

$$(x + 3)(x + 2) = x^2 + 5x + 6.$$

Let's look at this operation in its abstract form:

$$(x + a)(x + b) = x^2 + (a + b)x + ab.$$

The product of two factors of the form $(x + ?)$ is equal to a quadratic expression. Observe that the middle term on the right-hand side contains the *sum* of the two constants on the left-hand side $(a + b)$, while the third term contains their product ab.

It is very common for people to confuse these terms. If you are ever confused about an algebraic expression, go back to the distributive property and expand the expression using a step-by-step approach. As a second example, consider this slightly-more-complicated algebraic expression and its expansion:

$$\begin{aligned}(x+a)(bx^2+cx+d) &= x(bx^2+cx+d)+a(bx^2+cx+d)\\ &= bx^3+cx^2+dx+abx^2+acx+ad\\ &= bx^3+(c+ab)x^2+(d+ac)x+ad.\end{aligned}$$

Note how all terms containing x^2 are grouped into one term, and all terms containing x are grouped into another term. We can use this pattern to keep things organized when dealing with expressions containing many different powers of x.

Example Suppose we are asked to solve for t in the equation

$$7(3+4t) = 11(6t-4).$$

Since the unknown t appears on both sides of the equation, it is not immediately obvious how to proceed.

To solve for t, we must bring all t terms to one side and all constant terms to the other side. First, expand the two brackets to obtain

$$21+28t = 66t-44.$$

Then move things around to relocate all ts to the equation's right-hand side and all constants to the left-hand side:

$$21+44 = 66t-28t.$$

We see t is contained in both terms on the right-hand side, so we can rewrite the equation as

$$21+44 = (66-28)t.$$

The answer is within close reach: $t = \frac{21+44}{66-28} = \frac{65}{38}$.

Factoring

Factoring involves "taking out" the common parts of a complicated expression in order to make the expression more compact. Suppose we're given the expression $6x^2y + 15x$. We can simplify this expression by taking out the common factors and writing them in front of a bracket. Let's see how this is done step by step. The expression has two terms and each term can be split into its constituent factors:

$$6x^2y + 15x = (3)(2)(x)(x)y + (5)(3)x.$$

Since factors x and 3 appear in both terms, we can *factor them out* to the front like this:

$$6x^2y + 15x = 3x(2xy + 5).$$

The expression on the right shows $3x$ is common to both terms.

Here's another example where factoring is used:

$$2x^2y + 2x + 4x = 2x(xy + 1 + 2) = 2x(xy + 3).$$

Quadratic factoring

When dealing with a quadratic function, it is often useful to rewrite the function as a product of two factors. Suppose you're given the quadratic function $f(x) = x^2 - 5x + 6$ and asked to describe its properties. What are the *roots* of this function? In other words, for what values of x is this function equal to zero? For which values of x is the function positive, and for which values of x is the function negative?

Factoring the expression $x^2 - 5x + 6$ will help us see the properties of the function more clearly. To *factor* a quadratic expression is to express it as the product of two factors:

$$f(x) = x^2 - 5x + 6 = (x - 2)(x - 3).$$

We now see at a glance the solutions (the roots) are $x_1 = 2$ and $x_2 = 3$. We can also see for which x values the function will be overall positive: for $x > 3$, both factors will be positive, and for $x < 2$ both factors will be negative, and a negative times a negative gives a positive. For values of x such that $2 < x < 3$, the first factor will be positive, and the second factor negative, making the overall function negative.

For certain simple quadratics like the one above, you can simply *guess* what the factors will be. For more complicated quadratic expressions, you'll need to use the quadratic formula (page 34), which will be the subject of the next section. For now let us continue with more algebra tricks.

Completing the square

Any quadratic expression $Ax^2 + Bx + C$ can be rewritten in the form $A(x-h)^2 + k$ for some constants h and k. This process is called *completing the square* due to the reasoning we follow to find the value of k. The constants h and k can be interpreted geometrically as the horizontal and vertical shifts in the graph of the basic quadratic function. The graph of the function $f(x) = A(x-h)^2 + k$ is the same as the graph of the function $f(x) = Ax^2$ except it is shifted h units to the right and k units upward. We will discuss the geometric meaning of h and k in more detail in Section 1.13 (page 73). For now, let's focus on the algebra steps.

Let's try to find the values of k and h in the expression $(x-h)^2 + k$ needed to complete the square in the expression $x^2 + 5x + 6$. Assume the two expressions are equal, and then expand the bracket to obtain

$$\begin{aligned} \underline{x^2} + 5x + 6 &= A(x-h)^2 + k \\ &= A(x^2 - 2hx + h^2) + k \\ &= \underline{Ax^2} - 2Ahx + Ah^2 + k. \end{aligned}$$

Observe the structure in the above equation. On both sides of the equality there is one term which contains x^2 (the quadratic term), one term that contains x^1 (the linear term), and constant terms. If the expressions are equal, then the coefficient of all the terms must be equal. By focusing on the quadratic terms in the equation (they are underlined) we see $A = 1$, so we rewrite the equation as

$$x^2 + \underline{5x} + 6 = x^2 \underline{-2hx} + h^2 + k.$$

Next we look at the linear terms (underlined) and infer that $h = -2.5$. After rewriting, we obtain an equation in which k is the only unknown:

$$x^2 + 5x + \underline{6} = x^2 - 2(-2.5)x + \underline{(-2.5)^2 + k}.$$

We must pick a value of k that makes the constant terms equal:

$$k = 6 - (-2.5)^2 = 6 - (2.5)^2 = 6 - \left(\tfrac{5}{2}\right)^2 = 6 \times \tfrac{4}{4} - \tfrac{25}{4} = \tfrac{24-25}{4} = \tfrac{-1}{4}.$$

After completing the square we obtain

$$x^2 + 5x + 6 = (x+2.5)^2 - \tfrac{1}{4}.$$

The right-hand side of the expression above tells us our function is equivalent to the basic function x^2, shifted 2.5 units to the left and $\frac{1}{4}$ units down. This would be very useful information if you ever had to draw the graph of this function—you could simply plot the basic graph of x^2 and then shift it appropriately.

It is important you become comfortable with this procedure for completing the square. It is not extra difficult, but it does require you to think carefully about the unknowns h and k and to choose their values appropriately. There is no general formula for finding k, but you can remember the following simple shortcut for finding h. Given an equation $Ax^2 + Bx + C = A(x-h)^2 + k$, we have $h = \frac{-B}{2A}$. Using this shortcut will save you some time, but you will still have to go through the algebra steps to find k.

Take out a pen and a piece of paper now (yes, right now!) and verify that you can correctly complete the square in these expressions: $x^2 - 6x + 13 = (x-3)^2 + 4$ and $x^2 + 4x + 1 = (x+2)^2 - 3$.

Exercises

E1.7 Factor the following expressions:

a) $x^2 - 8x + 7$ **b)** $x^2 + 4x + 4$

E1.8 Expand the following expressions:

a) $(a+b)^2$ **b)** $(a+b)^3$ **c)** $(a+b)^4$ **d)** $(a+b)^5$

Can you spot a pattern in the coefficients of the different expressions? Do you think there is a general formula for $(a+b)^n$?

1.7 Solving quadratic equations

What would you do if asked to solve for x in the quadratic equation $x^2 = 45x + 23$? This is called a *quadratic equation* since it contains the unknown variable x squared. The name comes from the Latin *quadratus*, which means square. Quadratic equations appear often, so mathematicians created a general formula for solving them. In this section, we'll learn about this formula and use it to put some quadratic equations in their place.

Before we can apply the formula, we need to rewrite the equation we are trying to solve in the following form:

$$ax^2 + bx + c = 0.$$

We reach this form by moving all the numbers and xs to one side and leaving only 0 on the other side. This is called the *standard form* of the quadratic equation. For example, to transform the quadratic equation $x^2 = 45x + 23$ into standard form, subtract $45x + 23$ from both sides of the equation to obtain $x^2 - 45x - 23 = 0$. What are the values of x that satisfy this equation?

Claim

The solutions to the equation $ax^2 + bx + c = 0$ are

$$x_1 = \frac{-b + \sqrt{b^2 - 4ac}}{2a} \quad \text{and} \quad x_2 = \frac{-b - \sqrt{b^2 - 4ac}}{2a}.$$

This result is called the *quadratic formula*, and is usually abbreviated $x = \frac{-b \pm \sqrt{b^2-4ac}}{2a}$, where the sign "$\pm$" stands for both "$+$" and "$-$." The notation "$\pm$" allows us to express both solutions x_1 and x_2 in one equation, but you should keep in mind there are really two solutions.

Let's see how the quadratic formula is used to solve the equation $x^2 - 45x - 23 = 0$. Finding the two solutions requires the simple mechanical task of identifying $a = 1$, $b = -45$, and $c = -23$, then plugging these values into the two parts of the formula:

$$x_1 = \frac{45 + \sqrt{45^2 - 4(1)(-23)}}{2} = 45.5054\ldots,$$

$$x_2 = \frac{45 - \sqrt{45^2 - 4(1)(-23)}}{2} = -0.5054\ldots.$$

Verify using your calculator that both of the values above satisfy the original equation $x^2 = 45x + 23$.

Proof of claim

Understanding proofs is an important aspect of learning mathematics. Every claim made by a mathematician comes with a proof, which is a step-by-step argument that shows why the claim is true. It's not necessary to know the proofs of *all* math statements, but the more proofs you know the more solid your understanding of math will become. It's easy to spot where a proof starts and where a proof ends. Each proof begins with the heading *Proof* (usually in italics) and has the symbol "□" at its end. It's usually okay to skip proofs when reading a math book, but if you really want to hang with the mathematicians, you have to read the proofs.

I want you to see the proof of the quadratic formula because it's an important result. This proof is an example of an argument from first principles, which means it uses only basic rules of math and doesn't depend on any advanced math knowledge. You can totally handle this! The proof uses the completing-the-square technique from the previous section.

Proof. Starting from the quadratic equation $ax^2 + bx + c = 0$, we divide by a to obtain the equation

$$x^2 + \frac{b}{a}x + \frac{c}{a} = 0.$$

Next we'll *complete the square* by asking, "What are the values of h and k that satisfy the equation

$$(x-h)^2 + k \;=\; x^2 + \frac{b}{a}x + \frac{c}{a} \;?"$$

To find the values for h and k, let's expand the bracket on the left-hand side to obtain

$$x^2 - 2hx + h^2 + k \;=\; x^2 + \frac{b}{a}x + \frac{c}{a}.$$

We can identify h by looking at the coefficients in front of x on both sides of the equation. We have $-2h = \frac{b}{a}$ and hence $h = -\frac{b}{2a}$.

Let's now substitute the value $h = -\frac{b}{2a}$ into the above equation and see what we have so far:

$$x^2 + \frac{b}{a}x + \frac{b^2}{4a^2} + k \;=\; x^2 + \frac{b}{a}x + \frac{c}{a}.$$

To determine the value of k, we need to ensure the constant terms on both sides of the equation are equal, and then isolate k:

$$\frac{b^2}{4a^2} + k \;=\; \frac{c}{a} \qquad \Rightarrow \qquad k = \frac{c}{a} - \frac{b^2}{4a^2}.$$

Having found the values of both h and k, we can write the equation $ax^2 + bx + c = 0$ in the form $(x-h)^2 + k = 0$ as follows:

$$\left(x + \frac{b}{2a}\right)^2 + \frac{c}{a} - \frac{b^2}{4a^2} = 0.$$

From here on, we can use the standard procedure for "digging" toward the x, which we saw in Section 1.1. Move all constants to the right-hand side:

$$\left(x + \frac{b}{2a}\right)^2 = -\frac{c}{a} + \frac{b^2}{4a^2}.$$

Next, take the square root of both sides to undo the square function. Since the square function maps both positive and negative numbers to the same value, this step yields two solutions:

$$x + \frac{b}{2a} = \pm\sqrt{-\frac{c}{a} + \frac{b^2}{4a^2}}.$$

Let's take a moment to tidy up the mess under the square root:

$$\sqrt{-\frac{c}{a}+\frac{b^2}{4a^2}} = \sqrt{-\frac{(4a)c}{(4a)a}+\frac{b^2}{4a^2}} = \sqrt{\frac{-4ac+b^2}{4a^2}} = \frac{\sqrt{b^2-4ac}}{2a}.$$

We obtain

$$x + \frac{b}{2a} = \pm\frac{\sqrt{b^2-4ac}}{2a},$$

which is just one step from the final answer,

$$x = \frac{-b}{2a} \pm \frac{\sqrt{b^2-4ac}}{2a} = \frac{-b \pm \sqrt{b^2-4ac}}{2a}.$$

This completes the proof. □

Alternative proof of claim

To have a proof, we don't necessarily need to show the derivation of the formula as outlined above. The claim states that x_1 and x_2 are solutions. To prove the claim we can simply plug x_1 and x_2 into the quadratic equation and verify that the answers are zero. Verify this on your own.

Applications

The golden ratio

The *golden ratio* is an essential proportion in geometry, art, aesthetics, biology, and mysticism, and is usually denoted as $\varphi = \frac{1+\sqrt{5}}{2} = 1.6180339\ldots$. This ratio is determined as the positive solution to the quadratic equation

$$x^2 - x - 1 = 0.$$

Applying the quadratic formula to this equation yields two solutions,

$$x_1 = \frac{1+\sqrt{5}}{2} = \varphi \qquad \text{and} \qquad x_2 = \frac{1-\sqrt{5}}{2} = -\frac{1}{\varphi}.$$

You can learn more about the various contexts in which the golden ratio appears from the Wikipedia article on the subject. We'll discuss the golden ratio again on page 390 in Chapter 5.

Explanations

Multiple solutions

Often, we are interested in only one of the two solutions to the quadratic equation. It will usually be obvious from the context of the problem which of the two solutions should be kept and which should be discarded. For example, the *time of flight* of a ball thrown in the air from a height of 3 metres with an initial velocity of 12 metres per second is obtained by solving the equation $(-4.9)t^2 + 12t + 3 = 0$. The two solutions of the quadratic equation are $t_1 = -0.229$ and $t_2 = 2.678$. The first answer t_1 corresponds to a time in the past so we reject it as invalid. The correct answer is t_2. The ball will hit the ground after $t = 2.678$ seconds.

Relation to factoring

In the previous section we discussed the *quadratic factoring* operation by which we could rewrite a quadratic function as the product of two terms $f(x) = ax^2 + bx + c = (x - x_1)(x - x_2)$. The two numbers x_1 and x_2 are called the *roots* of the function: these points are where the function $f(x)$ touches the x-axis.

You now have the ability to factor any quadratic equation. Use the quadratic formula to find the two solutions, x_1 and x_2, then rewrite the expression as $(x - x_1)(x - x_2)$.

Some quadratic expressions cannot be factored, however. These "unfactorable" expressions correspond to quadratic functions whose graphs do not touch the x-axis. They have no solutions (no roots). There is a quick test you can use to check if a quadratic function $f(x) = ax^2 + bx + c$ has roots (touches or crosses the x-axis) or doesn't have roots (never touches the x-axis). If $b^2 - 4ac > 0$ then the function f has two roots. If $b^2 - 4ac = 0$, the function has only one root, indicating the special case when the function touches the x-axis at only one point. If $b^2 - 4ac < 0$, the function has no roots. In this case, the quadratic formula fails because it requires taking the square root of a negative number, which is not allowed. Think about it—how could you square a number and obtain a negative number?

Links

[Intuitive visual derivation of the quadratic formula derivation]
`https://www.youtube.com/watch?v=EBbtoFMJvFc`

Exercises

E1.9 Solve for x in the quadratic equation $2x^2 - x = 3$.

E1.10 Solve for x in the equation $x^4 - 4x^2 + 4 = 0$.
Hint: Use the substitution $y = x^2$.

1.8 Exponents

In math we must often multiply together the same number many times, so we use the notation

$$b^n = \underbrace{bbb \cdots bb}_{n \text{ times}}$$

to denote some number b multiplied by itself n times. In this section we'll review the basic terminology associated with exponents and discuss their properties.

Definitions

The fundamental ideas of exponents are:

- b^n: the number b raised to the power n
  - ▷ b: the *base*
  - ▷ n: the *exponent* or *power* of b in the expression b^n

By definition, the zeroth power of any number is equal to one, expressed as $b^0 = 1$.

We'll also discuss *exponential functions* of the form $f : \mathbb{R} \to \mathbb{R}$. In particular, we define the following important exponential functions:

- b^x: the exponential function base b
- 10^x: the exponential function base 10
- $\exp(x) \equiv e^x$: the exponential function base e. The number e is called *Euler's number*.
- 2^x: the exponential function base 2. This function is important in computer science.

The number $e = 2.7182818\ldots$ is a special base with many applications. We call e the *natural* base. Another special base is 10 because we use the decimal system for our numbers. We can write very large numbers and very small numbers as powers of 10. For example, one thousand can be written as $1\,000 = 10^3$, one million is $1\,000\,000 = 10^6$, and one billion is $1\,000\,000\,000 = 10^9$.

Formulas

The following properties follow from the definition of exponentiation as repeated multiplication.

Property 1 Multiplying together two exponential expressions that have the same base is the same as adding the exponents:

$$b^m b^n = \underbrace{bbb\cdots bb}_{m \text{ times}}\,\underbrace{bbb\cdots bb}_{n \text{ times}} = \underbrace{bbbbbbb\cdots bb}_{m+n \text{ times}} = b^{m+n}.$$

Property 2 Division by a number can be expressed as an exponent of minus one:

$$b^{-1} \equiv \frac{1}{b}.$$

A negative exponent corresponds to a division:

$$b^{-n} = \frac{1}{b^n}.$$

Property 3 By combining Property 1 and Property 2 we obtain the following rule:

$$\frac{b^m}{b^n} = b^{m-n}.$$

In particular we have $b^n b^{-n} = b^{n-n} = b^0 = 1$. Multiplication by the number b^{-n} is the inverse operation of multiplication by the number b^n. The net effect of the combination of both operations is the same as multiplying by one, i.e., the identity operation.

Property 4 When an exponential expression is exponentiated, the inner exponent and the outer exponent multiply:

$$(b^m)^n = \underbrace{(\underbrace{bbb\cdots bb}_{m \text{ times}})(\underbrace{bbb\cdots bb}_{m \text{ times}})\cdots(\underbrace{bbb\cdots bb}_{m \text{ times}})}_{n \text{ times}} = b^{mn}.$$

Property 5.1

$$(ab)^n = \underbrace{(ab)(ab)(ab)\cdots(ab)(ab)}_{n \text{ times}} = \underbrace{aaa\cdots aa}_{n \text{ times}}\,\underbrace{bbb\cdots bb}_{n \text{ times}} = a^n b^n.$$

Property 5.2

$$\left(\frac{a}{b}\right)^n = \underbrace{\left(\frac{a}{b}\right)\left(\frac{a}{b}\right)\left(\frac{a}{b}\right)\cdots\left(\frac{a}{b}\right)\left(\frac{a}{b}\right)}_{n \text{ times}} = \frac{\overbrace{aaa\cdots aa}^{n \text{ times}}}{\underbrace{bbb\cdots bb}_{n \text{ times}}} = \frac{a^n}{b^n}.$$

Property 6 Raising a number to the power $\frac{1}{n}$ is equivalent to finding the nth root of the number:

$$b^{\frac{1}{n}} \equiv \sqrt[n]{b}.$$

In particular, the square root corresponds to the exponent of one half: $\sqrt{b} = b^{\frac{1}{2}}$. The cube root (the inverse of x^3) corresponds to $\sqrt[3]{b} \equiv b^{\frac{1}{3}}$. We can verify the inverse relationship between $\sqrt[3]{x}$ and x^3 by using either Property 1: $(\sqrt[3]{x})^3 = (x^{\frac{1}{3}})(x^{\frac{1}{3}})(x^{\frac{1}{3}}) = x^{\frac{1}{3}+\frac{1}{3}+\frac{1}{3}} = x^1 = x$, or by using Property 4: $(\sqrt[3]{x})^3 = (x^{\frac{1}{3}})^3 = x^{\frac{3}{3}} = x^1 = x$.

Properties 5.1 and 5.2 also apply for fractional exponents:

$$\sqrt[n]{ab} = (ab)^{\frac{1}{n}} = a^{\frac{1}{n}} b^{\frac{1}{n}} = \sqrt[n]{a}\sqrt[n]{b}, \qquad \sqrt[n]{\left(\frac{a}{b}\right)} = \left(\frac{a}{b}\right)^{\frac{1}{n}} = \frac{a^{\frac{1}{n}}}{b^{\frac{1}{n}}} = \frac{\sqrt[n]{a}}{\sqrt[n]{b}}.$$

Discussion

Negative exponents

A negative sign in the exponent does not mean "subtract," but rather "divide by":

$$a^{-n} \equiv \frac{1}{a^n} = \frac{1}{\underbrace{aa a\cdots a}_{n \text{ times}}}.$$

To understand why negative exponents correspond to division, consider the following calculation:

$$a^m a^n = \underbrace{aaa\cdots a}_{m \text{ times}} \underbrace{aaa\cdots a}_{n \text{ times}} = \underbrace{aaaaaa\cdots\cdots aa}_{m+n \text{ times}} = a^{m+n}.$$

This calculation illustrates a general rule for multiplying exponential expressions: $a^m a^n = a^{m+n}$, or, if you prefer words, "add the exponents together when multiplying exponential expressions." Defining $a^{-n} \equiv \frac{1}{a^n}$ ensures the rule $a^m a^n = a^{m+n}$ is also valid for negative exponents:

$$a^m a^{-n} = \underbrace{aaaaa\cdots aa}_{m \text{ times}} \frac{1}{\underbrace{a\cdots a}_{n \text{ times}}} = \frac{\overbrace{aaaaa\cdots aa}^{m \text{ times}}}{\underbrace{a\cdots a}_{n \text{ times}}} = \underbrace{aa\cdots a}_{m-n \text{ times}} = a^{m-n}.$$

For example, the expression 2^{-3} corresponds to $\frac{1}{2^3} = \frac{1}{8}$. If we multiply together 2^5 and 2^{-3}, we obtain $2^5 \cdot 2^{-3} = 2^{5-3} = 2^2 = 4$.

Fractional exponents

We discussed positive and negative exponents, but what about exponents that are fractions? Fractional exponents describe square-root-like operations:

$$a^{\frac{1}{2}} \equiv \sqrt{a} \equiv \sqrt[2]{a}, \qquad a^{\frac{1}{3}} \equiv \sqrt[3]{a}, \qquad a^{\frac{1}{4}} \equiv \sqrt[4]{a}.$$

Recall the square-root operation $\sqrt{\ }$, which is used it to undo the effect of the x^2 operation. More generally, the "n^{th} root" function $\sqrt[n]{x}$ is the inverse of the function x^n.

If this is the first time you're seeing square roots, you might assume you'll need to learn lots of new rules for manipulating square-root expressions. Or maybe you have experience with the rules of "squiggle math" already. What kind of emotions do expressions like $\sqrt[3]{27}\sqrt[3]{8}$ stir up in you? Chill! There's no new math to learn and no rules to memorize. All the "squiggle math" rules are consequences of the general rule $a^b a^c = a^{b+c}$ applied to expressions where the exponents are fractions. For example, a cube root satisfies the equation

$$\sqrt[3]{a}\sqrt[3]{a}\sqrt[3]{a} = a^{\frac{1}{3}}a^{\frac{1}{3}}a^{\frac{1}{3}} = a^{\frac{1}{3}+\frac{1}{3}+\frac{1}{3}} = a^1 = a.$$

Do you see why $\sqrt[3]{x}$ and x^3 are inverse operations? The number $\sqrt[3]{a}$ is one third of the number a with respect to multiplication (since multiplying $\sqrt[3]{a}$ by itself three times produces a). We say "one third *with respect to multiplication*," because the usual meaning of "one third of a" is with respect to the addition operation (adding together three copies of $\frac{a}{3}$ produces a).

The nth root of a is a number which, when multiplied together n times, will give a. The "n^{th} root of a" can be denoted in two equivalent ways:

$$\sqrt[n]{a} \equiv a^{\frac{1}{n}}.$$

Using this definition and the general rule $a^b a^c = a^{b+c}$ allows us to simplify all kinds expressions. For example, we can simplify $\sqrt[4]{a}\sqrt[4]{a}$ by rewriting it as $\sqrt[4]{a}\sqrt[4]{a} = a^{\frac{1}{4}}a^{\frac{1}{4}} = a^{\frac{1}{4}+\frac{1}{4}} = a^{\frac{1}{2}} = \sqrt{a}$. We can also simplify the expression $\sqrt[3]{27}\sqrt[3]{8}$ by rewriting it as $27^{\frac{1}{3}}8^{\frac{1}{3}}$, then simplifying it as $27^{\frac{1}{3}}8^{\frac{1}{3}} = (3 \cdot 3 \cdot 3)^{\frac{1}{3}}(2 \cdot 2 \cdot 2)^{\frac{1}{3}} = 3 \cdot 2 = 6$.

Let's verify the claim that $\sqrt[n]{a}$ equals "one n^{th} of a with respect to multiplication." To obtain the whole number, we must multiply the number $\sqrt[n]{a}$ times itself n times:

$$\left(\sqrt[n]{a}\right)^n = \left(a^{\frac{1}{n}}\right)^n = \underbrace{a^{\frac{1}{n}}a^{\frac{1}{n}}a^{\frac{1}{n}}a^{\frac{1}{n}}\cdots a^{\frac{1}{n}}a^{\frac{1}{n}}}_{n \text{ times}} = a^{\frac{n}{n}} = a^1 = a.$$

The n-fold product of $\frac{1}{n}$-fractional exponents of any number produces that number raised to exponent one, and therefore the inverse operation of $\sqrt[n]{x}$ is x^n.

The commutative law of multiplication $ab = ba$ implies that we can write any fraction $\frac{a}{b}$ in two other equivalent ways: $\frac{a}{b} = a\frac{1}{b} = \frac{1}{b}a$. We multiply by a, then divide the result by b; or first we divide by b and then multiply the result by a. Similarly, when we have a fraction in the exponent, we can write the answer in two equivalent ways:

$$a^{\frac{2}{3}} = \sqrt[3]{a^2} = (\sqrt[3]{a})^2, \quad a^{-\frac{1}{2}} = \frac{1}{a^{\frac{1}{2}}} = \frac{1}{\sqrt{a}}, \quad a^{\frac{m}{n}} = \left(\sqrt[n]{a}\right)^m = \sqrt[n]{a^m}.$$

Make sure the above notation makes sense to you. As an exercise, try computing $5^{\frac{4}{3}}$ on your calculator and check that you obtain $8.54987973\ldots$ as the answer.

Even and odd exponents

The function $f(x) = x^n$ behaves differently depending on whether the exponent n is even or odd. If n is odd we have

$$\left(\sqrt[n]{b}\right)^n = \sqrt[n]{b^n} = b, \qquad \text{when } n \text{ is odd.}$$

However, if n is even, the function x^n destroys the sign of the number (see x^2, which maps both $-x$ and x to x^2). The successive application of exponentiation by n and the nth root has the same effect as the absolute value function:

$$\sqrt[n]{b^n} = |b|, \qquad \text{when } n \text{ is even.}$$

Recall that the absolute value function $|x|$ discards the information about the sign of x. The expression $(\sqrt[n]{b})^n$ cannot be computed whenever b is a negative number. The reason is that we can't evaluate $\sqrt[n]{b}$ for $b < 0$ in terms of real numbers, since there is no real number which, multiplied by itself an even number of times, gives a negative number.

Links

[Further reading on exponentiation]
`http://en.wikipedia.org/wiki/Exponentiation`

[More details on scientific notation]
`http://en.wikipedia.org/wiki/Scientific_notation`

Exercises

E1.11 Simplify the following exponential expressions.

a) $2^3 ef \frac{\sqrt{ef}}{(\sqrt{ef})^3}$ b) $\frac{abc}{a^2b^3c^4}$ c) $\frac{(2\alpha)^3}{\alpha}$ d) $(a^3)^2(\frac{1}{b})^2$

E1.12 Simplify the following expressions as much as possible:

a) $\sqrt{3}\sqrt{3}$ b) $\sqrt{9}\sqrt{16}$ c) $\frac{\sqrt[3]{8}\sqrt{3}}{\sqrt{4}}$ d) $\frac{\sqrt{aba}}{\sqrt{b}}$

E1.13 Calculate the values of the following exponential expressions:

a) $\sqrt{2}(\pi)2^{\frac{1}{2}}$ b) $8^{\frac{2}{3}} + 8^{-\frac{2}{3}}$ c) $\left(\frac{(\sqrt[3]{c})^3}{c}\right)^{77}$ d) $\left(\frac{x^2\sqrt{x^4}}{x^3}\right)^2$

E1.14 Find all the values of x that satisfy these equations:

a) $x^2 = a$ b) $x^3 = b$ c) $x^4 = c$ d) $x^5 = d$

E1.15 Coulomb's constant k_e is defined by the formula $k_e = \frac{1}{4\pi\varepsilon_0}$, where ε_0 is the permittivity of free space. Use a calculator to compute the value of k_e starting from $\varepsilon_0 = 8.854 \times 10^{-12}$ and $\pi = 3.14159265$. Report your answer with an appropriate number of digits, even if the calculator gives you a number with more digits.

1.9 Logarithms

Some people think the word "logarithm" refers to some mythical, mathematical beast. Legend has it that logarithms are many-headed, breathe fire, and are extremely difficult to understand. Nonsense! Logarithms are simple. It will take you at most a couple of pages to get used to manipulating them, and that is a good thing because logarithms are used all over the place.

The strength of your sound system is measured in logarithmic units called decibels [dB]. This is because your ears are sensitive only to exponential differences in sound intensity. Logarithms allow us to compare very large numbers and very small numbers on the same scale. If sound were measured in linear units instead of logarithmic units, your sound system's volume control would need to range from 1 to 1 048 576. That would be weird, no? This is why we use the logarithmic scale for volume notches. Using a logarithmic scale, we can go from sound intensity level 1 to sound intensity level 1 048 576 in 20 "progressive" steps. Assume each notch doubles the sound intensity, rather than increasing the intensity by a fixed amount. If the first notch corresponds to 2, the second notch is 4—still probably inaudible, turn it up! By the time you get to the sixth notch you're at $2^6 = 64$ sound intensity, which is the level of audible music. The tenth notch corresponds to sound intensity $2^{10} = 1024$ (medium-strength sound), and finally the twentieth notch reaches a max power of $2^{20} = 1\,048\,576$, at which point the neighbours come to complain.

Definitions

You're hopefully familiar with these following concepts from the previous section:

- b^x: the exponential function base b
- $\exp(x) = e^x$: the exponential function base e, Euler's number
- 2^x: exponential function base 2
- f: the notion of a function $f : \mathbb{R} \to \mathbb{R}$
- f^{-1}: the inverse function of f. The inverse function is defined in terms of f such that $f^{-1}(f(x)) = x$. In other words, if you apply f to some number x and get the output y, and then you pass y through f^{-1}, the output will be x again. The inverse function f^{-1} undoes the effects of the function f.

In this section we'll play with the following new concepts:

- $\log_b(x)$: the logarithm of x base b is the inverse function of b^x.
- $\ln(x)$: the "natural" logarithm base e. This is the inverse of e^x.
- $\log_2(x)$: the logarithm base 2 is the inverse of 2^x.

I say *play* because there is nothing much new to learn here: a logarithm is a clever way to talk about the size of a number; essentially, it tells us how many digits the number has.

Formulas

The main thing to realize is that logs don't really exist on their own. They are defined as the inverses of their corresponding exponential functions. The following statements are equivalent:

$$\log_b(x) = m \quad \Leftrightarrow \quad b^m = x.$$

Logarithms with base e are written $\ln(x)$ for "logarithme naturel" because e is the "natural" base. Another special base is 10 because our numbers are based on the decimal system. The logarithm base 10 $\log_{10}(x)$ tells us roughly the size of the number x—how many digits the number has.

Example When someone working for the System (say someone with a high-paying job in the financial sector) boasts about his or her "six-figure" salary, they are really talking about the log of how much money they make. The "number of figures" N_S in their salary is calculated as 1 plus the logarithm base 10 of their salary S. The formula is

$$N_S = 1 + \log_{10}(S).$$

A salary of $S = 100\,000$ corresponds to $N_S = 1 + \log_{10}(100\,000) = 1 + 5 = 6$ figures.

What is the smallest "seven-figure" salary? We must solve for S given $N_S = 7$ in the formula. We find $7 = 1 + \log_{10}(S)$, which means $6 = \log_{10}(S)$, and—using the inverse relationship between logarithm base 10 and exponentiation base 10—we discover $S = 10^6 = 1\,000\,000$. One million dollars per year! Yes, for this kind of money I see how someone might want to work for the System. But most system pawns never make it to the seven-figure level; I believe the average high-ranking salary is more in the $1 + \log_{10}(250\,000) = 1 + 5.397 = 6.397$ digits range. Wait, a lousy 0.397 extra digits is all it takes to convince some of the smartest people out there to sell their brains to the finance sector? What wankers! Who needs a six-digit salary anyway? Why not make $1 + \log_{10}(55\,000) = 5.74$ digits as a teacher and do something with your life that *actually* matters?

Properties

Moving on, let's discuss two important properties you'll need when dealing with logarithms. Pay attention because the arithmetic rules for logarithms are very different from the usual rules for numbers. Intuitively, you can think of logarithms as a convenient way to refer to the exponents of numbers. The following properties are the logarithmic analogues of the properties of exponents.

Property 1

The first property states that the sum of two logarithms is equal to the logarithm of the product of the *arguments*:

$$\log(x) + \log(y) = \log(xy).$$

From this property, we can derive two other useful ones:

$$\log(x^k) = k\log(x),$$

and

$$\log(x) - \log(y) = \log\left(\frac{x}{y}\right).$$

Proof: For all three equations above, we need to show that the expression on the left is equal to the expression on the right. We met logarithms a very short time ago, so we don't know each other too well yet. In fact, the only thing we know about logs is the inverse relationship with the exponential function. The only way to prove this property is to use this relationship.

The following statement is true for any base b:

$$b^m b^n = b^{m+n}.$$

This follows from first principles. Recall that exponentiation is nothing more than repeated multiplication. If you count the total number of bs multiplied on the left side, you'll find a total of $m+n$ of them, which is what we have on the right.

If we define some new variables x and y such that $b^m = x$ and $b^n = y$, then we can rewrite the equation $b^m b^n = b^{m+n}$ as

$$xy = b^{m+n}.$$

Taking the logarithm of both sides gives us

$$\log_b(xy) = \log_b\left(b^{m+n}\right) = m + n = \log_b(x) + \log_b(y).$$

The last step above uses the definition of the log function again, which states that

$$b^m = x \Leftrightarrow m = \log_b(x) \qquad \text{and} \qquad b^n = y \Leftrightarrow n = \log_b(y).$$

Property 2

This property helps us change from one base to another.

We can express the logarithm in any base B in terms of a ratio of logarithms in another base b. The general formula is

$$\log_B(x) = \frac{\log_b(x)}{\log_b(B)}.$$

For example, the logarithm base 10 of a number S can be expressed as a logarithm base 2 or base e as follows:

$$\log_{10}(S) = \frac{\log_{10}(S)}{1} = \frac{\log_{10}(S)}{\log_{10}(10)} = \frac{\log_2(S)}{\log_2(10)} = \frac{\ln(S)}{\ln(10)}.$$

This property is helpful when you need to compute a logarithm in a base that is not available on your calculator. Suppose you're asked to compute $\log_7(S)$, but your calculator only has a $\boxed{\log_{10}}$ button. You can simulate $\log_7(S)$ by computing $\log_{10}(S)$ and dividing by $\log_{10}(7)$.

Exercises

E1.16 Use the properties of logarithms to simplify the expressions

a) $\log(x) + \log(2y)$ **b)** $\log(z) - \log(z^2)$ **c)** $\log(x) + \log(y/x)$

d) $\log_2(8)$ **e)** $\log_3(\frac{1}{27})$ **f)** $\log_{10}(10000)$

1.10 The Cartesian plane

The Cartesian plane, named after famous philosopher and mathematician René Descartes, is used to visualize pairs of numbers (x, y).

Recall the number line representation for numbers that we introduced in Section 1.3.

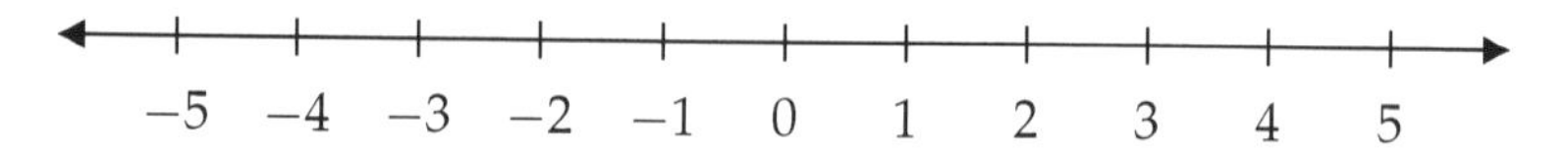

Figure 1.15: Every real number x corresponds to a point on the number line. The number line extends indefinitely to the left (toward negative infinity) and to the right (toward positive infinity).

The Cartesian plane is the two-dimensional generalization of the number line. Generally, we call the plane's horizontal axis "the x-axis" and its vertical axis "the y-axis." We put notches at regular intervals on each axis so we can measure distances.

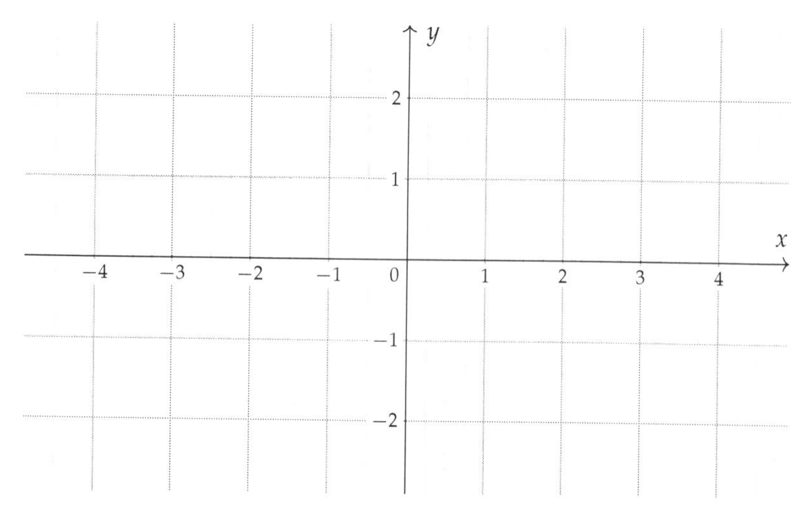

Figure 1.16: Every point in the Cartesian plane corresponds to a pair of real numbers (x, y). Points $P = (P_x, P_y)$, vectors $\vec{v} = (v_x, v_y)$, and graphs of functions $(x, f(x))$ live here.

Figure 1.16 is an example of an empty Cartesian coordinate system. Think of the coordinate system as an empty canvas. What can you draw on this canvas?

Vectors and points

A *point* $P = (P_x, P_y)$ in the Cartesian plane has an x-coordinate and a y-coordinate. To find this point, start from the origin—the point (0,0)—and move a distance P_x on the x-axis, then move a distance P_y on the y-axis.

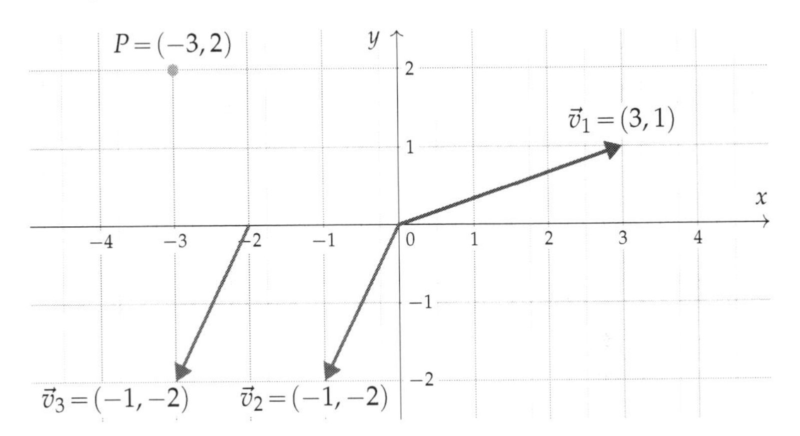

Figure 1.17: A Cartesian plane which shows the point $P = (-3, 2)$ and the vectors $\vec{v}_1 = (3, 1)$ and $\vec{v}_2 = \vec{v}_3 = (-1, -2)$.

Similar to a point, a vector $\vec{v} = (v_x, v_y)$ is a pair of coordinates. Unlike points, we don't necessarily start from the plane's origin when mapping vectors. We draw vectors as arrows that explicitly mark where the vector starts and where it ends. Note that vectors $\vec{v}_2$ and $\vec{v}_3$ illustrated in Figure 1.17 are actually the *same* vector—the "displace left by 1 and down by 2" vector. It doesn't matter where you draw this vector, it will always be the same whether it begins at the plane's origin or elsewhere.

Graphs of functions

The Cartesian plane is great for visualizing functions. You can think of a function as a set of input-output pairs $(x, f(x))$. You can *graph* a function by letting the y-coordinate represent the function's output value:

$$(x, y) = (x, f(x)).$$

For example, with the function $f(x) = x^2$, we can pass a line through the set of points

$$(x, y) = (x, x^2),$$

and obtain the graph shown in Figure 1.18.

When plotting functions by setting $y = f(x)$, we use a special terminology for the two axes. The x-axis represents the *independent* variable (the one that varies freely), and the y-axis represents the *dependent* variable $f(x)$, since $f(x)$ depends on x.

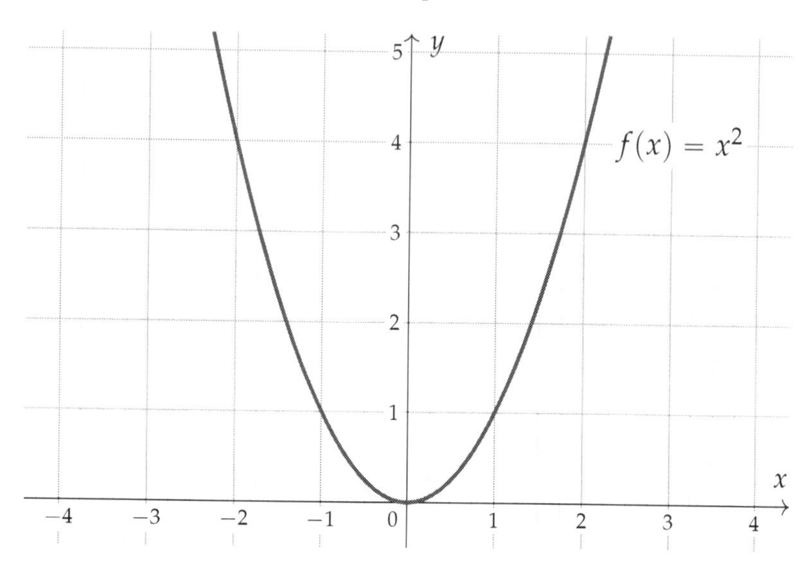

Figure 1.18: The graph of the function $f(x) = x^2$ consists of all pairs of points (x, y) in the Cartesian plane that satisfy $y = x^2$.

To draw the graph of any function $f(x)$, use the following procedure. Imagine making a sweep over all of the possible input values for the function. For each input x, put a point at the coordinates $(x, y) = (x, f(x))$ in the Cartesian plane. Using the graph of a function, you can literally *see* what the function does: the "height" y of the graph at a given x-coordinate tells you the value of the function $f(x)$.

Dimensions

The number line is one dimensional. Every number x can be visualized as a point on the number line. The Cartesian plane has two dimensions: the x dimension and the y dimension. If we need to visualize math concepts in 3D, we can use a three-dimensional coordinate system with x, y, and z axes.

1.11 Functions

We need to have a relationship talk. We need to talk about functions. We use functions to describe the relationships between variables. In particular, functions describe how one variable *depends* on another.

For example, the revenue R from a music concert depends on the number of tickets sold n. If each ticket costs \$25, the revenue from the concert can be written *as a function of* n as follows: $R(n) = 25n$. Solving for n in the equation $R(n) = 7000$ tells us the number of ticket sales needed to generate \$7000 in revenue. This is a simple model of a function; as your knowledge of functions builds, you'll learn how to build more detailed models of reality. For instance, if you need to include a 5% processing charge for issuing the tickets, you can update the revenue model to $R(n) = 0.95 \cdot 25 \cdot n$. If the estimated cost of hosting the concert is $C = \$2000$, then the profit from the concert P can be modelled as

$$\begin{aligned} P(n) &= R(n) \;-\; C \\ &= 0.95 \cdot \$25 \cdot n \;-\; \$2000 \end{aligned}$$

The function $P(n) = 23.75n - 2000$ models the profit from the concert as a function of the number of tickets sold. This is a pretty good model already, and you can always update it later as you learn more information.

The more functions you know, the more tools you have for modelling reality. To "know" a function, you must be able to understand and connect several of its aspects. First you need to know the function's mathematical **definition**, which describes exactly what the function does. Starting from the function's definition, you can use your existing math skills to find the function's domain, its image, and its inverse function. You must also know the **graph** of the function; what the function looks like if you plot x versus $f(x)$ in the Cartesian plane (page 48). It's also a good idea to remember the **values** of the function for some important inputs. Finally—and this is the part that takes time—you must learn about the function's **relations** to other functions.

Definitions

A *function* is a mathematical object that takes numbers as inputs and produces numbers as outputs. We use the notation

$$f\colon A \to B$$

to denote a function from the input set A to the output set B. In this book, we mostly study functions that take real numbers as inputs and give real numbers as outputs: $f\colon \mathbb{R} \to \mathbb{R}$.

We'll now define some fancy technical terms used to describe the input and output sets of functions.

- The *domain* of a function is the set of allowed input values.
- The *image* or *range* of the function f is the set of all possible output values of the function.
- The *codomain* of a function describes the type of outputs the function has.

To illustrate the subtle difference between the image of a function and its codomain, consider the function $f(x) = x^2$. The quadratic function is of the form $f\colon \mathbb{R} \to \mathbb{R}$. The function's domain is $\mathbb{R}$ (it takes real numbers as inputs) and its codomain is $\mathbb{R}$ (the outputs are real numbers too); however, not all outputs are possible. The *image* of the function $f(x) = x^2$ consists only of the nonnegative real numbers $[0, \infty) \equiv \{y \in \mathbb{R} \mid y \geqslant 0\}$.

A function is not a number; rather, it is a *mapping* from numbers to numbers. For any input x, the output value of f for that input is denoted $f(x)$.

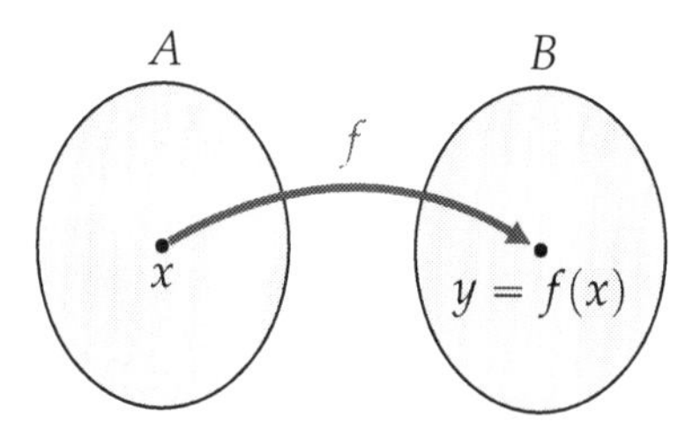

Figure 1.19: An abstract representation of a function f from the set A to the set B. The function f is the arrow which *maps* each input x in A to an output $f(x)$ in B. The output of the function $f(x)$ is also denoted y.

We say "f maps x to $f(x)$," and use the following terminology to classify the type of mapping that a function performs:

- A function is *one-to-one* or *injective* if it maps different inputs to different outputs.
- A function is *onto* or *surjective* if it covers the entire output set (in other words, if the image of the function is equal to the function's codomain).
- A function is *bijective* if it is both injective and surjective. In this case, f is a *one-to-one correspondence* between the input set and the output set: for each of the possible outputs $y \in Y$ (surjective part), there exists exactly one input $x \in X$, such that $f(x) = y$ (injective part).

The term *injective* is an allusion from the 1940s inviting us to picture the actions of injective functions as pipes through which numbers flow like fluids. Since a fluid cannot be compressed, the output space must be at least as large as the input space. A modern synonym for injective functions is to say they are *two-to-two*. If we imagine two specks of paint floating around in the "input fluid," an injective function will contain two distinct specks of paint in the "output fluid." In contrast, non-injective functions can map several different inputs to the same output. For example $f(x) = x^2$ is not injective since the inputs 2 and -2 are both mapped to the output value 4.

Function composition

We can combine two simple functions by chaining them together to build a more complicated function. This act of applying one function after another is called *function composition*. Consider for example the composition:

$$f \circ g\,(x) \equiv f(\,g(x)\,) = z.$$

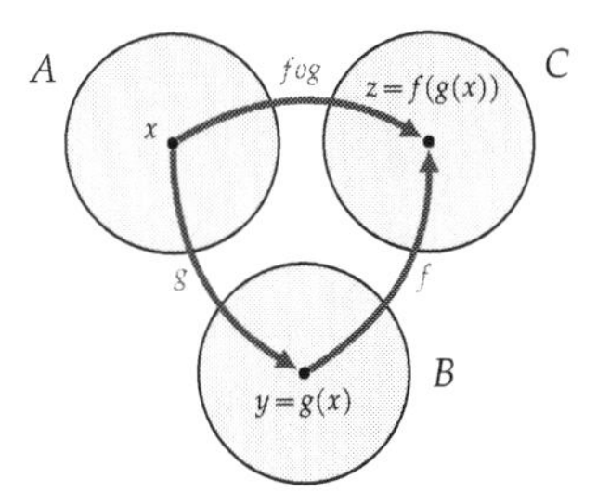

Figure 1.20: The function composition $f \circ g$ describes the combination of first applying the function g, followed by the function f: $f \circ g\,(x) \equiv f(g(x))$.

Figure 1.20 illustrates this concept. First, the function $g : A \to B$ acts on some input x to produce an intermediary value $y = g(x)$ in the set B. The intermediary value y is then passed through the function $f : B \to C$ to produce the final output value $z = f(y) = f(g(x))$ in the set C. We can think of the *composite function* $f \circ g$ as a function in its own right. The function $f \circ g : A \to C$ is defined through the formula $f \circ g\,(x) \equiv f(g(x))$.

Don't worry too much about the $\circ$ symbol—it's just a convenient math notation I wanted you to know about. Writing $f \circ g$ is just as good as writing $f(g(x))$. The important takeaway from Figure 1.20 is that functions can be combined by using the outputs of one function as the inputs to the next. This is a very useful idea for building math models. You can understand many complicated input-output transformations by describing them as compositions of simple functions.

Inverse function

Recall that a *bijective* function is a one-to-one correspondence between a set of input values and a set of output values. For every input value x, there is exactly one corresponding output value y. This means that we can start from any output value y and find the corresponding input value x that produced it.

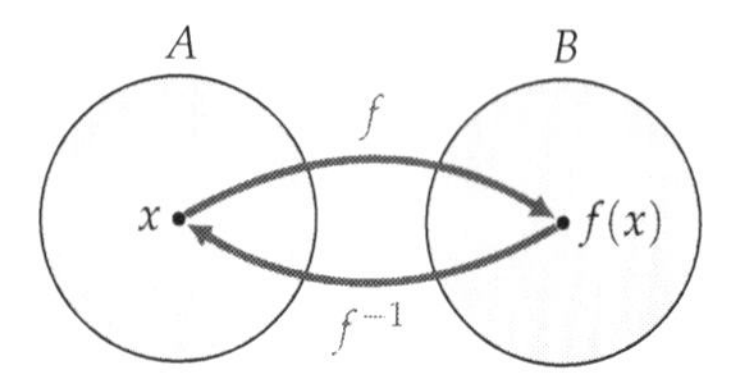

Figure 1.21: The inverse f^{-1} undoes the operation of the function f.

Given a bijective function $f : A \to B$, there exists an inverse function $f^{-1} : B \to A$, which performs the *inverse mapping* of f. If you start from some x, apply f, and then apply f^{-1}, you'll arrive—full circle—back to the original input x:

$$f^{-1}(\, f(x)\,) \equiv f^{-1} \circ f\ (x) = x.$$

In Figure 1.21 the function f is represented as a forward arrow, and the inverse function f^{-1} is represented as a backward arrow that puts the value $f(x)$ back to the x it came from.

Function names

We use short symbols like $+$, $-$, $\times$, and $\div$ to denote most of the important functions used in everyday life. We also use the weird *surd* notation to denote n^{th} root $\sqrt[n]{\ }$ and superscripts to denote exponents. All other functions are identified and denoted by their *name*. If I want to compute the *cosine* of the angle $60°$ (a function describing the ratio between the length of one side of a right-angle triangle and the hypotenuse), I write $\cos(60°)$, which means I want the value of the cos function for the input $60°$.

Incidentally, the function cos has a nice output value for that specific angle: $\cos(60°) \equiv \frac{1}{2}$. Therefore, seeing $\cos(60°)$ somewhere in an equation is the same as seeing $\frac{1}{2}$. To find other values of the function, say $\cos(33.13°)$, you'll need a calculator. All scientific calculators have a convenient little cos button for this very purpose.

Handles on functions

When you learn about functions you learn about the different "handles" by which you can "grab" these mathematical objects. The main handle for a function is its **definition**: it tells you the precise way to calculate the output when you know the input. The function definition is an important handle, but it is also important to "feel" what the function does intuitively. How does one get a feel for a function?

Table of values

One simple way to represent a function is to look at a list of input-output pairs: $\{\{\text{in} = x_1, \text{out} = f(x_1)\}, \{\text{in} = x_2, \text{out} = f(x_2)\}, \{\text{in} = x_3, \text{out} = f(x_3)\}, \ldots\}$. A more compact notation for the input-output pairs is $\{(x_1, f(x_1)), (x_2, f(x_2)), (x_3, f(x_3)), \ldots\}$. You can make your own little **table of values** by picking some random inputs and recording the output of the function in the second column:

$$\begin{array}{rcl} \text{input} = x & \rightarrow & f(x) = \text{output} \\ 0 & \rightarrow & f(0) \\ 1 & \rightarrow & f(1) \\ 55 & \rightarrow & f(55) \\ x_4 & \rightarrow & f(x_4). \end{array}$$

In addition to choosing random numbers for your table, it's also generally a good idea to check the function's values at $x = 0$, $x = 1$, $x = 100$, $x = -1$, and any other important-looking x value.

Function graph

One of the best ways to feel a function is to look at its graph. A graph is a line on a piece of paper that passes through all input-output pairs of a function. Imagine you have a piece of paper, and on it you draw a blank *coordinate system* as in Figure 1.22.

The horizontal axis, sometimes called the *abscissa*, is used to measure x. The vertical axis is used to measure $f(x)$. Because writing out $f(x)$ every time is long and tedious, we use a short, single-letter alias to denote the output value of f as follows:

$$y \equiv f(x) = \text{output}.$$

Think of each input-output pair of the function f as a point (x, y) in the coordinate system. The graph of a function is a representational drawing of everything the function does. If you understand how to interpret this drawing, you can infer everything there is to know about the function.

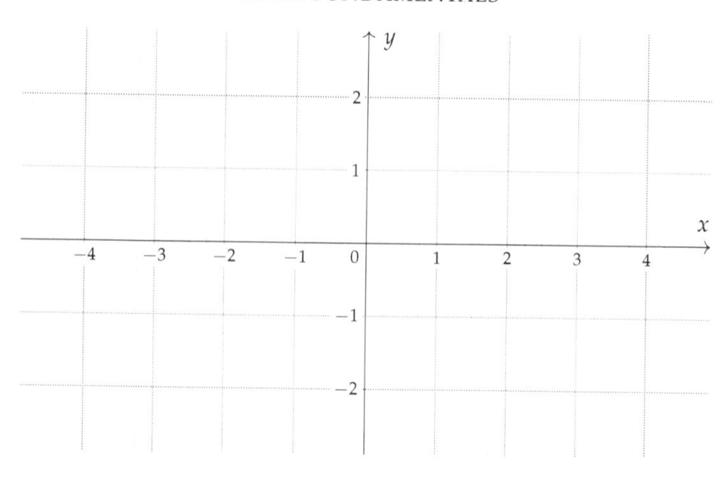

Figure 1.22: An empty (x, y)-coordinate system that you can use to plot the graph of *any* function $f(x)$. The graph of $f(x)$ consists of all the points for which $(x, y) = (x, f(x))$. See Figure 1.18 on page 50 for the graph of $f(x) = x^2$.

Facts and properties

Another way to feel a function is by knowing the function's properties. This approach boils down to learning facts about the function and its relation to other functions. An example of a mathematical fact is $\sin(30°) = \frac{1}{2}$. An example of a mathematical relation is the equation $\sin^2 x + \cos^2 x = 1$, which indicates a link between the sin function and the cos function.

The more you know about a function, the more "paths" your brain builds to connect to that function. Real math knowledge is not memorization; it requires establishing a graph of associations between different areas of information in your brain. Each concept is a *node* in this graph, and each fact you know about this concept is an *edge*. Mathematical thought is the usage of this graph to produce calculations and mathematical arguments called proofs. For example, by connecting your knowledge of the fact $\sin(30°) = \frac{1}{2}$ with the relation $\sin^2 x + \cos^2 x = 1$, you can show that $\cos(30°) = \frac{\sqrt{3}}{2}$. Note the notation $\sin^2(x)$ means $(\sin(x))^2$.

To develop mathematical skills, it is vital to practice path-building between related concepts by solving exercises and reading and writing mathematical proofs. With this book, I will introduce you to some of the many paths linking math concepts; it's up to you to reinforce these paths by using what you've learned to practice solving problems.

Example

Consider the function f from the real numbers to the real numbers ($f\colon \mathbb{R} \to \mathbb{R}$) defined by the quadratic expression,

$$f(x) = x^2 + 2x + 3.$$

The value of f when $x = 1$ is $f(1) = 1^2 + 2(1) + 3 = 1 + 2 + 3 = 6$. When $x = 2$, the output is $f(2) = 2^2 + 2(2) + 3 = 4 + 4 + 3 = 11$. What is the value of f when $x = 0$?

Example 2

Consider the exponential function with base 2:

$$f(x) = 2^x.$$

This function is crucial to computer systems. For instance, RAM memory chips come in powers of two because the memory space is exponential in the number of "address lines" used on the chip. When $x = 1$, $f(1) = 2^1 = 2$. When x is 2 we have $f(2) = 2^2 = 4$. The function is therefore described by the following input-output pairs: $(0,1)$, $(1,2)$, $(2,4)$, $(3,8)$, $(4,16)$, $(5,32)$, $(6,64)$, $(7,128)$, $(8,256)$, $(9,512)$, $(10,1024)$, $(11,2048)$, $(12,4096)$, etc. Recall that any number raised to exponent 0 gives 1. Thus, the exponential function passes through the point $(0,1)$. Recall also that negative exponents lead to fractions: $(-1, \frac{1}{2^1} = \frac{1}{2})$, $(-2, \frac{1}{2^2} = \frac{1}{4})$, $(-3, \frac{1}{2^3} = \frac{1}{8})$, etc.

Discussion

In this section we talked a lot about functions in general but we haven't said much about any function specifically. There are many useful functions out there, and we can't discuss them all here. In the next section, we'll introduce 10 functions of strategic importance for all of science. If you get a grip on these functions, you'll be able to understand all of physics and calculus and handle *any* problem your teacher may throw at you.

To build mathematical intuition, it is essential you understand functions' graphs. Trying to memorize the definitions and the properties of functions is a difficult task. Remembering what the function "looks like" is comparatively easier.

1.12 Functions reference

Your *function vocabulary* determines how well you can express yourself mathematically in the same way that your English vocabulary determines how well you can express yourself in English. The following pages aim to embiggen your function vocabulary so you you'll know how to handle the situation when a teacher tries to pull some trick on you at the final.

If you are seeing these functions for the first time, don't worry about remembering all the facts and properties on the first reading. We will use these functions throughout the rest of the book so you will have plenty of time to become familiar with them. Just remember to return to this section if you ever get stuck on a function.

Line

The equation of a line describes an input-output relationship where the change in the output is *proportional* to the change in the input. The equation of a line is

$$f(x) = mx + b.$$

The constant m describes the slope of the line. The constant b is called the y-intercept and it corresponds to the value of the function when $x = 0$.

The equation of the line $f(x) = mx + b$ is so important that it's worth taking the time to contemplate it for a few seconds. Consider what relationship the equation of $f(x)$ describes for different values of m and b. What happens when m is positive? What happens when m is negative?

I'll leave some blank space here to give you "pages-turned" credit for taking the time.

Graph

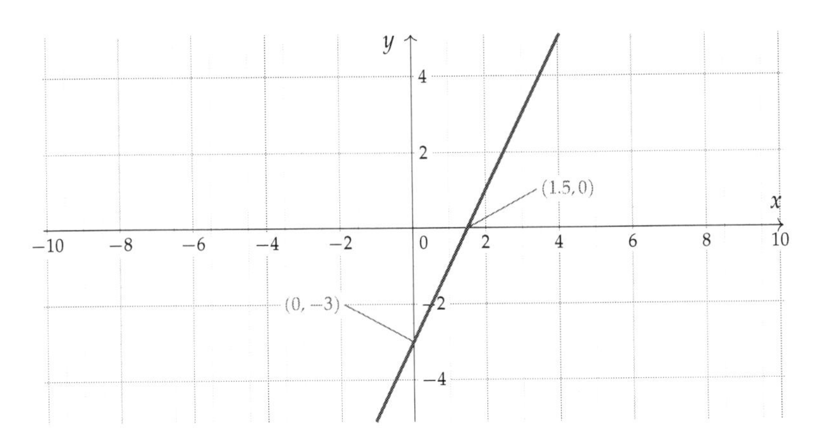

Figure 1.23: The graph of the function $f(x) = 2x - 3$. The slope is $m = 2$. The y-intercept of this line is at $y = -3$. The x-intercept is at $x = \frac{3}{2}$.

Properties

- Domain: $x \in \mathbb{R}$.
  The function $f(x) = mx + b$ is defined for all inputs $x \in \mathbb{R}$.
- Image: $x \in \mathbb{R}$ if $m \neq 0$. If $m = 0$ the function is constant $f(x) = b$, so the image set contains only a single number $\{b\}$.
- $x = -b/m$: the x-intercept of $f(x) = mx + b$. The x-intercept is obtained by solving $f(x) = 0$.
- A unique line passes through any two points (x_1, y_1) and (x_2, y_2) if $x_1 \neq x_2$.
- The inverse to the line $f(x) = mx + b$ is $f^{-1}(x) = \frac{1}{m}(x - b)$, which is also a line.

General equation

A line can also be described in a more symmetric form as a relation:

$$Ax + By = C.$$

This is known as the *general* equation of a line. The general equation for the line shown in Figure 1.23 is $2x - 1y = 3$.

Given the general equation of a line $Ax + By = C$, you can convert to the function form $y = f(x) = mx + b$ using $b = \frac{C}{B}$ and $m = \frac{-A}{B}$.

Square

The function x *squared*, is also called the *quadratic* function, or *parabola*. The formula for the quadratic function is

$$f(x) = x^2.$$

The name "quadratic" comes from the Latin *quadratus* for square, since the expression for the area of a square with side length x is x^2.

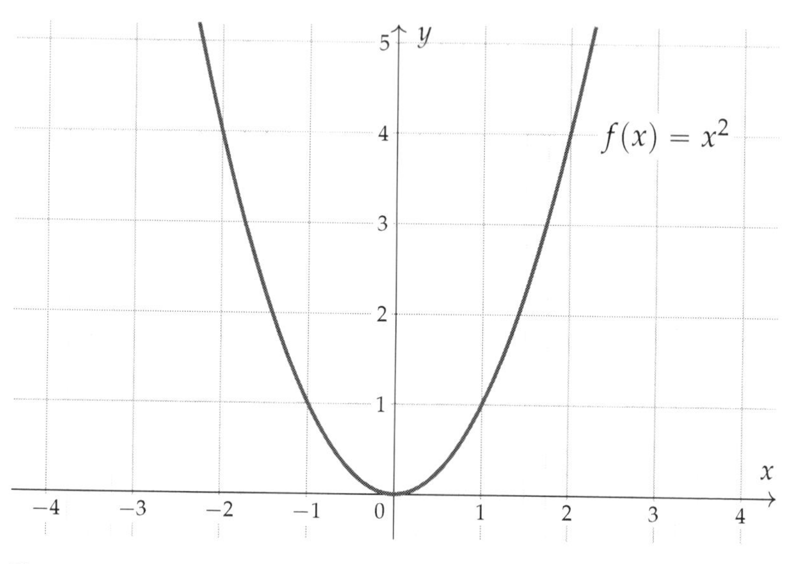

Figure 1.24: Plot of the quadratic function $f(x) = x^2$. The graph of the function passes through the following (x, y) coordinates: $(-2, 4)$, $(-1, 1)$, $(0, 0)$, $(1, 1)$, $(2, 4)$, $(3, 9)$, etc.

Properties

- Domain: $x \in \mathbb{R}$.
  The function $f(x) = x^2$ is defined for all input values $x \in \mathbb{R}$.
- Image: $f(x) \in [0, \infty)$.
  The outputs are never negative: $x^2 \geqslant 0$, for all $x \in \mathbb{R}$.
- The function x^2 is the inverse of the square root function $\sqrt{x}$.
- $f(x) = x^2$ is *two-to-one*: it sends both x and $-x$ to the same output value $x^2 = (-x)^2$.
- The quadratic function is *convex*, meaning it curves upward.

Square root

The square root function is denoted

$$f(x) = \sqrt{x} \equiv x^{\frac{1}{2}}.$$

The square root $\sqrt{x}$ is the inverse function of the square function x^2 for $x \geqslant 0$. The symbol $\sqrt{c}$ refers to the *positive* solution of $x^2 = c$. Note that $-\sqrt{c}$ is also a solution of $x^2 = c$.

Graph

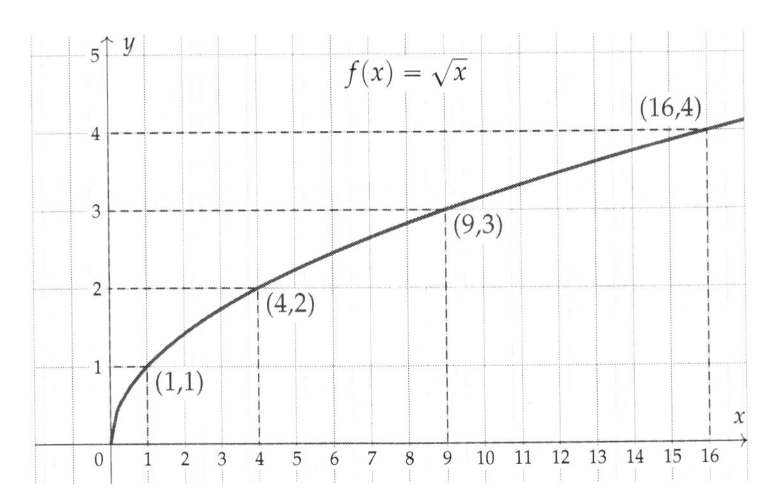

Figure 1.25: The graph of the function $f(x) = \sqrt{x}$. The domain of the function is $x \in [0, \infty)$. You can't take the square root of a negative number.

Properties

- Domain: $x \in [0, \infty)$.
  The function $f(x) = \sqrt{x}$ is only defined for nonnegative inputs $x \geqslant 0$. There is no real number y such that y^2 is negative, hence the function $f(x) = \sqrt{x}$ is not defined for negative inputs x.
- Image: $f(x) \in [0, \infty)$.
  The outputs of the function $f(x) = \sqrt{x}$ are never negative: $\sqrt{x} \geqslant 0$, for all $x \in [0, \infty)$.

In addition to *square* root, there is also *cube* root $f(x) = \sqrt[3]{x} \equiv x^{\frac{1}{3}}$, which is the inverse function for the cubic function $f(x) = x^3$. We have $\sqrt[3]{8} = 2$ since $2 \times 2 \times 2 = 8$. More generally, we can define the nth-root function $\sqrt[n]{x}$ as the inverse function of x^n.

Absolute value

The *absolute value* function tells us the size of numbers without paying attention to whether the number is positive or negative. We can compute a number's absolute value by *ignoring the sign* of the number. A number's absolute value corresponds to its distance from the origin of the number line.

Another way of thinking about the absolute value function is to say it multiplies negative numbers by -1 to "cancel" their negative sign:

$$f(x) = |x| = \begin{cases} x & \text{if } x \geqslant 0, \\ -x & \text{if } x < 0. \end{cases}$$

Graph

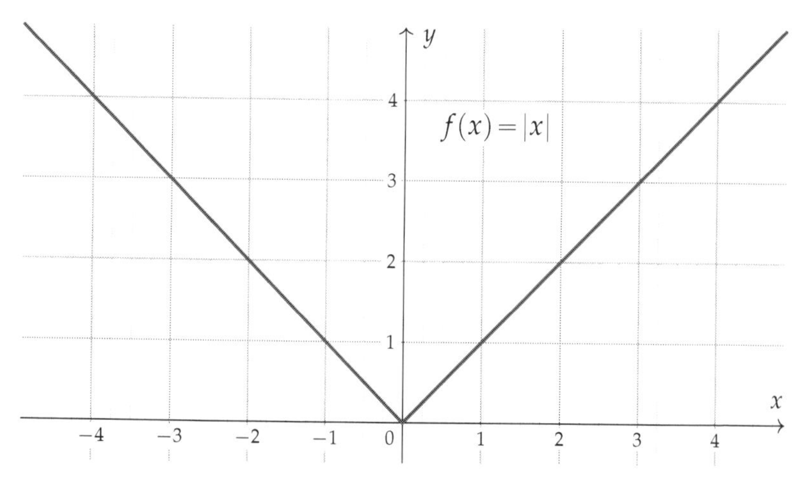

Figure 1.26: The graph of the absolute value function $f(x) = |x|$.

Properties

- Always returns a nonnegative number
- The combination of squaring followed by square-root is equivalent to the absolute value function:

$$\sqrt{x^2} \equiv |x|,$$

since squaring destroys the sign.

Polynomials

The polynomials are a very useful family of functions. For example, quadratic polynomials of the form $f(x) = ax^2 + bx + c$ often arise when describing physics phenomena. The general equation for a polynomial function of degree n is written,

$$f(x) = a_0 + a_1 x + a_2 x^2 + a_3 x^3 + \cdots + a_n x^n.$$

The constants a_i are known as the *coefficients* of the polynomial.

Parameters

- x: the variable
- a_0: the constant term
- a_1: the *linear* coefficient, or *first-order* coefficient
- a_2: the *quadratic* coefficient
- a_3: the *cubic* coefficient
- a_n: the nth order coefficient
- n: the *degree* of the polynomial. The degree of $f(x)$ is the largest power of x that appears in the polynomial.

A polynomial of degree n has $n+1$ coefficients: $a_0, a_1, a_2, \ldots, a_n$.

Properties

- Domain: $x \in \mathbb{R}$. Polynomials are defined for all inputs $x \in \mathbb{R}$.
- The roots of $f(x)$ are the values of x for which $f(x) = 0$.
- The image of a polynomial function depends on the coefficients.
- The sum of two polynomials is also a polynomial.

The most general first-degree polynomial is a line $f(x) = mx + b$, where m and b are arbitrary constants. The most general second-degree polynomial is $f(x) = a_2 x^2 + a_1 x + a_0$, where again a_0, a_1, and a_2 are arbitrary constants. We call a_k the *coefficient* of x^k, since this is the number that appears in front of x^k. Following the pattern, a third-degree polynomial will look like $f(x) = a_3 x^3 + a_2 x^2 + a_1 x + a_0$.

In general, a polynomial of degree n has the equation

$$f(x) = a_n x^n + a_{n-1} x^{n-1} + \cdots + a_2 x^2 + a_1 x + a_0.$$

You can add two polynomials by adding together their coefficients:

$$\begin{aligned} f(x) + g(x) &= (a_n x^n + \cdots + a_1 x + a_0) \; + \; (b_n x^n + \cdots + b_1 x + b_0) \\ &= (a_n + b_n) x^n + \cdots + (a_1 + b_1) x + (a_0 + b_0). \end{aligned}$$

The subtraction of two polynomials works similarly. We can also multiply polynomials together using the general algebra rules of for expanding brackets. The notion of polynomial division also exists, but that's a more advanced topic that we won't discuss for now. Instead let's focus on the basics.

Solving polynomial equations

Very often in math, you will have to *solve* polynomial equations of the form

$$A(x) = B(x),$$

where $A(x)$ and $B(x)$ are both polynomials. Recall from earlier that to *solve*, we must find the value of x that makes the equality true.

Say the revenue of your company is a function of the number of products sold x, and can be expressed as $R(x) = 2x^2 + 2x$. Say also the cost you incur to produce x objects is $C(x) = x^2 + 5x + 10$. You want to determine the amount of product you need to produce to break even, that is, so that revenue equals cost: $R(x) = C(x)$. To find the break-even value x, solve the equation

$$2x^2 + 2x = x^2 + 5x + 10.$$

This may seem complicated since there are xs all over the place. No worries! We can turn the equation into its "standard form," and then use the quadratic formula. First, move all the terms to one side until only zero remains on the other side:

$$\begin{aligned} 2x^2 + 2x \quad - x^2 &= \cancel{x^2} + 5x + 10 \quad -\cancel{x^2} \\ x^2 + 2x \quad - 5x &= \cancel{5x} + 10 \quad -\cancel{5x} \\ x^2 - 3x \quad - 10 &= \cancel{10} \quad -\cancel{10} \\ x^2 - 3x - 10 &= 0. \end{aligned}$$

Remember, if we perform the same operations on both sides of the equation, the resulting equation has the same solutions. Therefore, the values of x that satisfy

$$x^2 - 3x - 10 = 0,$$

namely $x = -2$ and $x = 5$, also satisfy

$$2x^2 + 2x = x^2 + 5x + 10,$$

which is the original problem we're trying to solve.

This "shuffling of terms" approach will work for any polynomial equation $A(x) = B(x)$. We can always rewrite it as $C(x) = 0$, where

$C(x)$ is a new polynomial with coefficients equal to the difference of the coefficients of A and B. Don't worry about which side you move all the coefficients to because $C(x) = 0$ and $0 = -C(x)$ have exactly the same solutions. Furthermore, the degree of the polynomial C can be no greater than that of A or B.

The form $C(x) = 0$ is the *standard form* of a polynomial, and we'll explore several formulas you can use to find its solution(s).

Formulas

The formula for solving the polynomial equation $P(x) = 0$ depends on the *degree* of the polynomial in question.

For a first-degree polynomial equation, $P_1(x) = mx + b = 0$, the solution is $x = \frac{-b}{m}$: just move b to the other side and divide by m.

For a second-degree polynomial,

$$P_2(x) = ax^2 + bx + c = 0,$$

the solutions are $x_1 = \frac{-b+\sqrt{b^2-4ac}}{2a}$ and $x_2 = \frac{-b-\sqrt{b^2-4ac}}{2a}$.

If $b^2 - 4ac < 0$, the solutions will involve taking the square root of a negative number. In those cases, we say no real solutions exist.

There is also a formula for polynomials of degree 3 and 4, but they are complicated. For polynomials with order $\geqslant 5$, there does not exist a general analytical solution.

Using a computer

When solving real-world problems, you'll often run into much more complicated equations. To find the solutions of anything more complicated than the quadratic equation, I recommend using a computer algebra system like `SymPy`: `http://live.sympy.org`.

To make `SymPy` solve the standard-form equation $C(x) = 0$, call the function `solve(expr,var)`, where the expression `expr` corresponds to $C(x)$, and `var` is the variable you want to solve for. For example, to solve $x^2 - 3x + 2 = 0$, type in the following:

```
>>> solve(x**2 - 3*x + 2, x)              # usage: solve(expr, var)
[1, 2]
```

The function `solve` will find the roots of any equation of the form `expr = 0`. Indeed, we can verify that $x^2 - 3x + 2 = (x-1)(x-2)$, so $x = 1$ and $x = 2$ are the two roots.

Substitution trick

Sometimes you can solve fourth-degree polynomials by using the quadratic formula. Say you're asked to solve for x in

$$g(x) = x^4 - 7x^2 + 10 = 0.$$

Imagine this problem is on your exam, where you are not allowed to use a computer. How does the teacher expect you to solve for x? The trick is to substitute $y = x^2$ and rewrite the same equation as

$$g(y) = y^2 - 7y + 10 = 0,$$

which you can solve by applying the quadratic formula. If you obtain the solutions $y = \alpha$ and $y = \beta$, then the solutions to the original fourth-degree polynomial are $x = \pm\sqrt{\alpha}$ and $x = \pm\sqrt{\beta}$, since $y = x^2$.

Since we're not taking an exam right now, we are allowed to use the computer to find the roots:

```
>>> solve(y**2 - 7*y + 10, y)
[2, 5]
>>> solve(x**4 - 7*x**2 + 10, x)
[sqrt(2), -sqrt(2), sqrt(5), -sqrt(5)]
```

Note how the second-degree polynomial has two roots, while the fourth-degree polynomial has four roots.

Even and odd functions

The polynomials form an entire family of functions. Depending on the choice of degree n and coefficients $a_0, a_1, \ldots, a_n$, a polynomial function can take on many different shapes. Consider the following observations about the symmetries of polynomials:

- If a polynomial contains only even powers of x, like $f(x) = 1 + x^2 - x^4$ for example, we call this polynomial *even*. Even polynomials have the property $f(x) = f(-x)$. The sign of the input doesn't matter.
- If a polynomial contains only odd powers of x, for example $g(x) = x + x^3 - x^9$, we call this polynomial *odd*. Odd polynomials have the property $g(x) = -g(-x)$.
- If a polynomial has both even and odd terms then it is neither even nor odd.

The terminology of *odd* and *even* applies to functions in general and not just to polynomials. All functions that satisfy $f(x) = f(-x)$ are called *even functions*, and all functions that satisfy $f(x) = -f(-x)$ are called *odd functions*.

Sine

The sine function represents a fundamental unit of vibration. The graph of $\sin(x)$ *oscillates* up and down and crosses the x-axis multiple times. The shape of the graph of $\sin(x)$ corresponds to the shape of a vibrating string. See Figure 1.27.

In the remainder of this book, we'll meet the function $\sin(x)$ many times. We'll define the function $\sin(x)$ more formally as a trigonometric ratio in Section 1.15 (page 83). In Chapter 3 we'll use $\sin(x)$ and $\cos(x)$ (another trigonometric ratio) to work out the *components* of vectors. Later in Chapter 4, we'll learn how the sine function can be used to describe waves and periodic motion.

At this point in the book, however, we don't want to go into too much detail about all these applications. Let's hold off on the discussion about vectors, triangles, angles, and ratios of lengths of sides and instead just focus on the graph of the function $f(x) = \sin(x)$.

Graph

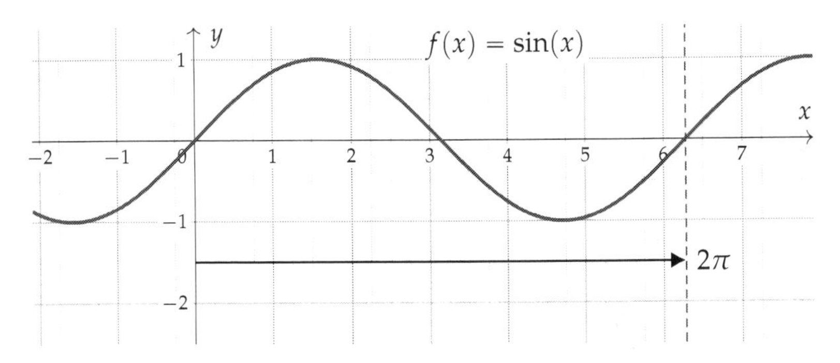

Figure 1.27: The graph of the function $y = \sin(x)$ passes through the following (x, y) coordinates: $(0,0)$, $(\frac{\pi}{6}, \frac{1}{2})$, $(\frac{\pi}{4}, \frac{\sqrt{2}}{2})$, $(\frac{\pi}{3}, \frac{\sqrt{3}}{2})$, $(\frac{\pi}{2}, 1)$, $(\frac{2\pi}{3}, \frac{\sqrt{3}}{2})$, $(\frac{3\pi}{4}, \frac{\sqrt{2}}{2})$, $(\frac{5\pi}{6}, \frac{1}{2})$, and $(\pi, 0)$. For $x \in [\pi, 2\pi]$ the function has the same shape as for $x \in [0, \pi]$ but with negative values.

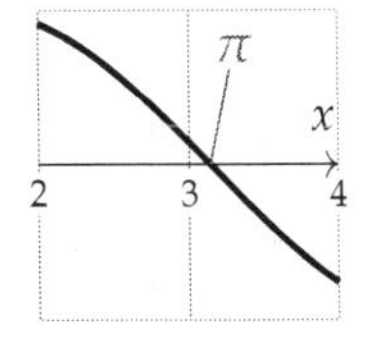

Figure 1.28: The function $f(x) = \sin(x)$ crosses the x-axis at $x = \pi$.

Let's start at $x = 0$ and follow the graph of the function $\sin(x)$

as it goes up and down. The graph starts from $(0,0)$ and smoothly increases until it reaches the maximum value at $x = \frac{\pi}{2}$. Afterward, the function comes back down to cross the x-axis at $x = \pi$. After π, the function drops below the x-axis and reaches its minimum value of -1 at $x = \frac{3\pi}{2}$. It then travels up again to cross the x-axis at $x = 2\pi$. This 2π-long cycle repeats after $x = 2\pi$. This is why we call the function *periodic*—the shape of the graph repeats.

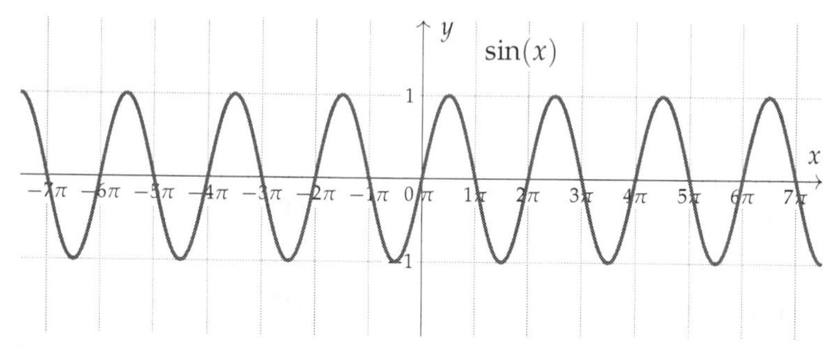

Figure 1.29: The graph of $\sin(x)$ from $x = 0$ to $x = 2\pi$ repeats periodically everywhere else on the number line.

Properties

- Domain: $x \in \mathbb{R}$.
  The function $f(x) = \sin(x)$ is defined for all input values $x \in \mathbb{R}$.
- Image: $\sin(x) \in [-1, 1]$.
  The outputs of the sine function are always between -1 and 1.
- Roots: $[\ldots, -3\pi, -2\pi, -\pi, 0, \pi, 2\pi, 3\pi, \ldots]$.
  The function $\sin(x)$ has roots at all multiples of π.
- The function is periodic, with period 2π: $\sin(x) = \sin(x + 2\pi)$.
- The sin function is *odd*: $\sin(x) = -\sin(-x)$
- Relation to cos: $\sin^2 x + \cos^2 x = 1$
- Relation to csc: $\csc(x) \equiv \frac{1}{\sin x}$ (csc is read *cosecant*)
- The inverse function of $\sin(x)$ is denoted as $\sin^{-1}(x)$, not to be confused with $(\sin(x))^{-1} = \frac{1}{\sin(x)} \equiv \csc(x)$. Sometimes the function $\sin^{-1}(x)$ is denoted "$\arcsin(x)$."
- The number $\sin(\theta)$ is the length-ratio of the vertical side and the hypotenuse in a right-angle triangle with angle θ at the base.

Links

[See the Wikipedia page for nice illustrations]
`http://en.wikipedia.org/wiki/Sine`

Cosine

The cosine function is the same as the sine function *shifted* by $\frac{\pi}{2}$ to the left: $\cos(x) = \sin(x + \frac{\pi}{2})$. Thus everything you know about the sine function also applies to the cosine function.

Graph

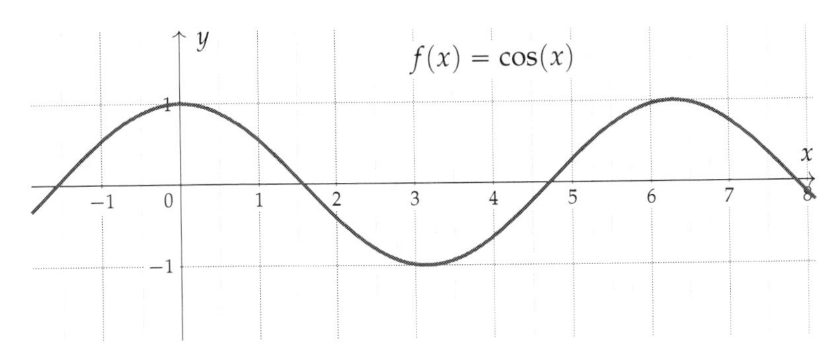

Figure 1.30: The graph of the function $y = \cos(x)$ passes through the following (x, y) coordinates: $(0,1)$, $(\frac{\pi}{6}, \frac{\sqrt{3}}{2})$, $(\frac{\pi}{4}, \frac{\sqrt{2}}{2})$, $(\frac{\pi}{3}, \frac{1}{2})$, $(\frac{\pi}{2}, 0)$, $(\frac{2\pi}{3}, -\frac{1}{2})$, $(\frac{3\pi}{4}, -\frac{\sqrt{2}}{2})$, $(\frac{5\pi}{6}, -\frac{\sqrt{3}}{2})$, and $(\pi, -1)$.

The cos function starts at $\cos(0) = 1$, then drops down to cross the x-axis at $x = \frac{\pi}{2}$. Cos continues until it reaches its minimum value at $x = \pi$. The function then moves upward, crossing the x-axis again at $x = \frac{3\pi}{2}$, and reaching its maximum value again at $x = 2\pi$.

Properties

- Domain: $x \in \mathbb{R}$
- Image: $\cos(x) \in [-1, 1]$
- Roots: $[\ldots, -\frac{3\pi}{2}, -\frac{\pi}{2}, \frac{\pi}{2}, \frac{3\pi}{2}, \frac{5\pi}{2}, \ldots]$
- Relation to sin: $\sin^2 x + \cos^2 x = 1$
- Relation to sec: $\sec(x) \equiv \frac{1}{\cos x}$ (sec is read *secant*)
- The inverse function of $\cos(x)$ is denoted $\cos^{-1}(x)$
- The cos function is *even*: $\cos(x) = \cos(-x)$
- The number $\cos(\theta)$ is the length-ratio of the horizontal side and the hypotenuse in a right-angle triangle with angle θ at the base

Tangent

The tangent function is the ratio of the sine and cosine functions:

$$f(x) = \tan(x) \equiv \frac{\sin(x)}{\cos(x)}.$$

Graph

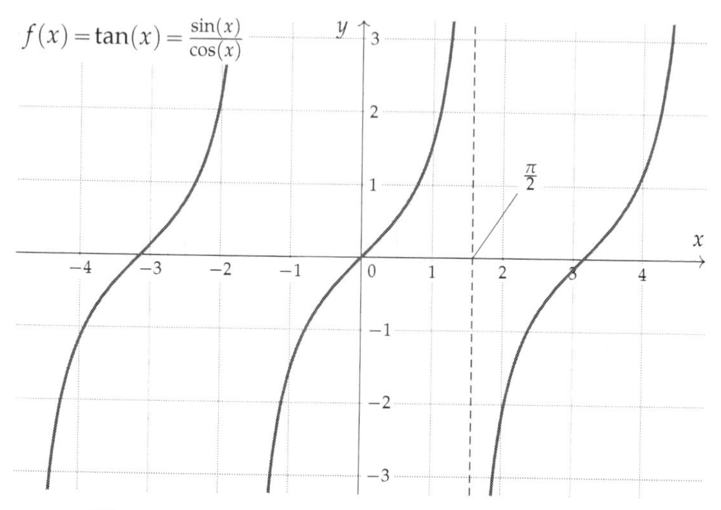

Figure 1.31: The graph of the function $f(x) = \tan(x)$.

Properties

- Domain: $\{x \in \mathbb{R} \mid x \neq \frac{(2n+1)\pi}{2}$ for any $n \in \mathbb{Z}\}$.
- Image: $x \in \mathbb{R}$.
- The function tan is periodic with period π.
- The tan function "blows up" at values of x where $\cos x = 0$. These are called *asymptotes* of the function and their locations are $x = \ldots, \frac{-3\pi}{2}, \frac{-\pi}{2}, \frac{\pi}{2}, \frac{3\pi}{2}, \ldots$.
- Value at $x = 0$: $\tan(0) = \frac{0}{1} = 0$, because $\sin(0) = 0$.
- Value at $x = \frac{\pi}{4}$: $\tan\left(\frac{\pi}{4}\right) = \frac{\sin(\frac{\pi}{4})}{\cos(\frac{\pi}{4})} = \frac{\frac{\sqrt{2}}{2}}{\frac{\sqrt{2}}{2}} = 1$.
- The number $\tan(\theta)$ is the length-ratio of the vertical and the horizontal sides in a right-angle triangle with angle θ.
- The inverse function of $\tan(x)$ is $\tan^{-1}(x)$.
- The inverse tangent function is used to compute the angle at the base in a right-angle triangle with horizontal side length ℓ_h and vertical side length ℓ_v: $\theta = \tan^{-1}\left(\frac{\ell_v}{\ell_h}\right)$.

Exponential

The exponential function base $e = 2.7182818\ldots$ is denoted

$$f(x) = e^x \equiv \exp(x).$$

Graph

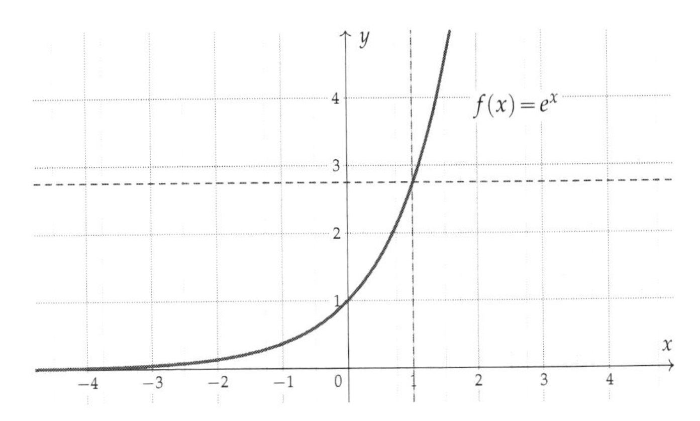

Figure 1.32: The graph of the exponential function $f(x) = e^x$ passes through the following (x, y) coordinates: $(-2, \frac{1}{e^2})$, $(-1, \frac{1}{e})$, $(0, 1)$, $(1, e)$, $(2, e^2)$, $(3, e^3 = 20.08\ldots)$, $(5, 148.41\ldots)$, and $(10, 22026.46\ldots)$.

Properties

- Domain: $x \in \mathbb{R}$
- Image: $e^x \in (0, \infty)$
- $f(a)f(b) = f(a+b)$ since $e^a e^b = e^{a+b}$
- The derivative (the slope of the graph) of the exponential function is the exponential function: $f(x) = e^x \;\; \Rightarrow \;\; f'(x) = e^x$

A more general exponential function would be $f(x) = Ae^{\gamma x}$, where A is the initial value, and γ (the Greek letter *gamma*) is the *rate* of the exponential. For $\gamma > 0$, the function $f(x)$ is increasing, as in Figure 1.32. For $\gamma < 0$, the function is decreasing and tends to zero for large values of x. The case $\gamma = 0$ is special since $e^0 = 1$, so $f(x)$ is a constant of $f(x) = A1^x = A$.

Links

[The exponential function 2^x evaluated]
`http://www.youtube.com/watch?v=e4MSN6IImpI`

Natural logarithm

The natural logarithm function is denoted

$$f(x) = \ln(x) = \log_e(x).$$

The function $\ln(x)$ is the inverse function of the exponential e^x.

Graph

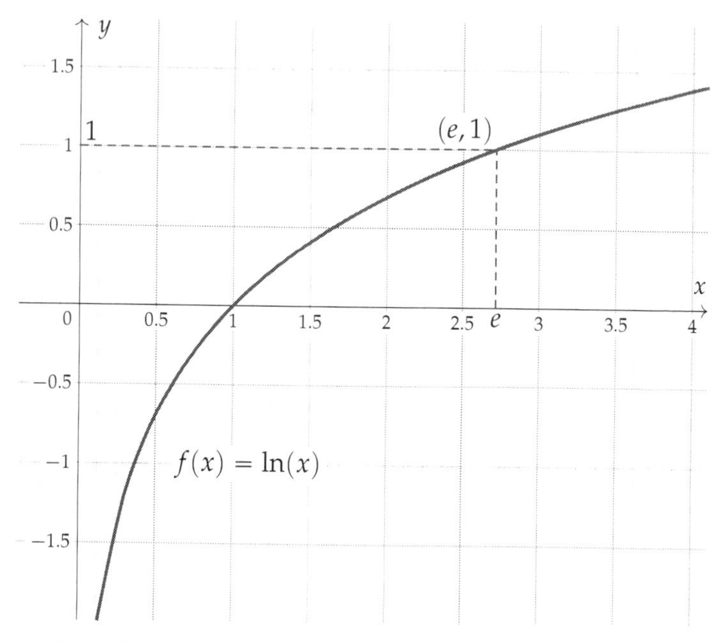

Figure 1.33: The graph of the function $\ln(x)$ passes through the following (x, y) coordinates: $(\frac{1}{e^2}, -2)$, $(\frac{1}{e}, -1)$, $(1, 0)$, $(e, 1)$, $(e^2, 2)$, $(e^3, 3)$, $(148.41\ldots, 5)$, and $(22026.46\ldots, 10)$.

Exercises

E1.17 Find the domain, the image, and the roots of $f(x) = 2\cos(x)$.

E1.18 What are the degrees of the following polynomials? Are they even, odd, or neither?

a) $p(x) = x^2 - 5x^4 + 1$ **b)** $q(x) = x - x^3 + x^5 - x^7$

E1.19 Solve for x in the following polynomial equations.

a) $3x + x^2 = x - 15 + 2x^2$ **b)** $3x^2 - 4x - 4 + x^3 = x^3 + 2x + 2$

1.13 Function transformations

Often, we're asked to adjust the shape of a function by scaling it or moving it, so that it passes through certain points. For example, if we wanted to make a function g with the same shape as the absolute value function $f(x) = |x|$, but moved up by three units so that $g(0) = 3$, we would use the function $g(x) = |x| + 3$.

In this section, we'll discuss the four basic transformations you can perform on *any* function f to obtain a transformed function g:

- Vertical translation: $g(x) = f(x) + k$
- Horizontal translation: $g(x) = f(x - h)$
- Vertical scaling: $g(x) = Af(x)$
- Horizontal scaling: $g(x) = f(ax)$

By applying these transformations, we can *move* and *stretch* a generic function to give it any desired shape.

The next couple of pages illustrate all of the above transformations on the function

$$f(x) = 6.75(x^3 - 2x^2 + x).$$

We'll work with this function because it has distinctive features in both the horizontal and vertical directions. By observing this function's graph, we see its x-intercepts are at $x = 0$ and $x = 1$. We can confirm this mathematically by factoring the expression:

$$f(x) = 6.75x(x^2 - 2x + 1) = 6.75x(x - 1)^2.$$

The function $f(x)$ also has a local maximum at $x = \frac{1}{3}$, and the value of the function at that maximum is $f(\frac{1}{3}) = 1$.

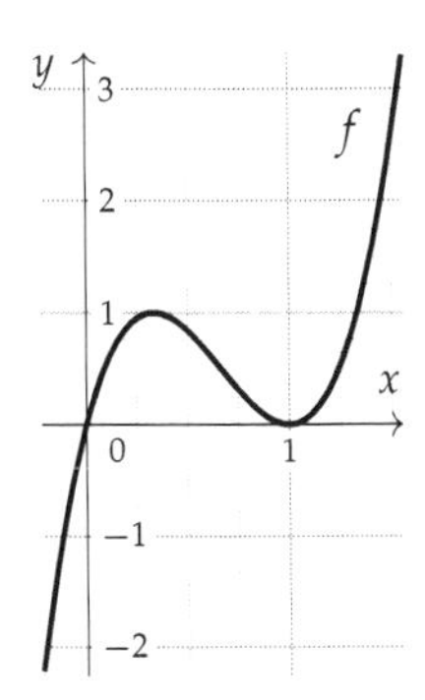

Figure 1.34: Graph of the function $f(x) = 6.75(x^3 - 2x^2 + x)$.

Vertical translations

To move a function $f(x)$ *up* by k units, add k to the function:

$$g(x) = f(x) + k.$$

The function $g(x)$ will have exactly the same shape as $f(x)$, but it will be *translated* (the mathematical term for moved) upward by k units.

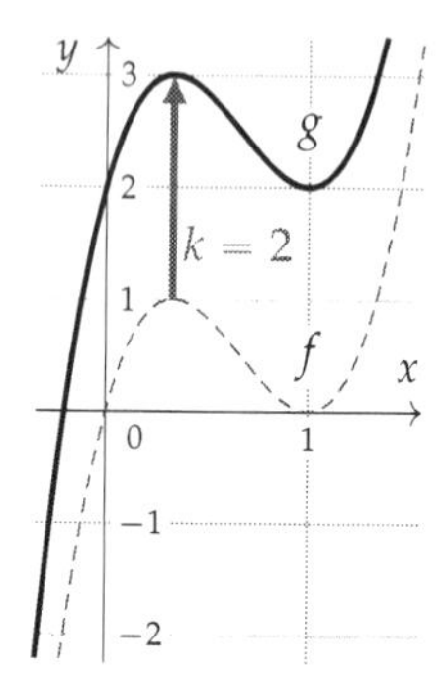

Figure 1.35: The graph of the function $g(x) = f(x) + 2$ has the same shape as the graph of $f(x)$ translated upward by two units.

Recall the function $f(x) = 6.75(x^3 - 2x^2 + x)$. To move the function up by $k = 2$ units, we can write

$$g(x) = f(x) + 2 = 6.75(x^3 - 2x^2 + x) + 2,$$

and the graph of $g(x)$ will be as it is shown in Figure 1.35. Recall the original function $f(x)$ crosses the x-axis at $x = 0$. The transformed function $g(x)$ has the property $g(0) = 2$. The maximum at $x = \frac{1}{3}$ has similarly shifted in value from $f(\frac{1}{3}) = 1$ to $g(\frac{1}{3}) = 3$.

Horizontal translation

We can move a function f to the right by h units by *subtracting* h from x and using $(x - h)$ as the function's input argument:

$$g(x) = f(x - h).$$

The point $(0, f(0))$ on $f(x)$ now corresponds to the point $(h, g(h))$ on $g(x)$.

Figure 1.36 shows the function $f(x) = 6.75(x^3 - 2x^2 + x)$, as well as the function $g(x)$, which is shifted to the right by $h = 2$ units:

$$g(x) = f(x - 2) = 6.75\left[(x-2)^3 - 2(x-2)^2 + (x-2)\right].$$

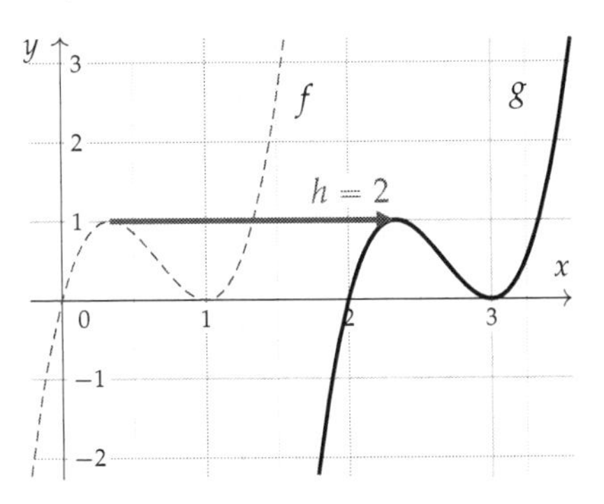

Figure 1.36: The graph of the function $g(x) = f(x-2)$ has the same shape as the graph of $f(x)$ translated to the right by two units.

The original function f gives us $f(0) = 0$ and $f(1) = 0$, so the new function $g(x)$ must give $g(2) = 0$ and $g(3) = 0$. The maximum at $x = \frac{1}{3}$ has similarly shifted by two units to the right, $g(2 + \frac{1}{3}) = 1$.

Vertical scaling

To stretch or compress the shape of a function vertically, we can multiply it by some constant A and obtain

$$g(x) = Af(x).$$

If $|A| > 1$, the function will be stretched. If $|A| < 1$, the function will be compressed. If A is negative, the function will flip upside down, which is a *reflection* through the x-axis.

There is an important difference between vertical translation and vertical scaling. Translation moves all points of the function by the same amount, whereas scaling moves each point proportionally to that point's distance from the x-axis.

The function $f(x) = 6.75(x^3 - 2x^2 + x)$, when stretched vertically by a factor of $A = 2$, becomes the function

$$g(x) = 2f(x) = 13.5(x^3 - 2x^2 + x).$$

The x-intercepts $f(0) = 0$ and $f(1) = 0$ do not move, and remain at $g(0) = 0$ and $g(1) = 0$. All values of $f(x)$ have been stretched upward by a factor of 2, as we can verify using the point $f(1.5) = 2.5$, which has become $g(1.5) = 5$. The maximum at $x = \frac{1}{3}$ has doubled in value to become $g(\frac{1}{3}) = 2$.

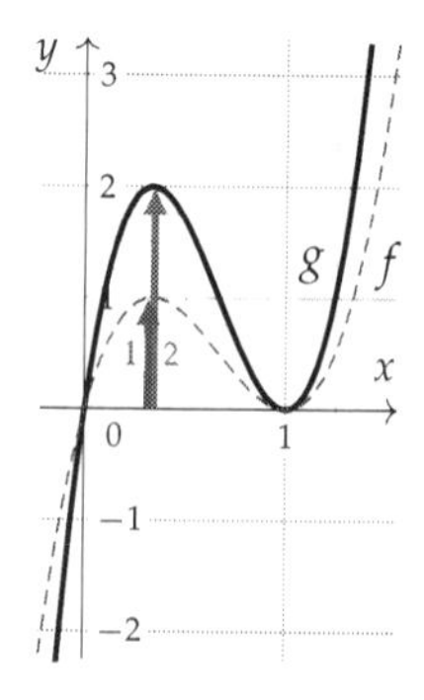

Figure 1.37: The graph of the function $g(x) = 2f(x)$ looks like $f(x)$ vertically stretched by a factor of two.

Horizontal scaling

To stretch or compress a function horizontally, we can multiply the input value by some constant a to obtain:

$$g(x) = f(ax).$$

If $|a| > 1$, the function will be compressed. If $|a| < 1$, the function will be stretched. Note that the behaviour here is the opposite of vertical scaling. If a is a negative number, the function will also flip horizontally, which is a reflection through the y-axis.

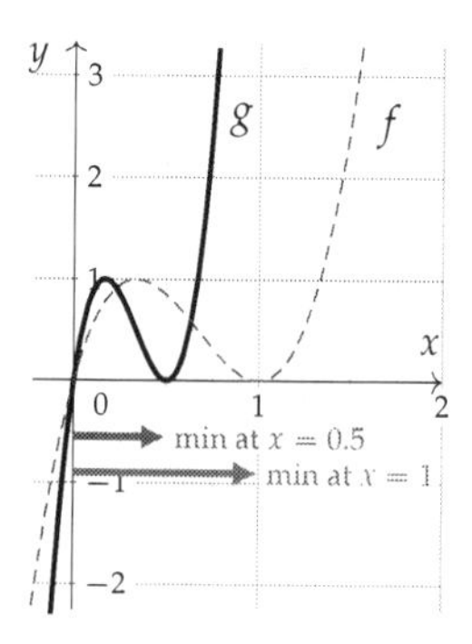

Figure 1.38: The graph of the function $g(x) = f(2x)$ looks like $f(x)$ horizontally compressed by a factor of two.

Figure 1.38 shows the function $f(x) = 6.75(x^3 - 2x^2 + x)$, as well as the function $g(x)$, which is $f(x)$ compressed horizontally by a factor of $a = 2$:

$$\begin{aligned} g(x) &= f(2x) \\ &= 6.75\Big[(2x)^3 - 2(2x)^2 + (2x)\Big]. \end{aligned}$$

The x-intercept $f(0) = 0$ does not move since it is on the y-axis. The x-intercept $f(1) = 0$ does move, however, and we have $g(0.5) = 0$. The maximum at $x = \frac{1}{3}$ moves to $g(\frac{1}{6}) = 1$. All points of $f(x)$ are compressed toward the y-axis by a factor of 2.

General quadratic function

The general quadratic function takes the form

$$f(x) = A(x-h)^2 + k,$$

where x is the input, and $A, h,$ and k are the *parameters*.

Parameters

- A: the slope multiplier
  - ▷ The larger the absolute value of A, the steeper the slope.
  - ▷ If $A < 0$ (negative), the function opens downward.
- h: the horizontal displacement of the function. Notice that subtracting a number inside the bracket $(\ )^2$ (positive h) makes the function go to the right.
- k: the vertical displacement of the function

Graph

The graph in Figure 1.39 illustrates a quadratic function with parameters $A = 1$, $h = 1$ (one unit shifted to the right), and $k = -2$ (two units shifted down).

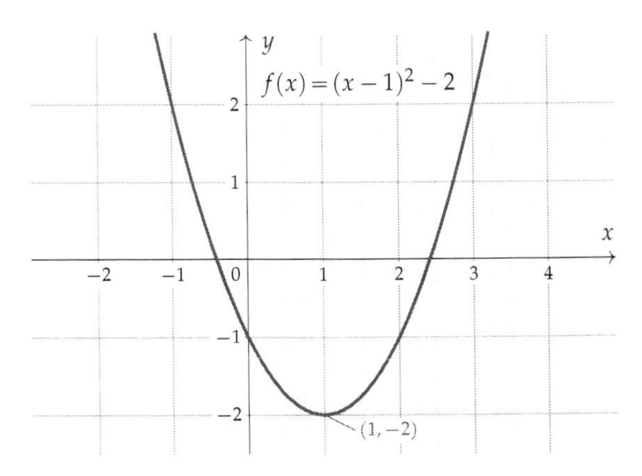

Figure 1.39: The graph of the function $f(x) = (x-1)^2 - 2$ is the same as the basic function $f(x) = x^2$, but shifted one unit to the right and two units down.

If a quadratic crosses the x-axis, it can be written in factored form:

$$f(x) = A(x-a)(x-b),$$

where a and b are the two roots. Another common way of writing a quadratic function is $f(x) = Ax^2 + Bx + C$.

Properties

- There is a unique quadratic function that passes through any three points (x_1, y_1), (x_2, y_2) and (x_3, y_3), if the points have different x-coordinates: $x_1 \neq x_2$, $x_2 \neq x_3$, and $x_1 \neq x_3$.

General sine function

Introducing all possible parameters into the sine function gives us:

$$f(x) = A\sin\left(\tfrac{2\pi}{\lambda}x - \phi\right),$$

where A, λ, and ϕ are the function's parameters.

Parameters

- A: the amplitude describes the distance above and below the x-axis that the function reaches as it oscillates.
- λ: the *wavelength* of the function:

  $$\lambda \equiv \{ \text{ the horizontal distance from one peak to the next } \}.$$

- ϕ: is a phase shift, analogous to the horizontal shift h, which we have seen. This number dictates where the oscillation starts. The default sine function has zero phase shift ($\phi = 0$), so it passes through the origin with an increasing slope.

The "bare" sine function $f(x) = \sin(x)$ has wavelength 2π and produces outputs that oscillate between -1 and $+1$. When we multiply the bare function by the constant A, the oscillations will range between $-A$ and A. When the input x is scaled by the factor $\frac{2\pi}{\lambda}$, the wavelength of the function becomes λ.

Exercises

E1.20 Given the functions $f(x) = x + 5$, $g(x) = x - 6$, $h(x) = 7x$, and $q(x) = x^2$, find the formulas for the following composite functions:

a) $q \circ f$ **b)** $f \circ q$ **c)** $q \circ g$ **d)** $q \circ h$

In each case, describe how the graph of the composite function is related to the graph of $q(x)$.
Hint: Recall, "$\circ$" denotes function composition: $(f \circ g)(x) \equiv f(g(x))$.

E1.21 Find the amplitude A, the wavelength λ, and the phase shift ϕ for the function $f(x) = 5\sin(62.83x - \frac{\pi}{8})$.

E1.22 Choose the coefficients a, b, and c for the quadratic function $f(x) = ax^2 + bx + c$ so that it passes through the points $(0,5)$, $(1,4)$, and $(2,5)$.
Hint: Find the equation $f(x) = A(x-h)^2 + k$ first.

E1.23 Find the values α and β that will make the function $g(x) = 2\sqrt{x-\alpha} + \beta$ pass through the points $(3,-2)$, $(4,0)$, and $(7,2)$.

1.14 Geometry

The word "geometry" comes from the Greek roots *geo*, which means "earth," and *metron*, which means "measurement." This name is linked to one of the early applications of geometry, which was to measure the total amount of land contained within a certain boundary region. Over the years, the study of geometry evolved to be more abstract. Instead of developing formulas for calculating the area of specific regions of land, mathematicians developed general area formulas that apply to *all* regions that have a particular shape.

In this section we'll present a number of formulas for calculating the perimeters, areas, and volumes for various shapes (also called "figures") commonly encountered in the real world. For two-dimensional figures, the main quantities of interest are the figures' areas and the figures' perimeters (the length of the walk around the figure). For three-dimensional figures, the quantities of interest are the surface area (how much paint it would take to cover all sides of the figure), and volume (how much water it would take to fill a container of this shape). The formulas presented are by no means an exhaustive list of everything there is to know about geometry, but they represent a core set of facts that you want to add to your toolbox.

Triangles

The area of a triangle is equal to $\frac{1}{2}$ times the length of its base times its height:

$$A = \tfrac{1}{2}ah_a.$$

Note that h_a is the height of the triangle *relative to* the side a.

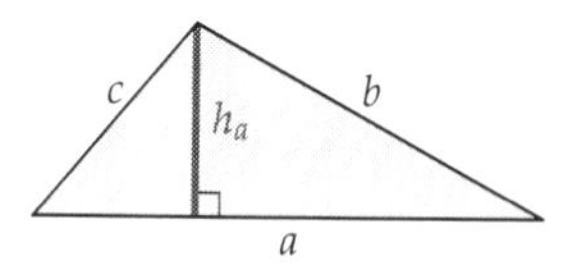

Figure 1.40: A triangle with side lengths a, b, and c. The height of the triangle with respect to the side a is denoted h_a.

The perimeter of a triangle is given by the sum of its side lengths:

$$P = a + b + c.$$

Interior angles of a triangle rule The sum of the inner angles in any triangle is equal to 180°. Consider a triangle with internal angles α, β and γ as shown in Figure 1.41. We may not know the values of the individual angles α, β, and γ, but we know their sum is $\alpha + \beta + \gamma = 180^\circ$.

Sine rule The sine rule states the following equation is true:

$$\frac{a}{\sin(\alpha)} = \frac{b}{\sin(\beta)} = \frac{c}{\sin(\gamma)},$$

where α is the angle opposite to side a, β is the angle opposite to side b, and γ is the angle opposite to side c, as shown in Figure 1.41.

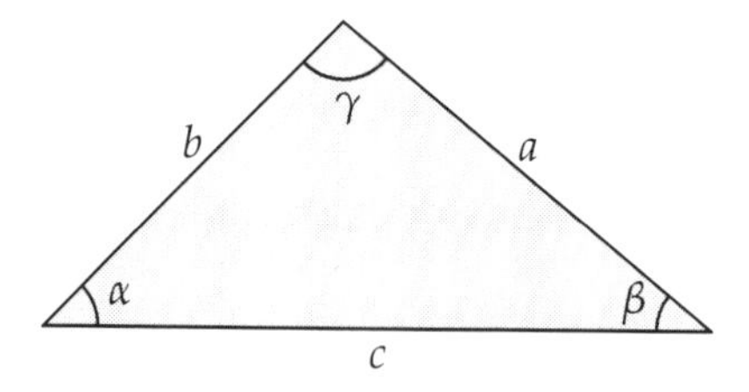

Figure 1.41: A triangle with inner angles α, β, and γ and sides a, b, and c.

Cosine rule The cosine rules states the following equations are true:

$$\begin{aligned} a^2 &= b^2 + c^2 - 2bc\cos(\alpha), \\ b^2 &= a^2 + c^2 - 2ac\cos(\beta), \\ c^2 &= a^2 + b^2 - 2ab\cos(\gamma). \end{aligned}$$

These equations are useful when you know two sides of a triangle and the angle between them, and you want to find the third side.

Circle

The circle is a beautiful shape. If we take the centre of the circle at the origin $(0,0)$, the circle of radius r corresponds to the equation

$$x^2 + y^2 = r^2.$$

This formula describes the set of points (x,y) with a distance from the centre equal to r.

The circumference of a circle of radius r is given by the formula

$$C = 2\pi r.$$

The circumference of a circle of radius 3 m is $C = 2\pi(3) = 18.85$ m. This is how far you'll need to walk to complete a full turn around a circle of radius $r = 3$ m.

The area enclosed by a circle of radius r is given by

$$A = \pi r^2.$$

Circles are so important that we dedicated a whole section (Section 1.17) to them. For now, let's continue discussing some other important geometric shapes.

Sphere

A sphere of radius r is described by the equation $x^2 + y^2 + z^2 = r^2$. The surface area of the sphere is $A = 4\pi r^2$, and its volume is given by $V = \frac{4}{3}\pi r^3$.

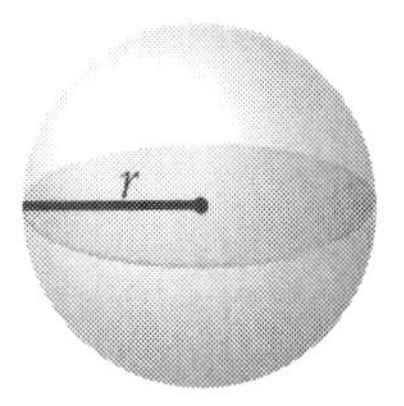

Figure 1.42: A sphere of radius r has surface area $4\pi r^2$ and volume $\frac{4}{3}\pi r^3$.

Cylinder

The surface area of a cylinder consists of the top and bottom circular surfaces, plus the area of the side of the cylinder:

$$A = 2\left(\pi r^2\right) + (2\pi r)h.$$

The volume of a cylinder is the product of the area of the cylinder's base times its height:

$$V = \left(\pi r^2\right) h.$$

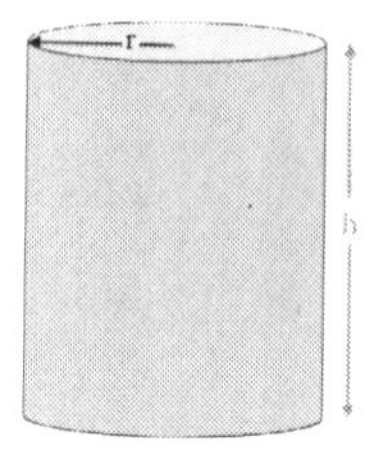

Figure 1.43: A cylinder with radius r and height h has volume $\pi r^2 h$.

Example You open the hood of your car and see 2.0 L written on top of the engine. The 2.0 L refers to the combined volume of the four pistons, which are cylindrical in shape. The owner's manual tells you the radius of each piston is 43.75 mm, and the height of each piston is 83.1 mm. Verify the total engine volume is 1998789 $\text{mm}^3 \approx 2$ L.

Cones and pyramids

The volume of a square pyramid with side length a and height h is given by the formula $V = \frac{1}{3}a^2h$. The volume of a cone of radius r and height h is given by the formula $V = \frac{1}{3}\pi r^2 h$. Note the factor $\frac{1}{3}$ appears in both formulas. These two formulas are particular cases of the general volume formula that applies to all pyramids:

$$V = \tfrac{1}{3}Ah,$$

where A is the area of the pyramid's base and h is its height. This formula applies for pyramids with a base that is a triangle (triangular pyramids), a square (square pyramids), a rectangle (rectangular pyramids), a circle (cones), or any other shape.

The System is obsessed with the pyramid shape. Many large organizations are structured like pyramids: the top boss tells vice-presidents what to do, vice-presidents tell directors what to do, directors tell upper management what to do, and so on until the commands reach regular employees. This pyramid-like structure allows for tight control of information and budgets within the organization.

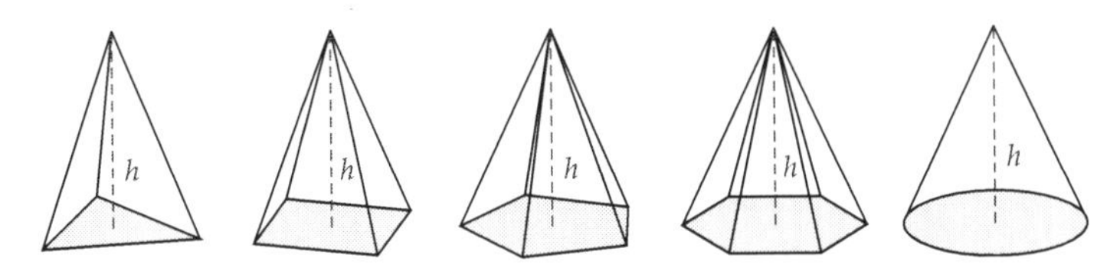

Figure 1.44: The volumes of pyramids and cones are described by the formula $V = \frac{1}{3}Ah$, where A is the area of the base and h is the height.

Pyramid structures are not *necessarily* bad; yet we often find some of the worst aspects of human nature concentrated at the tops of society's pyramids. It's wise to keep an eye on pyramid-shaped power structures, and watch out for any shenanigans the big bosses may try to pull.

Exercises

E1.24 Find the length of side x in the triangle below.

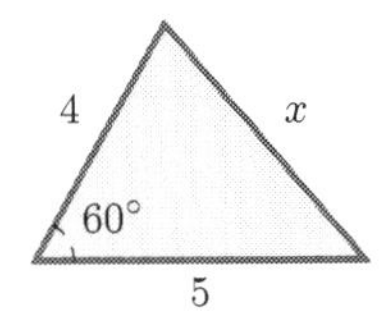

Hint: Use the cosine rule.

E1.25 Find the volume and the surface area of a sphere with radius 2.

1.15 Trigonometry

We can put any three lines together to make a triangle. What's more, if one of the triangle's angles is equal to 90°, we call this triangle a *right-angle triangle.*

In this section we'll discuss right-angle triangles in great detail and get to know their properties. We'll learn some fancy new terms like *hypotenuse, opposite,* and *adjacent,* which are used to refer to the different sides of a triangle. We'll also use the functions *sine, cosine,* and *tangent* to compute the *ratios of lengths* in right triangles.

Understanding triangles and their associated trigonometric functions is of fundamental importance: you'll need this knowledge for your future understanding of mathematical subjects like vectors and complex numbers, as well as physics subjects like oscillations and waves.

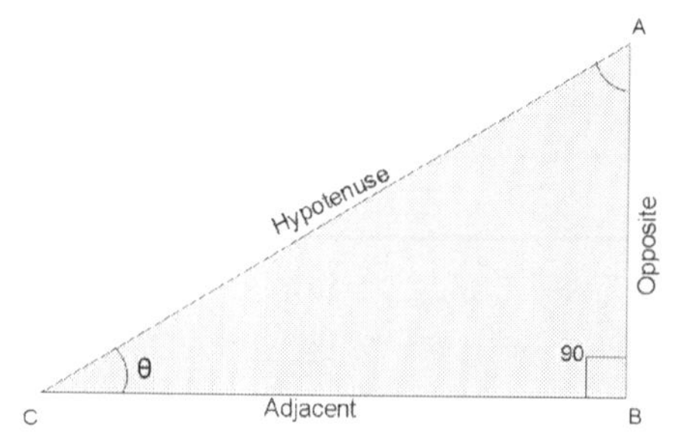

Figure 1.45: A right-angle triangle. The angle θ and the names of the sides of the triangle are indicated.

Concepts

- A, B, C: the three *vertices* of the triangle
- θ: the angle at the vertex C. Angles can be measured in degrees or radians.
- $\text{opp} \equiv \overline{AB}$: the length of the *opposite* side to θ
- $\text{adj} \equiv \overline{BC}$: the length of side *adjacent* to θ
- $\text{hyp} \equiv \overline{AC}$: the *hypotenuse*. This is the triangle's longest side.
- h: the "height" of the triangle (in this case $h = \text{opp} = \overline{AB}$)
- $\sin\theta \equiv \frac{\text{opp}}{\text{hyp}}$: the *sine* of theta is the ratio of the length of the opposite side and the length of the hypotenuse
- $\cos\theta \equiv \frac{\text{adj}}{\text{hyp}}$: the *cosine* of theta is the ratio of the adjacent length and the hypotenuse length
- $\tan\theta \equiv \frac{\sin\theta}{\cos\theta} \equiv \frac{\text{opp}}{\text{adj}}$: the *tangent* is the ratio of the opposite length divided by the adjacent length

Pythagoras' theorem

In a right-angle triangle, the length of the hypotenuse squared is equal to the sum of the squares of the lengths of the other sides:

$$|\text{adj}|^2 + |\text{opp}|^2 = |\text{hyp}|^2.$$

If we divide both sides of the above equation by $|\text{hyp}|^2$, we obtain

$$\frac{|\text{adj}|^2}{|\text{hyp}|^2} + \frac{|\text{opp}|^2}{|\text{hyp}|^2} = 1,$$

which can be rewritten as

$$\cos^2\theta + \sin^2\theta = 1.$$

This is a powerful *trigonometric identity* that describes an important relationship between sine and cosine.

Sin and cos

Meet the trigonometric functions, or trigs for short. These are your new friends. Don't be shy now, say hello to them.

"Hello."

"Hi."

"Soooooo, you are like functions right?"

"Yep," sin and cos reply in chorus.

"Okay, so what do you do?"

"Who me?" asks cos. "Well I tell the ratio... hmm... Wait, are you asking what I do as a *function* or specifically what *I* do?"

"Both I guess?"

"Well, as a function, I take angles as inputs and I give ratios as answers. More specifically, I tell you how 'wide' a triangle with that angle will be," says cos all in one breath.

"What do you mean wide?" you ask.

"Oh yeah, I forgot to say, the triangle must have a hypotenuse of length 1. What happens is there is a point P that moves around on a circle of radius 1, and we *imagine* a triangle formed by the point P, the origin, and the point on the x-axis located directly below the point P."

"I am not sure I get it," you confess.

"Let me try explaining," says sin. "Look on the next page, and you'll see a circle. This is the unit circle because it has a radius of 1. You see it, yes?"

"Yes."

"Now imagine a point P that moves along the circle of radius 1, starting from the point $P(0) = (1, 0)$. The x and y coordinates of the point $P(\theta) = (P_x(\theta),\ P_y(\theta))$ as a function of θ are

$$P(\theta) = (P_x(\theta),\ P_y(\theta)) = (\cos\theta,\ \sin\theta).$$

So, *either* you can think of us in the context of triangles, or in the context of the unit circle."

"Cool. I kind of get it. Thanks so much," you say, but in reality you are weirded out. Talking functions? "Well guys. It was nice to meet you, but I have to get going, to finish the rest of the book."

"See you later," says cos.

"Peace out," says sin.

The unit circle

The *unit circle* consists of all points (x, y) that satisfy the equation $x^2 + y^2 = 1$. A point $P = (P_x, P_y)$ on the unit circle has coordinates $(P_x, P_y) = (\cos\theta, \sin\theta)$, where θ is the angle P makes with the x-axis.

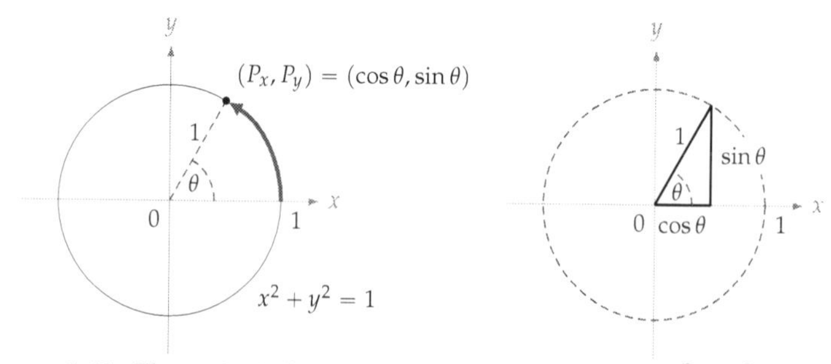

Figure 1.46: The unit circle corresponds to the equation $x^2 + y^2 = 1$. The coordinates of the point P on the unit circle are $P_x = \cos\theta$ and $P_y = \sin\theta$.

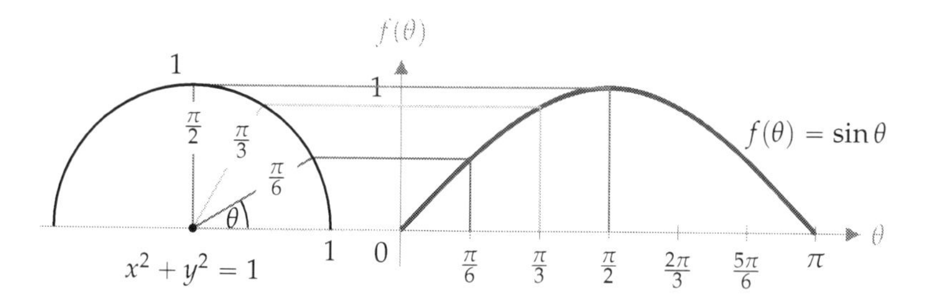

Figure 1.47: The function $f(\theta) = \sin\theta$ describes the vertical position of a point P that travels along the unit circle. The first half of a cycle is shown.

You should be familiar with the values of sin and cos for all angles that are multiples of $\frac{\pi}{6}$ (30°) or $\frac{\pi}{4}$ (45°). All of them are shown in Figure 1.48. For each angle, the x-coordinate (the first number in the bracket) is $\cos\theta$, and the y-coordinate is $\sin\theta$.

Maybe you're thinking that's way too much to remember. Don't worry, you just have to memorize one fact:

$$\sin(30^\circ) = \sin(\tfrac{\pi}{6}) = \tfrac{1}{2}.$$

Knowing this, you can determine all the other angles. Let's start with $\cos(30^\circ)$. We know that at 30°, point P on the unit circle has the vertical coordinate $\frac{1}{2} = \sin(30^\circ)$. We also know the cos quantity we are looking for is, by definition, the horizontal component:

$$P = (\cos(30^\circ), \sin(30^\circ)).$$

Key fact: all points on the unit circle are a distance of 1 from the origin. Knowing that P is a point on the unit circle, and knowing the value of $\sin(30^\circ)$, we can solve for $\cos(30^\circ)$. Start with the following identity,

$$\cos^2\theta + \sin^2\theta = 1,$$

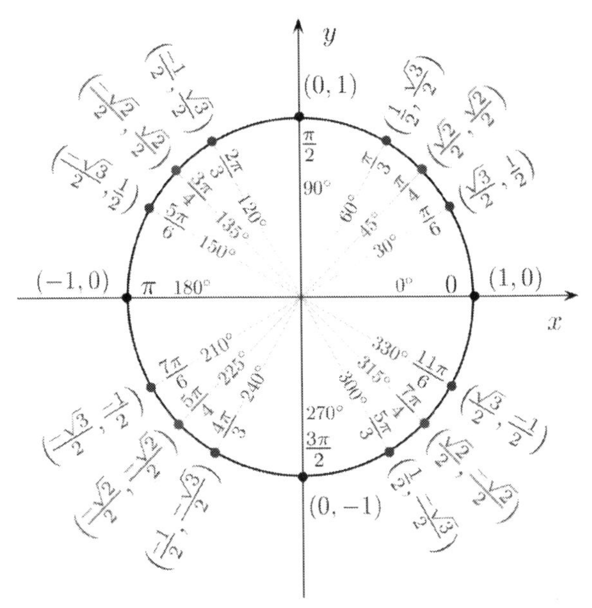

Figure 1.48: The unit circle. The coordinates of the point on the unit circle $(\cos\theta, \sin\theta)$ are indicated for several important values of the angle θ.

which is true for *all* angles θ. Moving things around, we obtain

$$\cos(30^\circ) = \sqrt{1 - \sin^2(30^\circ)} = \sqrt{1 - \tfrac{1}{4}} = \sqrt{\tfrac{3}{4}} = \tfrac{\sqrt{3}}{2}.$$

To find the values of $\cos(60^\circ)$ and $\sin(60^\circ)$, observe the symmetry of the circle. 60 degrees measured from the x-axis is the same as 30 degrees measured from the y-axis. From this, we know $\cos(60^\circ) = \sin(30^\circ) = \frac{1}{2}$. Therefore, $\sin(60^\circ) = \frac{\sqrt{3}}{2}$.

To find the values of sin and cos for angles that are multiples of 45°, we need to find the value a such that

$$a^2 + a^2 = 1,$$

since at 45°, the horizontal and vertical coordinates will be the same. Solving for a we find $a = \frac{1}{\sqrt{2}}$, but people don't like to see square roots in the denominator, so we write

$$\tfrac{\sqrt{2}}{2} = \cos(45^\circ) = \sin(45^\circ).$$

All other angles in the circle behave like the three angles above, with one difference: one or more of their components has a negative sign. For example, 150° is just like 30°, except its x component is negative.

Don't memorize all the values of sin and cos; if you ever need to determine their values, draw a little circle and use the symmetry of the circle to find the sin and cos components.

Non-unit circles

Consider a point $Q(\theta)$ at an angle of θ on a circle with radius $r \neq 1$. How can we find the x- and y-coordinates of the point $Q(\theta)$?

We saw that the coefficients $\cos\theta$ and $\sin\theta$ correspond to the x- and y-coordinates of a point on the *unit* circle ($r = 1$). To obtain the coordinates for a point on a circle of radius r, we must *scale* the coordinates by a factor of r:

$$Q(\theta) = (Q_x(\theta), Q_y(\theta)) = (r\cos\theta, r\sin\theta).$$

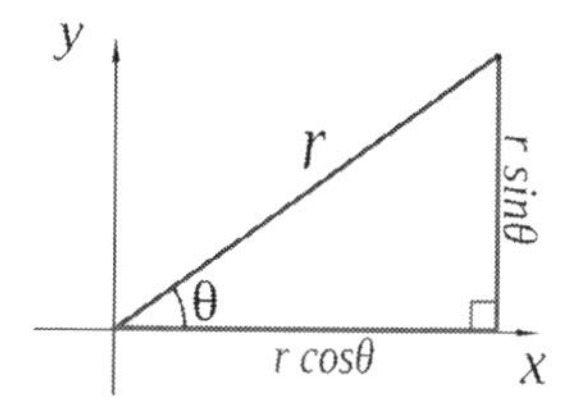

Figure 1.49: The x- and y-coordinates of a point at the angle θ and distance of r from the origin are given by $x = r\cos\theta$ and $y = r\sin\theta$.

The take-away message is that you can use the functions $\cos\theta$ and $\sin\theta$ to find the "horizontal" and "vertical" components of any length r. From this point on in the book, we'll always talk about the length of the *adjacent* side as $r_x = r\cos\theta$, and the length of the *opposite* side as $r_y = r\sin\theta$. It is extremely important you get comfortable with this notation.

The reasoning behind the above calculations is as follows:

$$\cos\theta \equiv \frac{\text{adj}}{\text{hyp}} = \frac{r_x}{r} \quad \Rightarrow \quad r_x = r\cos\theta,$$

and

$$\sin\theta \equiv \frac{\text{opp}}{\text{hyp}} = \frac{r_y}{r} \quad \Rightarrow \quad r_y = r\sin\theta.$$

Calculators

Make sure to set your calculator to the correct units for working with angles. What should you type into your calculator to compute the sine of 30 degrees? If your calculator is set to degrees, simply type: [30], [sin], [=].

If your calculator is set to radians, you have two options:

1. Change the `mode` of the calculator so it works in degrees.
2. Convert 30° to radians

$$30\,[^\circ] \times \frac{2\pi\,[\text{rad}]}{360\,[^\circ]} = \frac{\pi}{6}\,[\text{rad}],$$

and type: [π], [/], [6], [sin], [=] on your calculator.

Exercises

E1.26 Given a circle with radius $r = 5$, find the x- and y-coordinates of the point at $\theta = 45^\circ$. What is the circumference of the circle?

E1.27 Convert the following angles from degrees to radians.

a) 30° **b)** 45° **c)** 60° **d)** 270°

Links

[Unit-circle walkthrough and tricks by patrickJMT on YouTube]
`http://bit.ly/1mQg9Cj` and `http://bit.ly/1hvA702`

1.16 Trigonometric identities

There are a number of important relationships between the values of the functions sin and cos. Here are three of these relationships, known as *trigonometric identities*. There about a dozen other identities that are less important, but you should memorize these three.

The three identities to remember are:

1. Unit hypotenuse

$$\sin^2(\theta) + \cos^2(\theta) = 1.$$

The unit hypotenuse identity is true by the Pythagoras theorem and the definitions of sin and cos. The sum of the squares of the sides of a triangle is equal to the square of the hypotenuse.

2. sico + sico

$$\sin(a + b) = \sin(a)\cos(b) + \sin(b)\cos(a).$$

The mnemonic for this identity is "sico + sico."

3. coco − sisi

$$\cos(a+b) = \cos(a)\cos(b) - \sin(a)\sin(b).$$

The mnemonic for this identity is "coco − sisi." The negative sign is there because it's not good to be a sissy.

Derived formulas

If you remember the above three formulas, you can derive pretty much all the other trigonometric identities.

Double angle formulas

Starting from the sico + sico identity and setting $a = b = x$, we can derive the following identity:

$$\sin(2x) = 2\sin(x)\cos(x).$$

Starting from the coco-sisi identity, we obtain

$$\begin{aligned}\cos(2x) &= \cos^2(x) - \sin^2(x) \\ &= 2\cos^2(x) - 1 = 2\left(1 - \sin^2(x)\right) - 1 = 1 - 2\sin^2(x).\end{aligned}$$

The formulas for expressing $\sin(2x)$ and $\cos(2x)$ in terms of $\sin(x)$ and $\cos(x)$ are called *double angle formulas*.

If we rewrite the double-angle formula for $\cos(2x)$ to isolate the $\sin^2$ or the $\cos^2$ term, we obtain the *power-reduction formulas*:

$$\cos^2(x) = \frac{1}{2}\left(1 + \cos(2x)\right), \qquad \sin^2(x) = \frac{1}{2}\left(1 - \cos(2x)\right).$$

Self similarity

Sin and cos are periodic functions with period 2π. Adding a multiple of 2π to the function's input does not change the function:

$$\sin(x + 2\pi) = \sin(x + 124\pi) = \sin(x), \qquad \cos(x + 2\pi) = \cos(x).$$

Furthermore, sin and cos are self similar within each 2π cycle:

$$\sin(\pi - x) = \sin(x), \qquad \cos(\pi - x) = -\cos(x).$$

Sin is cos, cos is sin

It shouldn't be surprising if I tell you that sin and cos are actually $\frac{\pi}{2}$-shifted versions of each other:

$$\cos(x) = \sin\left(x + \frac{\pi}{2}\right) = \sin\left(\frac{\pi}{2} - x\right), \ \sin(x) = \cos\left(x - \frac{\pi}{2}\right) = \cos\left(\frac{\pi}{2} - x\right).$$

Sum formulas

$$\sin(a) + \sin(b) = 2\sin\left(\frac{1}{2}(a+b)\right)\cos\left(\frac{1}{2}(a-b)\right),$$

$$\sin(a) - \sin(b) = 2\sin\left(\frac{1}{2}(a-b)\right)\cos\left(\frac{1}{2}(a+b)\right),$$

$$\cos(a) + \cos(b) = 2\cos\left(\frac{1}{2}(a+b)\right)\cos\left(\frac{1}{2}(a-b)\right),$$

$$\cos(a) - \cos(b) = -2\sin\left(\frac{1}{2}(a+b)\right)\sin\left(\frac{1}{2}(a-b)\right).$$

Product formulas

$$\sin(a)\cos(b) = \frac{1}{2}(\sin(a+b) + \sin(a-b)),$$

$$\sin(a)\sin(b) = \frac{1}{2}(\cos(a-b) - \cos(a+b)),$$

$$\cos(a)\cos(b) = \frac{1}{2}(\cos(a-b) + \cos(a+b)).$$

Discussion

The above formulas will come in handy when you need to find some unknown in an equation, or when you are trying to simplify a trigonometric expression. I am not saying you should necessarily memorize them, but you should be aware that they exist.

Exercises

E1.28 Given $a = \pi$ and $b = \frac{\pi}{2}$, find

a) $\sin(a+b)$ **b)** $\cos(2a)$ **c)** $\cos(a+b)$

E1.29 Simplify the following expressions and compute their value without using a calculator.

a) $\cos(x) + \cos(\pi - x)$ **b)** $2\sin^2(x) + \cos(2x)$

c) $\sin(\frac{5\pi}{4})\sin(-\frac{\pi}{4})$ **d)** $2\cos(\frac{5\pi}{4})\cos(-\frac{\pi}{4})\cos(\pi)$

1.17 Circle

The *circle* is a set of points located a constant distance from a centre point. This geometric shape appears in many situations.

Definitions

- r: the radius of the circle
- A: the area of the circle
- C: the circumference of the circle
- (x, y): a point on the circle
- θ: the angle (measured from the x-axis) of a point on the circle

Formulas

A circle with radius r centred at the origin is described by the equation

$$x^2 + y^2 = r^2.$$

All points (x, y) that satisfy this equation are part of the circle.

Rather than staying centred at the origin, the circle's centre can be located at any point (p, q) on the plane as illustrated in Figure 1.50.

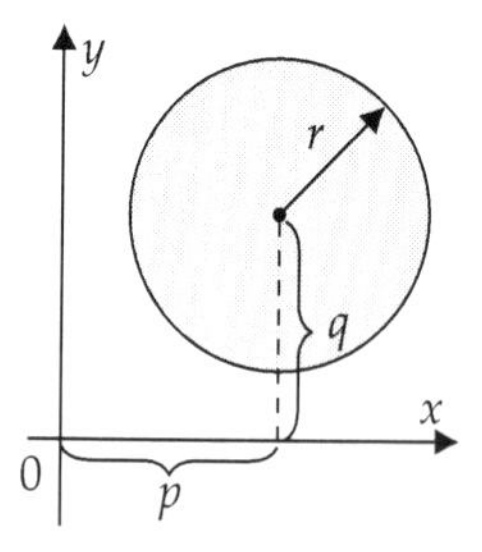

Figure 1.50: A circle of radius r centred at the point (p, q) is described by the formula $(x - p)^2 + (y - q)^2 = r^2$.

Explicit function

The equation of a circle is a *relation* or an *implicit function* involving x and y. To obtain an *explicit function* $y = f(x)$ for the circle, we can solve for y to obtain

$$y = \sqrt{r^2 - x^2}, \quad -r \leqslant x \leqslant r,$$

and

$$y = -\sqrt{r^2 - x^2}, \quad -r \leqslant x \leqslant r.$$

The explicit expression is really two functions, because a vertical line crosses the circle in two places. The first function corresponds to the top half of the circle, and the second function corresponds to the bottom half.

Polar coordinates

Circles are so common in mathematics that mathematicians developed a special "circular coordinate system" in order to describe them more easily.

It is possible to specify the coordinates (x, y) of any point on the circle in terms of the *polar coordinates* $r\angle\theta$, where r measures the distance of the point from the origin, and θ is the angle measured from the x-axis.

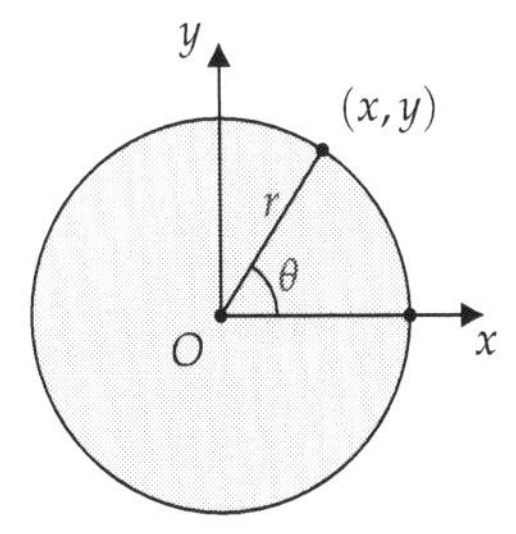

Figure 1.51: Polar coordinates $r\angle\theta$ can be used to describe any point (x, y).

To convert from the polar coordinates $r\angle\theta$ to the (x, y) coordinates, use the trigonometric functions cos and sin:

$$x = r\cos\theta \qquad \text{and} \qquad y = r\sin\theta.$$

Parametric equation

We can describe *all* the points on the circle if we specify a fixed radius r and vary the angle θ over all angles: $\theta \in [0, 360^\circ)$. A *parametric equation* specifies the coordinates $(x(\theta), y(\theta))$ for the points on a curve, for all values of the *parameter* θ. The parametric equation for a circle of radius r is given by

$$\{(x, y) \in \mathbb{R}^2 \mid x = r\cos\theta,\ y = r\sin\theta,\ \theta \in [0, 360^\circ)\}.$$

In words, this expression describes the set of points (x, y) in the Cartesian plane with x-coordinates that are described by $r\cos\theta$ and with y-coordinates that are described by $r\sin\theta$, where the angle θ varies from 0° to 360°. Try to visualize the curve traced by the point $(x(\theta), y(\theta)) = (r\cos\theta, r\sin\theta)$ as θ varies from 0° to 360°. The point will trace out a circle of radius r.

If we let the parameter θ vary over a smaller interval, we'll obtain subsets of the circle. For example, the parametric equation for the top half of the circle is

$$\{(x,y) \in \mathbb{R}^2 \mid x = r\cos\theta, y = r\sin\theta,\ \theta \in [0,180^\circ]\}.$$

The top half of the circle is also described by $\{(x,y) \in \mathbb{R}^2 \mid y = \sqrt{r^2 - x^2},\ x \in [-r,r]\}$, where the parameter used is the x-coordinate.

Area

The area of a circle of radius r is $A = \pi r^2$.

Circumference and arc length

The circumference of a circle is

$$C = 2\pi r.$$

This is the total length you can measure by following the curve all the way around to trace the outline of the entire circle.

What is the length of a part of the circle? Say you have a piece of the circle, called an *arc*, and that piece corresponds to the angle $\theta = 57^\circ$. What is the arc's length ℓ?

If the circle's total length $C = 2\pi r$ represents a full 360° turn around the circle, then the arc length ℓ for a portion of the circle corresponding to the angle θ is

$$\ell = 2\pi r \frac{\theta}{360}.$$

The arc length ℓ depends on r, the angle θ, and a factor of $\frac{2\pi}{360}$.

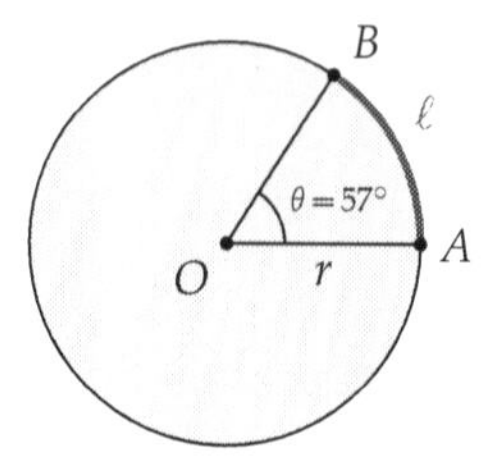

Figure 1.52: The arc length ℓ equals $\frac{57}{360}$ of the circle's circumference $2\pi r$.

Radians

Though degrees are commonly used as a measurement unit for angles, it's much better to measure angles in *radians*, since radians are the *natural* units for measuring angles. The conversion ratio between degrees and radians is

$$2\pi[\text{rad}] = 360^\circ.$$

When measuring angles in radians, the arc length is given by:

$$\ell = r\theta_{\text{rad}}.$$

Measuring angles in radians is equivalent to measuring arc length on a circle with radius $r = 1$.

Exercises

E1.30 On a rainy day, Laura brings her bike indoors, and the wet bicycle tires leave a track of water on the floor. What is the length of the water track left by the bike's rear tire (diameter 73[cm]) if the wheel makes five full turns along the floor?

E1.31 Describe the circle of radius 3 centred at $(1, 4)$ in terms of Cartesian coordinates and in terms of a parametric equation.

1.18 Ellipse

The *ellipse* is a fundamental shape that occurs in nature. The orbit of planet Earth around the Sun is an ellipse.

Parameters

- a: the half-length of the ellipse along the x-axis, also known as the semi-major axis
- b: the half-length of the ellipse along the y-axis
- ε: the *eccentricity* of the ellipse, $\varepsilon \equiv \sqrt{1 - \frac{b^2}{a^2}}$
- F_1, F_2: the two *focal points* of the ellipse
- r_1: the distance from a point on the ellipse to F_1
- r_2: the distance from a point on the ellipse to F_2

Definition

An ellipse is the curve found by tracing along all the points for which the sum of the distances to the two focal points is a constant:

$$r_1 + r_2 = \text{const.}$$

There's a neat way to draw a perfect ellipse using a piece of string and two tacks or pins. Take a piece of string and tack it to a picnic table at two points, leaving some loose slack in the middle of the string. Now take a pencil, and without touching the table, use the pencil to pull the middle of the string until it is taut. Make a mark at that point. With the two parts of string completely straight, make a mark at every point possible where the two "legs" of string remain taut.

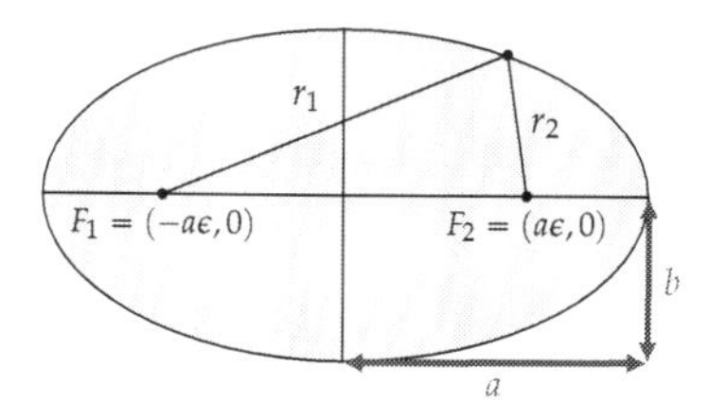

Figure 1.53: An ellipse with semi-major axis a and semi-minor axis b. The locations of the focal points F_1 and F_2 are indicated.

An ellipse is a set of points (x, y) that satisfy the equation

$$\frac{x^2}{a^2} + \frac{y^2}{b^2} = 1.$$

The *eccentricity* of an ellipse describes how elongated it is:

$$\varepsilon \equiv \sqrt{1 - \frac{b^2}{a^2}}.$$

The parameter $\varepsilon \in [0, 1)$ describes the *shape* of the ellipse in a scale-less fashion. The bigger ε is, the bigger the difference will be between the length of the semi-major axis and the semi-minor axis. In the special case when $\varepsilon = 0$, the equation of the ellipse becomes a circle with radius a.

The (x, y)-coordinates of the two focal points are

$$F_1 = (-a\varepsilon, 0) \qquad \text{and} \qquad F_2 = (a\varepsilon, 0).$$

The focal points correspond to the locations of the two tacks where the string is held in place. Recall that we defined the variables r_1 and r_2 to represent the distance from the focal points F_1 and F_2. Furthermore, we will denote by $q = a(1 - \varepsilon)$ the distance of the ellipse's closest approach to a focal point.

Polar coordinates

In polar coordinates, the ellipse can be described by a function $r_2(\theta)$ as illustrated in Figure 1.54. This function gives the distance of a point E from F_2 as a function of the angle θ. Recall in polar coordinates, the angle θ is the independent variable and the dependent variable is the distance $r_2(\theta)$.

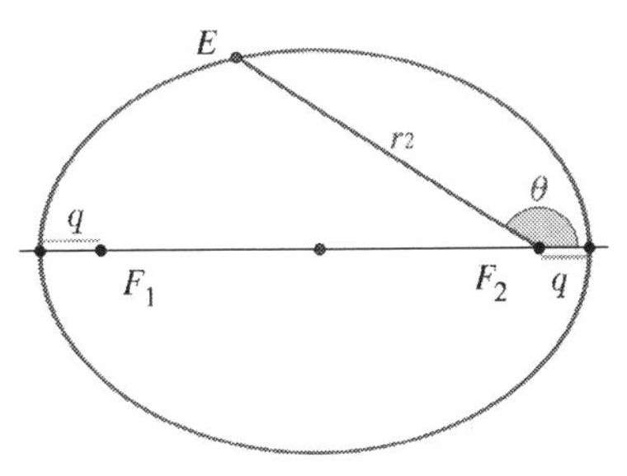

Figure 1.54: The shape of the ellipse is described by the function $r_2(\theta)$.

The equation of the ellipse in polar coordinates depends on the length of the semi-major axis a and the eccentricity ε. The equation that describes an ellipse in polar coordinates is

$$r_2(\theta) = \frac{a(1-\varepsilon^2)}{1+\varepsilon\cos(\theta)},$$

where the angle θ is measured with respect to the positive x-axis. The distance is smallest when $\theta = 0$ with $r_2(0) = a(1-\varepsilon) = q$ and largest when $\theta = \pi$ with $r_2(\pi) = a + a\varepsilon = a(1+\varepsilon)$.

Calculating the orbit of the Earth

To a close approximation, the motion of the Earth around the Sun is described by an ellipse with the Sun positioned at the focus F_2. We can therefore use the polar coordinates formula $r_2(\theta)$ to describe the distance of the Earth from the Sun.

The eccentricity of Earth's orbit around the Sun is $\varepsilon = 0.01671123$, and the half-length of the major axis is $a = 149\,598\,261$[km]. We substitute these values into the general formula for $r_2(\theta)$ and obtain the following equation:

$$r_2(\theta) = \frac{149\,556\,484.56}{1+0.01671123\cos(\theta)} \text{ [km]}.$$

The point where the Earth is closest to the Sun is called the *perihelion*. It occurs when $\theta = 0$, which happens around the 3rd of January. The moment where the Earth is most distant from the Sun is called the *aphelion* and corresponds to the angle $\theta = \pi$. Earth's *aphelion* happens around the 3rd of July.

We can use the formula for $r_2(\theta)$ to predict the *perihelion* and *aphelion* distances of Earth's orbit:

$$r_{2,\text{peri}} = r_2(0) = \frac{149556483}{1 + 0.01671123\cos(0)} = 147\,098\,290 \text{ [km]},$$

$$r_{2,\text{aphe}} = r_2(\pi) = \frac{149556483}{1 + 0.01671123\cos(\pi)} = 152\,098\,232 \text{ [km]}.$$

Google "perihelion" and "aphelion" to verify that the above predictions are accurate.

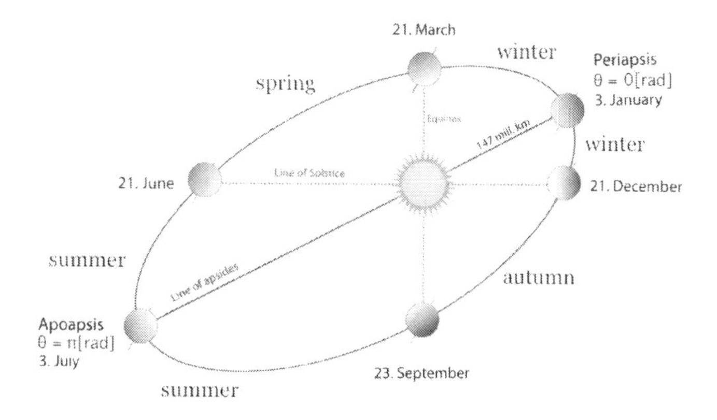

Figure 1.55: The orbit of the Earth around the Sun. Key points of the orbit are labelled. The seasons in the Northern hemisphere are also indicated.

The angle θ of the Earth relative to the Sun can be described as a function of time $\theta(t)$. The exact formula of the function $\theta(t)$ that describes the angle as a function of time is fairly complicated, so we won't go into the details. Let's simply look at some values of $\theta(t)$ with t measured in days. We'll begin on Jan 3rd.

Newton's insight

Contrary to common belief, Newton did not discover his theory of gravitation because an apple fell on his head while sitting under a tree. What actually happened is that he started from Kepler's laws of motion, which describe the exact elliptical orbit of the Earth as a function of time. Newton asked, "What kind of force would cause two bodies to spin around each other in an elliptical orbit?" He determined that the gravitational force between the Sun of mass M and

t [day]	1	2	.	182	.	365	365.242199
t [date]	Jan 3	Jan 4	.	July 3	.	Jan 2	?
$\theta(t)$ [°]	0		.	180	.	359.761356	360
$\theta(t)$ [rad]	0		.	π	.	6.27902	2π

Table 1.2: The angular position of the Earth as a function of time. Note the extra amount of "day" that is roughly equal to $\frac{1}{4} = 0.25$. We account for this discrepancy by adding an extra day to the calendar once every four years.

the Earth of mass m must be of the form $F_g = \frac{GMm}{r^2}$. We'll discuss more about the law of gravitation in Chapter 4.

For now, let's give props to Newton for connecting the dots, and props to Johannes Kepler for studying the orbital periods, and Tycho Brahe for doing all the astronomical measurements. Above all, we owe some props to the ellipse for being such an awesome shape!

By the way, the varying distance between the Earth and the Sun is not the reason we have seasons. The ellipse had nothing to do with seasons! Seasons are predominantly caused by the *axial tilt* of the Earth. The axis of rotation of the Earth is tilted by 23.4° relative to the plane of its orbit around the Sun. In the Northern hemisphere, the longest day of the year is the summer solstice, which occurs around the 21st of June. On that day, the Earth's spin axis is tilted toward the Sun so the Northern hemisphere receives the most sunlight.

Links

[Further reading about Earth-Sun geometry]
`http://www.physicalgeography.net/fundamentals/6h.html`

1.19 Hyperbola

The *hyperbola* is another fundamental shape of nature. A horizontal hyperbola is the set of points (x, y) which satisfy the equation

$$\frac{x^2}{a^2} - \frac{y^2}{b^2} = 1.$$

The numbers a and b are arbitrary constants. This hyperbola passes through the points $(-a, 0)$ and $(a, 0)$. The eccentricity of this hyperbola is defined as

$$\varepsilon = \sqrt{1 + \frac{b^2}{a^2}}.$$

Eccentricity is an important parameter of the hyperbola, as it determines the hyperbola's shape. Recall the ellipse is also defined by an eccentricity parameter, though the formula is slightly different. This could be a coincidence—or is there a connection? Let's see.

Graph

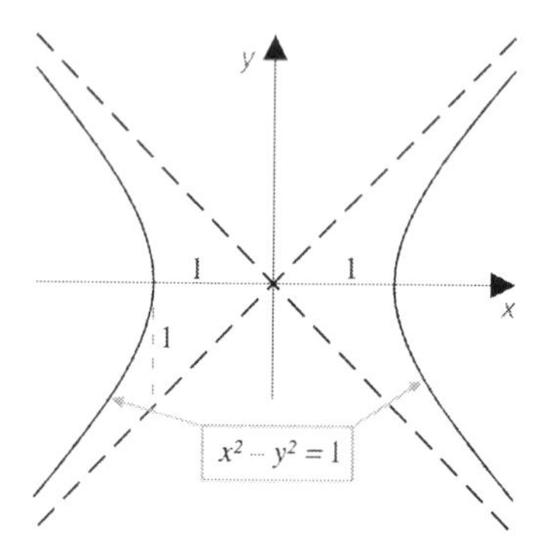

Figure 1.56: The unit hyperbola $x^2 - y^2 = 1$. The graph of the hyperbola has two branches, opening to the sides. The dashed lines are called the *asymptotes* of the hyperbola. The eccentricity determines the angle between the asymptotes. The eccentricity of $x^2 - y^2 = 1$ is $\varepsilon = \sqrt{1 + \frac{1}{1}} = \sqrt{2}$.

The graph of a hyperbola consists of two separate *branches*, as illustrated in Figure 1.56. We'll focus our discussion mostly on the right branch of the hyperbola.

Hyperbolic trigonometry

The trigonometric functions sin and cos describe the geometry of the unit circle. The point $P = (\cos\theta, \sin\theta)$ traces out the unit circle as the angle θ goes from 0 to 2π. The function cos is defined as the x-coordinate of the point P, and sin is the y-coordinate. The study of the geometry of the points on the unit circle is called *circular trigonometry*.

Instead of looking at a point P on the unit circle $x^2 + y^2 = 1$, let's trace out the path of a point Q on the unit hyperbola $x^2 - y^2 = 1$. We will now define *hyperbolic* variants of the sin and cos functions to describe the coordinates of the point Q. This is called *hyperbolic trigonometry*. Doesn't that sound awesome? Next time your friends ask what you have been up to, tell them you are learning about hyperbolic trigonometry.

The coordinates of a point Q on the unit hyperbola are $Q = (\cosh\mu, \sinh\mu)$, where μ is the *hyperbolic angle*. The x-coordinate of the point Q is $x = \cosh\mu$, and its y-coordinate is $y = \sinh\mu$. The name hyperbolic angle is a bit of a misnomer, since $\mu \in [0, \infty)$ actually measures an area. The area of the highlighted region in Figure 1.57 corresponds to $\frac{1}{2}\mu$.

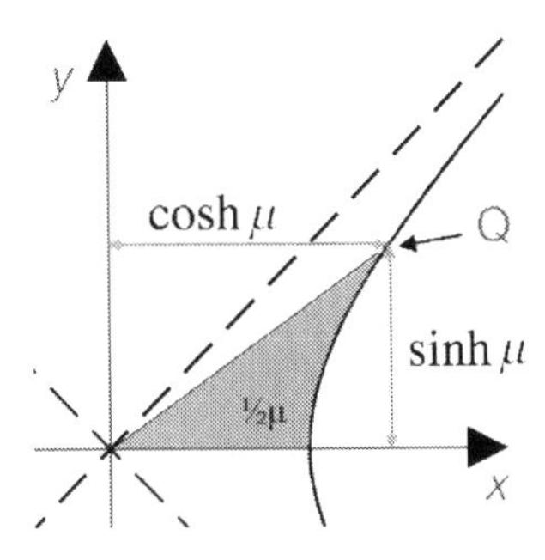

Figure 1.57: The functions $\cosh\mu$ and $\sinh\mu$ are defined as the x- and y-coordinates of a point moving on the unit hyperbola $x^2 - y^2 = 1$.

Recall the circular-trigonometric identity $\cos^2\theta + \sin^2\theta = 1$, which follows from the fact that all the points (x, y) on the unit circle obey $x^2 + y^2 = 1$. There is an analogous hyperbolic trigonometric identity:

$$\cosh^2\mu - \sinh^2\mu = 1.$$

This identity follows because we defined $x = \cosh\mu$ and $y = \sinh\mu$ to be the coordinates of a point Q which traces out the unit hyperbola $x^2 - y^2 = 1$.

The hyperbolic functions are related to the exponential function through the following formulas:

$$\cosh x = \frac{e^x + e^{-x}}{2}, \qquad \sinh x = \frac{e^x - e^{-x}}{2},$$

and

$$e^x = \cosh x + \sinh x.$$

Recall that even functions satisfy $f(-x) = f(x)$ and odd functions satisfy $g(-x) = -g(x)$. The cosh function is even, while sinh is odd. You can think of $\cosh x$ as the "even part" of e^x, and $\sinh x$ as the "odd part" of e^x.

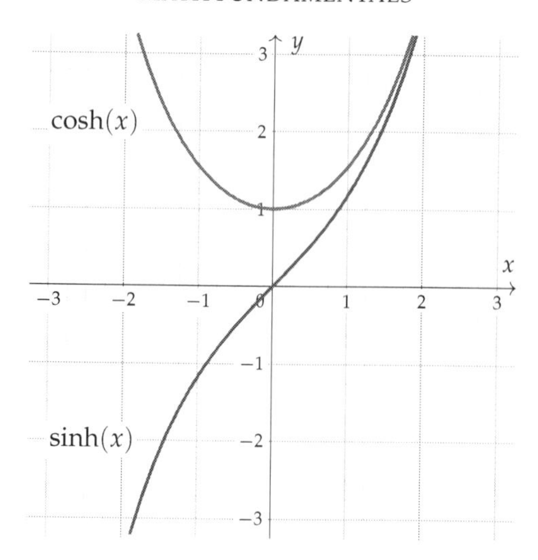

Figure 1.58: The graphs of the functions $\cosh x$ and $\sinh x$.

Don't worry about $\cosh x$ and $\sinh x$ too much. The hyperbolic trig functions are used much less often than the circular trigonometric functions $\cos\theta$ and $\sin\theta$. The main thing to remember is the general pattern: cosine functions are used to denote horizontal coordinates and sine functions are used to denote vertical coordinates.

The conic sections

There is a deep connection between the geometric shapes of the circle, the ellipse, the parabola, and the hyperbola. These seemingly different shapes can be obtained, geometrically speaking, from a single object: the cone. We can obtain the four curves by slicing the cone at different angles. Furthermore, we can use the eccentricity parameter ε to classify the curves.

A horizontal cut through the cone will produce a circle. The circle corresponds to an eccentricity parameter of $\varepsilon = 0$. For values of ε in the interval $[0, 1)$ the function $r(\theta)$ describes an ellipse. The value $\varepsilon = 1$ corresponds to the shape of a parabola. An eccentricity $\varepsilon > 1$ corresponds to the shape of a hyperbola.

Conic sections in polar coordinates

In polar coordinates, all four conic sections can be described by the same equation,

$$r(\theta) = \frac{q(1+\varepsilon)}{1+\varepsilon\cos(\theta)},$$

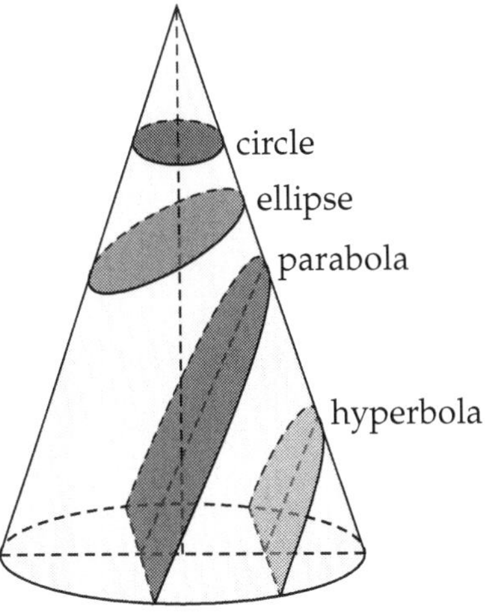

Figure 1.59: Taking slices through a cone at different angles produces different geometric shapes: a circle, an ellipse, a parabola, or a hyperbola.

where q is the curve's closest distance to a focal point. For a circle $q = a$, for an ellipse $q = a(1-\varepsilon)$, and for a hyperbola $q = a(\varepsilon - 1)$. In the context of a parabola, the length q is sometimes referred to as the focal length and denoted f.

Depending on the parameter ε, the equation $r(\theta)$ defines either a circle, an ellipse, a parabola, or a hyperbola. Table 1.4 summarizes all our observations regarding conic sections.

Conic section	Equation	Polar equation	Eccentricity
Circle	$x^2 + y^2 = a^2$	$r(\theta) = a$	$\varepsilon = 0$
Ellipse	$\frac{x^2}{a^2} + \frac{y^2}{b^2} = 1$	$r(\theta) = \frac{a(1-\varepsilon^2)}{1+\varepsilon\cos(\theta)}$	$\varepsilon = \sqrt{1 - \frac{b^2}{a^2}} \in [0,1)$
Parabola	$y^2 = 4qx$	$r(\theta) = \frac{2q}{1+\cos(\theta)}$	$\varepsilon = 1$
Hyperbola	$\frac{x^2}{a^2} - \frac{y^2}{b^2} = 1$	$r(\theta) = \frac{a(\varepsilon^2-1)}{1+\varepsilon\cos(\theta)}$	$\varepsilon = \sqrt{1 + \frac{b^2}{a^2}} \in (1,\infty)$

Table 1.4: The four conic sections and their eccentricity parameters.

The motion of the planets is explained by Newton's law of gravitation. The gravitational interaction between two bodies is always described by one of the four conic sections. Figure 1.60 illustrates four different trajectories for a satellite near planet F. The circle ($\varepsilon = 0$) and the ellipse ($\varepsilon \in [0,1)$) describe *closed orbits*, in which the satellite is captured in the gravitational field of the planet F and remains in orbit forever. The parabola ($\varepsilon = 1$) and the hyperbola ($\varepsilon > 1$)

describe *open orbits*, in which the satellite swings by the planet F and then continues.

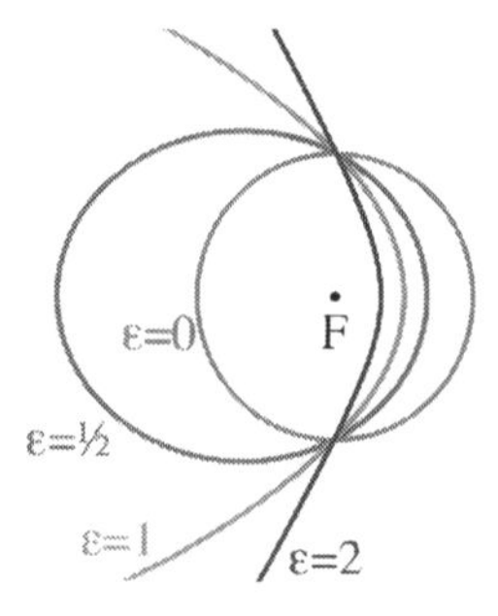

Figure 1.60: Four different trajectories for a satellite moving near a planet.

Links

[Lots of information about ellipses and orbits on Wikipedia]
`http://en.wikipedia.org/wiki/Eccentricity_(mathematics)`

[An in-depth discussion on the conic sections]
`http://astrowww.phys.uvic.ca/~tatum/celmechs/celm2.pdf`

1.20 Solving systems of linear equations

Solving equations with one unknown—like $2x + 4 = 7x$, for instance—requires manipulating both sides of the equation until the unknown variable is *isolated* on one side. For this instance, we can subtract $2x$ from both sides of the equation to obtain $4 = 5x$, which simplifies to $x = \frac{4}{5}$.

What about the case when you are given two equations and must solve for two unknowns? For example,

$$x + 2y = 5,$$
$$3x + 9y = 21.$$

Can you find values of x and y that satisfy both equations?

Concepts

- x, y: the two unknowns in the equations

- *eq*1, *eq*2: a system of two equations that must be solved *simultaneously*. These equations will look like

$$a_1x + b_1y = c_1,$$
$$a_2x + b_2y = c_2,$$

  where *a*s, *b*s, and *c*s are given constants.

Principles

If you have n equations and n unknowns, you can solve the equations simultaneously and find the values of the unknowns. There are several different approaches for solving equations simultaneously. We'll learn about three of these approaches in this section.

Solution techniques

When solving for two unknowns in two equations, the best approach is to *eliminate* one of the variables from the equations. By combining the two equations appropriately, we can simplify the problem to the problem of finding one unknown in one equation.

Solving by substitution

We want to solve the following system of equations:

$$x + 2y = 5,$$
$$3x + 9y = 21.$$

We can isolate x in the first equation to obtain

$$x = 5 - 2y,$$
$$3x + 9y = 21.$$

Now *substitute* the expression for x from the top equation into the bottom equation:

$$3(5 - 2y) + 9y = 21.$$

We just eliminated one of the unknowns by substitution. Continuing, we expand the bracket to find

$$15 - 6y + 9y = 21,$$

or

$$3y = 6.$$

We find $y = 2$, but what is x? Easy. To solve for x, plug the value $y = 2$ into any of the equations we started from. Using the equation $x = 5 - 2y$, we find $x = 5 - 2(2) = 1$.

Solving by subtraction

Let's return to our set of equations to see another approach for solving:

$$x + 2y = 5,$$
$$3x + 9y = 21.$$

Observe that any equation will remain true if we multiply the whole equation by some constant. For example, we can multiply the first equation by 3 to obtain an equivalent set of equations:

$$3x + 6y = 15,$$
$$3x + 9y = 21.$$

Why did I pick 3 as the multiplier? By choosing this constant, the x terms in both equations now have the same coefficient.

Subtracting two true equations yields another true equation. Let's subtract the top equation from the bottom one:

$$\cancel{3x} - \cancel{3x} + 9y - 6y = 21 - 15 \quad \Rightarrow \quad 3y = 6.$$

The $3x$ terms cancel. This subtraction eliminates the variable x because we multiplied the first equation by 3. We find $y = 2$. To find x, substitute $y = 2$ into one of the original equations:

$$x + 2(2) = 5,$$

from which we deduce that $x = 1$.

Solving by equating

There is a third way to solve the system of equations

$$x + 2y = 5,$$
$$3x + 9y = 21.$$

We can isolate x in both equations by moving all other variables and constants to the right-hand sides of the equations:

$$x = 5 - 2y,$$
$$x = \frac{1}{3}(21 - 9y) = 7 - 3y.$$

Though the variable x is unknown to us, we know two facts about it: x is equal to $5 - 2y$ and x is equal to $7 - 3y$. Therefore, we can eliminate x by equating the right-hand sides of the equations:

$$5 - 2y = 7 - 3y.$$

We solve for y by adding $3y$ to both sides and subtracting 5 from both sides. We find $y = 2$ then plug this value into the equation $x = 5 - 2y$ to find x. The solutions are $x = 1$ and $y = 2$.

Discussion

The three elimination techniques presented here will allow you to solve any system of n linear equations in n unknowns. Each time you perform a substitution, a subtraction, or an elimination by equating, you're simplifying the problem to a problem of finding $(n-1)$ unknowns in a system of $(n-1)$ equations. There is actually an entire course called linear algebra, in which you'll develop a more advanced, systematic approach for solving systems of linear equations.

Exercises

E1.32 Solve the system of equations simultaneously for x and y:

$$\begin{aligned} 2x + 4y &= 16, \\ 5x - y &= 7. \end{aligned}$$

E1.33 Solve the system of equations for the unknowns x, y, and z:

$$\begin{aligned} 2x + y - 4z &= 28, \\ x + y + z &= 8, \\ 2x - y - 6z &= 22. \end{aligned}$$

E1.34 Solve for p and q given the equations $p + q = 10$ and $p - q = 4$.

1.21 Compound interest

Soon after ancient civilizations invented the notion of numbers, they started computing *interest* on loans. It is a good idea to know how interest calculations work so that you will be able to make informed decisions about your finances.

Percentages

We often talk about ratios between quantities, rather than mentioning the quantities themselves. For example, we can imagine average Joe, who invests \$1000 in the stock market and loses \$300 because the boys on Wall Street keep pulling dirty tricks on him. To put the number \$300 into perspective, we can say Joe lost 0.3 of his investment, or alternatively, we can say Joe lost 30% of his investment.

To express a ratio as a percentage, multiply it by 100. The ratio of Joe's loss to investment is

$$R = 300/1000 = 0.3.$$

The same ratio expressed as a percentage gives

$$R = 300/1000 \times 100 = 30\%.$$

To convert from a percentage to a ratio, divide the percentage by 100.

Interest rates

Say you take out a \$1000 loan with an interest rate of 6% compounded annually. How much will you owe in interest at the end of the year?

Since 6% corresponds to a ratio of 6/100, and since you borrowed \$1000, the accumulated interest at the end of the year will be

$$I_1 = \frac{6}{100} \times \$1000 = \$60.$$

At year's end, you'll owe the bank a total of

$$L_1 = \left(1 + \frac{6}{100}\right) 1000 = (1 + 0.06)1000 = 1.06 \times 1000 = \$1060.$$

The total money owed after 6 years will be

$$L_6 = (1.06)^6 \times 1000 = \$1418.52.$$

You borrowed \$1000, but in six years you will need to give back \$1418.52. This is a terrible deal! But it gets worse. The above scenario assumes that the bank compounds interest only once per year. In practice, interest is compounded each month.

Monthly compounding

An annual compounding schedule is disadvantageous to the bank, and since the bank writes the rules, compounding is usually performed every month.

The monthly interest rate can be used to find the annual rate. The bank quotes the *nominal annual percentage rate* (APR), which is equal to

$$\text{nominal APR} = 12 \times r,$$

where r is the monthly interest rate.

Suppose we have a nominal APR of 6%, which gives a monthly interest rate of $r = 0.5\%$. If you borrow \$1000 at that interest rate, at the end of the first year you will owe

$$L_1 = \left(1 + \frac{0.5}{100}\right)^{12} \times 1000 = \$1061.68,$$

and after 6 years you will owe

$$L_6 = \left(1 + \frac{0.5}{100}\right)^{72} \times 1000 = 1.061677^6 \times 1000 = \$1432.04.$$

Note how the bank tries to pull a fast one: the *effective* APR is actually 6.16%, not 6%. Every twelve months, the amount due will increase by the following factor:

$$\text{effective APR} = \left(1 + \frac{0.5}{100}\right)^{12} = 1.0616.$$

Thus the effective annual percent rate is 6.16%, but it's legal for banks to advertise it as "6% nominal APR." Sneaky stuff.

Compounding infinitely often

We saw that more frequent compounding leads to higher effective interest rates. Let's find a formula for the effective APR if the nominal APR is 6% and the bank performs the compounding n times per year.

The annual growth ratio will be

$$\left(1 + \frac{6}{100n}\right)^{n},$$

where the interest rate per compounding period is $\frac{6}{n}\%$, and there are n periods per year.

Consider a scenario in which the compounding is performed infinitely often. This corresponds to the case when the number n in the above equation tends to infinity (denoted $n \to \infty$). This is not a practical question, but it is an interesting avenue to explore nevertheless because it leads to the definition of the natural exponential function $f(x) = e^x$.

When we set $n \to \infty$ in the above expression, the annual growth ratio will be described by the exponential function base e as follows:

$$\lim_{n\to\infty} \left(1 + \frac{6}{100n}\right)^{n} = \exp\!\left(\frac{6}{100}\right) = 1.0618365.$$

The expression "$\lim_{n\to\infty}$" is to be read as "In the limit when n tends to infinity." We will learn more about limits in Chapter 5.

A nominal APR of 6% with compounding that occurs infinitely often has effective APR of 6.183%. After six years you will owe

$$L_6 = \exp\left(\frac{6}{100}\right)^6 \times 1000 = \$1433.33.$$

The nominal APR is 6% in each case, yet, the more frequent the compounding schedule, the more money you'll owe after six years.

Exercises

E1.35 Studious Jack borrowed \$40 000 to complete his university studies and made no payments since graduation. Calculate how much money he owes after 10 years in each of the scenarios.

a) Nominal annual interest rate of 3% compounded monthly

b) Effective annual interest rate of 4%

c) Nominal annual interest rate of 5% with infinite compounding

E1.36 Entrepreneurial Kate borrowed \$20 000 to start a business. Initially her loan had an effective annual percentage rate of 6%, but after five years she negotiated with the bank to obtain a lower rate of 4%. How much money does she owe after 10 years?

1.22 Set notation

A *set* is the mathematically precise notion for describing a group of objects. You don't need to know about sets to perform simple math; but more advanced topics require an understanding of what sets are and how to denote set membership, set operations, and set containment relations. This section introduces all the relevant concepts.

Definitions

- *set*: a collection of mathematical objects
- S, T: the usual variable names for sets
- $s \in S$: this statement is read "s is an element of S" or "s is in S"
- $\mathbb{N}, \mathbb{Z}, \mathbb{Q}, \mathbb{R}$: some important number sets: the naturals, the integers, the rationals, and the real numbers, respectively.
- $\varnothing$: the *empty set* is a set that contains no elements

- { definition }: the curly brackets surround the definition of a set, and the expression inside the curly brackets describes what the set contains.

Set operations:

- $S \cup T$: the *union* of two sets. The union of S and T corresponds to the elements in either S or T.
- $S \cap T$: the *intersection* of the two sets. The intersection of S and T corresponds to the elements that are in both S and T.
- $S \backslash T$: *set difference* or *set minus*. The set difference $S \backslash T$ corresponds to the elements of S that are not in T.

Set relations:

- $\subset$: is a strict subset of
- $\subseteq$: is a subset of or equal to

Here is a list of special mathematical shorthand symbols and their corresponding meanings:

- $\in$: element of
- $\notin$: not an element of
- $\forall$: for all
- $\exists$: there exists
- $\nexists$: there doesn't exist
- $|$: such that

These symbols are used in math proofs because they allow us to express complex mathematical arguments succinctly and precisely.

An *interval* is a subset of the real line. We denote an interval by specifying its endpoints and surrounding them with either square brackets "[" or round brackets "(" to indicate whether or not the corresponding endpoint is included in the interval.

- $[a, b]$: the *closed* interval from a to b. This corresponds to the set of numbers between a and b on the real line, including the endpoints a and b. $[a, b] \equiv \{x \in \mathbb{R} \mid a \leqslant x \leqslant b\}$.
- (a, b): the *open* interval from a to b. This corresponds to the set of numbers between a and b on the real line, *not* including the endpoints a and b. $(a, b) \equiv \{x \in \mathbb{R} \mid a < x < b\}$.
- $[a, b)$: the half-open interval that includes the left endpoint a but not the right endpoint b. $[a, b) \equiv \{x \in \mathbb{R} \mid a \leqslant x < b\}$.

Sometimes we encounter intervals that consist of two disjointed parts. We use the notation $[a, b] \cup [c, d]$ to denote the union of the two intervals, which is the set of numbers *either* between a and b (inclusive) *or* between c and d (inclusive).

Sets

Much of math's power comes from *abstraction*: the ability to see the bigger picture and think *meta* thoughts about the common relationships between math objects. We can think of individual numbers like 3, -5, and π, or we can talk about the *set* of *all* numbers.

It is often useful to restrict our attention to a specific *subset* of the numbers as in the following examples.

Example 1: The nonnegative real numbers

Define $\mathbb{R}_+ \subset \mathbb{R}$ (read "$\mathbb{R}_+$ is a subset of $\mathbb{R}$") to be the set of nonnegative real numbers:

$$\mathbb{R}_+ \equiv \{\text{all } x \text{ in } \mathbb{R} \text{ such that } x \geqslant 0\},$$

or expressed more compactly,

$$\mathbb{R}_+ \equiv \{x \in \mathbb{R} \mid x \geqslant 0\}.$$

If we were to translate the above expression into plain English, it would read "The set $\mathbb{R}_+$ is defined as the set of all real numbers x such that x is greater or equal to zero."

Note we used the symbol "$\equiv$" instead of the basic "$=$" to give you an extra hint that we're defining a new variable $\mathbb{R}_+$ that is equal to the set expression on the right. In this book, we use the symbol "$\equiv$" whenever we define new variables and math quantities. Some other books use the notation "$:=$" for this purpose. The meaning of "$\equiv$" is identical to "$=$" but it tells you the variable on the left of the equality is new.

Example 2: Even and odd integers

Define the set of even integers as

$$E \equiv \{m \in \mathbb{Z} \mid m = 2n,\ n \in \mathbb{Z}\} = \{\ldots, -4, -2, 0, 2, 4, \ldots\}$$

and the set of odd integers as

$$O \equiv \{m \in \mathbb{Z} \mid m = 2n + 1,\ n \in \mathbb{Z}\} = \{\ldots, -3, -1, 1, 3, 5, \ldots\}.$$

Indeed, every even number is divisible by two, so it can be written in the form $2n$ for some integer n. Odd numbers can be obtained from the "template" $2n + 1$, with n varying over all integers.

In both of the above examples, we use the mathematical notation $\{\ldots \mid \ldots\}$ to define the sets. Inside the curly braces we first describe the general kind of objects we are talking about, followed by the symbol "$|$" (read "such that"), followed by the conditions that must be satisfied by all elements of the set.

Number sets

Recall the fundamental number sets we defined in Section 1.2 in the beginning of the book. It is worthwhile to review them briefly.

The *natural* numbers form the set derived when you start from 0 and add 1 any number of times:

$$\mathbb{N} \equiv \{0, 1, 2, 3, 4, 5, 6, \ldots\}.$$

The integers are the numbers derived by adding or subtracting 1 some number of times:

$$\mathbb{Z} \equiv \{x \mid x = \pm n, n \in \mathbb{N}\}.$$

When we allow for divisions between integers, we get the rational numbers:

$$\mathbb{Q} \equiv \left\{ z \,\middle|\, z = \frac{x}{y} \text{ where } x \text{ and } y \text{ are in } \mathbb{Z}, \text{ and } y \neq 0 \right\}.$$

The broader class of real numbers also includes all rationals as well as irrational numbers like $\sqrt{2}$ and π:

$$\mathbb{R} \equiv \{\pi, e, -1.53929411\ldots, 4.99401940129401\ldots, \ldots\}.$$

Finally, we have the set of complex numbers:

$$\mathbb{C} \equiv \{1, i, 1 + i, 2 + 3i, \ldots\},$$

where $i \equiv \sqrt{-1}$ is the unit imaginary number.

Note that the definitions of $\mathbb{R}$ and $\mathbb{C}$ are not very precise. Rather than give a precise definition of each set inside the curly braces as we did for $\mathbb{Z}$ and $\mathbb{Q}$, we instead stated some examples of the elements in the set. Mathematicians sometimes do this and expect you to guess the general pattern for all the elements in the set.

The following inclusion relationship holds for the fundamental sets of numbers:

$$\mathbb{N} \subset \mathbb{Z} \subset \mathbb{Q} \subset \mathbb{R} \subset \mathbb{C}.$$

This relationship means every natural number is also an integer. Every integer is a rational number. Every rational number is a real. And every real number is also a complex number. See Figure 1.2 (page 6) for an illustration of the subset relationship between the number sets.

Subsets of the real line

Recall that the real numbers $\mathbb{R}$ have a graphical representation as points on the number line. See Figure 1.13 on page 21 for a reminder.

The number line is also useful for representing various subsets of the real numbers, which we call *intervals*. We can graphically represent an interval by setting a section of the number line in **bold**. For example, the set of numbers that are strictly greater than 2 and strictly smaller than 4 is represented mathematically either as "$(2,4)$," or more explicitly as

$$\{x \in \mathbb{R} \mid 2 < x < 4\},$$

or graphically as in Figure 1.61.

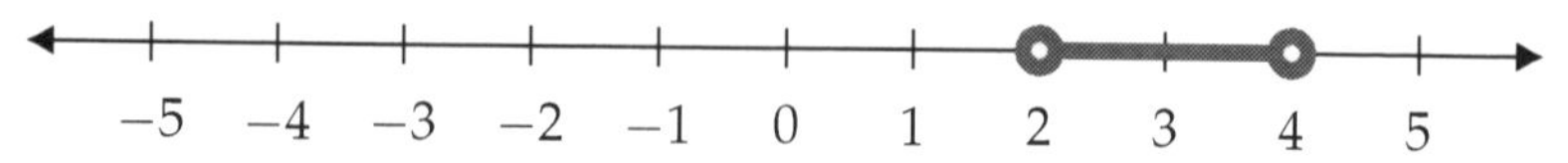

Figure 1.61: The open interval $(2,4) \equiv \{x \in \mathbb{R} \mid 2 < x < 4\}$.

Let's read the mathematical definition of this set carefully, and try to connect it with the graphical representation. Recall that the symbol $\in$ denotes set membership and the vertical bar stands for "such that," so the whole expression "$\{x \in \mathbb{R} \mid 2 < x < 4\}$" is read "the set of real numbers x, such that $2 < x < 4$." Indeed this is also the region shown in bold in Figure 1.61.

Note that this interval is described by *strict* inequalities, which means the subset contains 2.000000001 and 3.99999999, but doesn't contain the endpoints 2 and 4. These *open* endpoints 2 and 4 are denoted on the number line as empty dots. An empty dot indicates that the endpoint is not included in the set.

We use the *union* symbol ($\cup$) to denote subsets of the number line that consist of several parts. For example, the set of numbers that lies *either* between -3 and 0 *or* between 1 and 2 is written as

$$\{x \in \mathbb{R} \mid -3 \leqslant x \leqslant 0\} \cup \{x \in \mathbb{R} \mid 1 \leqslant x \leqslant 2\}.$$

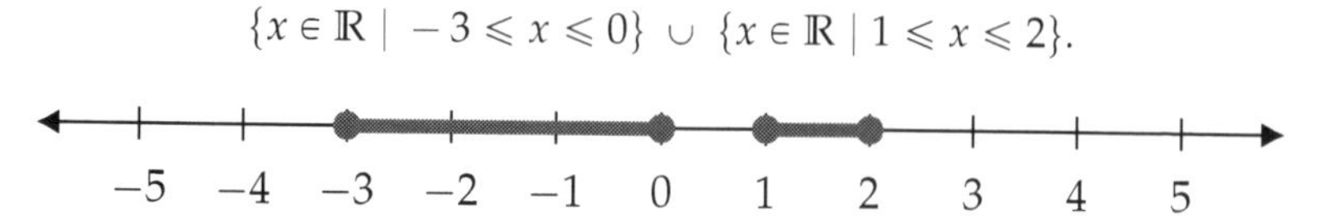

Figure 1.62: The graphical representation of the set $[-3,0] \cup [1,2]$.

This set is defined by less-than-or-equal inequalities, so the intervals contain their endpoints. These *closed* endpoints are denoted on the number line with filled-in dots.

Set relations and set operations

We'll now introduce a useful graphical representation for set relations and set operations. Although sets are purely mathematical constructs and they have no "shape," we can draw *Venn diagrams* to visualize relationships between sets and different subsets.

Consider the notion of a set B that is strictly contained in another set A. We write $B \subset A$ if $\forall b \in B$, $b \in A$ as well. Written in words, $B \subset A$ tells us every element of B is also an element of A.

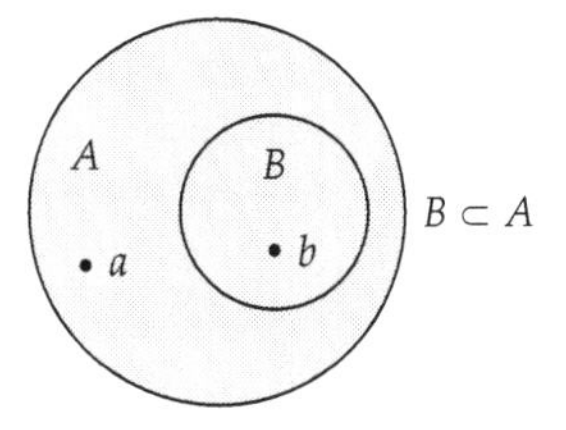

Figure 1.63: Venn diagram showing an example of the set relation $B \subset A$. The set B is strictly contained in the set A.

Figure 1.63 shows the picture that mathematicians have in mind when they say, "The set B is contained in the set A." Set containment is an abstract mathematical notion, but the picture helps us visualize the situation.

Mathematicians use two different symbols to describe set containment, in order to specify either a *strict* containment relation or a *subset-or-equal* relation. The two types of containment relations between sets are similar to the *less-than* ($<$) and *less-than-or-equal* ($\leqslant$) relations between numbers. A strict containment relation is denoted by the symbol $\subset$. We write $B \subset A$ if and only if every element of B is also an element of A, and there exists at least one element of A that is not an element of B. Using set notation, the previous sentence is expressed as

$$B \subset A \qquad \Leftrightarrow \qquad \forall b \in B, b \in A \text{ and } \exists a \in A \text{ such that } a \notin B.$$

For example, the expression $E \subset \mathbb{Z}$ shows that the even numbers are a strict subset of the integers. Every even number is an integer, but there exist integers that are not even (the odd numbers). Some mathematicians prefer the more descriptive symbol $\subsetneq$ to describe strict containment relations.

A subset-or-equal relation is denoted $B \subseteq A$. In writing $B \subseteq A$, a mathematician claims, "Every element of B is also an element of A," but makes no claim about the existence of elements that are contained in A but not in B. The statement $B \subset A$ implies $B \subseteq A$; however, $B \subseteq A$ does not imply $B \subset A$. This is analogous to how $b < a$ implies $b \leqslant a$, but $b \leqslant a$ doesn't imply $b < a$, since a and b could be equal.

Venn diagrams also help us visualize the subsets obtained from set operations. Figure 1.64 illustrates the set union $A \cup B$, the set intersection $A \cap B$, and the set difference $A \backslash B$, for two sets A and B.

The union $A \cup B$ describes all elements that are in either set A or set B, or both. If $e \in A \cup B$, then $e \in A$ or $e \in B$.

Recall the set of even numbers $E \subset \mathbb{Z}$ and the set of odd numbers $O \subset \mathbb{Z}$ defined above. Since every integer is either an even number or an odd number, we know $\mathbb{Z} \subseteq E \cup O$. The union of two subsets is always contained within the parent set, so we also know $E \cup O \subseteq \mathbb{Z}$. Combining these facts, we can establish the equality $E \cup O = \mathbb{Z}$, which states the fact, "The combination of all even and odd numbers is the same as all integers."

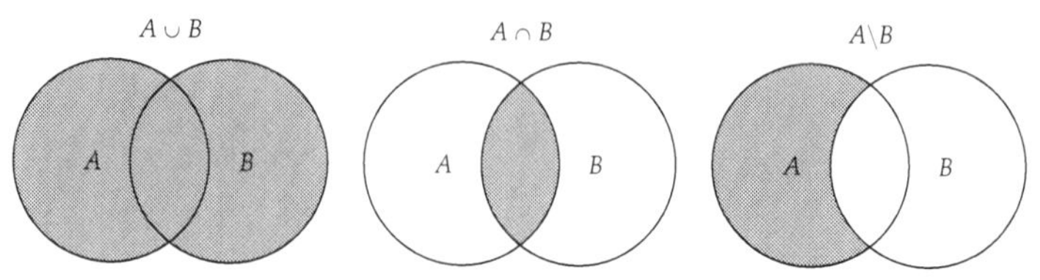

Figure 1.64: Venn diagrams showing different subsets obtained using the set operations: set union $A \cup B$, set intersection $A \cap B$, and set difference $A \backslash B$.

The set intersection $A \cap B$ and set difference $A \backslash B$ are also illustrated in Figure 1.64. The intersection of two sets contains the elements that are part of both sets. The set difference $A \backslash B$ contains all the elements that are in A but not in B.

Note the meaning of the conjunction "or" in English is ambiguous. The expression "in A or B" could be interpreted as either an "inclusive or," meaning "in A or B, or in both"—or as an "exclusive or," meaning "in A or B, but not both." Mathematicians always use "or" in the inclusive sense, so $A \cup B$ denotes elements that are in A or B, or in both sets. We can obtain an expression that corresponds to the "exclusive or" of two sets by taking the union of the sets and subtracting their intersection: $(A \cup B) \backslash (A \cap B)$.

Example 3: Set operations

Consider the three sets $A = \{a, b, c\}$, $B = \{b, c, d\}$, and $C = \{c, d, e\}$. Using set operations, we can define new sets, such as

$$A \cup B = \{a, b, c, d\}, \quad A \cap B = \{b, c\}, \quad \text{and} \quad A \backslash B = \{a\},$$

which correspond to elements in either A or B, the set of elements in A and B, and the set of elements in A but not in B, respectively.

We can also construct expressions involving three sets:

$$A \cup B \cup C = \{a, b, c, d, e\}, \qquad A \cap B \cap C = \{c\}.$$

And we can write more elaborate set expressions, like

$$(A \cup B) \setminus C = \{a, b\},$$

which is the set of elements that are in A or B but not in C.

Another example of a complicated set expression is

$$(A \cap B) \cup (B \cap C) = \{b, c, d\},$$

which describes the set of elements in both A and B or in both B and C. As you can see, set notation is a compact, precise language for writing complicated set expressions.

Example 4: Word problem

A startup is looking to hire student interns for the summer. Let S denote the whole set of students looking for a summer internship. Define C to be the subset of students who are good with computers, M the subset of students who know math, D the students with design skills, and L the students with good language skills.

Using set notation, we can specify different subsets of the students the startup might hire. Let's say the startup is a math textbook publisher; they want to hire students from the set $M \cap L$—the students who are good at math and who also have good language skills. A startup that builds websites needs both designers and coders, and therefore would choose students from the set $D \cup C$.

New vocabulary

The specialized notation used by mathematicians can be difficult to get used to. You must learn how to read symbols like $\exists$, $\subset$, $|$, and $\in$ and translate their meaning in the sentence. Indeed, learning advanced mathematics notation is akin to learning a new language.

To help you practice the new vocabulary, we'll look at some mathematical arguments that make use of the new symbols.

Simple proof example

Claim: Given $J(n) = 3n + 2 - n$, $J(n) \in E$ for all $n \in \mathbb{Z}$. The claim is that $J(n)$ is always an even number, whenever n is an integer. This means no matter which integer number n we choose, the function $J(n) = 3n + 2 - n$ will always output an even number.

Proof: We want to show $J(n) \in E$ for all $n \in \mathbb{Z}$. Let's first review the definition of the set of even numbers $E \equiv \{m \in \mathbb{Z} \mid m = 2n, n \in \mathbb{Z}\}$.

A number is even if it is equal to $2n$ for some integer n. Next let's simplify the expression for $J(n)$ as follows:

$$J(n) = 3n + 2 - n = 2n + 2 = 2(n+1).$$

Observe that the number $(n+1)$ is always an integer whenever n is an integer. Since the output of $J(n) = 2(n+1)$ is equal to $2m$ for some integer m, we've proven that $J(n) \in E$, for all $n \in \mathbb{Z}$. □

Less simple proof example: Square root of 2 is irrational

The following is an ancient mathematical proof expressed in terms of modern math symbols.

Claim: $\sqrt{2} \notin \mathbb{Q}$. The claim is that $\sqrt{2}$ is not part of the set of rational numbers. Recall the definition of the set of rational numbers: $\mathbb{Q} \equiv \left\{\frac{m}{n} \mid m, n \in \mathbb{Z}, n \neq 0\right\}$. If $\sqrt{2} \notin \mathbb{Q}$, this means no numbers $m \in \mathbb{Z}$ and $n \in \mathbb{Z}$ exist such that $m/n = \sqrt{2}$. Using mathematical notation, the previous sentence is expressed as

$$\nexists\, m \in \mathbb{Z}, n \in \mathbb{Z} \;\big|\; m/n = \sqrt{2}.$$

To prove the claim, we'll use a technique called *proof by contradiction*. We begin by assuming the opposite of what we want to prove: that there exist numbers $m \in \mathbb{Z}$ and $n \in \mathbb{Z}$ such that $m/n = \sqrt{2}$. We'll then carry out some simple algebra steps and in the end we'll obtain an equation that is not true—we'll arrive at a contradiction. Arriving at a contradiction means our original supposition is wrong: there are no numbers $m \in \mathbb{Z}$ and $n \in \mathbb{Z}$ such that $m/n = \sqrt{2}$.

Proof: Suppose there exist numbers $m \in \mathbb{Z}$ and $n \in \mathbb{Z}$ such that $m/n = \sqrt{2}$. We can assume the integers m and n have no common factors. In particular, m and n cannot both be even, otherwise they would both contain at least one factor of 2. Next, we'll investigate whether m is an even number $m \in E$, or an odd number $m \in O$. Look back to Example 2 (page 112) for the definitions of the sets O and E.

Before we check for even and oddness, it will help to point out the fact that the action of squaring an integer preserves its odd/even nature. An even number times an even number gives an even number: if $e \in E$ then $e^2 \in E$. Similarly, an odd number times an odd number gives an odd number: if $o \in O$ then $o^2 \in O$.

We proceed with the proof. We assume $m/n = \sqrt{2}$. Taking the square of both sides of this equation, we obtain

$$\frac{m^2}{n^2} = 2 \qquad \Rightarrow \qquad m^2 = 2n^2.$$

If we analyze the last equation in more detail, we can conclude that m cannot be an odd number, or written "$m \notin O$" in math. If m is an odd number then m^2 will also be odd, but this would contradict the above equation since the right-hand side of the equation contains the factor 2 and every number containing a factor 2 is even, not odd. If m is an integer ($m \in \mathbb{Z}$) and m is not odd ($m \notin O$) then it must be that m is even ($m \in E$).

If m is even, then it contains a factor of 2, so it can be written as $m = 2q$ where q is some other number $q \in \mathbb{Z}$. The exact value of q is not important. Let's revisit the equation $m^2 = 2n^2$ once more, this time substituting $m = 2q$ into the equation:

$$(2q)^2 = 2n^2 \quad \Rightarrow \quad 2q^2 = n^2.$$

By a similar reasoning as before, we can conclude n cannot be odd ($n \notin O$) so n must be even ($n \in E$). We've shown that both m and n must be even numbers, which means they both contain a factor 2. However, this statement contradicts our initial assumption that m and n do not have any common factors!

The fact that we arrived at a contradiction means there must be a mistake in our reasoning. Since each step we carried out was correct, the mistake must be in the original premise, namely that "There exist numbers $m \in \mathbb{Z}$ and $n \in \mathbb{Z}$ such that $m/n = \sqrt{2}$." Rather, the opposite must be true: "There do not exist numbers $m \in \mathbb{Z}$ and $n \in \mathbb{Z}$ such that $m/n = \sqrt{2}$." The last statement is equivalent to saying $\sqrt{2}$ is irrational, which is what we wanted to prove. □

Sets as solutions to equations

Another context where sets come up is when describing solutions to equations and inequalities. In Section 1.1 we learned how to solve for the unknown x in equations. To solve the equation $f(x) = c$ is to find all the values of x that satisfy this equation. For simple equations like $x - 3 = 6$, the solution is a single number $x = 9$, but more complex equations can have multiple solutions. For example, the solution to the equation $x^2 = 4$ is the set $\{-2, 2\}$, since both $x = -2$ and $x = 2$ satisfy the equation.

Please update your definition of the math verb "to solve" (an equation) to include the new notion of a *solution set*—the set of values that satisfy the equation. A solution set is the mathematically precise way to describe an equation's solutions:

- The solution set to the equation $x - 3 = 6$ is the set $\{9\}$.
- The solution set for the equation $x^2 = 4$ is the set $\{-2, 2\}$.
- The solution set of $\sin(x) = 0$ is the set $\{x \mid x = \pi n, \forall n \in \mathbb{Z}\}$.

- The solution set for the equation $\sin(x) = 2$ is $\varnothing$ (the empty set), since there is no number x that satisfies the equation.

The SymPy function solve returns the solutions of equations as a list. To solve the equation $f(x) = c$ using SymPy, we first rewrite it as expression that equals zero $f(x) - c = 0$, then call the function solve:

```
>>> solve(x-3 -6, x)          # usage: solve(expr, var)
[9]

>>> solve(x**2 -4, x)
[-2, 2]

>>> solve(sin(x), x)
[0, pi]                       # found only solutions in [0,2*pi)

>>> solve(sin(x) -2, x)
[]                            # empty list = empty set
```

Solution sets are also useful for describing the solutions to inequalities, which is what we'll learn about next.

Inequalities

In this section, we'll learn how to solve inequalities. The solution set to an inequality is an *interval*—a subset of the number line. Consider the inequality $x^2 \leqslant 4$, which is equivalent to asking the question, "For which values of x is x^2 less than or equal to 4?" The answer to this question is the interval $[-2,2] \equiv \{x \in \mathbb{R} \mid -2 \leqslant x \leqslant 2\}$.

Working with inequalities is essentially the same as working with their endpoints. To solve the inequality $x^2 \leqslant 4$, we first solve $x^2 = 4$ to find the endpoints and then use trial and error to figure out which part of the space to the left and right of the endpoints satisfies the inequality.

It's important to distinguish the different types of inequality conditions. The four different types of inequalities are

- $f(x) < g(x)$: a strict inequality. The function $f(x)$ is always *strictly less than* the function $g(x)$.
- $f(x) \leqslant g(x)$: the function $f(x)$ is *less than or equal to* $g(x)$.
- $f(x) > g(x)$: $f(x)$ is *strictly greater than* $g(x)$.
- $f(x) \geqslant g(x)$: $f(x)$ is *greater than or equal to* $g(x)$.

Depending on the type of inequality, the answer will be either a *open* or *closed* interval.

To solve inequalities we use the techniques we learned for solving equations: we perform simplifying steps **on both sides of the inequality** until we obtain the answer. The only new aspect when dealing with inequalities is the following. When multiplying an inequality by a negative number on both sides, we must flip the direction of the inequality:

$$f(x) \leqslant g(x) \qquad \Rightarrow \qquad -f(x) \geqslant -g(x).$$

Example 5 To solve the inequality $7 - x \leqslant 5$ we must *dig* toward the x and *undo* all the operations that stand in our way:

$$\begin{aligned} 7 - x &\leqslant 5, \\ (-x) + 7 &\leqslant 5, \\ (-x) + 7 - 7 &\leqslant 5 - 7, \\ -x &\leqslant -2, \\ x &\geqslant 2. \end{aligned}$$

To obtain the second line we simply rewrote the order of operations on the left side of the inequality. In the third line we subtracted 7 from both sides of the inequality to undo the $+7$ operation. In the last step we multiplied both sides of the inequality by -1, which had the effect of changing the inequality from $\leqslant$ to $\geqslant$. The solution set to the inequality $7 - x \leqslant 5$ is the interval $[2, \infty)$.

Example 6 To solve the inequality $x^2 \leqslant 4$, we must undo the quadratic function by taking the square root of both sides of the inequality. Note the equation $x^2 = 4$ has two solutions: $x = -2$ and $x = 2$. Similarly, we'll need to consider two separate cases for the inequality conditions. Simplifying the inequality $x^2 \leqslant 4$ by taking the square root on both sides results in two inequality conditions

$$x \geqslant -2 \qquad \text{and} \qquad x \leqslant 2,$$

which we can express more concisely as $-2 \leqslant x \leqslant 2$. If x is a negative number, it must be greater than -2; and if x is a positive number, it must be less than 2 in order for $x^2 \leqslant 4$. The solution set for the inequality $x^2 \leqslant 4$ is the interval $[-2, 2] = \{x \in \mathbb{R} \mid -2 \leqslant x \leqslant 2\}$. Note the solution is a closed interval (square brackets), which means the endpoints are included.

The best way to convince yourself that the above algebraic reasoning is correct is to think about the graph of the function $f(x) = x^2$. The inequality $x^2 \leqslant 4$ corresponds to the condition $f(x) \leqslant 4$. For what values of x is the graph of the function $f(x)$ below the line with equation $y = 4$?

As you can see, solving inequalities is no more complicated than solving equations. You can think about an inequality in terms of its endpoints, which correspond to the equality conditions. Whenever things get complicated (as in Example 6), you can sketch the function graphs for the different terms in the inequality and visually determine the appropriate directions for the inequality signs.

Sets related to functions

A function that takes real variables as inputs and produces real numbers as outputs is denoted $f : \mathbb{R} \to \mathbb{R}$. The *domain* of a function is the set of all possible inputs to the function that produce an output:

$$\text{Dom}(f) \equiv \{x \in \mathbb{R} \mid f(x) \in \mathbb{R}\}.$$

Inputs for which the function is undefined are not part of the domain. For instance the function $f(x) = \sqrt{x}$ is not defined for negative inputs, so we have $\text{Dom}(f) = \mathbb{R}_+$.

The *image* of a function is the set of all possible outputs of the function:

$$\text{Im}(f) \equiv \{y \in \mathbb{R} \mid \exists x \in \mathbb{R},\ y = f(x)\}.$$

For example, the function $f(x) = x^2$ has the image set $\text{Im}(f) = \mathbb{R}_+$ since the outputs it produces are always nonnegative.

Discussion

Knowledge of the precise mathematical jargon introduced in this section is not crucial to understanding basic mathematics. That said, I wanted to expose you to some technical math notation here because this is the language in which mathematicians think and communicate. Most advanced math textbooks will assume you understand technical math notation, so it's good to be prepared.

Exercises

E1.37 Given the three sets $A = \{1,2,3,4,5,6,7\}$, $B = \{1,3,5\}$, and $C = \{2,4,6\}$, compute the following set expressions.

a) $A \backslash B$ **b)** $B \cup C$ **c)** $A \cap B$ **d)** $B \cap C$

e) $A \cup B \cup C$ **f)** $A \backslash (B \cup C)$ **g)** $(A \backslash B) \cup C$ **h)** $(A \cap B) \cap C$

E1.38 Find the values of x that satisfy the following inequalities.

a) $2x < 3$ **b)** $-4x \geqslant 20$ **c)** $|2x - 3| < 5$

d) $3x + 3 < 5x - 5$ **e)** $\frac{1}{2}x - 2 \geqslant \frac{1}{3}$ **f)** $(x + 1)^2 \geqslant 9$

Express your answer as an interval with appropriate endpoints.

1.23 Math problems

We've now reached the first section of problems in this book. The purpose of these problems is to give you a way to comprehensively practice your math fundamentals. In the real world, you'll rarely have to solve equations by hand; however, knowing how to manipulate math expressions and solve math equations is a very useful skill to develop. At times, honing your math chops might seem like tough mental work, but at the end of each problem, you'll gain a stronger foothold on all the subjects you've been learning about. You'll also experience a small *achievement buzz* after each problem you vanquish.

I have a special message to readers who are learning math just for fun: you can either try the problems in this section or skip them. Since you have no upcoming exam on this material, you could skip ahead to Chapter 2 without any immediate consequences. However (and it's a big however), those readers who don't take a crack at these problems will be missing a significant opportunity.

Sit down to do them later today, or another time when you're properly caffeinated. If you take the initiative to make time for math, you'll find yourself developing lasting comprehension and true math fluency. Without the practice of solving problems, however, you're extremely likely to forget most of what you've learned in the next month or two, simple as that. You'll still remember the big ideas, but the details will be fuzzy and faded. Don't break the pace now: with math, it's very much *use it or lose it*!

By solving some of the problems in this section, you'll remember a lot more stuff. Make sure you step away from the pixels while you're solving problems. You don't need fancy technology to do math; grab a pen and some paper from the printer and you'll be fine. Do yourself a favour: put your phone in airplane-mode, close the lid of your laptop, and move away from desktop computers. Give yourself some time to think. Yes, I know you can look up the answer to any question in five seconds on the internet, and you can use `live.sympy.org` to solve any math problem, but that is like outsourcing the thinking. Mathematicians like Descartes, Hilbert, Leibniz, and Noether did most of their work with pen and paper and they did well. Spend some time with math the way they did.

P1.1 Solve for x in the equation $x^2 - 9 = 7$.

P1.2 Solve for x in the equation $\cos^{-1}\left(\frac{x}{A}\right) - \phi = \omega t$.

P1.3 Solve for x in the equation $\frac{1}{x} = \frac{1}{a} + \frac{1}{b}$.

P1.4 Use a calculator to find the values of the following expressions:

a) $\sqrt[4]{3^3}$ **b)** 2^{10} **c)** $7^{\frac{1}{4}} - 10$ **d)** $\frac{1}{2}\ln(e^{22})$

P1.5 Compute the following expressions involving fractions:

a) $\frac{1}{2} + \frac{1}{4}$ **b)** $\frac{4}{7} - \frac{23}{5}$ **c)** $1\frac{3}{4} + 1\frac{31}{32}$

P1.6 Use the basic rules of algebra to simplify the following expressions:

a) $ab\,\frac{1}{a}\,b^2cb^{-3}$ **b)** $\frac{abc}{bca}$ **c)** $\frac{27a^2}{\sqrt{9abba}}$

d) $\frac{a(b+c)-ca}{b}$ **e)** $\frac{a}{c\sqrt[3]{b}}\frac{b^{\frac{4}{3}}}{a^2}$ **f)** $(x+a)(x+b) - x(a+b)$

P1.7 Expand the brackets in the following expressions:

a) $(x+a)(x-b)$ **b)** $(2x+3)(x-5)$ **c)** $(5x-2)(2x+7)$

P1.8 Factor the following expressions as a product of linear terms:

a) $x^2 - 2x - 8$ **b)** $3x^3 - 27x$ **c)** $6x^2 + 11x - 21$

P1.9 Complete the square in the following quadratic expressions to obtain expressions of the form $A(x-h)^2 + k$.

a) $x^2 - 4x + 7$ **b)** $2x^2 + 12x + 22$ **c)** $6x^2 + 11x - 21$

P1.10 A golf club and a golf ball cost $1.10 together. The golf club costs one dollar more than the ball. How much does the ball cost?

P1.11 An ancient artist drew scenes of hunting on the walls of a cave, including 43 figures of animals and people. There were 17 more figures of animals than people. How many figures of people did the artist draw and how many figures of animals?

P1.12 A father is 35 years old and his son is 5 years old. In how many years will the father's age be four times the son's age?

P1.13 A boy and a girl collected 120 nuts. The girl collected twice as many nuts as the boy. How many nuts did each collect?

P1.14 Alice is 5 years older than Bob. The sum of their ages is 25 years. How old is Alice?

P1.15 A publisher needs to bind 4500 books. One print shop can bind these books in 30 days, another shop can do it in 45 days. How many days are necessary to bind all the books if both shops work in parallel?
Hint: Find the books-per-day rate of each shop.

P1.16 A plane leaves Vancouver travelling at 600 km/h toward Montreal. One hour later, a second plane leaves Vancouver heading for Montreal at 900 km/h. How long will it take for the second plane to overtake the first?
Hint: Distance travelled is equal to velocity multiplied by time: $d = vt$.

P1.17 There are 26 sheep and 10 goats on a ship. How old is the captain?

P1.18 The golden ratio, denoted φ, is the positive solution to the quadratic equation $x^2 - x - 1 = 0$. Find the golden ratio.

P1.19 Solve for x in the equation $\frac{1}{x} + \frac{2}{1-x} = \frac{4}{x^2}$.

Hint: Multiply both sides of the equation by $x^2(1-x)$.

P1.20 Use substitution to solve for x in the following equations:

a) $x^6 - 4x^3 + 4 = 0$ **b)** $\dfrac{1}{2-\sin x} = \sin x$

P1.21 Find the range of values of the parameter m for which the equation $2x^2 - mx + m = 0$ has no real solutions.
Hint: Use the quadratic formula.

P1.22 Use the properties of exponents and logarithms to simplify

a) $e^x e^{-x} e^z$ **b)** $\left(\dfrac{xy^{-2}z^{-3}}{x^2y^3z^{-4}}\right)^{-3}$ **c)** $(8x^6)^{-\frac{2}{3}}$

d) $\log_4(\sqrt{2})$ **e)** $\log_{10}(0.001)$ **f)** $\ln(x^2-1) - \ln(x-1)$

P1.23 When representing numbers on a computer, the number of digits of precision n in base b and the approximation error ϵ are related by the equation $n = -\log_b(\epsilon)$. A `float64` has 53 bits of precision (digits base 2). What is the approximation error ϵ for a `float64`? How many digits of precision does a `float64` have in decimal (base 10)?

P1.24 Find the values of x that satisfy the following inequalities:

a) $2x - 5 > 3$ **b)** $5 \leqslant 3x - 4 \leqslant 14$ **c)** $2x^2 + x \geqslant 1$

P1.25 Two algorithms, P and Q, can be used to solve a certain problem. The running time of Algorithm P as a function of the size of the problem n is described by the function $P(n) = 0.002n^2$. The running time of Algorithm Q is described by $Q(n) = 0.5n$. For small problems, Algorithm P runs faster. Starting from what n will Algorithm Q be faster?

P1.26 Consider a right-angle triangle in which the shorter sides are 8 cm and 6 cm. What is the length of the triangle's longest side?

P1.27 A television screen measures 26 inches on the diagonal. The screen height is 13 inches. How wide is the screen?

P1.28 A ladder of length 3.33 m leans against a wall and its foot is 1.44 m from the wall. What is the height h where the ladder touches the wall?

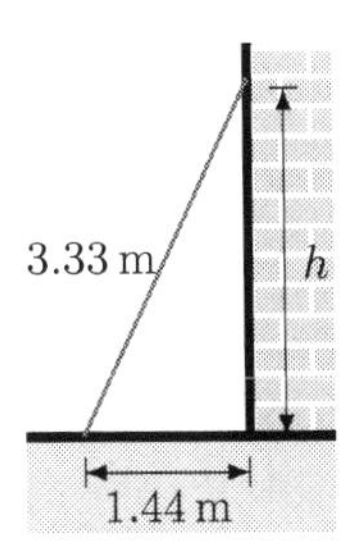

P1.29 **Kepler's triangle** Consider a right-angle triangle in which the hypotenuse has length $\varphi = \frac{\sqrt{5}+1}{2}$ (the golden ratio) and the adjacent side has length $\sqrt{\varphi}$. What is the length of the opposite side?

P1.30 Find the lengths x, y, and z in the figure below.

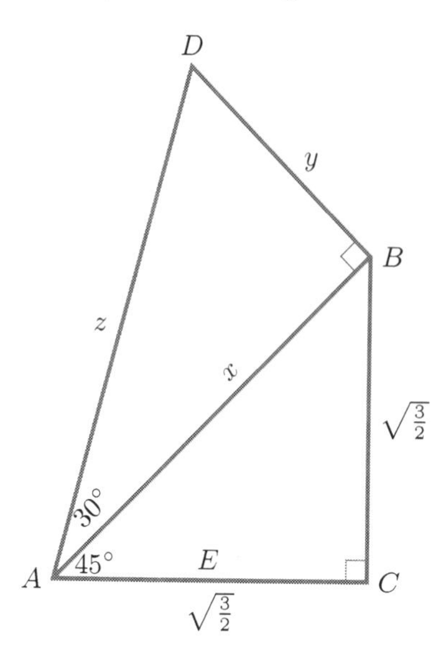

P1.31 Given the angle and distance measurements labelled in Figure 1.65, calculate the distance d and the height of the mountain peak h.

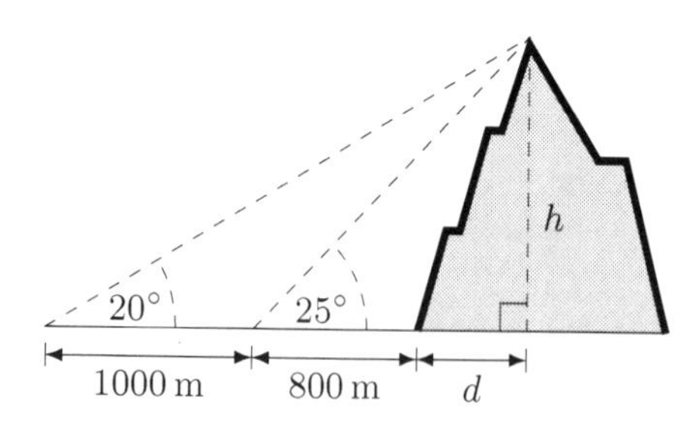

Figure 1.65: Measuring the height of a mountain using angles.

Hint: Use the definition of $\tan\theta$ to obtain two equations in two unknowns.

P1.32 You're observing a house from a blimp flying at an altitude of 2000 metres. From your point of view, the house appears at an angle 24° below the horizontal. What is the horizontal distance x between the blimp and the house?

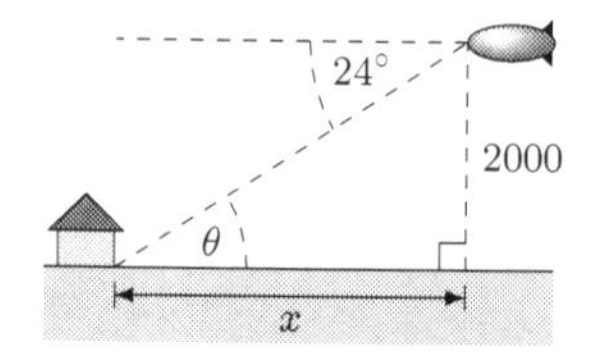

P1.33 Find x. Express your answer in terms of a, b, c and θ.

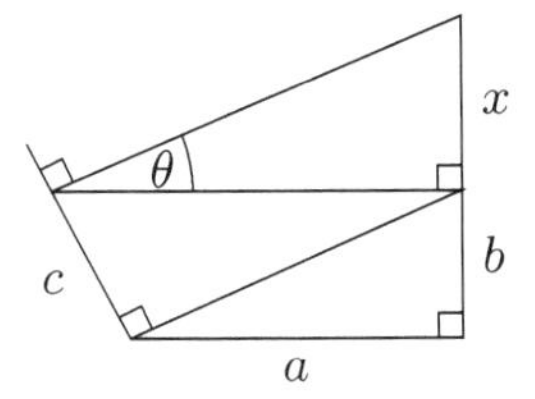

Hint: Use Pythagoras' theorem twice; then use the function tan.

P1.34 An equilateral triangle is inscribed in a circle of radius 1. Find the side length a and the area of the inscribed triangle $A_{\triangle}$.

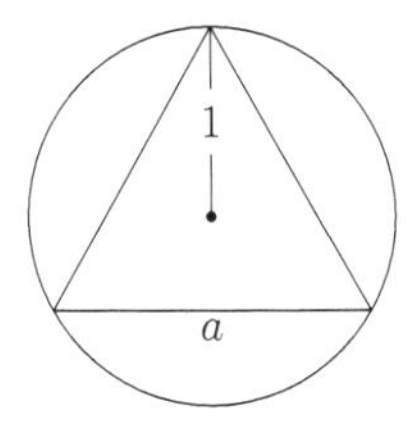

Hint: Split the triangle into three sub-triangles.

P1.35 Use the power-reduction trigonometric identities (page 90) to express $\sin^2\theta\cos^2\theta$ in terms of $\cos 4\theta$.

P1.36 A circle of radius 1 is inscribed inside a *regular octagon* (a polygon with eight sides of length b). Calculate the octagon's perimeter and its area.

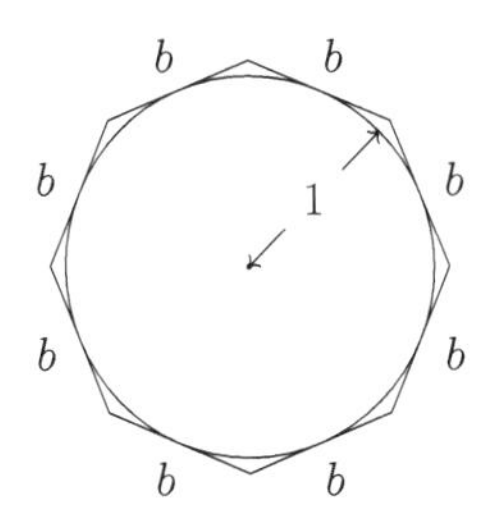

Hint: Split the octagon into eight isosceles triangles.

P1.37 Find the length of side c in the triangle:

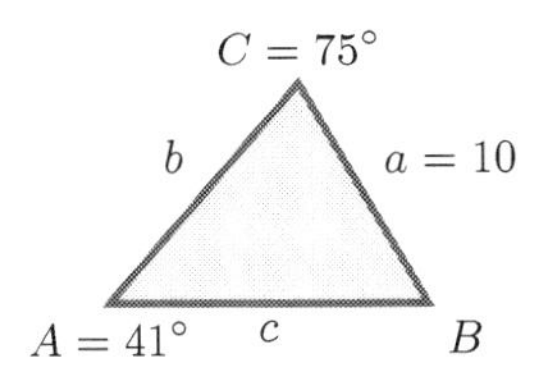

Hint: Use the sine rule.

P1.38 Consider the obtuse triangle shown in Figure 1.66.

a) Express h in terms of a and θ.

b) What is the area of this triangle?

c) Express c in terms of the variables a, b, and θ.

Hint: You can use the cosine rule for part **c)**.

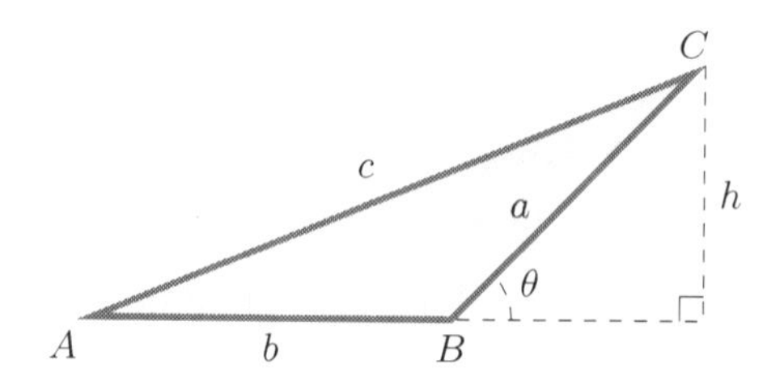

Figure 1.66: A triangle with base b and height h.

P1.39 Find the measure of the angle B and deduce the measure of the angle C. Find the length of side c.

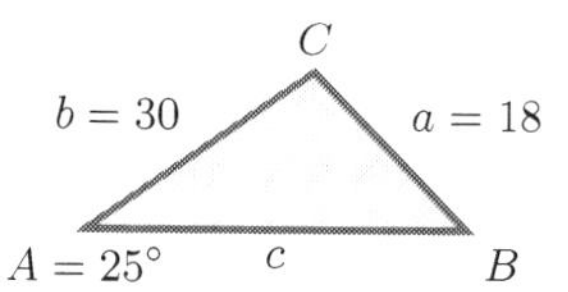

Hint: The sum of the internal angle measures of a triangle is $180°$.

P1.40 An observer on the ground measures an angle of inclination of $30°$ to an approaching airplane, and 10 seconds later measures an angle of inclination of $55°$. If the airplane is flying at a constant speed at an altitude of 2000 m in a straight line directly over the observer, find the speed of the airplane in kilometres per hour.

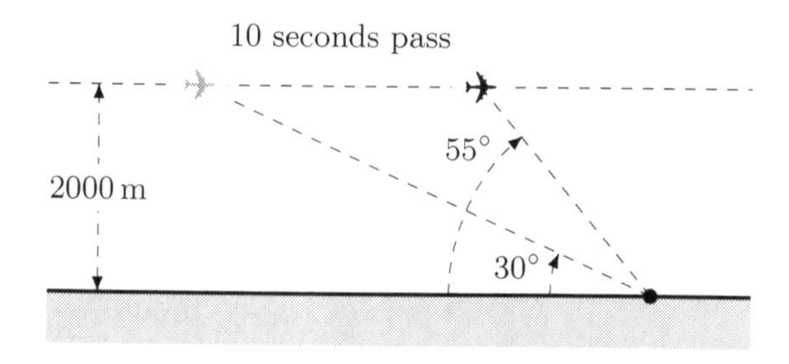

P1.41 Satoshi likes warm saké. He places 1 litre of water in a sauce pan with diameter 17 cm. How much will the height of the water level rise when Satoshi immerses a saké bottle with diameter 7.5 cm?

Hint: You'll need the volume conversion ratio 1 litre = $1000\,\text{cm}^3$.

P1.42 Find the length x of the diagonal of the quadrilateral below.

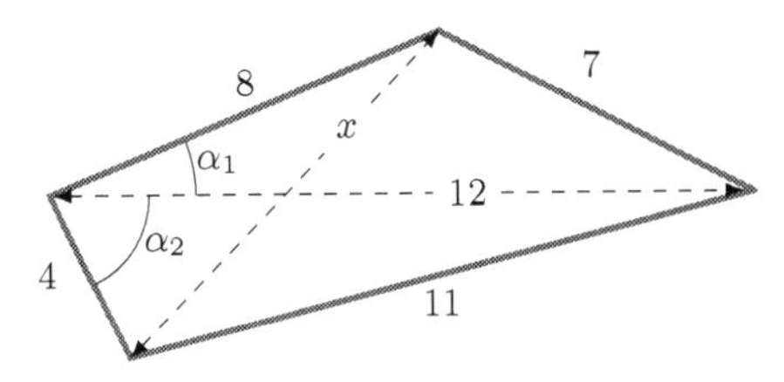

Hint: Use the law of cosines once to find α_1 and α_2, and again to find x.

P1.43 Find the area of the shaded region.

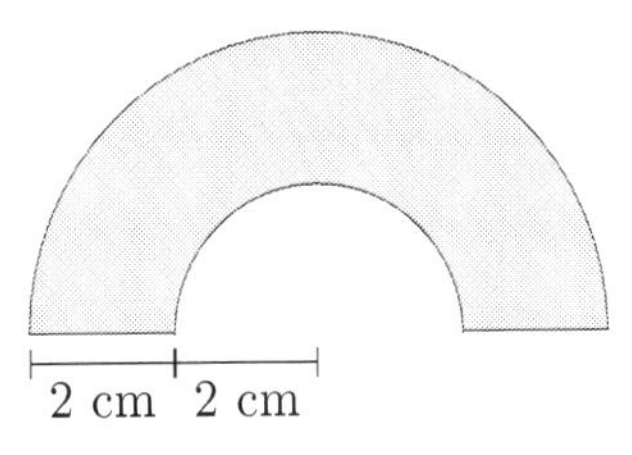

Hint: Find the area of the outer circle, subtract the area of missing centre disk, then divide by two.

P1.44 In preparation for the shooting of a music video, you're asked to suspend a wrecking ball hanging from a circular pulley. The pulley has a radius of 50 cm. The other lengths are indicated in the figure. What is the total length of the rope required?

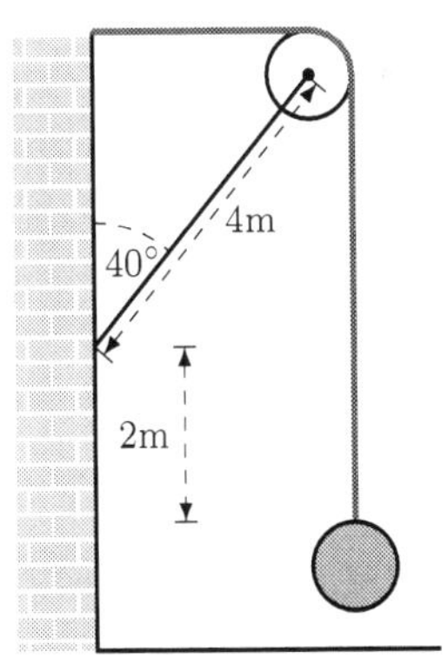

Hint: The total length of rope consists of two straight parts and the curved section that wraps around the pulley.

P1.45 The length of a rectangle is $c + 2$ and its height is 5. What is the area of the rectangle?

P1.46 A box of facial tissues has dimensions 10.5 cm by 7 cm by 22.3 cm. What is the volume of the box in litres?
Hint: $1\,\text{L} = 1000\,\text{cm}^3$.

P1.47 What is the measure of the angle θ in the figure below?

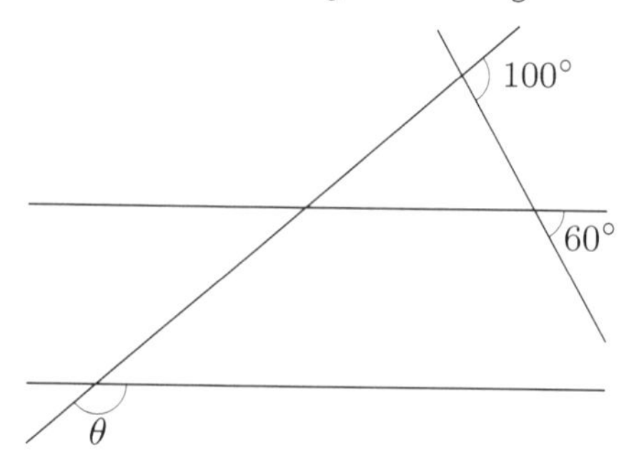

Hint: At the intersection of two lines, vertically opposite angles are equal.

P1.48 A large circle of radius R is surrounded by 12 smaller circles of radius r. Find the ratio $\frac{R}{r}$ rounded to four decimals.

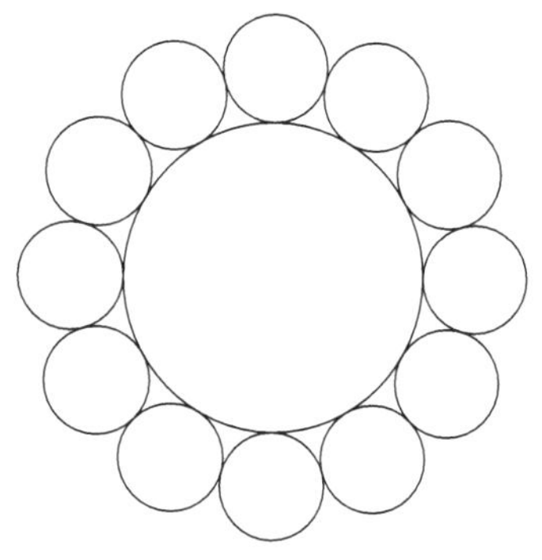

Hint: Draw an isosceles triangle with one vertex at the centre of the R-circle and the other vertices at the centres of two adjacent r-circles.

P1.49 The area of a rectangular figure is $35\,\text{cm}^2$. If one side is $5\,\text{cm}$, how long is the other side?

P1.50 A swimming pool has length $\ell = 20\,\text{m}$, width $w = 10\,\text{m}$, and depth $d = 1.5\,\text{m}$. Calculate the volume of water in the swimming pool in litres?
Hint: $1\,\text{m}^3 = 1000\,\text{L}$.

P1.51 How many litres of water remain in a tank that is $15\,\text{m}$ long, $6\,\text{m}$ wide, and $5\,\text{m}$ high, if 30% of its capacity is spent?

P1.52 A building has two water tanks, each with capacity $4000\,\text{L}$. One of them is $\frac{1}{4}$ full and the other contains three times more water. How many litres of water does the building have in total?

P1.53 The rectangular lid of a box has length $40\,\text{cm}$ and width $30\,\text{cm}$. A rectangular hole with area $500\,\text{cm}^2$ must be cut in the lid so that the hole's sides are equal distances from the sides of the lid. What will the distance be between the sides of the hole and the sides of the lid?
Hint: You'll need to define three variables to solve this problem.

P1.54 A man sells firewood. To make standard portions, he uses a standard length of rope ℓ to surround a pack of logs. One day, a customer asks him for a double portion of firewood. What length of rope should he use to measure this order? Assume the packs of logs are circular in shape.

P1.55 How much pure water should be added to 10 litres of a solution that is 60% acid to make a solution that is 20% acid?

P1.56 A tablet screen has a resolution of 768 pixels by 1024 pixels, and the physical dimensions of the screen are 6 inches by 8 inches. One might conclude that the best size of a PDF document for such a screen would be 6 inches by 8 inches. At first I thought so too, but I forgot to account for the status bar, which is 20 pixels tall. The actual usable screen area is only 768 pixels by 1004 pixels. Assuming the width of the PDF is chosen to be 6 inches, what height should the PDF be so that it fits perfectly in the content area of the tablet screen?

P1.57 Find the sum of the natural numbers 1 through 100.
Hint: Imagine pairing the biggest number with the smallest number in the sum, the second biggest number with the second smallest number, etc.

P1.58 Solve for x and y simultaneously in the following system of equations: $-x-2y=-2$ and $3x+3y=0$.

P1.59 Solve the following system of equations for the three unknowns:

$$\begin{aligned} 1x+2y+3z &= 14, \\ 2x+5y+6z &= 30, \\ -1x+2y+3z &= 12. \end{aligned}$$

P1.60 A hotel offers a 15% discount on rooms. Determine the original price of a room if the discounted room price is \$95.20.

P1.61 A set of kitchen tools normally retails for \$450, but today it is priced at the special offer of \$360. Calculate the percentage of the discount.

P1.62 You take out a \$5000 loan at a nominal annual percentage rate (nAPR) of 12% with monthly compounding. How much money will you owe after 10 years?

P1.63 Plot the graphs of $f(x) = 100e^{-x/2}$ and $g(x) = 100(1-e^{-x/2})$ by evaluating the functions at different values of x from 0 to 11.

P1.64 Starting from an initial quantity Q_o of Exponentium at $t = 0$ s, the quantity Q of Exponentium as a function of time varies according to the expression $Q(t) = Q_o e^{-\lambda t}$, where $\lambda = 5.0$ and t is measured in seconds. Find the *half-life* of Exponentium, that is, the time it takes for the quantity of Exponentium to reduce to half the initial quantity Q_o.

P1.65 A hot body cools so that every 24 min its temperature decreases by a factor of two. Deduce the time-constant and determine the time it will take the body to reach 1% of its original temperature.
Hint: The temperature function is $T(t) = T_o e^{-t/\tau}$ and τ is the *time constant*.

P1.66 A capacitor of capacitance $C = 4.0 \times 10^{-6}$ farads, charged to an initial potential of $V_o = 20$ volts, is discharging through a resistance of $R = 10\,000\,\Omega$ (read Ohms). Find the potential V after 0.01 s and after 0.1 s, knowing the decreasing potential follows the rule $V(t) = V_o e^{-\frac{t}{RC}}$.

P1.67 Let B be the set of people who are bankers and C be the set of crooks. Rewrite the math statement $\exists b \in B \mid b \notin C$ in plain English.

P1.68 Let M denote the set of people who run Monsanto, and H denote the people who ought to burn in hell for all eternity. Write the math statement $\forall p \in M, p \in H$ in plain English.

P1.69 When starting a business, one sometimes needs to find investors. Define M to be the set of investors with money, and C to be the set of investors with connections. Describe the following sets in words: **a)** $M \backslash C$, **b)** $C \backslash M$, and the most desirable set **c)** $M \cap C$.

P1.70 Write the formulas for the functions $A_1(x)$ and $A_2(x)$ that describe the areas of the following geometric shapes.

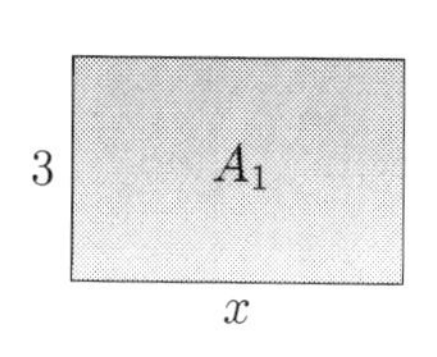

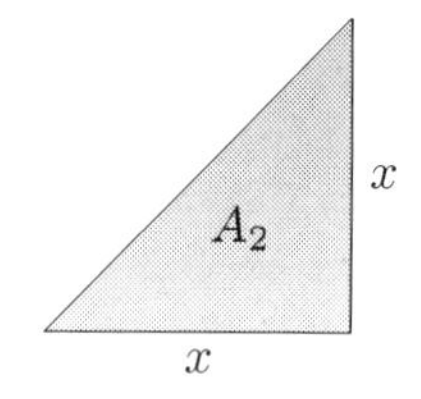

Chapter 2

Introduction to physics

2.1 Introduction

One of the coolest things about understanding math is that you will automatically start to understand the laws of physics too. Indeed, most physics laws are expressed as mathematical equations. If you know how to manipulate equations and you know how to solve for the unknowns in them, then you know half of physics already.

Ever since Newton figured out the whole $F = ma$ thing, people have used mechanics to achieve great technological feats, like landing spaceships on the Moon and Mars. You can be part of this science thing too. Learning physics will give you the following superpowers:

1. The power to **predict the future motion of objects** using equations. For most types of motion, it is possible to find an equation that describes the position of an object as a function of time $x(t)$. You can use this equation to predict the position of the object at all times t, including the future. "Yo G! Where's the particle going to be at $t = 1.3$ seconds?" you are asked. "It is going to be at $x(1.3)$ metres, bro." Simple as that. The equation $x(t)$ describes the object's position for *all* times t during the motion. Knowing this, you can plug $t = 1.3$ seconds into $x(t)$ to find the object's location at that time.

2. Special **physics vision** for seeing the world. After learning physics, you will start to think in terms of concepts like force, acceleration, and velocity. You can use these concepts to precisely describe all aspects of the motion of objects. Without physics vision, when you throw a ball into the air you will

see it go up, reach the top, then fall down. Not very exciting. Now *with* physics vision, you will see that at $t = 0$[s], the same ball is thrown in the positive y-direction with an initial velocity of $v_i = 12$[m/s]. The ball reaches a maximum height of $y_{\max} = \frac{12^2}{2\times 9.81} = 7.3$[m] at $t = 12/9.81 = 1.22$[s], then hits the ground after a total flight time of $t_f = 2\sqrt{\frac{2\times 7.3}{9.81}} = 2.44$[s].

The *measurement units* of physical quantities throughout this book are denoted in square brackets, like in the example above. Learning about the different measurement units is an important aspect of *physics vision*.

Why learn physics?

The main reason why you should learn physics is for the *knowledge buzz*. You will learn how to calculate the motion of objects, predict the outcomes of collisions, describe oscillations, and many other useful things. As you develop your physics skills, you will be able to use physics equations to derive one physical quantity from another. For example, we can predict the maximum height reached by a ball, if we know its initial velocity when thrown. The equations of physics are a lot like LEGO blocks; your job is to figure out different ways to connect them together.

By learning how to solve complicated physics problems, you will develop your analytical skills. Later on, you can apply these skills to other areas of life. Even if you don't go on to study science, the expertise you develop in solving physics problems will help you tackle complicated problems in general. As proof of this statement, consider the fact that companies like to hire physicists even for positions unrelated to physics: they feel confident that candidates who understand physics will be able to figure out all the business stuff easily.

Intro to science

Perhaps the most important reason you should learn physics is because it represents the golden standard for the scientific method. First of all, physics deals only with concrete things that can be **measured**. There are no feelings or subjectivities in physics. Physicists must derive mathematical models that **accurately describe** and **predict** the outcomes of experiments. Above all, we can **test** the validity of the physical models by running experiments and comparing the predicted outcome with what actually happens in the lab.

The key ingredient in scientific thinking is skepticism. Scientists must convince their peers that their equations are true without a doubt. The peers shouldn't need to *trust* the scientist; rather, they can carry out their own tests to see if the equation accurately predicts what happens in the real world. For example, let's say I claim that the height of a ball thrown up in the air with speed 12[m/s] is described by the equation $y_c(t) = \frac{1}{2}(-9.81)t^2 + 12t + 0$. To test whether this equation is true, you can perform a throwing-the-ball-in-the-air experiment and record the motion of the ball as a video. You can then compare the motion parameters observed in the video with those predicted by the claimed equation $y_c(t)$.

- **Maximum height reached** One thing you can check is whether the equation $y_c(t)$ predicts the ball's maximum height y_{max}. The claimed equation predicts the ball will reach its maximum height at $t = 1.22$[s]. The maximum height predicted is $\max_t\{y_c(t)\} = y_c(1.22) = 7.3$[m]. You can compare this value with the maximum height y_{max} you observe in the video.

- **Total time of flight** You can also check whether the equation $y_c(t)$ correctly predicts the time when the ball will fall back to the ground. Using the video, suppose you measure the time it took the ball to fall back to the ground to be $t_{\text{fall}} = 2.44$[s]. If the equation $y_c(t)$ is correct, it should predict a height of zero metres for the time t_{fall}.

If both predictions of the equation $y_c(t)$ match your observations from the video, you can start to believe the claimed equation of motion $y_c(t)$ is truly an accurate model for the real world.

The scientific method depends on this interplay between experiment and theory. Theoreticians prove theorems and derive equations, while experimentalists test the validity of equations. The equations that accurately predict the laws of nature are kept while inaccurate models are rejected. At the same time, experimentalists constantly measure new data and challenge theoreticians to come up with equations that correctly describe the new measurements.

Equations of physics

The best physics equations are collected in textbooks. Physics textbooks contain only equations that have been extensively tested and are believed to be true. Good physics textbooks also explain how the equations are *derived* from first principles. This is important, because it is much easier to understand a few fundamental principles of physics, rather than memorize a long list of formulas. Understanding trumps memorization any day of the week.

The next section will teach you about three equations that fully describe the motion of any object: $x(t)$, $v(t)$, and $a(t)$. Using these equations and the equation-solving techniques from Chapter 1, we can predict pretty much anything we want about the position and velocity of objects undergoing *constant acceleration*.

Instead of asking you to memorize these equations, I'll show you a cool trick for obtaining one equation of motion from another. These three equations describe different aspects of the same motion, so it's no surprise the equations are related. While you are not required to know how to derive the equations of physics, you do need to know how to use all these equations. Learning a bit of theory is a good deal: just a few pages of "difficult" theory (integrals) will give you a deep understanding of the relationship between $a(t)$, $v(t)$, and $x(t)$. This way, you can rely on your newly expanded math knowledge, rather than remember three separate formulas!

2.2 Kinematics

Kinematics (from the Greek word *kinema* for *motion*) is the study of trajectories of moving objects. The equations of kinematics can be used to calculate how long a ball thrown upward will stay in the air, or to calculate the acceleration needed to go from 0 to 100[km/h] in 5 seconds. To carry out these calculations, we need to choose the right *equation of motion* and figure out the values of the *initial conditions* (the initial position x_i and the initial velocity v_i). Afterward, we plug the known values into the appropriate equation of motion and solve for the unknown using one or two simple algebra steps. This entire section boils down to three equations and the plug-number-into-equation skill.

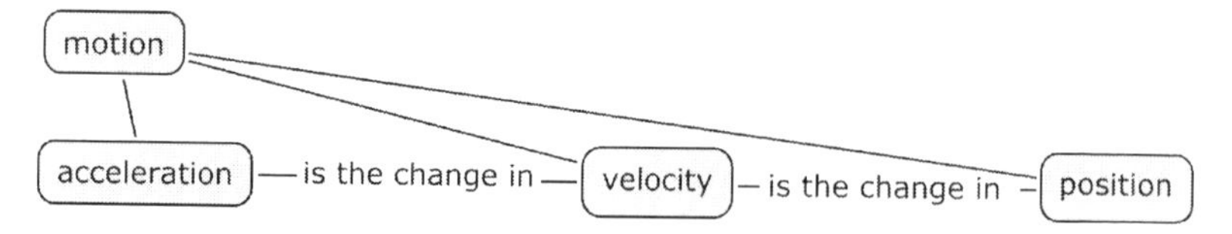

Figure 2.1: The motion of an object is described by its position, velocity, and acceleration functions.

This section is here to teach you how to use the equations of motion and help you understand the concepts of velocity and acceleration. You'll also learn how to recognize which equations to use when solving different types of physics problems.

Concepts

The key notions for describing the motion of objects are:

- t: the time. Time is measured in seconds [s].
- $x(t)$: an object's position as a function of time—also known as the equation of motion. Position is measured in metres [m] and depends on the time t.
- $v(t)$: the object's velocity as a function of time. Velocity is measured in metres per second [m/s].
- $a(t)$: the object's acceleration as a function of time. Acceleration is measured in metres per second squared [m/s^2].
- $x_i = x(0), v_i = v(0)$: the object's initial position and velocity, as measured at $t = 0$. Together x_i and v_i are known as the *initial conditions*.

Position, velocity, and acceleration

The motion of an object is characterized by three functions: the position function $x(t)$, the velocity function $v(t)$, and the acceleration function $a(t)$. The functions $x(t)$, $v(t)$, and $a(t)$ are connected—they all describe different aspects of the same motion.

You are already familiar with these notions from your experience of riding in a car. The equation of motion $x(t)$ describes the position of the car as a function of time. The *velocity* describes the change in the position of the car, or mathematically,

$$v(t) \equiv \text{rate of change in } x(t).$$

If we measure x in metres [m] and time t in seconds [s], then the units of $v(t)$ will be metres per second [m/s]. For example, an object moving with a constant velocity of $+30$[m/s] will increase its position by 30[m] each second. Note that the velocity $v(t)$ could be positive or negative. The *speed* of an object is defined as the absolute value of its velocity $|v(t)|$. The speed is always a nonnegative quantity, whereas velocity is positive or negative depending on the direction of motion.

The rate of change of an object's velocity is called *acceleration*:

$$a(t) \equiv \text{rate of change in } v(t).$$

Acceleration is measured in metres per second squared [m/s^2]. A constant positive acceleration means the velocity of the motion is steadily increasing, similar to pressing the gas pedal. A constant negative acceleration means the velocity is steadily decreasing, similar to pressing the brake pedal.

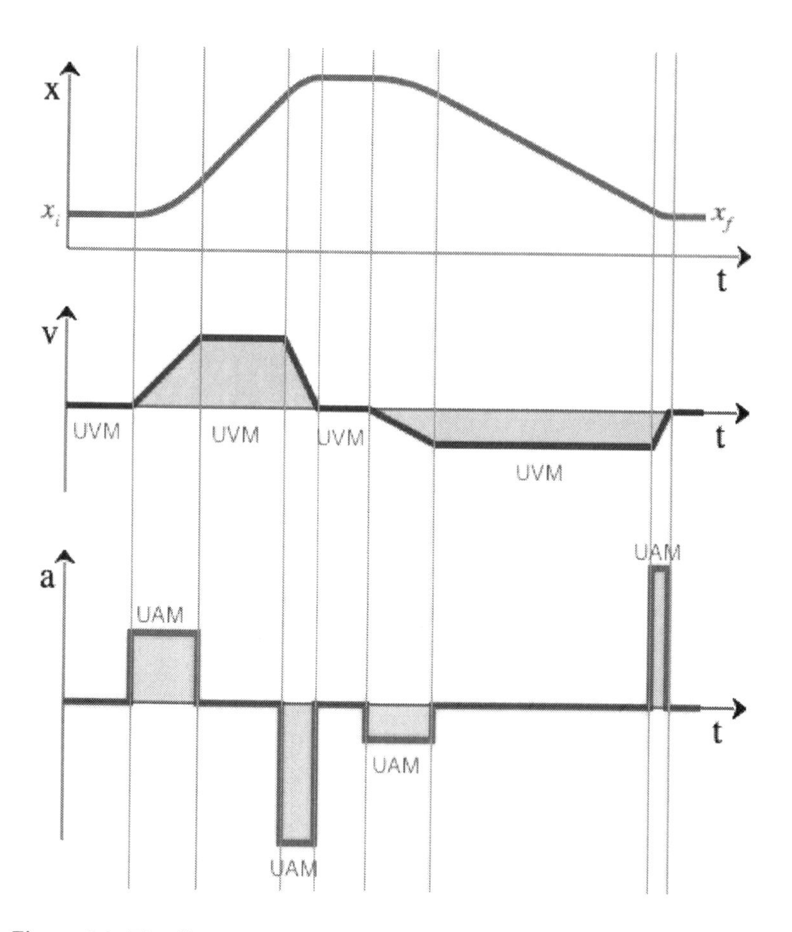

Figure 2.2: The illustration shows the simultaneous graphs of the position, velocity, and acceleration of a car during some time interval. The car starts from an initial position x_i where it sits still for some time. The driver then floors the pedal to produce a maximum acceleration for some time, and the car picks up speed. The driver then eases off the accelerator, keeping it pressed enough to maintain a constant speed. Suddenly the driver sees a police vehicle in the distance and slams on the brakes (negative acceleration) and shortly afterward brings the car to a stop. The driver waits for a few seconds to make sure the cops have passed. Next, the driver switches into reverse gear and adds gas. The car accelerates backward for a bit, then maintains a constant backward speed for an extended period of time. Note how "moving backward" corresponds to negative velocity. Finally, the driver slams on the brakes and stops the car. Notice that braking corresponds to positive acceleration when the motion is in the negative direction. The car's final position is x_f.

In a couple of paragraphs, we'll discuss the exact mathematical equations for $x(t)$, $v(t)$, and $a(t)$, but before we dig into the math, let's look at the example of the motion of a car illustrated in Figure 2.2. We can observe two distinct types of motion. During some times, the car undergoes motion at a constant velocity (uniform velocity motion, UVM). During other times, the car undergoes motion with constant acceleration (uniform acceleration motion, UAM). There exist many other types of motion, but for the purpose of this section we'll focus on these two types of motion.

- UVM: During times when there is no acceleration, the car maintains a uniform velocity and therefore $v(t)$ is a constant function. For motion with constant velocity, the position function is a line with a constant slope because, by definition, $v(t) = \text{slope of } x(t)$.
- UAM: During times where the car experiences a constant acceleration $a(t) = a$, the velocity of the function changes at a constant rate. The rate of change of the velocity is constant $a = \text{slope of } v(t)$, so the velocity function looks like a line with slope a. The position function $x(t)$ has a curved shape (quadratic) during moments of constant acceleration.

Formulas

There are basically four equations you need to know for this entire section. Together, these four equations fully describe all aspects of motion with constant acceleration.

Uniformly accelerated motion (UAM)

If the object undergoes a *constant* acceleration $a(t) = a$—like a car when you floor the *accelerator*—then its motion can be described by the following equations:

$$a(t) = a, \tag{2.1}$$

$$v(t) = at + v_i, \tag{2.2}$$

$$x(t) = \tfrac{1}{2}at^2 + v_i t + x_i, \tag{2.3}$$

where v_i is the initial velocity of the object and x_i is its initial position.

Here is another useful equation to remember:

$$[v(t)]^2 = v_i^2 + 2a[x(t) - x_i],$$

which is usually written

$$v_f^2 = v_i^2 + 2a\Delta x, \tag{2.4}$$

where v_f denotes the final velocity (at $t = t_f$) and Δx denotes the *change* in the x-coordinate between $t = 0$ and $t = t_f$. The triangle thing Δ is the capital Greek letter *delta*, which is often used to denote the change in quantities. Using the Δ-notation, we can rewrite equation (2.2) as follows: $\Delta v = a\Delta t$, where $\Delta v \equiv v_f - v_i$ and $\Delta t \equiv t_f - t_i$.

That's it! Memorize these four equations, plug-in the right numbers, and you can solve any kinematics problem humanly imaginable.

Uniform velocity motion (UVM)

The special case where there is zero acceleration ($a = 0$), is called *uniform velocity motion* or UVM. The velocity stays uniform (constant) because there is no acceleration. The following three equations describe the motion of an object with uniform velocity:

$$\begin{aligned} a(t) &= 0, \\ v(t) &= v_i, \\ x(t) &= v_i t + x_i. \end{aligned}$$

As you can see, these are really the same equations as in the UAM case above, but because $a = 0$, some terms are missing.

Free fall

We say an object is in *free fall* if the only force acting on it is the force of gravity. On the surface of the Earth, the force of gravity produces a constant acceleration of $a_y = -9.81[\text{m/s}^2]$. The negative sign is there because the gravitational acceleration is directed downward, and we assume the y-axis points upward. Since the gravitational acceleration is constant, we can use the UAM equations to find the height $y(t)$ and velocity $v(t)$ of objects in free fall.

Examples

Now we'll illustrate how the equations of kinematics are used.

Moroccan example Suppose your friend wants to send you a ball wrapped in aluminum foil by dropping it from his balcony, which is located at a height of $y_i = 44.145[\text{m}]$. How long will it take for the ball to hit the ground?

We recognize this is a problem with acceleration, so we start by writing the general UAM equations:

$$y(t) = \tfrac{1}{2}at^2 + v_i t + y_i,$$
$$v(t) = at + v_i.$$

To find the answer, substitute the following known values into the $y(t)$ equation: $y(0) = y_i = 44.145$[m]; $a = -9.81$ (since the ball is in free fall); and $v_i = 0$[m/s] (since the ball was released from rest). We want to find the time t_{fall} when the height of the ball will be zero:

$$0 = y(t_{\text{fall}}),$$
$$0 = \tfrac{1}{2}(-9.81)(t_{\text{fall}})^2 + 0(t_{\text{fall}}) + 44.145.$$

Solving for t_{fall} we find the answer $t_{\text{fall}} = \sqrt{\frac{44.145\times 2}{9.81}} = 3[\text{s}]$.

As another variation of this type of kinematics question, suppose you're given the time it takes for the ball to fall $t_{\text{fall}} = 3$[s], and you're asked to find the height of the balcony. You already know $y(3) = 0$, and are looking for the initial height y_i. You can solve for y_i in the equation $0 = \frac{1}{2}(-9.81)3^2 + y_i$. The answer gives $y_i = 44.145$[m].

0 to 100 in 5 seconds Say you're in the driver's seat of a car and you want to accelerate from 0 to 100[km/h] in 5 seconds. How much acceleration must the car's engine produce, assuming it produces a constant amount of acceleration?

We can calculate the necessary a by plugging the required values into the velocity equation for UAM:

$$v(t) = at + v_i.$$

Before we tackle that, we need to convert the velocity in [km/h] to velocity in [m/s]: $100[\text{km/h}] = \frac{100[\cancel{\text{km}}]}{1[\cancel{\text{h}}]} \cdot \frac{1000[\text{m}]}{1[\cancel{\text{km}}]} \cdot \frac{1[\cancel{\text{h}}]}{3600[\text{s}]} = 27.8$ [m/s]. We substitute the desired values $v_f = 27.8$[m/s], $v_i = 0$, and $t = 5$[s] into the equation for $v(t)$ and solve for a:

$$27.8 = v(5) = a5 + 0.$$

After solving for a, we find the car's engine must produce a constant acceleration of $a = \frac{27.8}{5} = 5.56[\text{m/s}^2]$ or greater.

Moroccan example II Some time later, your friend wants to send you another aluminum ball from his apartment located on the 14th floor (height of 44.145[m]). To decrease the time of flight, he *throws* the ball straight down with an initial velocity of 10[m/s]. How long does it take for the ball to hit the ground?

Imagine the apartment building as a y-axis that measures distance upward starting from the ground floor. We know the balcony is located at a height of $y_i = 44.145$[m], and that at $t = 0$[s] the ball starts with $v_i = -10$[m/s]. The initial velocity is negative because it points in the opposite direction of the y-axis. We also know there is an acceleration due to gravity of $a_y = -9.81$[m/s^2].
We start by writing the general UAM equation:

$$y(t) = \tfrac{1}{2}a_y t^2 + v_i t + y_i.$$

To find the time when the ball will hit the ground, we can solve for t in the equation $y(t) = 0$, then plug the values into the UAM equation,

$$y(t) = 0 = \tfrac{1}{2}(-9.81)t^2 - 10t + 44.145,$$

and solve for t using the quadratic formula. First, rewrite the quadratic equation in standard form: $0 = \underbrace{4.905}_{a}\,t^2 + \underbrace{10.0}_{b}\,t \underbrace{-44.145}_{c}$.

Then solve using the quadratic equation:

$$t_{\text{fall}} = \frac{-b \pm \sqrt{b^2 - 4ac}}{2a} = \frac{-10 \pm \sqrt{100 + 866.12}}{9.81} = 2.15 \qquad [\text{s}].$$

We ignore the negative-time solution because it corresponds to a time in the past. Compared to the first Moroccan example, we see that throwing the ball downward makes it fall to the ground in less time.

Discussion

Most kinematics problems you'll be solving follow the same pattern as the examples above. Given some initial values, you'll be asked to solve for some unknown quantity.

It's important to keep in mind the *signs* of the numbers you plug into the equations. You should always draw the coordinate system and indicate clearly (to yourself) the x-axis, which measures the object's displacement. A velocity or acceleration quantity that points in the same direction as the x-axis is a positive number, while quantities pointing in the opposite direction are negative numbers.

By the way, all this talk about $v(t)$ being the "rate of change of $x(t)$" is starting to get on my nerves. The expression "rate of change of" is an indirect way of saying the calculus term *derivative*. In order to use this more precise terminology throughout the remainder of the book, we'll now take a short excursion into the land of calculus to define two fundamental concepts: derivatives and integrals.

Exercises

E2.1 Calculate the time it will take a rocket launched with initial velocity v_i[m/s] and constant acceleration of a[m/s^2] to reach the velocity of 100[m/s]. What is the total distance travelled?

a) $v_i = 20$[m/s], $a = 5$[m/s^2] **b)** $v_i = 30$[m/s], $a = 10$[m/s^2]

2.3 Introduction to calculus

Calculus is the study of functions and their properties. The two operations in the study of calculus are derivatives—which describe how quantities *change over time*—and integrals, which are used to calculate the total amount of a quantity *accumulated* over a time period.

Derivatives

The derivative function $f'(t)$ describes how the function $f(t)$ changes over time. The derivative encodes the information about the *instantaneous rate of change* of the function $f(t)$, which is the same as the *slope* of the graph of the function at that point:

$$f'(t) \equiv \text{slope}_f(t) = \frac{\text{change in } f(t)}{\text{change in } t} = \frac{f(t+\Delta t) - f(t)}{\Delta t}.$$

If the derivative $f'(t)$ is equal to 5 units per second, this means that $f(t)$ changes by 5 units each second. The derivative of the constant function is zero because it has zero rise-over-run everywhere. The derivative of the function $f(t) = mt + b$ (a line) is the constant function $f'(t) = m$. More generally, the instantaneous slope of a function is different for different values of t, as illustrated in Figure 2.3.

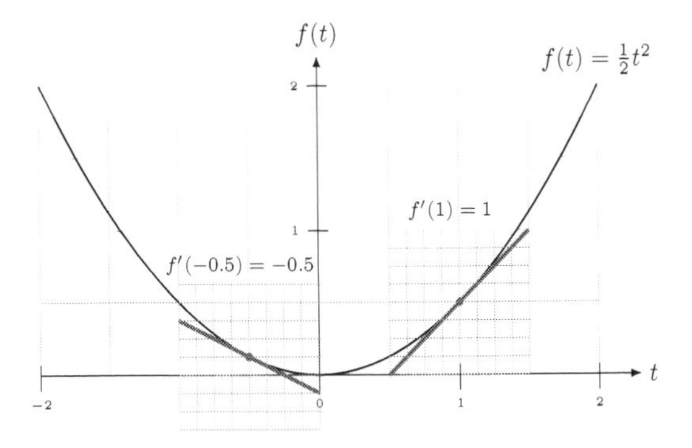

Figure 2.3: The derivative of the function at $t = a$ is denoted $f'(a)$ and describes the slope function at that point.

The derivative operation is denoted by several symbols: $Df(t) = f'(t) = \frac{df}{dt} = \frac{d}{dt}\{f(t)\} = \dot{f}$. All these symbols carry the same meaning. Think of $f'(t)$ not as a separate entity from $f(t)$, but as a *property* of the function $f(t)$. It's best to think of the derivative as an *operator* $\frac{d}{dt}$ that you apply to functions to obtain their slope information.

Integrals

An integral corresponds to the computation of the *area* enclosed between the curve $f(t)$ and the t-axis over some interval:

$$A(a,b) \equiv \int_{t=a}^{t=b} f(t)\, dt.$$

The symbol $\int$ is shorthand for *sum*. Indeed, the area under the curve corresponds to the sum of the values of the function $f(t)$ between $t = a$ and $t = b$. The integral is the total of f between a and b.

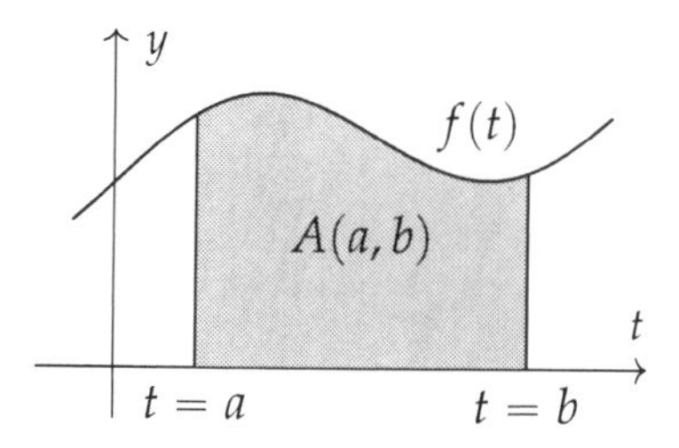

Figure 2.4: The integral of the function $f(t)$ between $t = a$ and $t = b$.

Example 1

We can easily find the area under the graph of the constant function $f(t) = 3$ between any two points because the region under the curve is rectangular. Choosing $t = 0$ as the starting point, we obtain the integral function $F(\tau)$, which corresponds to the area under $f(t)$ between $t = 0$ and $t = \tau$:

$$F(\tau) \equiv A(0,\tau) = \int_0^\tau f(t)\, dt = 3\tau.$$

The area is equal to the rectangle's height times its width as illustrated in Figure 2.5.

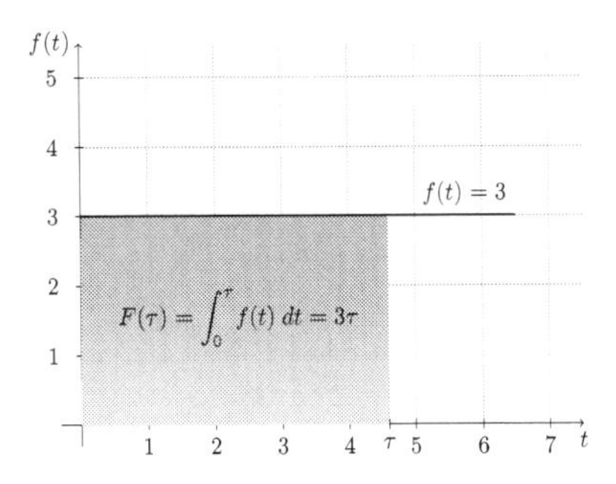

Figure 2.5: The area of a rectangle of height 3 and width τ is equal to 3τ.

Example 2

Consider now the area under the graph of the line $g(t) = t$, starting from $t = 0$. Since the region under the curve is triangular, we can compute its area. Recall the area of a triangle is given by the length of its base times its height divided by 2.

The general formula for the area under $g(t)$ from $t = 0$ until $t = \tau$ is described by the following integral calculation:

$$G(\tau) \equiv A(0,\tau) = \int_0^\tau g(t)\, dt = \frac{\tau \times \tau}{2} = \tfrac{1}{2}\tau^2.$$

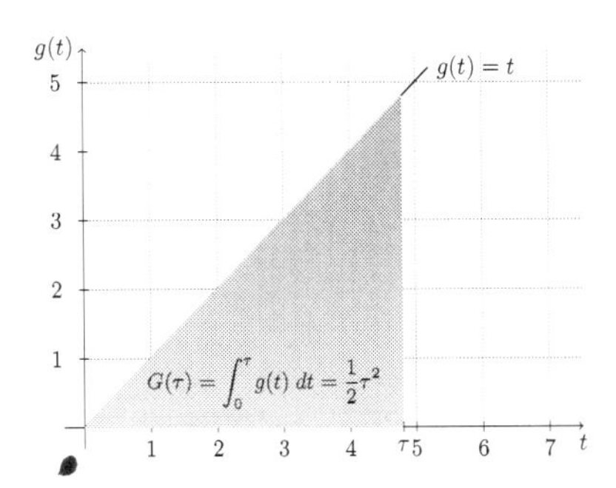

Figure 2.6: The area of a triangle with base τ and height τ is equal to $\frac{1}{2}\tau^2$.

We're able to compute the above integrals thanks to the simple geometries of the areas under the graphs. Later in this book (Chapter 5), we'll develop techniques for finding integrals (areas under the curve) of more complicated functions. In fact, there is an entire course called integral calculus, which is dedicated to the task of finding integrals.

But don't worry, you don't need to know *everything* about integrals to learn physics. What is important right now is that you understand the concept of integration. The integral of a function is the area under the graph of the function, which is in some sense the total amount of the function accumulated during some interval of time. For the most part of the first-year physics, the only integral formulas you'll need to know are

$$\int_0^\tau a\, dt = a\tau \qquad \text{and} \qquad \int_0^\tau at\, dt = \tfrac{1}{2}a\tau^2.$$

The first integral describes the general calculation of the area under a constant function, like in Example 1. The second formula is a generalization of the formula we derived in Example 2. Using these formulas in combination, you can compute the integral of an arbitrary line $h(t) = mt + b$ as follows:

$$H(\tau) = \int_0^\tau h(t)\, dt = \int_0^\tau (mt + b)\, dt = \int_0^\tau mt\, dt + \int_0^\tau b\, dt = \tfrac{1}{2}m\tau^2 + b\tau.$$

Regroup

At this point you might be on the fence about the new calculus concepts. On one hand, calculating slopes (derivatives) and areas under the curve (integrals) seem like trivial tasks. On the other hand, seeing five different notations for the derivative and the weird integral sign has probably put some fear in you. You might be wondering whether you *really* need to learn about derivatives and integrals. How often do you have to compute the area under the graph of a function in the real world? It turns out that "calculating the area under a curve" is very useful since it is the "undo operation" for the derivative.

Inverse operations

The integral is the inverse operation of the derivative. Many equations in math and physics involve the *derivative* of some unknown function. Understanding the inverse relationship between integrals and derivatives will allow you to solve for the unknown function in these equations.

You should already be familiar with the inverse relationship between functions. When solving equations, we use inverse functions to *undo* functions that stand in our way as we try to isolate the unknown x. Similarly, we use the integral operation to *undo* the effects of the derivative operation when we try to solve for some unknown function $f(t)$. For example, suppose $g(t)$ is a known function and we're trying to solve for $f(t)$ in the equation

$$\frac{d}{dt}\{f(t)\} = g(t).$$

Taking the integral on the left-hand side of the equation will undo the derivative operation. To keep the equality true, we must apply the "integrate over t" operation on both sides of the equation. We obtain

$$\int \frac{d}{dt}\{f(t)\}\, dt = \int g(t)\, dt,$$
$$f(t) = \int g(t)\, dt.$$

The take-home message is that every time you want to *undo* a derivative, you can apply the integral operation, however, there is a little technical detail we must clarify to make this statement precise.

The integral isn't *exactly* the inverse of the derivative—there is a tricky extra constant factor that appears when we integrate. Let's analyze in more detail what happens when we perform the combo of the derivative operation followed by the integral operation on some function $f(t)$. Suppose we are given the derivative function $f'(t)$ and asked to integrate it between $t = 0$ and $t = \tau$. Intuitively, this integral corresponds to calculating the **total of the changes** in $f(t)$ during that time interval. Recall the notation for "change in f" $\Delta f \equiv f(\tau) - f(0)$, which we used previously. This notation makes it easy to see how the integral over $f'(t)$ corresponds to the total change in $f(t)$ between $t = 0$ and $t = \tau$:

$$\int_0^\tau f'(t)\, dt \;=\; \Delta f \equiv f(\tau) - f(0).$$

Calculating the total of the instantaneous changes in f during the interval $[0, \tau]$ is the same as finding the change in $f(t)$ between the endpoints of the interval. If we rewrite the above equation to isolate $f(\tau)$, we obtain

$$f(\tau) \;=\; f(0) + \int_0^\tau f'(t)\, dt.$$

Note that the expression for $f(\tau)$ depends on the value of $f(t)$ at $t = 0$, which we call the *initial value* of the function. In physics problems, the initial values of the equations of motion $x(0) \equiv x_i$ and $v(0) \equiv v_i$ are called the *initial conditions*.

Banking example To illustrate how derivative and integral operations apply to the real world, I'll draw an analogy from a scenario that every student is familiar with. Consider the function $\text{ba}(t)$, which represents your bank account balance at time t. Also consider the function $\text{tr}(t)$, which corresponds to the transactions (deposits and withdrawals) on your account.

The function $\text{tr}(t)$ is the derivative of the function $\text{ba}(t)$. If you ask, "How does my balance change over time?" the answer is the function $\text{tr}(t)$. Using mathematical symbols, we can represent this relationship as

$$\text{tr}(t) = \frac{d}{dt}\left\{\text{ba}(t)\right\}.$$

If the derivative is positive, your account balance is growing. If the derivative is negative, your account balance is depleting.

Suppose you have a record of all the transactions on your account $\text{tr}(t)$, and you want to compute the final account balance at the end of the month. Since $\text{tr}(t)$ is the derivative of $\text{ba}(t)$, you can use an integral (the inverse operation of the derivative) to obtain $\text{ba}(t)$. Knowing the balance of your account at the beginning of the month, you can predict the balance at the end of the month by using the following integral calculation:

$$\text{ba}(30) = \text{ba}(0) + \int_0^{30} \text{tr}(t)\, dt.$$

This calculation makes sense since $\text{tr}(t)$ represents the instantaneous changes in $\text{ba}(t)$. If you want to find the overall change in the account balance from day 0 until day 30, you can compute the total of all the transactions on the account.

We use integrals every time we need to calculate the total of some quantity over a time period. In the next section, we'll see how these integration techniques can be applied to the subject of kinematics, and how the equations of motion for UAM are derived from first principles.

2.4 Kinematics with calculus

To carry out kinematics calculations, all we need to do is plug the initial conditions (x_i and v_i) into the correct equation of motion. But how did Newton come up with the equations of motion in the first place? Now that you know Newton's mathematical techniques (calculus), you can learn to derive the equations of motion by yourself.

Concepts

Recall the kinematics concepts related to the motion of objects:

- t: time
- $x(t)$: position as a function of time
- $v(t)$: velocity as a function of time
- $a(t)$: acceleration as a function of time
- $x_i \equiv x(0), v_i \equiv v(0)$: the initial conditions

Position, velocity, and acceleration revisited

The equations of kinematics are used to predict the motion of objects. Suppose you know the acceleration of the object $a(t)$ at all times t. Can you find $x(t)$ starting from $a(t)$?

The equations of motion $x(t)$, $v(t)$, and $a(t)$ are related:

$$a(t) \overset{\frac{d}{dt}}{\longleftarrow} v(t) \overset{\frac{d}{dt}}{\longleftarrow} x(t).$$

The velocity function is the derivative of the position function and the acceleration function is the derivative of the velocity function.

General procedure

If you know the acceleration of an object as a function of time $a(t)$, and you know its initial velocity $v_i = v(0)$, you can find its velocity function $v(t)$ for all later times using integration. This is because the acceleration function $a(t)$ describes the change in the object's velocity.

Let's see how this works. The object started with an initial velocity of $v_i \equiv v(0)$ at $t = 0$. The velocity at a later time $t = \tau$ is equal to v_i plus the total acceleration of the object between $t = 0$ and $t = \tau$:

$$v(\tau) = v_i + \int_0^\tau a(t)\, dt.$$

If you know the initial position x_i and the velocity function $v(t)$, you can find the position function $x(t)$ by using integration. We find the position at time $t = \tau$ by adding all the velocities (the changes in the object's position) that occurred between $t = 0$ and $t = \tau$:

$$x(\tau) = x_i + \int_0^\tau v(t)\, dt.$$

The procedure for finding $x(t)$ starting from $a(t)$ can be summarized as follows:

$$a(t) \overset{v_i+\int dt}{\longrightarrow} v(t) \overset{x_i+\int dt}{\longrightarrow} x(t).$$

Next, I'll illustrate how you can apply this procedure to the important special case of an object undergoing uniformly accelerated motion.

Derivation of the UAM equations of motion

Consider an object undergoing uniformly accelerated motion (UAM) with acceleration function $a(t) = a$. Suppose we know the initial velocity of $v_i \equiv v(0)$, and we want to find the velocity at a later time $t = \tau$. We compute $v(\tau)$ using the following integral:

$$v(\tau) = v_i + \int_0^\tau a(t)\, dt = v_i + \int_0^\tau a\, dt = v_i + a\tau.$$

Velocity as a function of time is given by the initial velocity v_i added to the integral of the acceleration. The integration can be visualized as the calculation of the area of a rectangle, similar to the calculation we saw in Example 1 on page 144.

You can also use integration to find the position function $x(t)$ if you know the initial position x_i and the velocity function $v(t)$. The formula is

$$x(\tau) = x_i + \int_0^\tau v(t)\, dt = x_i + \int_0^\tau (v_i + at)\, dt = x_i + v_i\tau + \tfrac{1}{2}a\tau^2.$$

The integration step can be visualized as the calculation of the area of a triangle with slope a stacked on top of a rectangle of height v_i.

Note that the above calculations required knowing the initial conditions x_i and v_i. These initial values were required because the integral calculations we performed only told us the *change* in the quantities relative to their initial values.

The fourth equation

We can derive the fourth equation of motion,

$$v_f^2 = v_i^2 + 2a(x_f - x_i),$$

by combining the equations of motion $v(t)$ and $x(t)$. Let's see how. Start by squaring both sides of the velocity equation $v_f = v_i + at$ to obtain

$$v_f^2 = (v_i + at)^2 = v_i^2 + 2av_it + a^2t^2 = v_i^2 + 2a[v_it + \tfrac{1}{2}at^2].$$

The term in the square bracket is equal to $\Delta x = x(t) - x_i = x_f - x_i$.

Applications of derivatives

Recall that the velocity and the acceleration functions are obtained by taking derivatives of the position function:

$$x(t) \xrightarrow{\frac{d}{dt}} v(t) \xrightarrow{\frac{d}{dt}} a(t).$$

We just saw how to use integration to follow this chain of operations in reverse to obtain $x(t)$ for the special case of constant acceleration:

$$\begin{aligned} a(t) &\equiv a, \\ v(t) &\equiv v_i + \int_0^t a(\tau)\, d\tau = v_i + at, \\ x(t) &\equiv x_i + \int_0^t v(\tau)\, d\tau = x_i + v_i t + \tfrac{1}{2}at^2. \end{aligned}$$

Note that, in addition to the integral calculations, the formulas for $v(t)$ and $x(t)$ require some additional information—the initial value of the function.

Earlier we defined the derivative operator $\frac{d}{dt}$ that computes the derivative function $f'(t)$, which tells us the slope of the function $f(t)$. There are several derivative formulas that you need to learn to be proficient at calculus. We'll get to them in Chapter 5. For now, the only derivative formula you'll need is the *power rule* for derivatives:

$$\text{if} \quad f(t) = At^n \quad \text{then} \quad f'(t) = nAt^{n-1}.$$

Using this formula on each term in the function $f(t) = A + Bt + Ct^2$ we find its derivative is $\frac{df}{dt} \equiv f'(t) = 0 + B + 2Ct$.

Let's now use the derivative to verify that the equations of motion we obtained above satisfy $v'(t) = a(t)$ and $x'(t) = v(t)$. Applying the derivative operation to both sides of the equations we obtain

$$\begin{aligned} a'(t) &\equiv 0, \\ v'(t) &\equiv \tfrac{d}{dt}\{v_i + at\} = \cancel{\tfrac{d}{dt}\{v_i\}} + \tfrac{d}{dt}\{at\} = 0 + a &&= a(t), \\ x'(t) &\equiv \cancel{\tfrac{d}{dt}\{x_i\}} + \tfrac{d}{dt}\{v_i t\} + \tfrac{d}{dt}\{\tfrac{1}{2}at^2\} = 0 + v_i + at &&= v(t). \end{aligned}$$

Note that computing the derivative of a function kills the information about its initial value; the derivative contains only information about the changes in $f(t)$.

Let's summarize what we've learned so far about derivatives and integrals. Integrals are useful because they allow us to compute $v(t)$ from $a(t)$, and $x(t)$ from $v(t)$. The derivative operation is useful because it allows us to obtain $v(t)$ if we know $x(t)$, and/or obtain $a(t)$ if we know $v(t)$. Recall that $x(t)$, $v(t)$, and $a(t)$ correspond to three different aspects of the same motion, as shown in Figure 2.2 on page 138. The operations of calculus allow us to move freely between the different descriptions of the motion.

Discussion

According to Newton's second law of motion, forces are the cause of acceleration and the formula that governs this relationship is

$$F_{\text{net}} = ma,$$

where F_{net} is the magnitude of the net force acting on the object.

In Chapter 4 we'll learn about *dynamics*, the study of the different kinds of forces that can act on objects: gravitational force $\vec{F}_g$, spring force $\vec{F}_s$, friction force $\vec{F}_f$, and other forces. To find an object's acceleration, we must add together all the forces acting on the object and divide by the object's mass:

$$\sum F_i = F_{\text{net}} \qquad \Rightarrow \qquad a = \frac{1}{m} F_{\text{net}}.$$

The physics procedure for predicting the motion of an object given the forces acting on it can be summarized as follows:

$$\underbrace{\frac{1}{m}\left(\sum \vec{F} = \vec{F}_{\text{net}}\right)}_{\text{dynamics}} = \underbrace{a(t) \overset{v_i + \int dt}{\longrightarrow} v(t) \overset{x_i + \int dt}{\longrightarrow} x(t)}_{\text{kinematics}}.$$

Free fall revisited

The force of gravity acting on an object of mass m on the surface of the Earth is given by $\vec{F}_g = -mg\hat{y}$,

where $g = 9.81[\text{m/s}^2]$ is the *gravitational acceleration* on the surface of the Earth. We previously discussed that an object is in *free fall* when the only force acting on it is the force of gravity. In this case, Newton's second law tells us

$$\begin{aligned} \vec{F}_{\text{net}} &= m\vec{a} \\ -mg\hat{y} &= m\vec{a}. \end{aligned}$$

Dividing both sides by the mass, we see the acceleration of an object in free fall is $\vec{a} = -9.81\hat{y}$.

It's interesting to note that an object's mass does not affect its acceleration during free fall. The force of gravity is proportional to the mass of the object, but acceleration is inversely proportional to the mass of the object; overall, it holds that $a_y = -g$ for objects in free fall, regardless of their mass. This observation was first made by Galileo in his famous Leaning Tower of Pisa experiment. Galileo dropped a wooden ball and a metal ball (same shape, different mass) from the Leaning Tower of Pisa, and observed that they fell to the ground at the same time. Search for "Apollo 15 feather and hammer drop" on YouTube to see this experiment performed on the Moon.

What next?

You might have noticed that in the last couple of paragraphs we started putting little arrows on top of certain quantities. The arrows are there to remind you that forces, velocities, and accelerations are *vector quantities*. In the next chapter, we'll make a short mathematical digression to introduce all the vectors concepts necessary to understand physics.

Before we proceed with the vectors lessons and more advanced physics topics, it's a good idea to practice using the physics equations you just learned. Take the time to solve a couple of the practice problems in the next section.

2.5 Kinematics problems

We spent an entire chapter learning about position, velocity, and acceleration equations used to describe the motion of objects. It's now time to practice using these equations to solve problems.

Here are some general tips for solving kinematics problems. First, try to determine which equation you'll need to solve the problem. There are just four of them: $x(t) = x_i + v_i t + \frac{1}{2}at^2$, $v(t) = v_i + at$, $a(t) = a = \frac{F_{\text{net}}}{m}$, and $v_f^2 = v_i^2 + 2a\Delta x$, so it can't be that hard. If you can't figure it out, check the hint then try solving the problem. Always draw a diagram labelling all the variables that appear in your equations. This way you'll always have a picture of what is going on. Check your answer against the answer provided on page 433. If you didn't get the right answer, check your work and try again. Don't look at the solution yet. Try to figure out the problem by revisiting the assumptions you made, the equations you wrote, and the steps you followed. Look at the solution only if you can't figure out the problem after 10 minutes and you're running out of ideas.

P2.1 Below is a velocity-vs-time graph of a moving particle. Is the particle gaining or losing speed? Does the graph describe uniformly accelerated motion (UAM) or not?

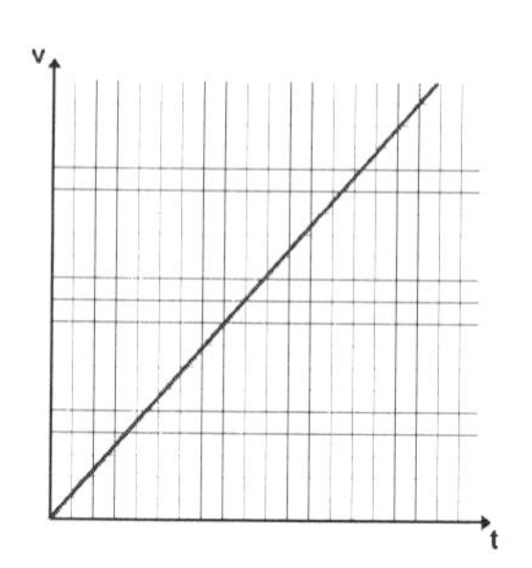

Hint: Acceleration is the slope of the velocity graph.

P2.2 You're running away from point A. At $t = 2$[s] you're 3[m] away from A, at $t = 4$[s] you're 8[m] away from A, and at $t = 6$[s] you're 14[m] away from A. Are you running with uniform velocity (UVM)?
Hint: Calculate the velocity during each time interval.

P2.3 A car is moving on a straight road. Indicate whether the car's speed is increasing or decreasing in the following cases:

1. Velocity is negative, acceleration is positive.
2. Velocity is negative, acceleration is negative.

Hint: Pay attention to the relative direction of acceleration to velocity.

P2.4 A body is pushed by a constant force F, and at time $t = t_0$ the force becomes zero. Determine when the particle is in uniformly accelerated motion (UAM) and when it is in uniform velocity motion (UVM).
Hint: Remember Newton's 2nd law of motion.

P2.5 A car has the following acceleration-vs-time graph. The car starts from rest at $t = 0$[s]. Find the velocity of the car at times A, B, C, D, and E.

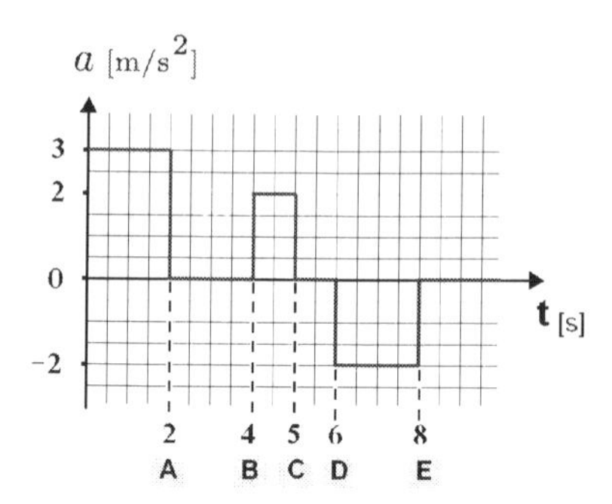

Hint: The change in velocity is the area under the acceleration graph.

P2.6 The position of a rocket as a function of time is described by the equation $x(t) = 3t^3 + 5t^2 - 3t + 5$. Find the velocity and the acceleration of the rocket as functions of time.
Hint: Differentiate the function with respect to t.

P2.7 You're on a mission to Jupiter where you design an experiment to measure the planet's gravitational acceleration. In the experiment, you let go of a ball from a height of 4[m] and watch it fall to the ground. When the ball hits the ground, its speed is 14[m/s].

1. What is the gravitational acceleration on Jupiter?
2. Find the position of the ball as a function of time.

Hint: Use the fourth equation of motion.

P2.8 You're pulling a 5[kg] cart in a straight path. The position of the cart as a function of time is $x(t) = 6t^2 + 2t + 1$[m].

1. Find the velocity and acceleration of the cart as functions of time.
2. Calculate the force you're using to pull the cart.

Hint: Take the derivative of the position with respect to time. Use Newton's 2nd law $F = ma$.

P2.9 A remote controlled car has a mass of 0.5[kg]. The electric engine pushes the car with a force of 1.0[N] starting from rest at point A.

1. Find the acceleration, velocity, and position of the car as functions of time, assuming $x = 0$ at point A.
2. Calculate the velocity of the car at $t = 4$[s].
3. What is the car's velocity when it is 9[m] away from point A?

Hint: Use Newton's 2nd law and integration.

P2.10 Below is an acceleration-vs-time graph of a particle. At $t = 0$[s], the particle starts moving from rest at $x = 0$[m]. The particle's acceleration from $t = 0$[s] to $t = 3$[s] is given by $a(t) = 3t$[m/s^2]. After $t = 2$[s], the acceleration is constant $a = 6$[m/s^2].

1. Find the velocity $v(2)$ and position $x(2)$ of the particle at $t = 2$[s].
2. Construct the functions of time that describe the acceleration, the velocity, and the position of the particle after $t = 2$[s].
3. How much time is needed for the particle to reach $x = 49$[m]?
4. At what distance from the origin will the particle's velocity reach 12[m/s]?

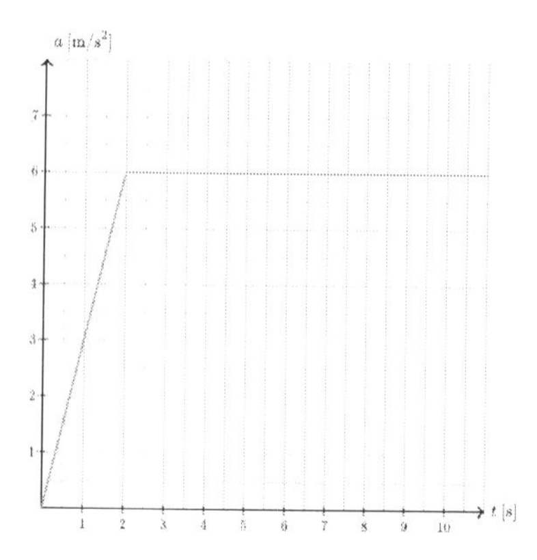

Hint: Use integration to find the velocity and the position. The integral of $f(t) = t^2$ is $F(t) = \frac{1}{3}t^3$. Make sure that when $t = 2$[s], the functions $v(t)$ and $x(t)$ in Part 2 match your answer from Part 1.

P2.11 The graph below shows the position-vs-time graph of a squirrel running in a field where x is in metres and t is in seconds.

1. Calculate the squirrel's velocity during the time intervals A to B, C to D, and E to F.
2. Indicate whether the squirrel is standing still, moving forward (in the positive x-direction), or moving backward during the following intervals: 0[s] to 2[s], 2[s] to 6[s], and 6[s] to 9[s].

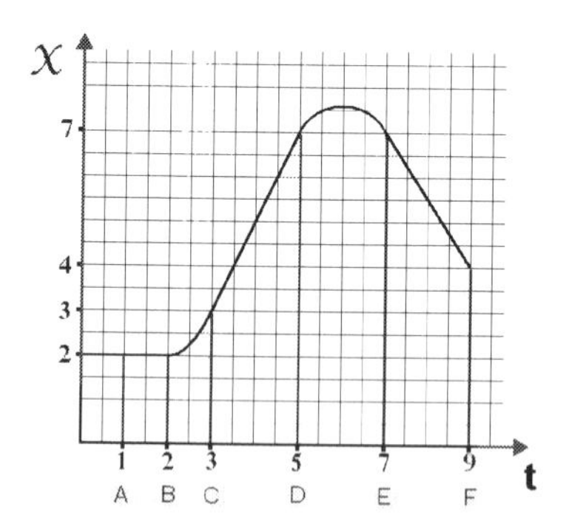

Hint: Velocity is Δx divided by Δt.

P2.12 A car passes point A with velocity v_i[m/s] at $t = 0$[s], with an acceleration of -2[m/s^2]. The car comes to rest 9[m] from point A.

1. What is v_i?
2. What is the position of the car as a function of time?

Hint: Use the fourth equation of motion.

P2.13 Two dogs are running after a tennis ball. At $t = 0[s]$ the first dog starts running from rest with an acceleration of $3[m/s^2]$. The other dog is $4[m]$ ahead of the first dog at $t = 0[s]$, running with velocity $3[m/s]$ and acceleration $1[m/s^2]$.

1. Construct the positions of the two dogs as functions of time.
2. At what time will the dogs meet?

Hint: Equate the positions of both dogs.

P2.14 A car has the position function $x(t) = 2t^2 + 5t + 7[m]$.

1. What is the car's position and velocity at $t = 0[s]$?
2. Find the velocity and acceleration of the car as functions of time.
3. Find the position and the velocity of the car at $t = 5[s]$?

Hint: Use differentiation to find the velocity and acceleration functions.

P2.15 A car moving with initial velocity v_i applies the brakes. After $2[m]$ the car's speed is $4[m/s]$, and $4[m]$ after applying the brakes the car comes to a stop. What is v_i and how much time was needed for the car to stop? Assume the car's acceleration (deceleration) is constant starting from the point the brakes are applied until it stops.

Hint: Use the fourth equation of motion. Find the position function.

Chapter 3

Vectors

In this chapter we'll learn how to manipulate multi-dimensional objects called vectors. Vectors are the precise way to describe directions in space. We need vectors in order to describe physical quantities like the velocity of an object, its acceleration, and the net force acting on the object.

Vectors are built from ordinary numbers, which form the *components* of the vector. You can think of a vector as a list of numbers, and *vector algebra* as operations performed on the numbers in the list. Vectors can also be manipulated as geometric objects, represented by arrows in space. For instance, the arrow that corresponds to the vector $\vec{v} = (v_x, v_y)$ starts at the origin $(0,0)$ and ends at the point (v_x, v_y). The word vector comes from the Latin *vehere*, which means *to carry*. Indeed, the vector $\vec{v}$ takes the point $(0,0)$ and carries it to the point (v_x, v_y).

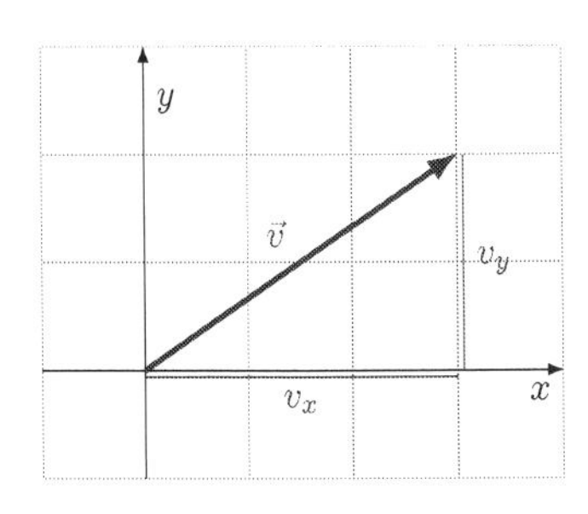

Figure 3.1: The vector $\vec{v} = (3,2)$ can be represented as an arrow in the Cartesian plane. The horizontal component of $\vec{v}$ is $v_x = 3$. The vertical component of $\vec{v}$ is $v_y = 2$.

This chapter will introduce you to vectors, vector algebra, and vector operations, which are very useful for solving physics problems.

What you'll learn here applies more broadly to current problems in computer graphics, probability theory, machine learning, and other fields of science and mathematics. It's all about vectors these days, so you'd best get to know them.

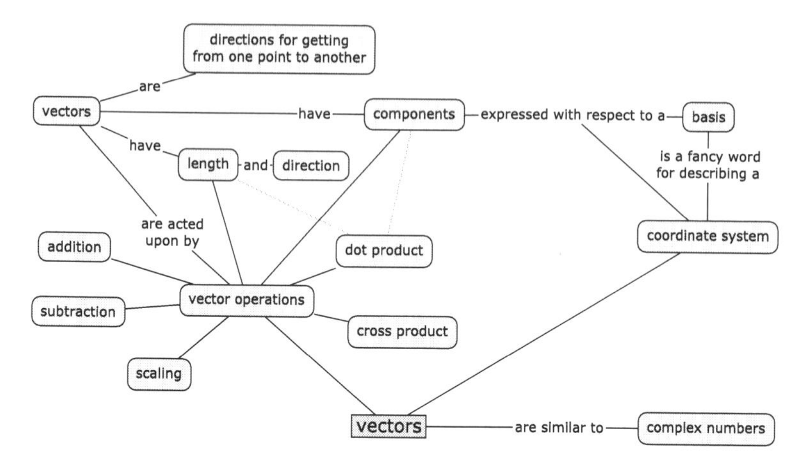

Figure 3.2: This figure illustrates the new concepts related to vectors. As you can see, there is quite a bit of new vocabulary to learn, but don't be fazed—all these terms are just fancy ways of talking about arrows.

3.1 Great outdoors

Vectors are directions for getting from point A to point B. Directions can be given in terms of street names and visual landmarks, or with respect to a coordinate system.

While on vacation in British Columbia, you want to visit a certain outdoor location your friend told you about. Your friend isn't available to take you there himself, but he has sent you *directions* for how to get to the place from the bus stop:

```
Sup G. Go to bus stop number 345. Bring a compass.
Walk 2 km north then 3 km east. You will find X there.
```

This text message contains all the information you need to find X.

Act 1: Following directions

You arrive at the bus station, located at the top of a hill. From this height you can see the whole valley, and along the hillside below spreads a beautiful field of tall crops. The crops are so tall they prevent anyone standing in them from seeing too far; good thing you have a compass. You align the compass needle so the red arrow points north. You walk 2 km north, then turn right (east) and walk another 3 km. You arrive at X.

Okay, back to vectors. In this case, the *directions* can be also written as a vector $\vec{d}$, expressed as:

$$\vec{d} = 2\text{km}\,\hat{N} + 3\text{km}\,\hat{E}.$$

This is the mathematical expression that corresponds to the directions "Walk 2 km north then 3 km east." Here, $\hat{N}$ is a *direction* and the number in front of the direction tells you the distance to walk in that direction.

Act 2: Equivalent directions

Later during your vacation, you decide to return to the location X. You arrive at the bus stop to find there is a slight problem. From your position, you can see a kilometre to the north, where a group of armed and threatening-looking men stand, waiting to ambush anyone who tries to cross what has now become a trail through the crops. Clearly the word has spread about X and constant visitors have drawn too much attention to the location.

Well, technically speaking, there is no problem at X. The problem lies on the route that starts north and travels through the ambush squad. Can you find an alternate route that leads to X?

```
"Use math, Luke! Use math!"
```

Recall the commutative property of number addition: $a + b = b + a$. Maybe an analogous property holds for vectors? Indeed, it does:

$$\vec{d} = 2\text{km}\,\hat{N} + 3\text{km}\,\hat{E} = 3\text{km}\,\hat{E} + 2\text{km}\,\hat{N}.$$

The $\hat{N}$ directions and the $\hat{E}$ directions obey the commutative property. Since the directions can be followed in any order, you can first walk the 3 km east, then walk 2 km north and arrive at X again.

Act 3: Efficiency

It takes 5 km of walking to travel from the bus stop to X, and another 5 km to travel back to the bus stop. Thus, it takes a total of 10 km walking every time you want to go to X. Can you find a quicker route? What is the fastest way from the bus stop to the destination?

Instead of walking in the east and north directions, it would be quicker if you take the diagonal to the destination. Using Pythagoras' theorem you can calculate the length of the diagonal. When the side lengths are 3 and 2, the diagonal has length $\sqrt{3^2+2^2} = \sqrt{9+4} = \sqrt{13} = 3.60555\ldots$. The length of the diagonal route is just 3.6 km, which means the diagonal route saves you a whole 1.4 km of walking in each direction.

But perhaps seeking efficiency is not always necessary! You could take a longer path on the way back and give yourself time to enjoy the great outdoors.

Discussion

Vectors are directions for getting from one point to another point. To indicate directions on maps, we use the four cardinal directions: $\hat{N}$, $\hat{S}$, $\hat{E}$, $\hat{W}$. In math, however, we will use only two of the cardinals—$\hat{E} \equiv \hat{x}$ and $\hat{N} \equiv \hat{y}$—since they fit nicely with the usual way of drawing the Cartesian plane. We don't need an $\hat{S}$ direction because we can represent downward distances as negative distances in the $\hat{N}$ direction. Similarly, $\hat{W}$ is the same as negative $\hat{E}$.

From now on, when we talk about vectors we will always represent them with respect to the standard coordinate system $\hat{x}$ and $\hat{y}$, and use *bracket notation*,

$$(v_x, v_y) \equiv v_x\,\hat{x} + v_y\,\hat{y}.$$

Bracket notation is nice because it's compact, which is good since we will be doing a lot of calculations with vectors. Instead of explicitly writing out all the directions, we will automatically assume that the first number in the bracket is the $\hat{x}$ distance and the second number is the $\hat{y}$ distance.

3.2 Vectors

Vectors are extremely useful in all areas of life. In physics, for example, we use a vector to describe the velocity of an object. It is not sufficient to say that the speed of a tennis ball is 20[m/s]: we must also specify the direction in which the ball is moving. Both of the two velocities

$$\vec{v}_1 = (20, 0) \qquad \text{and} \qquad \vec{v}_2 = (0, 20)$$

describe motion at the speed of 20[m/s]; but since one velocity points along the x-axis, and the other points along the y-axis, they are *completely* different velocities. The velocity vector contains information about the object's speed *and* direction. The direction makes a big difference. If it turns out the tennis ball is hurtling toward you, you'd better get out of the way!

This section's main idea is that **vectors are not the same as numbers**. A vector is a special kind of mathematical object that is *made up of* numbers. Before we begin any calculations with vectors, we need to think about the basic mathematical operations that we can perform on vectors. We will define vector addition $\vec{u}+\vec{v}$, vector subtraction $\vec{u}-\vec{v}$, vector scaling $\alpha\vec{v}$, and other operations. We will also discuss two different notions of *vector product*, which have useful geometric properties.

Definitions

The two-dimensional vector $\vec{v} \in \mathbb{R}^2$ is equivalent to a *pair of numbers* $\vec{v} \equiv (v_x, v_y)$. We call v_x the x-component of $\vec{v}$, and v_y is the y-component of $\vec{v}$.

Vector representations

We'll use three equivalent ways to denote vectors:

- $\vec{v} = (v_x, v_y)$: component notation, where the vector is represented as a pair of coordinates with respect to the x-axis and the y-axis.
- $\vec{v} = v_x\hat{\imath} + v_y\hat{\jmath}$: unit vector notation. The vector is expressed in terms of the unit vectors $\hat{\imath} = (1,0)$ and $\hat{\jmath} = (0,1)$.
- $\vec{v} = \|\vec{v}\|\angle\theta$: length-and-direction notation, where the vector is expressed in terms of its *length* $\|\vec{v}\|$ and the angle θ that the vector makes with the x-axis.

These three notations describe different aspects of vectors, and we will use them throughout the rest of the book. We'll learn how to convert between them—both algebraically (with pen, paper, and calculator) and intuitively (by drawing arrows).

Vector operations

Consider two vectors, $\vec{u} = (u_x, u_y)$ and $\vec{v} = (v_x, v_y)$, and assume that $\alpha \in \mathbb{R}$ is an arbitrary constant. The following operations are defined for these vectors:

- **Addition:** $\vec{u}+\vec{v} = (u_x + v_x, u_y + v_y)$
- **Subtraction:** $\vec{u}-\vec{v} = (u_x - v_x, u_y - v_y)$
- **Scaling:** $\alpha\vec{u} = (\alpha u_x, \alpha u_y)$

- **Dot product:** $\vec{u} \cdot \vec{v} = u_x v_x + u_y v_y$
- **Length:** $\|\vec{u}\| = \sqrt{\vec{u} \cdot \vec{u}} = \sqrt{u_x^2 + u_y^2}$. We will also sometimes simply use the letter u to denote the length of $\vec{u}$.
- **Cross product:** $\vec{u} \times \vec{v} = (u_y v_z - u_z v_y,\ u_z v_x - u_x v_z,\ u_x v_y - u_y v_x)$. The cross product is only defined for three-dimensional vectors like $\vec{u} = (u_x, u_y, u_z)$ and $\vec{v} = (v_x, v_y, v_z)$.

Pay careful attention to the dot product and the cross product. Although they're called products, these operations behave much differently from taking the product of two numbers. Also note, there is no notion of vector division.

Vector algebra

Addition and subtraction Just like numbers, you can add vectors

$$\vec{v} + \vec{w} = (v_x, v_y) + (w_x, w_y) = (v_x + w_x, v_y + w_y),$$

subtract them

$$\vec{v} - \vec{w} = (v_x, v_y) - (w_x, w_y) = (v_x - w_x, v_y - w_y),$$

and solve all kinds of equations where the unknown variable is a vector. This is not a formidably complicated new development in mathematics. Performing arithmetic calculations on vectors simply requires **carrying out arithmetic operations on their components**. Given two vectors, $\vec{v} = (4, 2)$ and $\vec{w} = (3, 7)$, their difference is computed as $\vec{v} - \vec{w} = (4, 2) - (3, 7) = (1, -5)$.

Scaling We can also *scale* a vector by any number $\alpha \in \mathbb{R}$:

$$\alpha\vec{v} = (\alpha v_x, \alpha v_y),$$

where each component is multiplied by the scaling factor α. Scaling changes the length of a vector. If $\alpha > 1$ the vector will get longer, and if $0 \leqslant \alpha < 1$ then the vector will become shorter. If α is a negative number, the scaled vector will point in the opposite direction.

Length A vector's length is obtained from Pythagoras' theorem. Imagine a right-angle triangle with one side of length v_x and the other side of length v_y; the length of the vector is equal to the length of the triangle's hypotenuse:

$$\|\vec{v}\|^2 = v_x^2 + v_y^2 \qquad \Rightarrow \qquad \|\vec{v}\| = \sqrt{v_x^2 + v_y^2}.$$

A common technique is to scale a vector $\vec{v}$ by one over its length $\frac{1}{\|\vec{v}\|}$ to obtain a unit vector that points in the same direction as $\vec{v}$:

$$\hat{v} \equiv \frac{\vec{v}}{\|\vec{v}\|} = \left(\frac{v_x}{\|\vec{v}\|}, \frac{v_y}{\|\vec{v}\|}\right).$$

Unit vectors (denoted with a hat instead of an arrow) are useful when you want to describe only a direction in space without any specific length in mind. Verify that $\|\hat{v}\| = 1$.

Vector as arrows

So far, we described how to perform algebraic operations on vectors in terms of their components. Vector operations can also be interpreted geometrically, as operations on two-dimensional arrows in the Cartesian plane.

Vector addition The sum of two vectors corresponds to the combined displacement of the two vectors. Figure 3.3 illustrates the addition of two vectors, $\vec{v}_1 = (3,0)$ and $\vec{v}_2 = (2,2)$. The sum of the two vectors is the vector $\vec{v}_1 + \vec{v}_2 = (3,0) + (2,2) = (5,2)$.

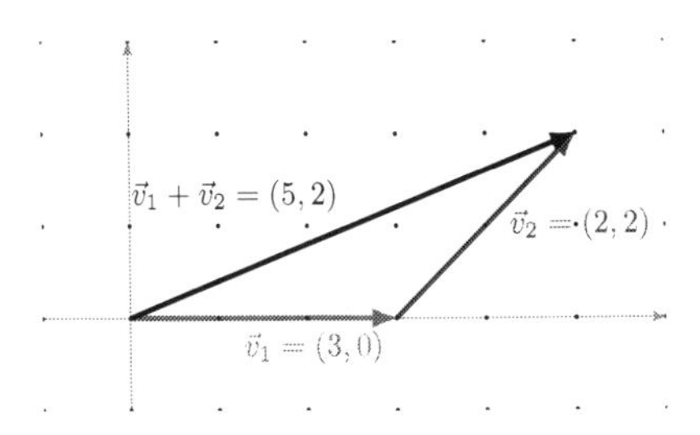

Figure 3.3: The addition of the vectors $\vec{v}_1$ and $\vec{v}_2$ produces the vector $(5,2)$.

Vector subtraction Before we describe vector subtraction, note that multiplying a vector by a scaling factor $\alpha = -1$ gives a vector of the same length as the original, but pointing in the opposite direction.

This fact is useful if you want to subtract two vectors using the graphical approach. Subtracting a vector is the same as adding the negative of the vector:

$$\vec{w} - \vec{v}_1 = \vec{w} + (-\vec{v}_1) = \vec{v}_2.$$

Figure 3.4 illustrates the graphical procedure for subtracting the vector $\vec{v}_1 = (3,0)$ from the vector $\vec{w} = (5,2)$. Subtraction of $\vec{v}_1 = (3,0)$ is the same as addition of $-\vec{v}_1 = (-3,0)$.

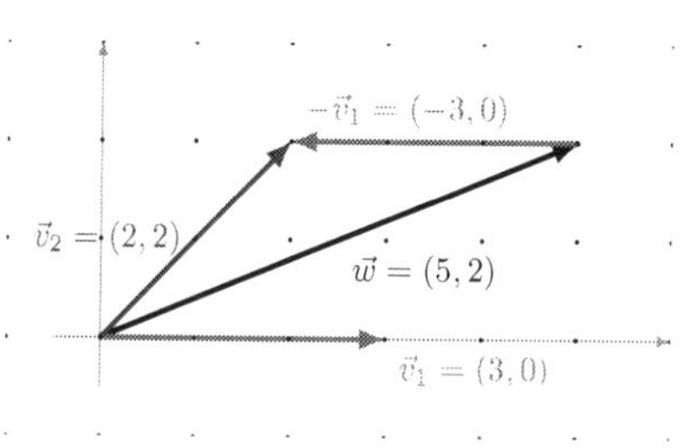

Figure 3.4: The vector subtraction $\vec{w} - \vec{v}_1$ is equivalent to the vector addition $\vec{w} + (-\vec{v}_1)$, where $(-\vec{v}_1)$ is like $\vec{v}_1$ but points in the opposite direction.

Scaling The scaling operation acts to change the length of a vector. Suppose we want to obtain a vector in the same direction as the vector $\vec{v} = (3, 2)$, but half as long. "Half as long" corresponds to a scaling factor of $\alpha = 0.5$. The scaled-down vector is $\vec{w} = 0.5\vec{v} = (1.5, 1)$.

Conversely, we can think of the vector $\vec{v}$ as being twice as long as the vector $\vec{w}$.

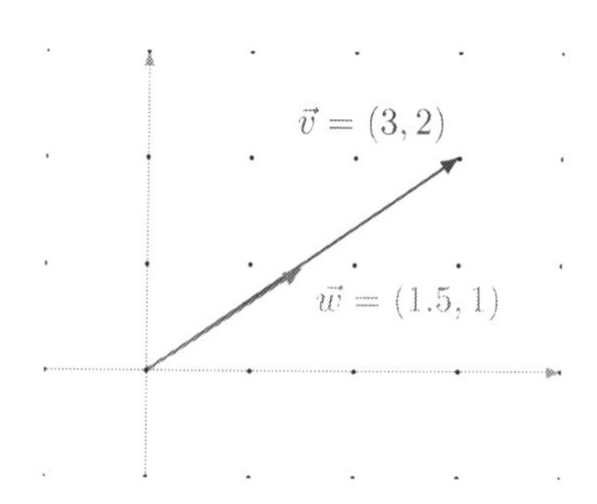

Figure 3.5: Vectors $\vec{v}$ and $\vec{w}$ are related by the equation $\vec{v} = 2\vec{w}$.

Length-and-direction representation

So far, we've seen how to represent a vector in terms of its components. There is also another way of representing vectors: we can specify a vector in terms of its length $||\vec{v}||$ and its direction—the angle it makes with the x-axis. For example, the vector $(1, 1)$ can also be written as $\sqrt{2}\angle 45°$. This magnitude-and-direction notation is useful because it makes it easy to see the "size" of vectors. On the other hand, vector arithmetic operations are much easier to carry out in the component notation. We will use the following formulas for converting between the two notations.

To convert the length-and-direction vector $\|\vec{r}\|\angle\theta$ into an x-

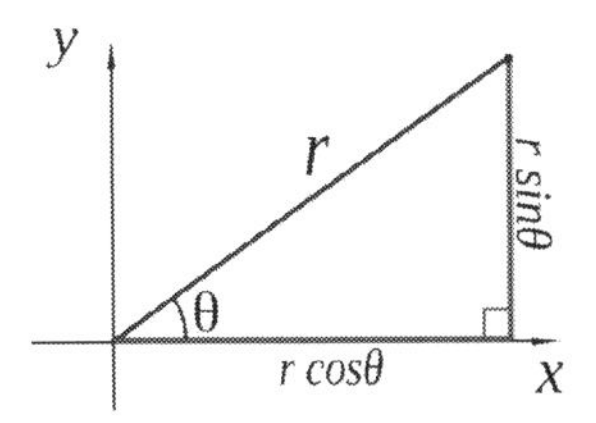

Figure 3.6: The x- and y-coordinates of a vector with length r and direction θ are given by $r_x = r\cos\theta$ and $r_y = r\sin\theta$.

component and a y-component (r_x, r_y), use the formulas

$$r_x = \|\vec{r}\|\cos\theta \quad \text{and} \quad r_y = \|\vec{r}\|\sin\theta.$$

To convert from component notation (r_x, r_y) to length-and-direction $\|\vec{r}\|\angle\theta$, use

$$r = \|\vec{r}\| = \sqrt{r_x^2 + r_y^2} \qquad \text{and} \qquad \theta = \tan^{-1}\left(\frac{r_y}{r_x}\right).$$

Note that the second part of the equation involves the inverse tangent function. By convention, the function $\tan^{-1}$ returns values between $\pi/2$ (90°) and $-\pi/2$ (−90°). You should be careful when finding the θ of vectors with an angle outside of this range. Specifically, for vectors with $v_x < 0$, you must add π (180°) to $\tan^{-1}(r_y/r_x)$ to obtain the correct θ.

Unit vector notation

In three dimensions, we can think of a vector $\vec{v} = (v_x, v_y, v_z)$ as a command to "Go a distance v_x in the x-direction, a distance v_y in the y-direction, and v_z in the z-direction."

To write this set of commands more explicitly, we can use multiples of the vectors $\hat{\imath}, \hat{\jmath}$, and $\hat{k}$. These are the unit vectors pointing in the x, y, and z directions, respectively:

$$\hat{\imath} = (1,0,0), \qquad \hat{\jmath} = (0,1,0), \quad \text{and} \quad \hat{k} = (0,0,1).$$

Any number multiplied by $\hat{\imath}$ corresponds to a vector with that number in the first coordinate. For example, $3\hat{\imath} \equiv (3,0,0)$. Similarly, $4\hat{\jmath} \equiv (0,4,0)$ and $5\hat{k} \equiv (0,0,5)$.

In physics, we tend to perform a lot of numerical calculations with vectors; to make things easier, we often use unit vector notation:

$$v_x\hat{\imath} + v_y\hat{\jmath} + v_z\hat{k} \qquad \Leftrightarrow \qquad \vec{v} \qquad \Leftrightarrow \qquad (v_x, v_y, v_z).$$

The addition rule remains the same for the new notation:

$$\underbrace{2\hat{\imath} + 3\hat{\jmath}}_{\vec{v}} + \underbrace{5\hat{\imath} - 2\hat{\jmath}}_{\vec{w}} = \underbrace{7\hat{\imath} + 1\hat{\jmath}}_{\vec{v}+\vec{w}}.$$

It's the same story repeating all over again: we need to add $\hat{\imath}$s with $\hat{\imath}$s, and $\hat{\jmath}$s with $\hat{\jmath}$s.

Examples

Simple example

Compute the sum $\vec{s} = 4\hat{\imath} + 5\angle 30°$. Express your answer in the length-and-direction notation.

Since we want to carry out an addition, and since addition is performed in terms of components, our first step is to convert $5\angle 30°$ into component notation: $5\angle 30° = 5\cos 30°\hat{\imath} + 5\sin 30°\hat{\jmath} = 5\frac{\sqrt{3}}{2}\hat{\imath} + \frac{5}{2}\hat{\jmath}$. We can now compute the sum:

$$\vec{s} = 4\hat{\imath} + 5\tfrac{\sqrt{3}}{2}\hat{\imath} + \tfrac{5}{2}\hat{\jmath} = (4 + 5\tfrac{\sqrt{3}}{2})\hat{\imath} + (\tfrac{5}{2})\hat{\jmath}.$$

The x-component of the sum is $s_x = (4 + 5\frac{\sqrt{3}}{2})$ and the y-component of the sum is $s_y = (\frac{5}{2})$. To express the answer as a length and a direction, we compute the length $\|\vec{s}\| = \sqrt{s_x^2 + s_y^2} = 8.697$ and the direction $\tan^{-1}(s_y/s_x) = 16.7°$. The answer is $\vec{s} = 8.697\angle 16.7°$.

Vector addition example

You're heading to physics class after a "safety meeting" with a friend, and are looking forward to two hours of finding absolute amazement and awe in the laws of Mother Nature. As it turns out, there is no enlightenment to be had that day because there is going to be an in-class midterm. The first question involves a block sliding down an incline. You look at it, draw a little diagram, and then wonder how the hell you are going to find the net force acting on the block. The three forces acting on the block are $\vec{W} = 300\angle -90°$, $\vec{N} = 260\angle 120°$, and $\vec{F}_f = 50\angle 30°$.

You happen to remember the net force formula:

$$\sum \vec{F} = \vec{F}_{\text{net}} = m\vec{a} \qquad [\text{ Newton's } 2^{\text{nd}} \text{ law }].$$

You get the feeling Newton's 2nd law is the answer to all your troubles. You sense this formula is certainly the key because you saw the keyword "net force" when reading the question, and notice "net force" also appears in this very equation.

The net force is the sum of all forces acting on the block:

$$\vec{F}_{\text{net}} = \sum \vec{F} = \vec{W} + \vec{N} + \vec{F}_f.$$

All that separates you from the answer is the addition of these vectors. Vectors have components, and there is the whole sin/cos procedure for decomposing length-and-direction vectors into their components. If you have the vectors as components you'll be able to add them and find the net force.

Okay, chill! Let's do this one step at a time. The net force must have an x-component, which, according to the equation, must equal the sum of the x-components of all the forces:

$$\begin{aligned} F_{\text{net},x} &= W_x + N_x + F_{f,x} \\ &= 300\cos(-90^\circ) + 260\cos(120^\circ) + 50\cos(30^\circ) \\ &= -86.7. \end{aligned}$$

Now find the y-component of the net force using the sin of the angles:

$$\begin{aligned} F_{\text{net},y} &= W_y + N_y + F_{f,y} \\ &= 300\sin(-90^\circ) + 260\sin(120^\circ) + 50\sin(30^\circ) \\ &= -49.8. \end{aligned}$$

Combining the two components of the vector, we get the final answer:

$$\begin{aligned} \vec{F}_{\text{net}} &\equiv (F_{\text{net},x}, F_{\text{net},y}) \\ &= (-86.7, -49.8) = -86.7\hat{\imath} - 49.8\hat{\jmath} \\ &= 100\angle 209.9^\circ. \end{aligned}$$

Bam! Just like that you're done, because you overstand them vectors!

Relative motion example

A boat can reach a top speed of 12 knots in calm seas. Instead of cruising through a calm sea, however, the boat's crew is trying to sail up the St-Laurence river. The speed of the current is 5 knots.

If the boat travels directly upstream at full throttle $12\hat{\imath}$, then the speed of the boat relative to the shore will be

$$12\hat{\imath} - 5\hat{\imath} = 7\hat{\imath},$$

since we must "deduct" the speed of the current from the speed of the boat relative to the water. See the vector diagram in Figure 3.7.

Figure 3.7: A boat travels with speed 12 knots against a current of 5 knots.

If the crew wants to cross the river perpendicular to the current flow, they can use some of the boat's thrust to counterbalance the current, and the remaining thrust to push across. The situation is illustrated in Figure 3.8. In what direction should the boat sail to cross the river? We are looking for the direction of $\vec{v}$ the boat should take such that, after adding in the velocity of the current, the boat moves in a straight line between the two banks (in the $\hat{\jmath}$ direction).

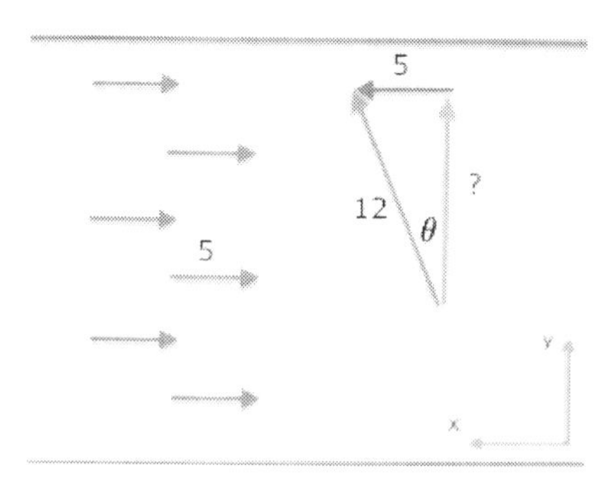

Figure 3.8: Part of the boat's thrust cancels the current.

Let's analyze the vector diagram. The opposite side of the triangle is parallel to the current flow and has length 5. We take the up-the-river component of the speed $\vec{v}$ to be equal to $5\hat{\imath}$, so that it cancels exactly the $-5\hat{\imath}$ flow of the river. The hypotenuse has length 12 since this is the speed of the boat relative to the surface of the water.

From all of this we can answer the question like professionals. You want the angle? Well, we have that $\frac{\text{opp}}{\text{hyp}} = \frac{5}{12} = \sin(\theta)$, where θ is the angle of the boat's course relative to the straight line between the two banks. We can use the inverse-sin function to solve for the angle:

$$\theta = \sin^{-1}\left(\tfrac{5}{12}\right) = 24.62^\circ.$$

The across-the-river component of the velocity can be calculated using $v_y = 12\cos(\theta) = 10.91$, or from Pythagoras' theorem if you prefer $v_y = \sqrt{\|\vec{v}\|^2 - v_x^2} = \sqrt{12^2 - 5^2} = 10.91$.

Vector dimensions

The most common types of vectors are two-dimensional vectors (like the ones in the Cartesian plane), and three-dimensional vectors (directions in 3D space). 2D and 3D vectors are easier to work with because we can visualize them and draw them in diagrams. In general, vectors can exist in any number of dimensions. An example of a n-dimensional vector is

$$\vec{v} = (v_1, v_2, \ldots, v_n) \in \mathbb{R}^n.$$

The rules of vector algebra apply in higher dimensions, but our ability to visualize stops at three dimensions.

Coordinate system

Vector components depend on the coordinate system in which the vectors are represented. Throughout this section we used the x, y, and z axes as the coordinate system, and we described vectors as components along each of these axes. This is a very convenient coordinate system; we have a set of three *perpendicular* axes, and a set of three unit vectors $\{\hat{\imath}, \hat{\jmath}, \hat{k}\}$ that point along each of the three axis directions. Every vector is implicitly defined in terms of this coordinate system. When we talk about the vector $\vec{v} = 3\hat{\imath} + 4\hat{\jmath} + 2\hat{k}$, we are really saying, "Start from the origin $(0,0,0)$, move 3 units in the x-direction, then move 4 units in the y-direction, and finally move 2 units in the z-direction." It is simpler to express these directions as $\vec{v} = (3,4,2)$, while remembering that the numbers in the bracket measure distances *relative* to the xyz-coordinate system.

It turns out, using the xyz-coordinate system and the vectors $\{\hat{\imath}, \hat{\jmath}, \hat{k}\}$ is just one of many possible ways we can represent vectors. We can represent a vector $\vec{v}$ as coefficients (v_1, v_2, v_3) with respect to any *basis* $\{\hat{e}_1, \hat{e}_2, \hat{e}_3\}$ as follows: $\vec{v} = v_1\hat{e}_1 + v_2\hat{e}_2 + v_3\hat{e}_3$. What is a basis, you ask? I'm glad you asked, because this is the subject of the next section.

Exercises

E3.1 Given the vectors $\vec{v}_1 = (2,1)$, $\vec{v}_2 = (2,-1)$, and $\vec{v}_3 = (3,3)$, calculate the following expressions:

a) $\vec{v}_1 + \vec{v}_2$ **b)** $\vec{v}_2 - 2\vec{v}_1$ **c)** $\vec{v}_1 + \vec{v}_2 + \vec{v}_3$

E3.2 Express the following vectors as components:

a) $\vec{v}_1 = 10\angle 30^\circ$ **b)** $\vec{v}_2 = 12\angle -90^\circ$ **c)** $\vec{v}_3 = 3\angle 170^\circ$

E3.3 Express the following vectors in length-and-direction notation:

a) $\vec{u}_1 = (4,0)$ **b)** $\vec{u}_2 = (1,1)$ **c)** $\vec{u}_3 = (-1,3)$

3.3 Basis

One of the most important concepts in the study of vectors is the concept of a *basis*. Consider the three-dimensional vector space $\mathbb{R}^3$. A *basis* for $\mathbb{R}^3$ is a set of vectors $\{\hat{e}_1, \hat{e}_2, \hat{e}_3\}$ that can be used as a coordinate system for $\mathbb{R}^3$. If the set of vectors $\{\hat{e}_1, \hat{e}_2, \hat{e}_3\}$ is a basis, then you can *represent* any vector $\vec{v} \in \mathbb{R}^3$ as coefficients (v_1, v_2, v_3) *with respect to* that basis:

$$\vec{v} = v_1\hat{e}_1 + v_2\hat{e}_2 + v_3\hat{e}_3.$$

The vector $\vec{v}$ is obtained by measuring out a distance v_1 in the $\hat{e}_1$ direction, a distance v_2 in the $\hat{e}_2$ direction, and a distance v_3 in the $\hat{e}_3$ direction.

You are already familiar with the *standard* basis $\{\hat{\imath}, \hat{\jmath}, \hat{k}\}$, which is associated with the xyz-coordinate system. You know that any vector $\vec{v} \in \mathbb{R}^3$ can be expressed as a triple (v_x, v_y, v_z) with respect to the basis $\{\hat{\imath}, \hat{\jmath}, \hat{k}\}$ through the formula $\vec{v} = v_x\hat{\imath} + v_y\hat{\jmath} + v_z\hat{k}$.

An analogy

Let's start with a simple example of a basis. If you look at the HTML source code behind any web page, you're sure to find at least one mention of the colour stylesheet directive such as `color:#336699;`. The numbers should be interpreted as a triple of values $(33, 66, 99)$, each value describing the amount of red, green, and blue needed to create a given colour. Let us call the colour described by the triple $(33, 66, 99)$ CoolBlue. This convention for colour representation is called the RGB colour model and we can think of it as the *RGB basis*. A basis is a set of elements that can be combined together to express something more complicated. In our case, the **R**, **G**, and **B** elements are pure colours that can create any colour when mixed appropriately. Schematically, we can write this mixing idea as

$$\text{CoolBlue} = (33, 66, 99)_{RGB} = 33\mathbf{R} + 66\mathbf{G} + 99\mathbf{B},$$

where the *coefficients* determine the strength of each colour component. To create the colour, we combine its components as symbolized by the $+$ operation.

The cyan, magenta, and yellow (CMY) colour model is another basis for representing colours. To express the "cool blue" colour in the CMY basis, you will need the following coefficients:

$$(33, 66, 99)_{RGB} = \text{CoolBlue} = (222, 189, 156)_{CMY} = 222\mathbf{C} + 189\mathbf{M} + 156\mathbf{Y}.$$

The *same* colour CoolBlue is represented by a *different* set of coefficients when the CMY colour basis is used.

Note that a triple of coefficients by itself does not mean anything unless we know the basis being used. For example, if we were to interpret the triple of coordinates $(33, 66, 99)$ with respect to the CMY basis, will would obtain a completely different colour, which would not be cool at all.

A basis is required to convert mathematical objects like the triple (a, b, c) into real-world ideas like colours. As exemplified above, to avoid any ambiguity we can use a subscript after the bracket to indicate the basis associated with each triple of coefficients.

Discussion

It's hard to over-emphasize the importance of the basis—the coordinate system you will use to describe vectors. The choice of coordinate system is the bridge between real-world vector quantities and their mathematical representation in terms of components. Every time you solve a problem with vectors, the first thing you should do is draw a coordinate system. Always keep in mind the coordinate system you're using when computing the components of vectors.

3.4 Vector products

Since adding two vectors $\vec{v}$ and $\vec{w}$ corresponds to adding their components $(v_x + w_x, v_y + w_y, v_z + w_z)$, you might logically think that the product of two vectors also corresponds to the product of their components $(v_x w_x, v_y w_y, v_z w_z)$, but this type of product is not used. Instead, we'll define the *dot product* and the *cross product*, which allow us to perform useful geometric operations with vectors.

Dot product

The *dot product* takes two vectors as inputs and produces a single, real number as an output:

$$\cdot : \mathbb{R}^3 \times \mathbb{R}^3 \quad \to \quad \mathbb{R}.$$

The dot product between two vectors can be computed using either the algebraic formula,

$$\vec{v} \cdot \vec{w} \equiv v_x w_x + v_y w_y + v_z w_z,$$

or the geometric formula,

$$\vec{v} \cdot \vec{w} \equiv \|\vec{v}\|\|\vec{w}\| \cos(\varphi),$$

where φ is the angle between the two vectors. Note the value of the dot product depends on the vectors' lengths and the cosine of the angle between them.

The name *dot product* comes from the symbol used to denote it. It is also known as the *scalar product*, since the result of the dot product is a scalar number—a number that does not change when the basis changes. The dot product is also sometimes called the *inner product*.

We can combine the algebraic and the geometric formulas for the dot product to obtain the formula,

$$\cos(\varphi) = \frac{\vec{v} \cdot \vec{w}}{\|\vec{v}\|\|\vec{w}\|} = \frac{v_x w_x + v_y w_y + v_z w_z}{\|\vec{v}\|\|\vec{w}\|} \quad \text{and} \quad \varphi = \cos^{-1}(\cos(\varphi)).$$

This formula makes it possible to find the angle between two vectors if we know their components.

The geometric factor $\cos(\varphi)$ depends on the relative orientation of the two vectors as follows:

- If the vectors point in the same direction, then $\cos(\varphi) = \cos(0°) = 1$, so $\vec{v} \cdot \vec{w} = \|\vec{v}\|\|\vec{w}\|$.
- If the vectors are perpendicular to each other, then $\cos(\varphi) = \cos(90°) = 0$, so $\vec{v} \cdot \vec{w} = 0$.
- If the vectors point in exactly opposite directions, then $\cos(\varphi) = \cos(180°) = -1$, so $\vec{v} \cdot \vec{w} = -\|\vec{v}\|\|\vec{w}\|$.

The dot product is defined for vectors of any dimension; as long as two vectors have the same number of components, we can compute their dot product.

Cross product

The *cross product* takes two vectors as inputs and produces another vector as the output:

$$\times : \mathbb{R}^3 \times \mathbb{R}^3 \quad \to \quad \mathbb{R}^3.$$

The cross product of two vectors is perpendicular to both vectors:

$$\vec{v} \times \vec{w} = \{ \text{ a vector perpendicular to both } \vec{v} \text{ and } \vec{w} \ \} \quad \in \mathbb{R}^3.$$

If you take the cross product of one vector pointing in the x-direction with another vector pointing in the y-direction, the result will be a vector in the z-direction: $\hat{\imath} \times \hat{\jmath} = \hat{k}$. The name *cross product* comes from the symbol used to denote it. It is also sometimes called the *vector product*, since the output of this operation is a vector.

The cross products of individual basis elements are defined as

$$\hat{\imath} \times \hat{\jmath} = \hat{k}, \qquad \hat{\jmath} \times \hat{k} = \hat{\imath}, \qquad \hat{k} \times \hat{\imath} = \hat{\jmath}.$$

The cross product is *anticommutative*, which means swapping the order of the inputs introduces a negative sign in the output:

$$\hat{\jmath} \times \hat{\imath} = -\hat{k}, \qquad \hat{k} \times \hat{\jmath} = -\hat{\imath}, \qquad \hat{\imath} \times \hat{k} = -\hat{\jmath}.$$

It's likely that, until now, the products you've seen in math have been *commutative*, which means the order of the inputs doesn't matter. The product of two numbers is commutative $ab = ba$, and the dot product is commutative $\vec{u} \cdot \vec{v} = \vec{v} \cdot \vec{u}$, but the cross product of two vectors is *anti*commutative $\vec{v} \times \vec{w} = -\vec{w} \times \vec{v}$.

For two arbitrary vectors $\vec{a} = (a_x, a_y, a_z)$ and $\vec{b} = (b_x, b_y, b_z)$, the cross product is calculated as

$$\vec{a} \times \vec{b} = \left(a_y b_z - a_z b_y,\ a_z b_x - a_x b_z,\ a_x b_y - a_y b_x\right).$$

The cross product's output has a length that is proportional to the sine of the angle between the vectors:

$$\|\vec{a} \times \vec{b}\| = \|\vec{a}\|\|\vec{b}\| \sin(\varphi).$$

The direction of the vector $(\vec{a} \times \vec{b})$ is perpendicular to both $\vec{a}$ and $\vec{b}$.

The right-hand rule

Consider the plane formed by the vectors $\vec{a}$ and $\vec{b}$. There are actually *two* vectors perpendicular to this plane: one above the plane and one below the plane. We use the *right-hand rule* to figure out which of these vectors corresponds to the cross product $\vec{a} \times \vec{b}$.

Make a fist with your right hand and then extend your thumb, first finger, and middle finger. When your index finger points in the same direction as the vector $\vec{a}$ and your middle finger points in the direction of $\vec{b}$, your thumb will point in the direction of $\vec{a} \times \vec{b}$. The relationship encoded in the right-hand rule matches the relationship between the standard basis vectors: $\hat{\imath} \times \hat{\jmath} = \hat{k}$.

Links

[A nice illustration of the cross product]
`http://1ucasvb.tumblr.com/post/76812811092/`

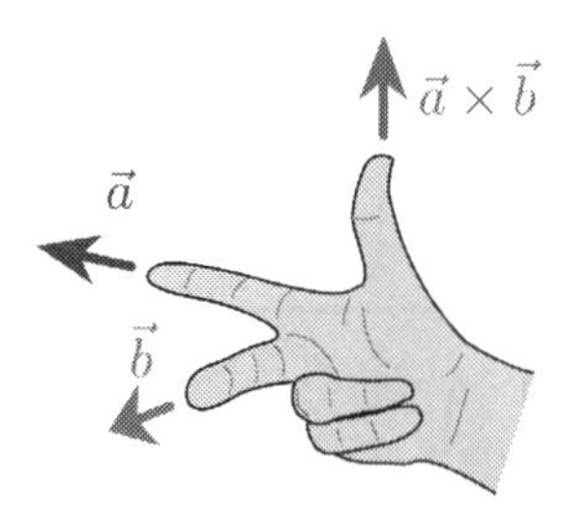

Figure 3.9: Using the right-hand rule to determine the direction of the cross product $\vec{a} \times \vec{b}$ based on directions of $\vec{a}$ and $\vec{b}$.

3.5 Complex numbers

By now, you've heard about complex numbers $\mathbb{C}$. The word "complex" is an intimidating word. Surely it must be a complex task to learn about the complex numbers. That may be true in general, but it helps if you know about vectors. Complex numbers are similar to two-dimensional vectors $\vec{v} \in \mathbb{R}^2$. We add and subtract complex numbers like vectors. Complex numbers also have components, length, and "direction." If you understand vectors, you will understand complex numbers at almost no additional mental cost.

We'll begin with a practical problem.

Example

Suppose you're asked to solve the following quadratic equation:

$$x^2 + 1 = 0.$$

You're looking for a number x, such that $x^2 = -1$. If you are only allowed to give real answers (the set of real numbers is denoted $\mathbb{R}$), then there is no answer to this question. In other words, this equation has no solutions. Graphically speaking, this is because the quadratic function $f(x) = x^2 + 1$ does not cross the x-axis.

However, we're not taking no for an answer! If we insist on solving for x in the equation $x^2 + 1 = 0$, we can imagine a new number i that satisfies $i^2 = -1$. We call i the unit imaginary number. The solutions to the equation are therefore $x_1 = i$ and $x_2 = -i$. There are two solutions because the equation is quadratic. We can check that $i^2 + 1 = -1 + 1 = 0$ and also $(-i)^2 + 1 = (-1)^2 i^2 + 1 = i^2 + 1 = 0$.

Thus, while the equation $x^2 + 1 = 0$ has no real solutions, it *does* have solutions if we allow the answers to be imaginary numbers.

Definitions

Complex numbers have a real part and an imaginary part:

- i: the unit imaginary number $i \equiv \sqrt{-1}$ or $i^2 = -1$
- bi: an imaginary number that is equal to b times i
- $\mathbb{R}$: the set of real numbers
- $\mathbb{C}$: the set of complex numbers $\mathbb{C} = \{a + bi \mid a, b \in \mathbb{R}\}$
- $z = a + bi$: a complex number
    - ▷ $\text{Re}\{z\} = a$: the real part of z
    - ▷ $\text{Im}\{z\} = b$: the imaginary part of z
- $\bar{z}$: the *complex conjugate* of z. If $z = a + bi$, then $\bar{z} = a - bi$.

The polar representation of complex numbers:

- $z = |z|\angle\varphi_z = |z|\cos\varphi_z + i|z|\sin\varphi_z$
- $|z| = \sqrt{\bar{z}z} = \sqrt{a^2 + b^2}$: the *magnitude* of $z = a + bi$
- $\varphi_z = \tan^{-1}(b/a)$: the *phase* or *argument* of $z = a + bi$
- $\text{Re}\{z\} = |z|\cos\varphi_z$
- $\text{Im}\{z\} = |z|\sin\varphi_z$

Formulas

Addition and subtraction

Just as we performed the addition of vectors component by component, we perform addition on complex numbers by adding the real parts together and adding the imaginary parts together:

$$(a + bi) + (c + di) = (a + c) + (b + d)i.$$

Polar representation

We can give a geometric interpretation of the complex numbers by extending the real number line into a two-dimensional plane called the *complex plane*. The horizontal axis in the complex plane measures the *real* part of the number. The vertical axis measures the *imaginary* part. Complex numbers are points in the complex plane.

It is possible to represent any complex number $z = a + bi$ in terms of its *magnitude* and its *phase*:

$$z = |z|\angle\varphi_z = \underbrace{|z|\cos\varphi_z}_{a} + \underbrace{|z|\sin\varphi_z}_{b}\, i.$$

The *magnitude* (or *absolute value*) of a complex number $z = a + bi$ is

$$|z| = \sqrt{a^2 + b^2}.$$

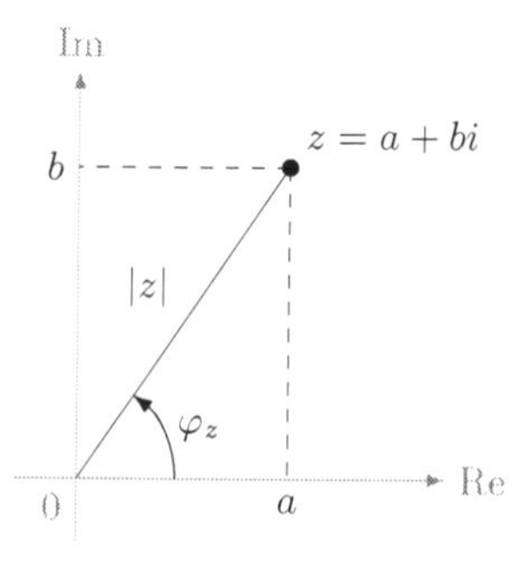

Figure 3.10: The complex number $z = a + bi$ corresponds to the point with coordinates (a, b) in the complex plane.

This corresponds to the *length* of the vector that represents the complex number in the complex plane. The formula is obtained by using Pythagoras' theorem.

The *phase*, also known as the *argument* of the complex number $z = a + bi$ is

$$\varphi_z \equiv \arg z \; = \; \texttt{atan2}(b,a) \; =^{\dagger} \; \tan^{-1}(b/a).$$

The phase corresponds to the angle that z forms with the real axis. Note the equality labelled † is true only when $a > 0$, because the function $\tan^{-1}$ always returns numbers in the range $[-\frac{\pi}{2}, \frac{\pi}{2}]$. Manual corrections of the output of $\tan^{-1}(b/a)$ are required for complex numbers with $a < 0$.

Some programming languages provide the two-input math function `atan2(y,x)` that correctly computes the angle that the vector (x, y) makes with the x-axis in all four quadrants. Because complex numbers behave like two-dimensional vectors, you can use `atan2` to compute their phase.

In addition to the vector-like properties of complex numbers, like magnitude and phase, we can also perform other operations with complex numbers that are not defined for vectors. The set of complex numbers $\mathbb{C}$ is a *field*. This means, in addition to the addition and subtraction operations, we can also perform multiplication and division with complex numbers.

Multiplication

The product of two complex numbers is computed using the usual rules of algebra:

$$(a + bi)(c + di) = (ac - bd) + (ad + bc)i.$$

In the polar representation, the product formula is

$$(p\angle\phi)(q\angle\psi) = pq\angle(\phi+\psi).$$

To multiply two complex numbers, multiply their magnitudes and add their phases.

Division

Let's look at the procedure for dividing complex numbers:

$$\frac{(a+bi)}{(c+di)} = \frac{(a+bi)}{(c+di)}\frac{(c-di)}{(c-di)} = (a+bi)\frac{(c-di)}{(c^2+d^2)} = (a+bi)\frac{\overline{c+di}}{|c+di|^2}.$$

In other words, to divide the number z by the complex number s, compute $\bar{s}$ and $|s|^2 = s\bar{s}$ and then use

$$z/s = z\frac{\bar{s}}{|s|^2}.$$

You can think of $\frac{\bar{s}}{|s|^2}$ as being equivalent to s^{-1}.

Cardano's example One of the earliest examples of reasoning involving complex numbers was given by Gerolamo Cardano in his 1545 book *Ars Magna*. Cardano wrote, "If someone says to you, divide 10 into two parts, one of which multiplied into the other shall produce 40, it is evident that this case or question is impossible." We want to find numbers x_1 and x_2 such that $x_1 + x_2 = 10$ and $x_1x_2 = 40$. This sounds kind of impossible. Or is it?

"Nevertheless," Cardano said, "we shall solve it in this fashion:

$$x_1 = 5+\sqrt{15}i \text{ and } x_2 = 5-\sqrt{15}i."$$

When you add $x_1 + x_2$ you obtain 10. When you multiply the two numbers the answer is

$$\begin{aligned} x_1x_2 &= \left(5+\sqrt{15}i\right)\left(5-\sqrt{15}i\right) \\ &= 25 - 5\sqrt{15}i + 5\sqrt{15}i - \sqrt{15}^2 i^2 = 25 + 15 = 40. \end{aligned}$$

Hence $5+\sqrt{15}i$ and $5-\sqrt{15}i$ are two numbers whose sum is 10 and whose product is 40.

Example 2 Compute the product of i and -1. Both i and -1 have a magnitude of 1 but different phases. The phase of i is $\frac{\pi}{2}$ (90°), while -1 has phase π (180°). The product of these two numbers is

$$(i)(-1) = (1\angle\tfrac{\pi}{2})(1\angle\pi) = 1\angle(\tfrac{\pi}{2}+\pi) = 1\angle\tfrac{3\pi}{2} = -i.$$

Multiplication by i is effectively a rotation by $\frac{\pi}{2}$ (90°) to the left.

Example 3 Find the polar representation of $z = -3 - i$ and compute z^6. Let's denote the polar representation of z by $z = r\angle\varphi$ as shown in Figure 3.11. We find $r = \sqrt{3^2 + 1^2} = \sqrt{10}$ and $\varphi = \tan^{-1}(\frac{1}{3}) + \pi = 0.322 + \pi$. Using the polar representation, we can easily compute z^6:

$$z^6 = r^6\angle(6\varphi) = (\sqrt{10})^6\angle 6(0.322 + \pi) = 10^3\angle 1.932 + 6\pi = 10^3\angle 1.932.$$

Note we can ignore multiples of 2π in the phase. In component form, z^6 is equal to $1000\cos(1.932) + 1000\sin(1.932)i = -353.4 + 935.5i$.

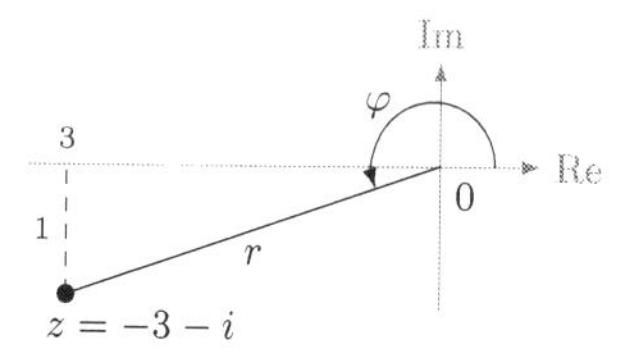

Figure 3.11: The complex number $z = 3 - i$ has magnitude $r = \sqrt{10}$ and phase $\varphi = 0.322 + \pi = 3.463$.

Fundamental theorem of algebra

The solutions to *any* polynomial equation $a_0 + a_1x + \cdots + a_nx^n = 0$ are of the form

$$z = a + bi.$$

In particular, any polynomial $P(x)$ of nth degree can be written as

$$P(x) = (x - z_1)(x - z_2)\cdots(x - z_n),$$

where $z_i \in \mathbb{C}$ are the polynomial's *complex* roots. Before today, you might have said the equation $x^2 + 1 = 0$ has no solutions. Now you know its solutions are the complex numbers $z_1 = i$ and $z_2 = -i$.

The theorem is "fundamental" because it tells us we won't ever need to invent any "fancier" set of numbers to solve polynomial equations. Recall that each set of numbers is associated with a different class of equations. The natural numbers $\mathbb{N}$ appear as solutions of the equation $m + n = x$, where m and n are natural numbers (denoted $m, n \in \mathbb{N}$). The integers $\mathbb{Z}$ are the solutions to equations of the form $x + m = n$, where $m, n \in \mathbb{N}$. The rational numbers $\mathbb{Q}$ are necessary to solve for x in $mx = n$, with $m, n \in \mathbb{Z}$. To find the solutions of $x^2 = 2$, we need the real numbers $\mathbb{R}$. The process of requiring new types of numbers for solving more complicated types of equations stops at $\mathbb{C}$; any polynomial equation—no matter how complicated it is—has solutions that are complex numbers $\mathbb{C}$.

Euler's formula

You already know $\cos\theta$ is a shifted version of $\sin\theta$, so it's clear these two functions are related. It turns out the exponential function is also related to sin and cos. Lo and behold, we have Euler's formula:

$$e^{i\theta} = \cos\theta + i\sin\theta\,.$$

Inputting an imaginary number to the exponential function outputs a complex number that contains both cos and sin. Euler's formula gives us an alternate notation for the polar representation of complex numbers: $z = |z|\angle\varphi_z = |z|e^{i\varphi_z}$.

If you want to impress your friends with your math knowledge, plug $\theta = \pi$ into the above equation to find

$$e^{i\pi} = \cos(\pi) + i\sin(\pi) = -1,$$

which can be rearranged into the form, $e^{\pi i} + 1 = 0$. This equation shows a relationship between the five most important numbers in all of mathematics: Euler's number $e = 2.71828\ldots$, $\pi = 3.14159\ldots$, the imaginary number i, 1, and zero. It's kind of cool to see all these important numbers reunited in one equation, don't you agree?

De Moivre's formula

By replacing θ in Euler's formula with $n\theta$, we obtain de Moivre's formula:

$$(\cos\theta + i\sin\theta)^n = \cos n\theta + i\sin n\theta.$$

De Moivre's formula makes sense if you think of the complex number $z = e^{i\theta} = \cos\theta + i\sin\theta$, raised to the nth power:

$$(\cos\theta + i\sin\theta)^n = z^n = (e^{i\theta})^n = e^{in\theta} = \cos n\theta + i\sin n\theta.$$

Setting $n = 2$ in de Moivre's formula, we can derive the double angle formulas (page 90) as the real and imaginary parts of the following equation:

$$(\cos^2\theta - \sin^2\theta) + (2\sin\theta\cos\theta)i = \cos(2\theta) + \sin(2\theta)i.$$

Links

[Mini tutorial on the complex numbers]
`http://paste.lisp.org/display/133628`

3.6 Vectors problems

You learned a bunch of vector formulas and you saw some vector diagrams, but did you really learn how to solve problems with vectors? There is only one way to find out: test yourself by solving problems.

I've said it before and I don't want to repeat myself too much, but it's worth saying again: the more problems you solve, the better you'll understand the material. It's now time for you to try the following vector problems to make sure you're on top of things.

P3.1 Express the following vectors in length-and-direction notation:

a) $\vec{u}_1 = (0,5)$ **b)** $\vec{u}_2 = (1,2)$ **c)** $\vec{u}_3 = (-1,-2)$

P3.2 Express the following vectors as components:

a) $\vec{v}_1 = 20\angle 30°$ **b)** $\vec{v}_2 = 10\angle -90°$ **c)** $\vec{v}_3 = 5\angle 150°$

P3.3 Express the following vectors in terms of unit vectors $\hat{\imath}$, $\hat{\jmath}$, and $\hat{k}$:

a) $\vec{w}_1 = 10\angle 25°$ **b)** $\vec{w}_2 = 7\angle -90°$ **c)** $\vec{w}_3 = (3,-2,3)$

P3.4 Given the vectors $\vec{v}_1 = (1,1)$, $\vec{v}_2 = (2,3)$, and $\vec{v}_3 = 5\angle 30°$, calculate the following expressions:

a) $\vec{v}_1 + \vec{v}_2$ **b)** $\vec{v}_2 - 2\vec{v}_1$ **c)** $\vec{v}_1 + \vec{v}_2 + \vec{v}_3$

P3.5 Starting from the point $P = (2,6)$, the three displacement vectors shown in Figure 3.12 are applied to obtain the point Q. What are the coordinates of the point Q?

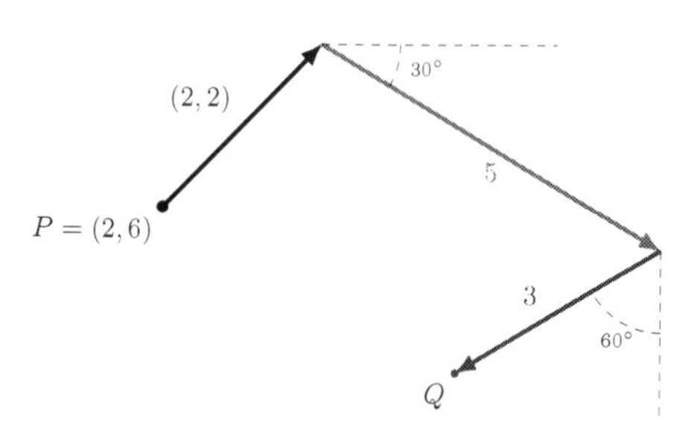

Figure 3.12: A point P is displaced by three vectors to obtain point Q.

P3.6 Given the vectors $\vec{u} = (1,1,1)$, $\vec{v} = (2,3,1)$, and $\vec{w} = (-1,-1,2)$, compute the following products:

a) $\vec{u} \cdot \vec{v}$ **b)** $\vec{u} \cdot \vec{w}$ **c)** $\vec{v} \cdot \vec{w}$

d) $\vec{u} \times \vec{v}$ **e)** $\vec{u} \times \vec{w}$ **f)** $\vec{v} \times \vec{w}$

P3.7 Given the vectors $\vec{p} = (1,1,0,3,3)$ and $\vec{q} = (1,2,3,4,5)$, calculate the following expressions:

a) $\vec{p} + \vec{q}$ **b)** $\vec{p} - \vec{q}$ **c)** $\vec{p} \cdot \vec{q}$

P3.8 Find a unit vector that is perpendicular to both $\vec{u} = (1,0,1)$ and $\vec{v} = (1,2,0)$.
Hint: Use the cross product.

P3.9 Find a vector that is orthogonal to both $\vec{u}_1 = (1,0,1)$ and $\vec{u}_2 = (1,3,0)$, and whose dot product with the vector $\vec{v} = (1,1,0)$ is equal to 8.

P3.10 Compute the following expressions:

a) $\sqrt{-4}$ **b)** $\dfrac{2+3i}{2+2i}$ **c)** $e^{3i}(2+i)e^{-3i}$

P3.11 Solve for $x \in \mathbb{C}$ in the following equations:

a) $x^2 = -4$ **b)** $\sqrt{x} = 4i$

c) $x^2 + 2x + 2 = 0$ **d)** $x^4 + 4x^2 + 3 = 0$

Hint: To solve **d)**, use the substitution $u = x^2$.

P3.12 Given the numbers $z_1 = 2 + i$, $z_2 = 2 - i$, and $z_3 = -1 - i$, compute

a) $|z_1|$ **b)** $\dfrac{z_1}{z_3}$ **c)** $z_1 z_2 z_3$

P3.13 A real business is a business that is profitable. An imaginary business is an idea that is just turning around in your head. We can model the real-imaginary nature of a business project by representing the *project state* as a complex number $p \in \mathbb{C}$. For example, a business idea is described by the state $p_o = 100i$. In other words, it is 100% imaginary.

To bring an idea from the imaginary into the real, you must work on it. We'll model the work done on the project as a multiplication by the complex number $e^{-i\alpha h}$, where h is the number of hours of work and α is a constant that depends on the project. After h hours of work, the initial state of the project is transformed as follows: $p_f = e^{-i\alpha h} p_o$. Working on the project for one hour "rotates" its state by $-\alpha$[rad], making it less imaginary and more real.

If you start from an idea $p_o = 100i$ and the cumulative number of hours invested after t weeks of working on the project is $h(t) = 0.2t^2$, how long will it take for the project to become 100% real? Assume $\alpha = 2.904 \times 10^{-3}$.
Hint: A project is 100% real if $\operatorname{Re}\{p\} = p$.

P3.14 A farmer with a passion for robotics has built a prototype of a robotic tractor. The tractor is programmed to move with a speed of 0.524[km/h] and follow the direction of the hour-hand on a conventional watch. Assume the tractor starts at 12:00 p.m. (noon) and is left to roam about in a field until 6:00 p.m. What is the shape of the trajectory that the tractor will follow? What is the total distance travelled by the tractor after six hours?

Chapter 4

Mechanics

4.1 Introduction

Mechanics is the precise study of the motion of objects, the forces acting on them, and more abstract concepts such as momentum and energy. You probably have an intuitive understanding of these concepts already. In this chapter we will learn how to use precise mathematical equations to support your intuition.

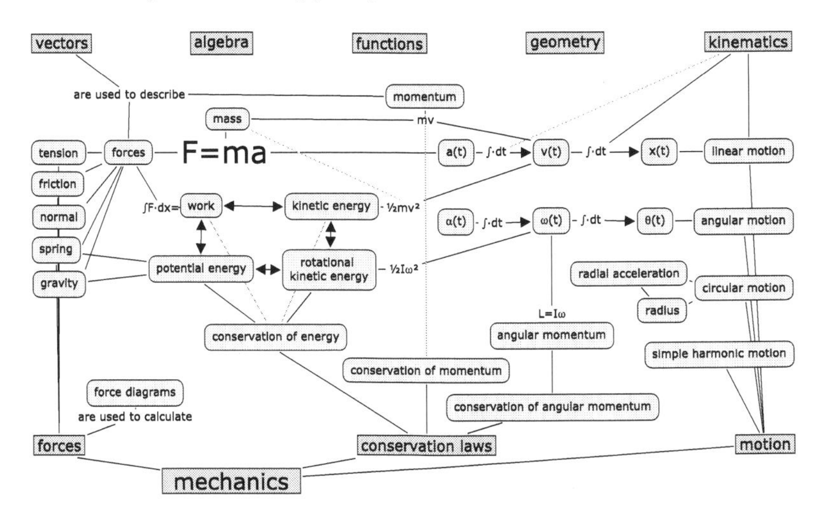

Figure 4.1: The concepts of mechanics. Forces are the cause of motion. We can also analyze the motion of objects in terms of the concepts of energy and momentum. If you understand the connections between all of the above concepts, you understand mechanics.

Newton's laws

Mechanics is the part of physics that is easiest to understand. Starting from three general principles known as *Newton's laws*, we can figure out pretty much everything about the motion of objects.

Newton's three laws of motion:

1. In the absence of external forces, objects will maintain their velocity and their direction of motion.
2. A force acting on an object causes an acceleration inversely proportional to the mass of the object: $\vec{F} = m\vec{a}$.
3. For each force $\vec{F}_{12}$ applied by Object 1 on Object 2, there is an equal and opposite force $\vec{F}_{21}$ that Object 2 exerts on Object 1.

The cool part of learning physics is that it teaches us to think about the laws of nature in terms of simple principles. Complicated phenomena can be broken down and understood in terms of basic theories. The laws of physics can be expressed in terms of mathematical equations. There are about 20 such equations (see page 484 in the back of the book). In this chapter you will learn how to use these equations to solve all kinds of physics problems.

Kinematics is the study of motion

To solve a physics problem is to obtain the *equation of motion* $x(t)$, which describes the position of the object as a function of time. Once you know $x(t)$, you can answer any question pertaining to the object's motion. To find the initial position x_i of the object, plug $t = 0$ into the equation of motion $x_i = x(0)$. To find the time(s) when the object reaches a certain distance, let's say 20[m] from the origin, solve for t in $x(t) = 20$[m]. Many of the problems on the mechanics final exam will be of this kind, so if you know how to find $x(t)$, you'll be in good shape to ace the exam.

In Chapter 2, we learned about the kinematics of objects moving in one dimension. More specifically, we used integration to obtain the velocity function of an object starting from the knowledge of its acceleration. Integrating the velocity function, we obtain its position function:

$$a(t) \quad \overset{v_i+\int dt}{\longrightarrow} \quad v(t) \quad \overset{x_i+\int dt}{\longrightarrow} \quad x(t).$$

Okay, but how do we obtain the acceleration?

Dynamics is the study of forces

The first step toward finding $x(t)$ is to calculate all the *forces* that act on the object. The forces are the *cause* of the object's acceleration. Newton's second law $F = ma$ states that **a force acting on an object produces an acceleration inversely proportional to the mass of the object**. There are many kinds of forces: the weight of an object $\vec{W}$ is a type of force, the force of friction $\vec{F}_f$ is another type of force, the tension in a rope $\vec{T}$ is yet another type of force, and so on. Note the little arrow on top of each force, which is there to remind you that forces are *vector quantities*. To find the *net force* acting on the object, calculate the sum of all the forces acting on the object $\vec{F}_{\text{net}} \equiv \sum \vec{F}$.

Once you know the net force, you can use the formula $\vec{a}(t) = \frac{\vec{F}_{\text{net}}}{m}$ to find the object's acceleration. Once you know the acceleration $a(t)$, you can compute $x(t)$ using the calculus steps we learned in Chapter 2. The entire procedure for predicting the motion of objects can be summarized as

$$\frac{1}{m}\underbrace{\left(\sum \vec{F} = \vec{F}_{\text{net}}\right)}_{\text{dynamics}} = \underbrace{a(t) \overset{v_i+\int dt}{\longrightarrow} v(t) \overset{x_i+\int dt}{\longrightarrow} x(t)}_{\text{kinematics}}.$$

If you understand the above equation, then you understand mechanics. The goal of this chapter is to introduce you to all the concepts that appear in this equation and explore the relationships between them.

Other stuff

In addition to dynamics and kinematics, this chapter covers a number of other physics topics.

Newton's second law can also be applied to the study of objects in rotation. Angular motion is described by the angle of rotation $\theta(t)$, the angular velocity $\omega(t)$, and the angular acceleration $\alpha(t)$. Angular acceleration is caused by angular force, which we call *torque* $\mathcal{T}$. The principles behind circular motion are almost exactly the same as the principles of linear motion; the only difference being we use *angular* quantities to describe circular motion—instead of describing the motion in terms of [m], [m/s], and [m/s^2], we describe angular motion in terms of [radians], [radians/s], and [radians/s^2].

During a collision between two objects, the sudden spike in the contact force between them can be difficult to measure and quantify. It is therefore not possible to use Newton's law $F = ma$ to find the accelerations of the objects occurring during collisions and predict the motion of the objects using the kinematics approach described above.

To predict the motion of objects after a collision, we can use a *momentum* calculation. An object of mass m moving with velocity $\vec{v}$ has momentum $\vec{p} \equiv m\vec{v}$. The principle of conservation of momentum states that **the total amount of momentum in a system before and after a collision is conserved**. Thus, if two objects with initial momenta $\vec{p}_{i1}$ and $\vec{p}_{i2}$ collide, the total momentum before the collision must be equal to the total momentum after the collision:

$$\sum \vec{p}_i = \sum \vec{p}_f \qquad \Rightarrow \qquad \vec{p}_{i1} + \vec{p}_{i2} = \vec{p}_{f1} + \vec{p}_{f2}.$$

We use this equation to calculate the final momenta $\vec{p}_{f1}$, $\vec{p}_{f2}$ of the objects after the collision.

There is another way to solve physics problems by applying the concept of *energy*. Instead of trying to describe the entire motion of the object, we can focus only on the initial parameters and the final parameters of an object's movement. The law of conservation of energy states that **the total energy of the system is conserved**:

$$\sum E_i = \sum E_f.$$

By knowing the total initial energy of a system, we can find the final energy in the system, and from the final energy we can calculate the final motion parameters.

Units

In math we work with numbers—we solve questions where the answers are numbers without dimensions like 3, 5 or 12.34. The universal power of math comes precisely from this abstraction of things into numbers. We could be solving for the number of sheep in a pen, the surface area of a sphere, or the annual revenue of your startup; we can apply the same mathematical techniques to each example, even though the numbers we use will represent very different kinds of quantities.

Because physics deals with real-world concepts and quantities, each number in physics always comes with a *measurement unit*. We must pay attention to the units of physical quantities and—most importantly—distinguish between the different *dimensions* of numerical quantities. An answer in physics is a number that represents a length, a time, a velocity, an acceleration, or some other physical quantity. It doesn't make sense to add a *time* and a *mass*, because the two numbers measure different kinds of quantities.

Here's a list of some kinds of quantities discussed in this chapter:

Dimension	SI unit	Other units	Measured with
time	[s]	[h], [min]	clock
length	[m]	[cm], [mm], [ft], [in]	metre tape
velocity	[m/s]	[km/h], [mi/h]	speedometer
acceleration	[m/s^2]		accelerometer
mass	[kg]	[g], [lb]	scale

Appendix C (see page 452 in the back of the book) provides a more detailed list of the International System of Units (abbreviated SI for *Système International*).

The units of physical quantities are indicated in square brackets throughout the lessons of this chapter. In your equations, you should always try to keep in mind the units for different physics quantities. Sometimes you'll be able to catch yourself making an error because the units will not come out right. If I ask you to calculate the maximum height a ball will reach, I expect your answer to be a length measured in [m] and not some other kind of quantity like a velocity [m/s] or an acceleration [m/s^2] or an area [m^2]. An answer in [ft] would also be acceptable since this is also a length, and it can be converted to metres using $1[\text{ft}] = 0.3048[\text{m}]$ (see page 453 for other conversion ratios). Learn to watch out for the units and dimensions of physical quantities, and you'll have an easy time in physics. They are an excellent error-checking mechanism.

We'll begin our physics journey by starting with the familiar subject of kinematics which we studied in Chapter 2. Now that you know about vectors, we can study two-dimensional kinematics problems, such as the motion of a projectile.

4.2 Projectile motion

Ever since the invention of gun powder, generation after generation of men have thought of countless different ways to hurtle shrapnel at each other. Indeed, mankind has been stuck to the idea of two-dimensional projectile motion like flies on shit. As long as there is money to be made in selling weapons, and so long as the media continues to justify the legitimacy of the use of these weapons, it is likely the trend will continue.

It is therefore imperative for anyone interested in reversing this trend to learn about the physics of projectile motion. You need to know the techniques of the enemy (the industrial military complex) before you can fight them. We'll see that projectile motion is nothing more than a pair of parallel one-dimensional kinematics problems: UVM in the x-direction and UAM in the y-direction.

Concepts

The basic concepts of kinematics in two dimensions are:

- $\hat{x}, \hat{y}$: the xy-coordinate system
- t: time, measured in seconds
- $\vec{r}(t) \equiv (x(t), y(t))$: the position vector of the object at time t
- $\vec{v}(t) \equiv (v_x(t), v_y(t))$: the velocity vector of the object
- $\vec{a}(t) \equiv (a_x(t), a_y(t))$: the acceleration vector of the object

We will use the following terminology when analyzing the motion of an object that starts from an *initial* position and travels to a *final* position:

- $t_i = 0$: the initial time
- t_f: the final time
- $\vec{v}_i = (v_x(0), v_y(0)) = (v_{ix}, v_{iy})$: the initial velocity at $t = 0$
- $\vec{r}_i = (x(0), y(0)) = (x_i, y_i)$: the initial position at $t = 0$
- $\vec{r}_f = \vec{r}(t_f) = (x(t_f), y(t_f)) = (x_f, y_f)$: the position at $t = t_f$

Definitions

Motion in two dimensions

We use the position vector $\vec{r}(t)$ to describe the x and y coordinates of the projectile as a function of time:

$$\vec{r}(t) \equiv (x(t), y(t)).$$

We use x to describe the horizontal distance travelled by the projectile and y to describe the height of the projectile.

The velocity of the projectile is the derivative of its position:

$$\vec{v}(t) = \frac{d}{dt}(\vec{r}(t)) = \left(\frac{dx(t)}{dt}, \frac{dy(t)}{dt}\right) = (v_x(t), v_y(t)).$$

The initial velocity is an important parameter of the motion:

$$\vec{v}(0) = (v_x(0), v_y(0)) = (v_{ix}, v_{iy}) = (\|\vec{v}_i\| \cos\theta, \|\vec{v}_i\| \sin\theta) = \|\vec{v}_i\| \angle\theta.$$

The initial velocity vector can be expressed as components (v_{ix}, v_{iy}), or in the length-and-direction form $\|\vec{v}_i\| \angle\theta$, where θ measures the angle between $\vec{v}_i$ and the x-axis.

On Earth, the acceleration of the projectile is

$$\vec{a}(t) = \frac{d}{dt}\left(\vec{v}(t)\right) = (a_x(t), a_y(t)) = (0, -9.81).$$

We know the exact value of the object's acceleration in both the x-direction and the y-direction. There is zero acceleration in the x-direction because there are no horizontal forces acting on the projectile (we ignore the effects of air friction). In the y-direction we have a uniform downward acceleration due to gravity.

Projectile motion

The motion of a projectile can be described by two sets of equations.

In the x-direction, the motion is described by the uniform velocity motion (UVM) equations of motion:

$$x(t) = v_{ix}t + x_i, \tag{4.1}$$

$$v_x(t) = v_{ix}. \tag{4.2}$$

We use the UVM equations of motion for $x(t)$ and $v_x(t)$ because there are no horizontal forces acting on the object, and by extension the object experiences zero acceleration in the x-direction: $a_x = 0$.

In the y-direction, the constant, downward pull of gravity produces uniformly accelerated motion (UAM). The equations of motion in the y-direction are

$$y(t) = \tfrac{1}{2}(-9.81)t^2 + v_{iy}t + y_i, \tag{4.3}$$

$$v_y(t) = (-9.81)t + v_{iy}, \tag{4.4}$$

$$v_{yf}^2 = v_{iy}^2 + 2(-9.81)(\Delta y). \tag{4.5}$$

The equations in the y-direction correspond to the standard UAM equations with $a = -9.81[\text{m/s}^2]$.

Example

In this example, we'll analyze all aspects of the motion of a projectile shown in Figure 4.2. An object is thrown from an initial height of 1[m], with initial velocity of 8.96[m/s] at an angle of 51.3° to the ground. Calculate the maximum height h the object will reach, and the distance d where the object will hit the ground.

Our first step when reading any physics problem is to extract all quantitative information from the problem statement. The object's initial position is $\vec{r}(0) = (x_i, y_i) = (0, 1)[\text{m}]$. Its initial velocity is $\vec{v}_i = 8.96\angle 51.3°[\text{m/s}]$, which is $\vec{v}_i = (8.96\cos 51.3°, 8.96\sin 51.3°) = (5.6, 7)[\text{m/s}]$ in component form.

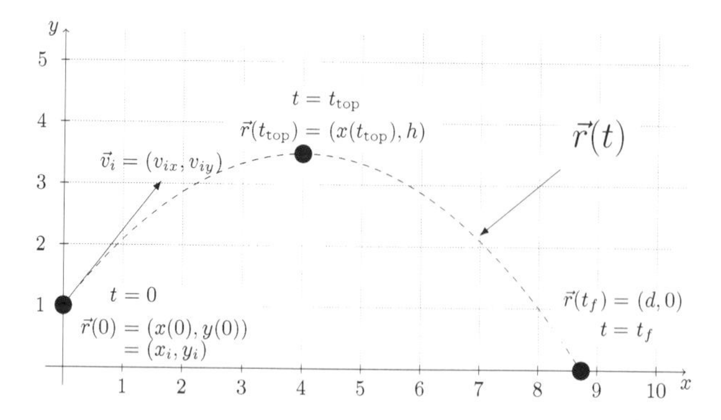

Figure 4.2: The trajectory of a projectile that starts at $\vec{r}_i = (0, 1)$[m] with initial velocity $\vec{v}_i = 8.96\angle 51.3°$[m/s], rises to a maximum height of $h = 3.5$[m], then hits the ground at a distance of $d = 8.68$[m] from the origin.

Next, plug the values of $\vec{r}_i = (0, 1)$[m] and $\vec{v}_i = (5.6, 7)$[m/s] into the equations of motion for the x and y directions:

$$x(t) = 5.6t + 0, \qquad y(t) = \tfrac{1}{2}(-9.81)t^2 + 7t + 1,$$
$$v_x(t) = 5.6, \qquad v_y(t) = (-9.81)t + 7.$$

When the object reaches its maximum height, it will have zero velocity in the y-direction: $v_y(t_{\text{top}}) = 0$. We can use this fact along with the $v_y(t)$ equation to find $t_{\text{top}} = 7/9.81 = 0.714$[s]. The maximum height is then obtained by evaluating the function $y(t)$ at $t = t_{\text{top}}$. We obtain $h = y(t_{\text{top}}) = \frac{1}{2}(-9.81)(0.714)^2 + 7(0.714) + 1 = 3.5$[m].

To find d, we must find the time t_f when the object hits the ground. We can find t_f by solving the quadratic equation $0 = y(t_f) = \frac{1}{2}(-9.81)(t_f)^2 + 7(t_f) + 1$. The solution is $t_f = 1.55$[s]. We then plug this time value into the equation for $x(t)$ to find $d = x(t_f) = 5.6(1.55) + 0 = 8.68$[m]. Can you verify that these answers match the trajectory illustrated in the figure?

Explanations

Coordinate system

Before you begin solving any projectile motion problem, you should make a diagram of what is going on. In your diagram, be sure to clearly indicate the coordinate system with respect to which you'll measure x, y, v_x, and v_y. The values you plug into the equations of motion are measured with respect to this coordinate system; for example, a velocity v_x in the opposite direction of the x-axis is represented as a negative number.

Uniform velocity motion in the x-direction

Ignoring the effects of air friction means there are no forces and no acceleration in the x-direction, so $a_x = 0$. As a consequence, the velocity will be constant. Constant velocity means the projectile will keep whatever x-velocity you give it when you throw it. Therefore the UVM equations describe the projectile's motion in the x-direction:

$$\begin{aligned} a_x(t) &= 0\,, \\ v_x(t) &= v_{ix}\,, \\ x(t) &= v_{ix}t + x_i\,. \end{aligned}$$

Uniform acceleration motion in the y-direction

The pull of gravity acts in the negative y-direction. Gravity is a constant downward acceleration equal to $g = 9.81[\text{m/s}^2]$. The motion in the y-direction is therefore described by the UAM equations with acceleration $a_y = -g = -9.81[\text{m/s}^2]$:

$$\begin{aligned} a_y(t) &= -g\,, \\ v_y(t) &= (-g)t + v_{iy}\,, \\ y(t) &= \tfrac{1}{2}(-g)t^2 + v_{iy}t + y_i\,. \end{aligned}$$

We can combine the equations for $v_y(t)$ and $y(t)$ to obtain a fourth equation of motion:

$$v_{fy}^2 = v_{iy}^2 + 2(-g)(\Delta y),$$

which relates the object's final velocity to its initial velocity and its displacement in the y-direction, $\Delta y = y_f - y_i$.

Examples

Roach throw

You are sitting comfortably on a bench in the park and you have a small piece of garbage in your hand. Not far from you is a garbage bin. Since you're feeling lazy and relaxed, you can't be bothered to walk to the bin and dispose of said garbage particle, so you decide to throw it into the bin from where you are sitting. Let's call the garbage particle r for short. Imagine a coordinate system centred below your feet. The point $(0, 0)$ is where you are sitting, and the point $(x = 0, y = 1.4)$[m] is the initial position of the particle r as you prepare to throw it.

Suppose the distance to the garbage bin is 3 metres and the bin is 1 metre tall. Can you calculate the initial velocity $\vec{v}_i$ the particle r needs in order to land in the garbage bin? Assume you flick the particle from your fingers so it flies straight along the x-axis; in other words, you do not give the particle any initial y-velocity so $v_{iy} = 0$.

To describe the motion of r, all you need to know is the initial position $\vec{r}(0) = (x(0), y(0))$, and the initial velocity $\vec{v}_i = \vec{v}(0) = (v_x(0), v_y(0))$. You can then plug these values into the projectile equations of motion:

$$x(t) = v_{ix}t + x_i,$$
$$y(t) = \tfrac{1}{2}a_y t^2 + v_{iy}t + y_i.$$

Most physics word problems will follow this pattern. The problem statement gives you some information about the initial conditions and the desired final conditions, and asks you to solve for the *unknown*—the one variable that is not given in the problem statement.

Can you carry out the necessary calculations in this case? I don't mean to stress you out, but sitting next to you is your 110[kg] pure-muscle Chilean friend who has two kids and *really* gets pissed off at people who throw garbage around in the park. You don't want to piss him off so you better get that initial velocity right!

Okay, from here we can switch into high gear because we have everything set up nicely. We know the general equations of motion for UVM in x and UAM in y are

$$x(t) = v_{ix}t + x_i,$$
$$y(t) = \tfrac{1}{2}a_y t^2 + v_{iy}t + y_i\,.$$

More specifically, we know the y acceleration is due to gravity, so we have

$$x(t) = v_{ix}t + x_i,$$
$$y(t) = \tfrac{1}{2}(-9.81)t^2 + v_{iy}t + y_i\,.$$

We also know the position at $t = 0$ is $(x_i, y_i) = (0, 1.4)$[m], and that at some $t_f > 0$ the particle will be flying into the bin at $(x(t_f), y(t_f)) = (3, 1)$[m].

Substituting all the known quantities into the general equations, we obtain

$$x(t_f) = 3 = v_{ix}t_f + 0,$$
$$y(t_f) = 1 = \tfrac{1}{2}(-9.81)t_f^2 + v_{iy}t_f + 1.4\,.$$

Furthermore, as the problem specifies, we can assume the initial velocity of the projectile is purely horizontal ($v_{iy} = 0$). Thus, we must solve the pair of equations,

$$\begin{aligned} 3 &= v_{ix} t_f, \\ 1 &= 1.4 - 4.9 t_f^2, \end{aligned}$$

where v_{ix} and t_f are the two unknowns.

From this step, it should be clear where the story is going. First we solve for t_f in the second equation:

$$t_f = \sqrt{\frac{(1-1.4)}{-4.9}} = \sqrt{\frac{-0.4}{-4.9}} = \sqrt{4/49} = 2/7 \approx 0.2857[\text{s}].$$

We can now solve for v_{ix} in the first equation:

$$v_{ix} = \frac{3}{t_f} = \frac{3 \cdot 7}{2} = \frac{21}{2} = 10.5[\text{m/s}].$$

You flick r with your finger at an initial velocity of $\vec{v}_i = (10.5, 0)[\text{m/s}]$ and it flies straight into the garbage bin. Success!

Freedom and democracy

An American F-18 is flying above Iraq. It is carrying two bombs. One bomb is named "freedom" and weighs 200[kg]; the other is called "democracy" and weighs 500[kg]. If the plane is flying horizontally with speed $v_i = 300[\text{m/s}]$ and drops both bombs from a height of 2000[m], how far will each bomb travel horizontally before it hits the ground? Which city will get freedom and which city will get democracy?

The equations of motion for the bombs are

$$x(t) = v_{ix} t + x_i = 300t + 0$$

and

$$y(t) = \tfrac{1}{2}(-9.81)t^2 + v_{iy} t + y_i = -4.9t^2 + 2000.$$

To find where the bombs will land, the first step is to calculate the time of flight. We solve for t_f in the equation $y(t_f) = 0$ and find $t_f = 20.20[\text{s}]$. We can then find the final x-position where the bombs hit the ground from the first equation: $x_f = x(20.20) = 6060[\text{m}]$. Both bombs hit the point located 6.06[km] from the launch point. Observe that the bombs' masses did not play any part in the equations of motion.

Let's be real. The scenario at hand is essentially what the people in Washington are talking about when they say they are bringing freedom and democracy to the Middle East. A monstrous amalgamation of warmongering corporations, weak politicians, and special-interest lobby groups make a complete mockery of the political process. In order to see an end to world conflict, I think the entire military-industrial complex needs to be dismantled. How can we stop them, you ask? In my opinion, the best way to fight the System is not to work for the System. If some recruiters from that sector comes to offer you a job one day because you're a math expert, tell them to scram.

Interception

With all those people launching explosive projectiles at each other, a need develops for *interception* systems that can throw counter-projectiles at the incoming projectiles and knock them out of the air.

Let's see how we can intercept an incoming ball (A) launched from $\vec{r}_{Ai} = (0,3)$ with initial velocity $\vec{v}_{Ai} = (8\cos(40), 8\sin(40))$. As an interception device, you have at your disposal a ball launcher placed at $\vec{r}_{Bi} = (10,0)$ with a fixed firing angle of 50°. You position the launcher so it faces the incoming ball as illustrated in Figure 4.3.

The launcher has a variable launch speed w[m/s], which you can choose. You want to fire an intercepting ball, which will have an initial velocity $\vec{v}_{Bi} = (-w\cos(50), w\sin(50))$, so it intercepts the ball (A) in midair. What initial velocity w is required for the balls to hit each other? At which time t will the collision occur?

As far as kinematics is concerned, this is a standard projectile motion problem **times two**. You have ball (A), which has the equations of motion,

$$
\begin{aligned}
x_A(t) &= v_{Aix}t + x_{Ai} = 8\cos(40)t + 0, \\
y_A(t) &= \tfrac{1}{2}(-9.81)t^2 + v_{Aiy}t + y_{Ai} = -4.9t^2 + 8\sin(40)t + 3.
\end{aligned}
$$

You also have ball (B), which has the equations of motion,

$$
\begin{aligned}
x_B(t) &= v_{Bix}t + x_{Bi} = -w\cos(50)t + 10, \\
y_B(t) &= \tfrac{1}{2}(-9.81)t^2 + v_{Biy}t + y_{Bi} = -4.9t^2 + w\sin(50)t + 0.
\end{aligned}
$$

We want the balls to collide, so at some point they will have the same coordinates $\vec{r}_A = \vec{r}_B$, which is another way of saying

$$
(x_A(t), y_A(t)) = (x_B(t), y_B(t)).
$$

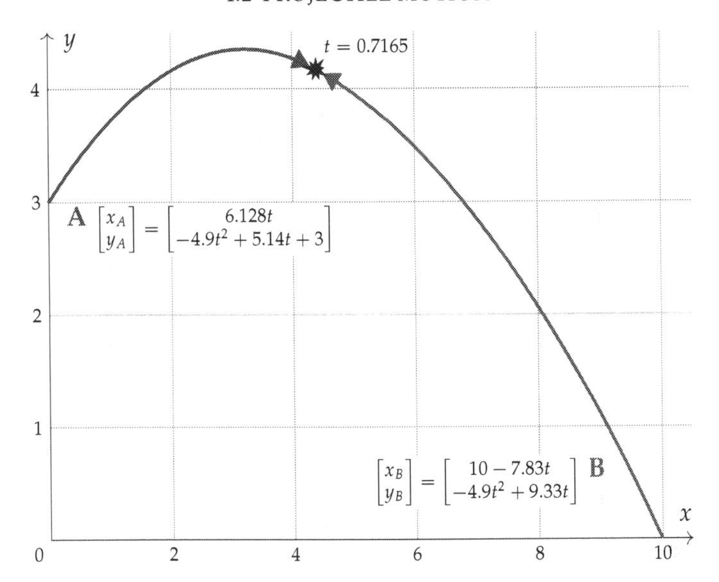

Figure 4.3: The incoming ball (A) is intercepted by the ball (B) coming from the right. The collision occurs at $t = 0.7165$[s].

The x-coordinates must match, and the y-coordinates must match. We express these conditions through the following two equations:

$$\begin{aligned} 8\cos(40)t + 0 &= -w\cos(50)t + 10, \\ -4.9t^2 + 8\sin(40)t + 3 &= -4.9t^2 + w\sin(50)t + 0, \end{aligned}$$

which we must solve simultaneously.

To solve, we cancel $-4.9t^2$ on both sides of the bottom equation:

$$\begin{aligned} 8\cos(40)t &= -w\cos(50)t + 10, \\ 8\sin(40)t + 3 &= w\sin(50)t. \end{aligned}$$

This is a set of two equations with two unknowns, and we can solve it. It's not going to be easy, since we can't cleanly isolate t or w using standard substitution techniques. However, there is a trick! We can divide the two equations. If $A = B$ and $C = D \neq 0$ then $A/C = B/D$, and this is what we'll use. To prepare for this step, let's rearrange the equations a bit so all the w-containing terms stand alone on the right side:

$$\begin{aligned} 10 - 8\cos(40)t &= w\cos(50)t, \\ 8\sin(40)t + 3 &= w\sin(50)t. \end{aligned}$$

We'll now divide the bottom equation by the top equation to obtain

$$\frac{8\sin(40)t + 3}{10 - 8\cos(40)t} = \frac{w\sin(50)t}{w\cos(50)t} = \tan(50).$$

Rearranging the expression, we find

$$8\sin(40)t + 3 = \tan(50)(10 - 8\cos(40)t).$$

Collect all the t terms to one side to obtain

$$[8\sin(40) + 8\cos(40)\tan(50)]t = 10\tan(50) - 3,$$

and finally

$$t = \frac{10\tan(50) - 3}{8\sin(40) + 8\cos(40)\tan(50)} = 0.7165[\text{s}].$$

We can now plug values into any of the above equations to find the value of w. For example, try plugging the value of $t = 0.7165[\text{s}]$ into

$$10 - 8\cos(40)t = w\cos(50)t$$

to find

$$10 - 8\cos(40)(0.7165) = w\cos(50)(0.7165),$$

which leads to $w = \frac{10-8\cos(40)(0.7165)}{\cos(50)(0.7165)} = 12.1788\ [\text{m/s}]$.

Let's check this answer. If we substitute $w = 12.1788[\text{m/s}]$ into the equations of motion and plot the two trajectories on the computer we obtain the graph shown in Figure 4.3. As you can see, the trajectories intersect at time $t = 0.7165[\text{s}]$ as expected.

Discussion

I want to point out that you need no new physics information to understand the motion of projectiles. Projectile motion is a two-dimensional kinematics problem that can be broken down into two parts: the x-direction (described by the UVM equations) and the y-direction (described by the UAM equations).

Links

[Pres. Eisenhower's warning about the military-industrial complex]

> *"Only an alert and knowledgeable citizenry can compel the proper meshing of the huge industrial and military machinery of defence with our peaceful methods and goals."*

`http://www.youtube.com/watch?v=8y06NSBBRtY`

4.3 Forces

Like a shepherd who brings back stray sheep, we need to rescue the word *force* and give it precise meaning. In physics, force means something very specific. I'm not talking about "the force" from Star Wars, nor the "force of public opinion," nor the "*force* in the battle of good versus evil."

In physics, force refers to an amount of push or pull exerted on an object. Forces are vector quantities measured in Newtons [N]. In this section, we'll explore all the different kinds of forces.

Concepts

- $\vec{F}$: a force. This is something the object "feels" as a pull or a push. Forces are vector quantities, so you must always keep in mind the direction in which they act.
- $k, G, m, \mu_s, \mu_k, \ldots$: parameters on which the force F may depend. For example, the heavier an object is (the larger the m parameter), the larger its gravitational pull will be. This relationship is expressed by the equation $\vec{W} = -9.81m\hat{\jmath}$, where $\hat{\jmath}$ points toward the sky.

Kinds of forces

Next, we'll review all the forces you're supposed to know for a standard mechanics class, and define the relevant parameters for each kind of force. You need to practice exercises using each of these forces, until you start to *feel* how they act.

Gravitation

The force of gravity exists between any two objects with mass. The magnitude of the gravitational force between two objects of mass M[kg] and m[kg] separated by a distance r[m] is given by the formula

$$F_g = \frac{GMm}{r^2}, \tag{4.6}$$

where $G = 6.67 \times 10^{-11}[\frac{\text{Nm}^2}{\text{kg}^2}]$ is the *gravitational constant*. This is one of Newton's biggest discoveries—the famous one-over-r-squared law of gravitation.

On the surface of the Earth, which has mass $M = 5.972 \times 10^{24}$[kg] and radius $r = 6.367 \times 10^{6}$[m], the force of gravity on an object of

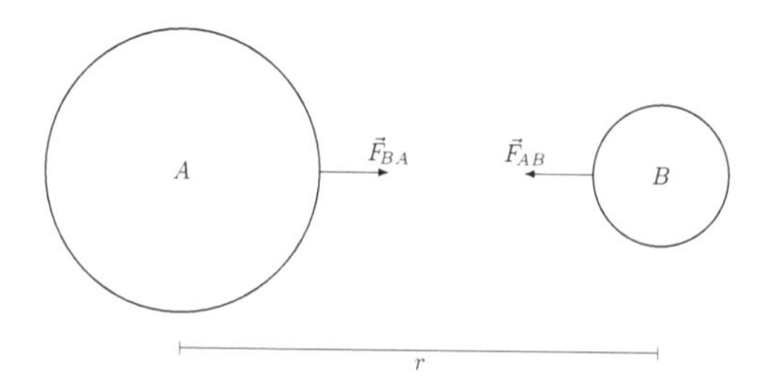

Figure 4.4: The gravitational force between two planets acts to pull them together. Assume Planet A has mass m_A and Planet B has mass m_B. The force vector $\vec{F}_{AB}$ describes "Planet A's pull on Planet B." The force vector $\vec{F}_{BA}$ describes "Planet B's pull on Planet A." The magnitude of the gravitational pull is $F_g = \frac{Gm_Am_B}{r^2} = \|\vec{F}_{AB}\| = \|\vec{F}_{BA}\|$.

mass m is given by

$$F_g = \frac{GMm}{r^2} = \underbrace{\frac{GM}{r^2}}_{g} m = 9.81m = W.$$

We call this force the *weight* of the object, and to be precise we write $\vec{W} = -mg\hat{\jmath}$ to indicate that the weight acts *downward*, in the negative y-direction. Verify using a calculator that $\frac{GM}{r^2} = 9.81 \equiv g$.

Force of a spring

A spring is a piece of metal twisted into a coil that has a certain natural length. The spring will resist any attempts to stretch or compress it. The force exerted by a spring is given by

$$\vec{F}_s = -kx,$$

where x is the amount by which the spring is displaced from its natural length, and the constant k[N/m] is a measure of the spring's *strength*. Note the negative sign indicates that the spring always acts to oppose the displacement.

If you try to stretch the spring, displacing it in the positive x-direction, then the force of the spring will pull against you (the spring will pull in the negative x-direction). Similarly, if you try to compress the spring (a displacement in the negative x-direction), the spring will push back against you, in the positive x-direction.

Normal force

The *normal* force is the force between two surfaces in contact. In this context, the word *normal* means "perpendicular to the surface of."

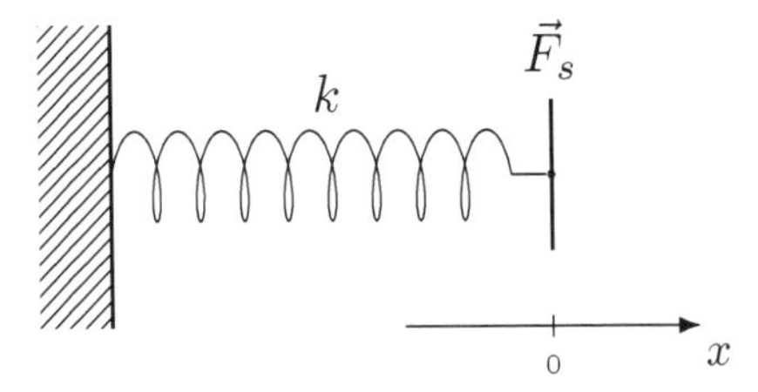

Figure 4.5: The force exerted by a spring is proportional to its displacement from its natural length, denoted x. When $x > 0$ the spring is stretched. When $x < 0$ the spring is compressed. When one end of the spring is fixed, the force exerted by the spring at the other end is $\vec{F}_s = -kx$.

The reason my coffee mug is not falling to the floor right now is that the table exerts a normal force $\vec{N}$ on the mug, keeping it in place.

Force of friction

In addition to the normal force between surfaces, there is also the force of friction $\vec{F}_f$, which acts to impede any sliding motion between the surfaces. There are two kinds of friction forces, and both are proportional to the amount of normal force between the surfaces:

$$\max\{\vec{F}_{fs}\} = \mu_s\|\vec{N}\| \text{ (static)}, \quad \text{and} \quad \vec{F}_{fk} = \mu_k\|\vec{N}\| \text{ (kinetic)},$$

where μ_s and μ_k are the static and kinetic *friction coefficients*. It makes sense that the force of friction should be proportional to the magnitude of the normal force $\|\vec{N}\|$, since the harder the two surfaces push against each other, the more difficult it becomes to make them slide. The above equations give mathematical precision to this intuitive logic.

The static force of friction acts on objects that are not moving. It describes the *maximum* amount of friction that can exist between two objects. If a horizontal force greater than $F_{fs} = \mu_s N$ is applied to the object, then it will start to slip. The kinetic force of friction acts when two objects are sliding relative to each other. It always acts in the direction opposite to the motion.

Tension

A force can also be exerted on an object remotely by attaching a rope to the object, and pulling the rope. The force exerted on the object will be equal to the rope's *tension* $\vec{T}$. Note that tension always pulls *away* from an object: you can pull but you can't push a dog by its leash.

Discussion

Viewing the interactions between objects in terms of the forces that act between them gives us a powerful tool for thinking and analyzing physics problems. The following section shows you how to draw force diagrams that account for all the forces acting on an object.

4.4 Force diagrams

Welcome to Force-Accounting 101. Here, we'll learn how to identify all the forces acting on an object and use Newton's 2nd law $\sum \vec{F} = \vec{F}_{\text{net}} = m\vec{a}$ to predict the resulting acceleration of the object.

Concepts

Newton's second law describes a relationship between three quantities:

- m: the *mass* of an object
- $\vec{F}_{\text{net}}$: the net force acting on the object
- $\vec{a}$: the *acceleration* of the object

Forces and accelerations are vectors. To work with vectors, we work with their *components*:

- F_x: the *component* of $\vec{F}$ in the x-direction
- F_y: the *component* of $\vec{F}$ in the y-direction

Vectors are meaningless unless it is clearly explained which *coordinate system* they are expressed in respect to.

- The x-axis: The x-axis is usually horizontal and points to the right. For problems with inclines, it will be more convenient to use an inclined x-axis that is parallel to the slope.
- The y-axis: The y-axis is always *perpendicular* to the x-axis.
- The $\hat{\imath}$ and $\hat{\jmath}$ vectors: These are unit vectors in the x and y directions, respectively. Any vector can be written as $\vec{v} = v_x\hat{\imath} + v_y\hat{\jmath}$ or as $\vec{v} = (v_x, v_y)$.

We can write any force vector in three equivalent ways:

$$\vec{F} \equiv F_x\hat{\imath} + F_y\hat{\jmath} \equiv (F_x, F_y) \equiv \|\vec{F}\|\angle\theta.$$

What types of forces are represented in force diagrams?

- $\vec{W} \equiv \vec{F}_g$: the force of gravity. The *weight* of an object is the force the object feels due to gravity. The gravitational pull always points downward, toward the centre of the Earth.
- $\vec{T}$: the tension in a rope. Tension always pulls *away* from the object.
- $\vec{N}$: the normal force. The normal force is part of the contact force between two surfaces.
- $\vec{F}_{fs} = \mu_s \|\vec{N}\|$: the static force of friction
- $\vec{F}_{fk} = \mu_k \|\vec{N}\|$: the kinetic force of friction
- $\vec{F}_s = -kx$: the force (pull or push) of a spring that is displaced (stretched or compressed) by x metres

Formulas

Newton's 2nd law

The net force $\vec{F}_{\text{net}}$ is the sum of the forces acting on an object. Assuming the object is rigid, the location where the forces act on the object is not important, so we can assume all forces act at the object's centre of mass.

The net force acting on an object, divided by the object's mass, gives the acceleration of the object:

$$\sum \vec{F} \equiv \vec{F}_{\text{net}} = m\vec{a}. \tag{4.7}$$

Vector components

If a vector $\vec{v}$ makes an angle θ with the x-axis, then

$$v_x = \|\vec{v}\| \cos\theta \qquad \text{and} \qquad v_y = \|\vec{v}\| \sin\theta.$$

The vector $v_x\hat{\imath}$ corresponds to the part of $\vec{v}$ that points in the x-direction.

Shortly, I'll be asking you over and over again to

find the component of $\vec{F}$ in the ? direction,

which is another way of asking you to find the number $v_?$.

The answer is usually equal to the length $\|\vec{F}\|$ multiplied by either cos or sin or sometimes -1, **depending on way the coordinate system is chosen**. So don't guess. Look at the coordinate system. If the vector points in the direction where x increases, then v_x should be a positive number. If $\vec{v}$ points in the opposite direction, then v_x should be negative.

To add forces $\vec{F}_1$ and $\vec{F}_2$, you need to add their components:

$$\vec{F}_1 + \vec{F}_2 = (F_{1x}, F_{1y}) + (F_{2x}, F_{2y}) = (F_{1x} + F_{2x}, F_{1y} + F_{2y}) = \vec{F}_{\text{net}}.$$

However, instead of dealing with vectors in the bracket notation, when solving force diagrams it is easier to simply write the x equation on one line, and the y equation on a separate line below it:

$$F_{\text{net},x} = F_{1x} + F_{2x},$$

$$F_{\text{net},y} = F_{1y} + F_{2y}.$$

It's a good idea to always write those two equations together as a block, so it's clear the first row represents the x dimension and the second row represents the y dimension for the same problem.

Force check

It is important to account for *all* the forces acting on an object. First of all, any object with mass on the surface of the Earth will feel a downward gravitational pull of magnitude $F_g = W = m\vec{g}$. Then you must consider whether any of the other forces are present: $\vec{T}$, $\vec{N}$, $\vec{F}_f$, and $\vec{F}_s$. Any time you see a rope tugging on the object, you can know there must be some tension $\vec{T}$, which is a force vector pulling on the object. Any time you have an object sitting on a surface, the surface pushes back with a *normal* force $\vec{N}$. If the object slides on the surface, then a force of friction acts against the direction of motion:

$$F_{fk} = \mu_k \|\vec{N}\|.$$

If the object is not moving, you must use the equation for the static force of friction. The maximum static friction force that the contact between the object and the ground can support before the object starts to slip is

$$\max\{F_{fs}\} = \mu_s \|\vec{N}\|.$$

If you see a spring that is either stretched or compressed by the object, then you must account for the spring force. The force of a spring is *restorative*; it always acts against the deformation you exert on the spring. If you stretch the spring by x[m], it will try to pull itself back to its normal length with a force of

$$\vec{F}_s = -kx\hat{\imath}.$$

The constant of proportionality k is called the *spring constant* and is measured in [N/m].

Solving force diagrams

We'll now explain how to solve dynamics problems. We'll first describe the general procedure in terms of a sequence of steps. Afterward, we'll illustrate how to use this procedure through a series of examples.

The steps for solving dynamics problems are as follows:

1. Draw a force diagram focused on the object, and indicate all the forces acting on the object.
2. Choose a coordinate system, and indicate clearly in the diagram what you are calling the positive x-direction, and what you are calling the positive y-direction. All quantities in the subsequent equations will be expressed *with respect to* this coordinate system.
3. Write the $\vec{F} = m\vec{a}$ template:

$$\sum F_x = \qquad\qquad\qquad = ma_x,$$
$$\sum F_y = \qquad\qquad\qquad = ma_y.$$

4. Fill in the template by calculating the x and y components of each force acting on the object ($\vec{W}$, $\vec{N}$, $\vec{T}$, $\vec{F}_{fs}$, $\vec{F}_{fk}$, $\vec{F}_s$, as applicable).
5. Solve the equations for the unknown quantities.

I highly recommend you perform some consistency checks after Step 4 by checking the sign of each force: if a force in the diagram is acting in the x-direction, then its component must be positive. If the force is acting in the direction opposite to the x-axis, then its component must be negative. You should also check to make sure that whenever $F_x = \|\vec{F}\| \cos\theta$, then $F_y = \|\vec{F}\| \sin\theta$. If, instead of θ, you use the angle ϕ defined with respect to the y-axis, then the roles of sin and cos will change: $F_x = \|\vec{F}\| \sin\phi$ and $F_y = \|\vec{F}\| \cos\phi$.

Examples

Block on a table

You place a block of mass m on the table. Since the block has mass m, its weight $\vec{W}$ pulls down on it, yet the table stops the block from dropping to the floor. The table pushes back on the block with a normal force $\vec{N}$.

Steps 1 and 2: Draw the force diagram and choose a coordinate system:

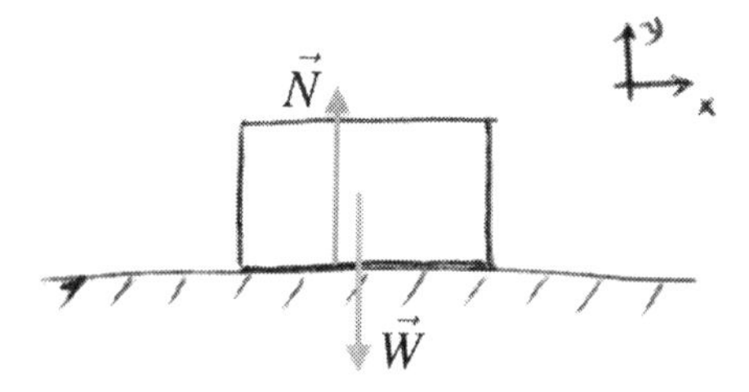

Figure 4.6: A block sitting on a table. The weight of the block $\vec{W}$ is counteracted by the normal force $\vec{N}$.

Step 3: Next, write the empty force diagram equations template:

$$\sum F_x = \qquad\qquad = ma_x,$$
$$\sum F_y = \qquad\qquad = ma_y.$$

Step 4: There are no forces acting in the x-direction, and the block is not moving, so $a_x = 0$. In the y-direction, we have the force of gravity and the normal force exerted by the table:

$$\sum F_x = 0 = 0,$$
$$\sum F_y = N - mg = 0.$$

We set $a_y = 0$, as we can *see* that the block is just sitting there on the table without moving. The technical term for situations where $a_x = 0, a_y = 0$ is called *static equilibrium*. Force diagrams with static equilibrium are easy to solve because the entire right-hand side is equal to zero, which means the forces acting on the object must be counter-balancing each other.

Step 5: Suppose the teacher now asks, "What is the magnitude of the normal force?" By looking at the second equation, you can answer, "$N = mg$ bro!"

Moving the fridge

You are trying to push your fridge across the kitchen floor. It weighs quite a lot, and is strongly "gripping" the floor when you try to push it. The static coefficient of friction between the bottom of your fridge and the tiles on the floor is μ_s. How much force $\vec{F}_{\text{ext}}$ will it take to cause the fridge to start moving?

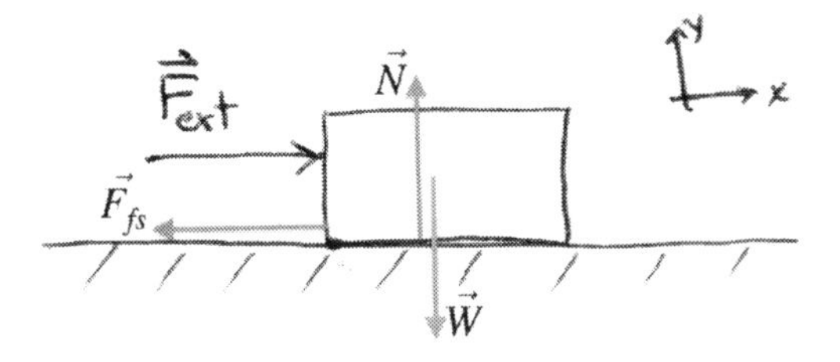

Figure 4.7: How hard do you need to push before the fridge starts to slip?

$$\sum F_x = F_{\text{ext}} - F_{fs} = 0,$$
$$\sum F_y = N - mg = 0.$$

If you push with a force of $F_{\text{ext}} = 30[\text{N}]$, the fridge will push back via its connection to the floor with a force $F_{fs} = 30[\text{N}]$. If you push harder, the fridge will push back harder and it still will not move. Only when you reach the slipping threshold will the fridge move. This means you'll need to push with a force equal to the *maximum* static friction force $F_{fs} = \mu_s N$, so we have

$$\sum F_x = F_{\text{ext}} - \mu_s N = 0,$$
$$\sum F_y = N - mg = 0.$$

To solve for F_{ext}, look at the bottom equation, isolate $N = mg$, then substitute the value of N in the top equation to find $F_{\text{ext}} = \mu_s mg$.

Friction slowing you down

Okay, now you're moving the fridge at a steady pace across the room. The forces acting on the fridge are illustrated in Figure 4.8.

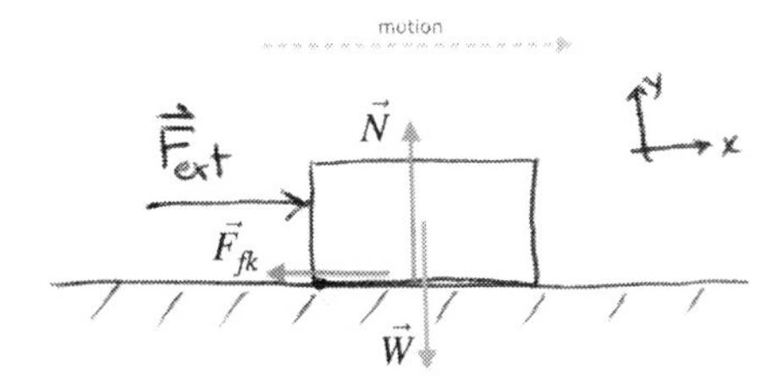

Figure 4.8: The fridge is moving. What is the magnitude of the external force $\vec{F}_{\text{ext}}$ required to counterbalance the kinetic force of friction?

Your equation of motion is expressed as

$$\sum F_x = F_{\text{ext}} - F_{fk} = ma_x,$$
$$\sum F_y = N - mg = 0.$$

In particular, if you want to keep a steady speed (v = const) as you move the fridge across the room, you'll need to push the fridge with a force that exactly balances the friction force and keeps $a_x = 0$.

To find the value of F_{ext} that allows you to keep a constant speed, solve

$$\sum F_x = F_{\text{ext}} - \mu_k N = 0,$$
$$\sum F_y = N - mg = 0.$$

The above set of equations are similar to the equations we obtained for the fridge that was not moving. The only difference is the kinetic coefficient of friction μ_k replaces the static coefficient of friction μ_s. Keeping the fridge moving with a constant velocity requires an external force $F_{\text{ext}} = \mu_k mg$. Generally, $\mu_k < \mu_s$, so less force is needed to keep the fridge moving than is needed to start the fridge moving.

Let's approach this whole friction thing from a different slant.

Incline

At this point, my dear readers, we're delving into the crucial question that you will—without a doubt—be asked to solve in your homework or at the final exam. A block is sliding down an incline as in Figure 4.9. What is its acceleration?

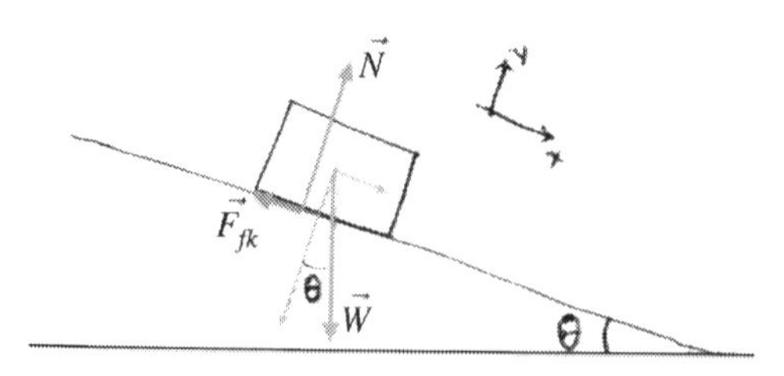

Figure 4.9: A block sliding down an incline with angle θ. What is the block's acceleration?

Step 1: Draw a diagram that includes the block's weight $\vec{W}$, the normal force $\vec{N}$, and the friction force $\vec{F}_{fk}$.

Step 2: Choose the coordinate system to be tilted along the incline. This is important because, in this coordinate system, the block's motion is purely in the x-direction, while the y-direction remains static.

Steps 3 and 4: Let's copy the empty template and fill in the equations:

$$\sum F_x = \|\vec{W}\| \sin\theta - F_{fk} = ma_x,$$
$$\sum F_y = N - \|\vec{W}\| \cos\theta \quad = 0;$$

or, substituting the values that we know,

$$\sum F_x = mg\sin\theta - \mu_k N = ma_x,$$
$$\sum F_y = N - mg\cos\theta \quad = 0.$$

Step 5: From the y equation, we obtain $N = mg\cos\theta$, which we substitute into the x equation to obtain

$$a_x = \frac{1}{m}(mg\sin\theta - \mu_k mg\cos\theta) = g\sin\theta - \mu_k g\cos\theta.$$

Bathroom scale

You have a spring in your bathroom scale with spring constant k, on which you place a block of mass m. By what length Δy will the spring be compressed?

Step 1, 2: Draw a before and after picture with the y-axis placed at the *natural* length of the spring.

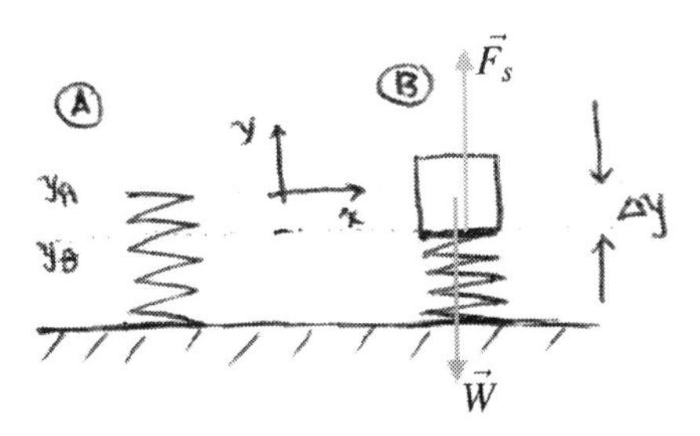

Figure 4.10: A bathroom scale is compressed by a distance Δy when an object of mass m is placed on it.

Steps 3 and 4: Filling in the template, we find

$$\sum F_x = 0 = 0,$$
$$\sum F_y = F_s - mg = 0.$$

Step 5: We know the force exerted by a spring is proportional to its displacement according to

$$F_s = -ky_B,$$

so we can find $y_B = -\frac{mg}{k}$. The length of compression is therefore

$$|\Delta y| = \frac{mg}{k}.$$

Two blocks

Now you're ready for a more involved example with two blocks. One block is sitting on a surface, and the other block is falling straight down. The two blocks are connected by a rope. What is the acceleration of the *system* as a whole?

Steps 1 and 2: We have two objects, so we need to draw two force diagrams.

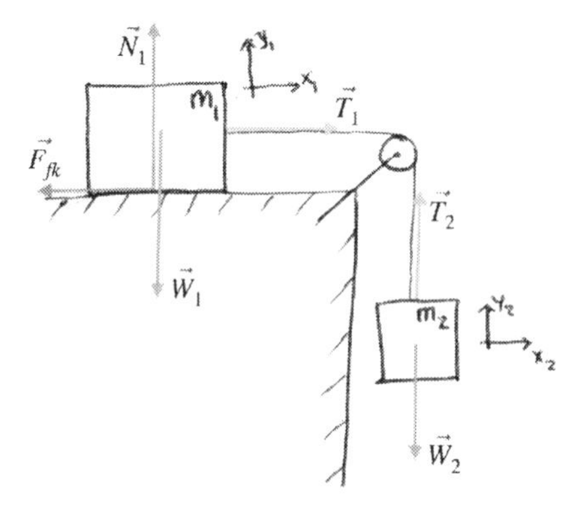

Figure 4.11: A block of mass m_1 is dragged along horizontally by a second block of mass m_2 which is falling vertically. What is the acceleration of the system?

Step 3: We need two sets of equations; one set for the block on the horizontal surface, and one set for the falling block:

$$\sum F_{1x} = \quad = m_1 a_{x_1} \qquad \sum F_{2x} = \quad = m_2 a_{x_2}$$
$$\sum F_{1y} = \quad = m_1 a_{y_1} \qquad \sum F_{2y} = \quad = m_2 a_{y_2}$$

Step 4: We fill in the equations with all the forces drawn in the diagram:

$$\sum F_{1x} = -F_{fk} + T_1 = m_1 a_{x_1} \qquad \sum F_{2x} = 0 = 0$$
$$\sum F_{1y} = N_1 - W_1 = 0 \qquad \sum F_{2y} = -W_2 + T_2 = m_2 a_{y_2}$$

Step 5: What connections exist between the two blocks? Since the blocks are connected by the rope, the tension in the rope is equal on both ends, and $T_1 = T_2 = T$. Also, since the rope is a fixed length, the x_1 and y_2 coordinates are related by a constant (though they point in different directions), so it must be that $a_{x_1} = -a_{y_2} = a$.

We'll rewrite the equations in terms of the new *common* variables T and a:

$$\sum F_{1x} = -\mu_k N_1 + T = m_1 a \qquad \sum F_{2x} = 0 = 0$$
$$\sum F_{1y} = N_1 - m_1 g = 0 \qquad \sum F_{2y} = -m_2 g + T = -m_2 a$$

Isolate N_1 on the bottom left, and isolate T on the bottom right:

$$\sum F_{1x} = -\mu_k N_1 + T = m_1 a \qquad \sum F_{2x} = 0 = 0$$
$$N_1 = m_1 g \qquad T = -m_2 a + m_2 g$$

Substitute the values of N_1 and T into the top left equation:

$$\sum F_{1x} = -\mu_k(m_1 g) + (-m_2 a + m_2 g) = m_1 a.$$

Moving all terms containing a to the right-hand side gives

$$-\mu_k m_1 g + m_2 g = m_1 a + m_2 a = (m_1 + m_2)a.$$

This makes sense if you think about it: two blocks attached with a rope form a single system of collective mass $(m_1 + m_2)$ with two external forces acting on it. From this point of view, the tension T is an *internal* force of the system, so it does not appear in the external force equation.

The acceleration of the whole two-block system is

$$a = \frac{m_2 g - \mu_k m_1 g}{m_1 + m_2}.$$

Two inclines

Two inclines? Things just got crazy! We have two inclines, two blocks, a rope, and friction everywhere. As usual, we want to find the acceleration of the system.

Steps 1 and 2: Draw a force diagram with two different coordinate systems, each system adapted for the angle of the incline:

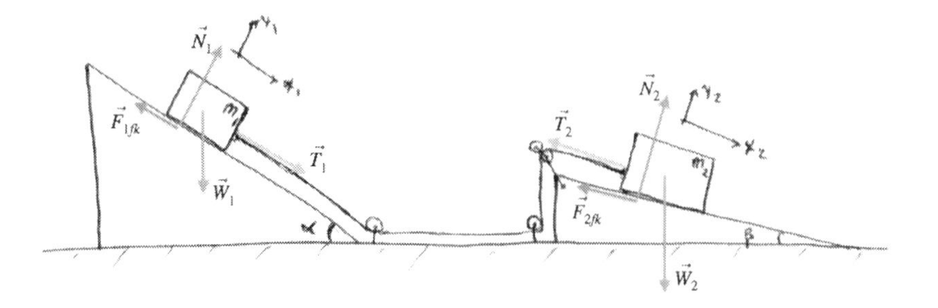

Steps 3 and 4: Make two copies of the template, fill in known forces, and set $a_{y_1} = 0$ and $a_{y_2} = 0$:

$$\sum F_{1x} = W_1 \sin\alpha - F_{1fk} + T_1 = m_1 a_{x_1},$$
$$\sum F_{1y} = -W_1 \cos\alpha + N_1 \qquad = 0,$$
$$\sum F_{2x} = W_2 \sin\beta - F_{2fk} - T_2 = m_2 a_{x_2},$$
$$\sum F_{2y} = -W_2 \cos\beta + N_2 \qquad = 0.$$

Before we continue with this problem, we must identify the connections between the two sets of equations. The tension in the rope is the same, which we will call $T = T_1 = T_2$. Also the two blocks must have the same acceleration since the blocks are moving together $a = a_{x_1} = a_{x_2}$.

Step 5: Rewriting the expression in terms of the common variables T and a, we obtain the new sets of equations:

$$\sum F_{1x} = m_1 g \sin\alpha - \mu_k N_1 + T = m_1 a,$$
$$N_1 = m_1 g \cos\alpha,$$
$$\sum F_{2x} = m_2 g \sin\beta - \mu_k N_2 - T = m_2 a,$$
$$N_2 = m_2 g \cos\beta.$$

Substitute the values of N_1 and N_2 into the x equations:

$$\sum F_{1x} = m_1 g \sin\alpha - \mu_k m_1 g \cos\alpha + T = m_1 a,$$
$$\sum F_{2x} = m_2 g \sin\beta - \mu_k m_2 g \cos\beta - T = m_2 a.$$

There are many ways to solve for the two unknowns in this pair of equations. We can isolate T in one of the equations, then substitute the value of T into the second equation. Another option is to isolate a in both equations, then set the equations equal to each other.

We'll use the first approach and isolate T in the bottom equation:

$$m_1 g \sin\alpha - \mu_k m_1 g \cos\alpha + T = m_1 a,$$
$$m_2 g \sin\beta - \mu_k m_2 g \cos\beta - m_2 a = T.$$

Finally, we'll substitute the expression for T into the top equation to obtain

$$m_1 g \sin\alpha - \mu_k m_1 g \cos\alpha + (m_2 g \sin\beta - \mu_k m_2 g \cos\beta - m_2 a) = m_1 a,$$

which can be rewritten as

$$m_1 g \sin\alpha - \mu_k m_1 g \cos\alpha + m_2 g \sin\beta - \mu_k m_2 g \cos\beta = (m_1 + m_2) a.$$

Since we know the values of m_1, m_2, μ_k, α, and β, we can calculate all the quantities on the left-hand side and solve for a. We thus obtain $a = \frac{m_1 g(\sin\alpha - \mu_k \cos\alpha) + m_2 g(\sin\beta - \mu_k \cos\beta)}{m_1 + m_2}$. Observe the final answer has the form $a = \frac{F_T}{m_T}$, where F_T is sum of forces acting on the system divided by the total mass of the system.

Other types of problems

Each of the previous examples asked you to find the acceleration, but sometimes a problem might give you the acceleration and ask you to solve for a different unknown. Regardless of what you must solve for, you should always start with a diagram and a sum-of-the-forces template. Once these equations are in front of you, you'll be able to reason through the problem more easily.

Experiment

You remove the spring from a retractable pen, and from the spring you suspend an object of known mass—say a 100[g] chocolate bar. With a ruler, you measure how much the spring stretches in the process. What is the spring constant k?

Discussion

In previous sections we discussed the *kinematics* problem of finding an object's position $x(t)$ given its acceleration function $a(t)$, and given the initial conditions x_i and v_i. In this section we studied the *dynamics* problem, which involves drawing force diagrams and calculating the net force acting on an object. Understanding these topics means you fully understand Newton's equation $F = ma$, which is perhaps the most important equation in this book.

We can summarize the entire procedure for predicting the position of an object $x(t)$ from first principles in the following equation:

$$\frac{1}{m}\underbrace{\left(\sum \vec{F} = \vec{F}_{\text{net}}\right)}_{\text{dynamics}} = \underbrace{\vec{a}(t) \overset{\vec{v}_i+\int dt}{\longrightarrow} \vec{v}(t) \overset{\vec{r}_i+\int dt}{\longrightarrow} \vec{r}(t)}_{\text{kinematics}}.$$

The left-hand side calculates the net force acting on an object, which is the *cause* of acceleration. The right-hand side indicates how we can calculate the position vector $\vec{r}(t)$ starting from the acceleration and the initial conditions. If you know the forces acting on any object (rocks, projectiles, cars, stars, planets, etc.) then you can predict the object's motion using this equation, which is pretty cool.

So far we discussed one approach for analyzing the motion of objects. Calculating the forces and the acceleration of objects, then using integration to find the position function $\vec{r}(t)$ is a very useful approach for solving physics problems. There are several other ways of looking at the motion of objects that are equally useful and provide us with different insights. In the next two sections, we'll discuss how to model physical situations in terms of momentum and energy.

4.5 Momentum

A collision between two objects creates a sudden spike in the contact force between them, which can be difficult to measure and quantify. It is not possible to use Newton's law $F = ma$ to predict the accelerations that occur during collisions. To predict the motion of the objects after the collision, we need a *momentum* calculation. According to the law of conservation of momentum, the total amount of momentum before and after the collision is the same. Once we know the momenta of the objects before the collision, it becomes possible to calculate their momenta after the collision, and from this determine their subsequent motion.

To illustrate the importance of momentum, consider the following situation. Say you have a 1[g] paper ball and a 1000[kg] car moving at the same speed of 100[km/h]. Which of the two objects would you rather be hit by? Momentum, denoted $\vec{p}$, is the precise physical concept that measures the *quantity* of motion. An object of mass m moving with velocity $\vec{v}$ has a momentum of $\vec{p} \equiv m\vec{v}$. Momentum plays a key role in collisions. Your gut feeling about the piece of paper and the car is correct. The car weighs $1000 \times 1000 = 10^6$ times more than the piece of paper, so the car has 10^6 times more momentum when moving at the same speed. Colliding with the car will "hurt" one-million times more than colliding with the piece of paper, even though both objects approach at the same velocity.

In this section, we'll learn how to use the law of conservation of momentum to predict the outcomes of collisions.

Concepts

- m: the *mass* of the moving object
- $\vec{v}$: the *velocity* of the moving object
- $\vec{p} = m\vec{v}$: the *momentum* of the moving object
- $\sum \vec{p}_{\text{in}}$: the sum of the momenta of particles before a collision
- $\sum \vec{p}_{\text{out}}$: the sum of the momenta of particles after a collision

Definition

The *momentum* of a moving object is equal to the velocity of the object multiplied by its mass:

$$\vec{p} = m\vec{v} \qquad [\text{kg m/s}]. \tag{4.8}$$

If an object's velocity is $\vec{v} = 20\hat{\imath} = (20, 0)$[m/s] and its mass is 100[kg], then its momentum is $\vec{p} = 2000\hat{\imath} = (2000, 0)$[kg m/s].

Momentum is a vector quantity, and we will often need to convert momentum from the length-and-direction form into the component form:

$$\vec{p} = \|\vec{p}\|\angle\theta = (\|\vec{p}\|\cos\theta, \|\vec{p}\|\sin\theta) = (p_x, p_y).$$

The component form makes it easy to add and subtract vectors: $\vec{p}_1 + \vec{p}_2 = (p_{1x} + p_{2x}, p_{1y} + p_{2y})$. To express the final answer, we will need to convert the component form back to the length-and-direction form:

$$\|\vec{p}\| = \sqrt{p_x^2 + p_y^2}, \qquad \theta = \tan^{-1}\left(\frac{p_y}{p_x}\right).$$

Conservation of momentum

Newton's first law states that in the absence of acceleration ($\vec{a} = 0$), an object maintains a constant velocity. This becomes kind of obvious if you apply the logic of calculus: $\vec{a}$ is the change in $\vec{v}$, so if $\vec{a} = 0$ then $\vec{v}$ must be constant.

In the absence of acceleration, objects conserve their velocity: $\vec{v}_{\text{in}} = \vec{v}_{\text{out}}$. When we multiply both sides of this equation by the object's mass, we obtain an equivalent statement saying that objects conserve their momentum:

$$\vec{p}_{\text{in}} = m\vec{v}_{\text{in}} = m\vec{v}_{\text{out}} = \vec{p}_{\text{out}}.$$

More generally, for situations involving multiple moving objects, the *sum* of the momenta of all the objects stays constant even if the objects interact. This reasoning is useful when analyzing collisions, since it allows us to equate the sum of the momenta before and after the collision:

$$\sum \vec{p}_{\text{in}} = \sum \vec{p}_{\text{out}}. \tag{4.9}$$

Any momentum that goes into a collision must also come out. This equation expresses the law of conservation of momentum.

The law of conservation of momentum is one of the furthest-reaching laws of physics you will learn by studying mechanics. We discussed the conservation of momentum in the simple context of two colliding particles, but the law applies widely, to multiple particles, fluids, fields, and even collisions involving atomic particles described by quantum mechanics. The quantity of motion (a.k.a. momentum) cannot be created or destroyed—it can only be exchanged between systems.

Examples

Example 1 It's a rainy day, and from your balcony you throw—horizontally, at a speed of 10[m/s]—a piece of rolled-up carton with a mass of 0.4[g]. Shortly after it leaves your hand, the piece collides with a rain drop that weighs 2[g] and is falling straight down at a speed of 30[m/s]. What will the resulting velocity be if the two objects stick together after the collision?

The conservation of momentum equation says,

$$\vec{p}_{\text{in},1} + \vec{p}_{\text{in},2} = \vec{p}_{\text{out}}.$$

Plugging in the values, we obtain the equation

$$\begin{array}{ccccc} m_1\vec{v}_1 & + & m_2\vec{v}_2 & = & (m_1+m_2)\vec{v}_{\text{out}}, \\ 0.4\times(10,0) & + & 2\times(0,-30) & = & 2.4\times\vec{v}_{\text{out}}. \end{array}$$

Solving for $\vec{v}_{\text{out}}$ we find

$$\vec{v}_{\text{out}} = \frac{0.4(10,0)+2(0,-30)}{2.4} = (1.666,-25.0) = 1.666\hat{\imath} - 25.0\hat{\jmath}.$$

Example 2: Hipsters on bikes Two hipsters on fixed-gear bikes are headed toward the same intersection as shown in Figure 4.12. Both hipsters have a speed of 50[km/h]. The first hipster crosses the street at a diagonal of 30 degrees when the two bikers collide. Did anyone else see this coming? Apparently, the second hipster didn't, because the thick frames of his glasses were blocking his peripheral vision.

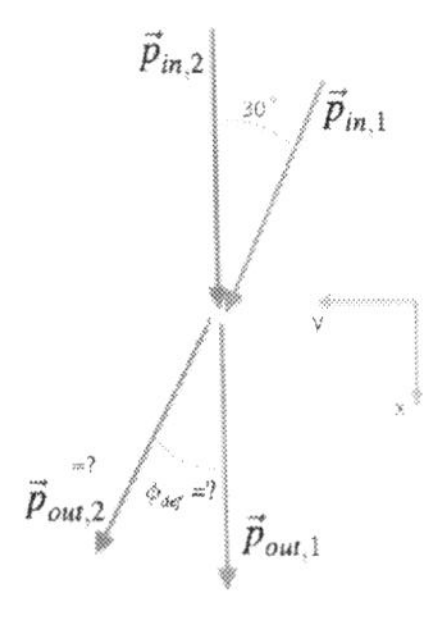

Figure 4.12: Momentum diagram of the collision between two cyclists.

Assume the weight of the street-crossing-at-30-degrees hipster combined with the weight of his bike totals 90[kg]. And assume the weight of the hipster moving in the straight line combined with the weight of his bike is 100[kg].

The story will continue in a moment, but first let's review the information I've given you so far:

$$\begin{aligned}\vec{p}_{\text{in},1} &= 90 \times 50\angle 30 \\ &= 90(50\cos 30, 50\sin 30),\end{aligned}$$

$$\begin{aligned}\vec{p}_{\text{in},2} &= 100 \times 50\angle 0 \\ &= 100(50, 0),\end{aligned}$$

where the x-coordinate points down the street, and the y-coordinate is perpendicular to the street.

Surprisingly, nobody gets hurt in this collision. The bikers bump shoulder-to-shoulder and bounce off each other. The hipster who was trying to cross the street is redirected down the street, while the hipster travelling down the street is deflected to the side and rerouted onto a bike path. I know what you are thinking: couldn't they get hurt at least a little bit? Okay, let's say the whiplash from the shoulder-to-shoulder collision sends the hipsters' heads flying toward each other and smashes their glasses. There you have it.

Suppose the velocity of the first hipster after the collision is 60 [km/h]. What is the velocity and the deflected direction of the second hipster? As given above, the outgoing momentum of the first hipster is $\vec{p}_{\text{out},1} = 90(60, 0)$, and we're looking to find $\vec{p}_{\text{out},2}$.

We can solve this problem with the conservation of momentum formula, which tells us that

$$\vec{p}_{\text{in},1} + \vec{p}_{\text{in},2} = \vec{p}_{\text{out},1} + \vec{p}_{\text{out},2}.$$

We know three of the above quantities, so we can solve for the remaining unknown vector by isolating it on one side of the equation:

$$\vec{p}_{\text{out},2} = \vec{p}_{\text{in},1} + \vec{p}_{\text{in},2} - \vec{p}_{\text{out},1},$$

$$\vec{p}_{\text{out},2} = 90(50\cos 30, 50\sin 30) + 100(50,0) - 90(60,0).$$

The x-component of the momentum $\vec{p}_{\text{out},2}$ is

$$p_{\text{out},2,x} = 90 \times 50\cos 30 + 5000 - 90 \times 60 = 3497.11,$$

and the y-component is $p_{\text{out},2,y} = 90 \times 50\sin 30 = 2250$.

The magnitude of the momentum of hipster 2 is given by

$$\|\vec{p}_{\text{out},2}\| = \sqrt{p_{\text{out},2,x}^2 + p_{\text{out},2,y}^2} = 4158.39 \quad [\text{kg km/h}].$$

Note the unit of the momentum is not the standard choice [kg m/s]. That is fine. As long as you keep in mind which units you're using, it's not always necessary to convert to SI units.

The final velocity of hipster 2 is $v_{\text{out},2} = 4158.39/100 = 41.58[\text{km/h}]$. The deflection angle is obtained by

$$\phi_{\text{def}} = \tan^{-1}\left(\frac{p_{\text{out},2,y}}{p_{\text{out},2,x}}\right) = 32.76°.$$

Discussion

We previously defined the concept of momentum in terms of an object's velocity; but in fact, momentum can be traced to a concept more fundamental than velocity. If you go on to take more advanced physics classes, you'll learn about the *natural* variables—position and momentum $(\vec{x}, \vec{p})$—that describe the *state* of a particle. You'll also learn that the *real* form of Newton's second law is written in terms of momentum:

$$\vec{F} = \frac{d\vec{p}}{dt} \quad \text{for } m \text{ constant} \quad \Rightarrow \quad \vec{F} = \frac{d(m\vec{v})}{dt} = m\frac{d\vec{v}}{dt} = m\vec{a}.$$

In most physics problems, objects will maintain a constant mass, so using $\vec{F} = m\vec{a}$ is perfectly fine.

The law of conservation of momentum follows from Newton's third law: for each force $\vec{F}_{12}$ exerted by Object 1 on Object 2, there exists a counter force $\vec{F}_{21}$ of equal magnitude and opposite direction, which is the force of Object 2 pushing back on Object 1. Earlier, I mentioned it is difficult to quantify the magnitude of the exact forces $\vec{F}_{12}$ and $\vec{F}_{21}$ that occur during a collision. Indeed, the amount of force suddenly shoots up as the two objects collide, then suddenly drops again. Complicated as these forces may be, we know that during the entire collision they obey Newton's third law. Assuming there are no other forces acting on the objects, we have

$$\vec{F}_{12} = -\vec{F}_{21} \quad \text{using the above} \Rightarrow \quad \frac{d\vec{p}_1}{dt} = -\frac{d\vec{p}_2}{dt}.$$

If we move the negative term to the left-hand side of the equation we obtain

$$\frac{d\vec{p}_1}{dt} + \frac{d\vec{p}_2}{dt} = 0 = \frac{d}{dt}\left(\vec{p}_1 + \vec{p}_2\right).$$

The second part of the equation implies that the quantity $(\vec{p}_1 + \vec{p}_2)$ is constant over time, and so $\vec{p}_{\text{in},1} + \vec{p}_{\text{in},2} = \vec{p}_{\text{out},1} + \vec{p}_{\text{out},2}$.

In this section, we saw how to use a momentum calculation to predict the motion of particles after a collision. In the next section we'll learn about *energy*, which is another useful concept for understanding and predicting the motion of objects.

Links

[Animations of simple collisions between objects]
`http://en.wikipedia.org/wiki/Conservation_of_linear_momentum`

Exercise

E4.1 A sticky ball of mass 3[g] and velocity 20[m/s] collides with a stationary ball of mass 5[g]. The balls stick together. What is their velocity after the collision?
Hint: Use conservation of momentum $\vec{p}_{1,\text{in}} + \vec{p}_{2,\text{in}} = \vec{p}_{\text{out}}$.

4.6 Energy

Instead of thinking in terms of velocities $v(t)$ and motion trajectories $x(t)$, we can solve physics problems by using *energy* calculations. In this section, we'll precisely define different kinds of energies, and we'll learn the rules for converting one energy into another. The key idea to keep in mind is the principle of *total energy conservation*, which says that in any physical process, the sum of the initial energies is equal to the sum of the final energies.

Example

You drop a ball from a height h[m] and want to predict its speed just before it hits the ground. Through the kinematics approach, you would set up the general equation of motion,

$$v_f^2 = v_i^2 + 2a(y_f - y_i),$$

substitute $y_i = h$, $y_f = 0$, $v_i = 0$, and $a = -g$, and solve for the ball's final speed at impact v_f. The answer is $v_f = \sqrt{2gh}$[m/s].

Alternately, we can use an energy calculation. The ball starts from a height h, which means it has $U_i = mgh$[J] of potential energy. As the ball falls, potential energy is converted into kinetic energy. Just before the ball hits the ground, its final kinetic energy is equal to the initial potential energy: $K_f = U_i$. Since the formula for kinetic energy is $K = \frac{1}{2}mv^2$[J], we have $\frac{1}{2}mv_f^2 = mgh$. We cancel the mass on both sides of the equation and solve for v_f to obtain $v_f = \sqrt{2gh}$[m/s].

Both methods of solving the example problem lead us to the same answer, but the energy reasoning is arguably more intuitive than blindly plugging values into a formula. In science, it is really important to know different ways of arriving at the same answer. Knowing about these alternate routes will allow you to check your answers and better understand concepts.

Concepts

Energy is measured in Joules [J] and it arises in several contexts:

- K = **kinetic energy**: the type of energy objects have by virtue of their motion
- W = **work**: the amount of energy an external force adds or subtracts from a system. Positive work corresponds to energy added to the system while negative work corresponds to energy withdrawn from the system.
- U_g = **gravitational potential energy**: the energy an object has by virtue of its position above the ground. We say this energy is *potential* because it is a form of *stored work*. Potential energy corresponds to the amount of work the force of gravity will add to an object when the object falls to the ground.
- U_s = **spring potential energy**: the energy stored in a spring when it is displaced (stretched or compressed) from its relaxed position.

There are many other kinds of energy—electrical energy, magnetic energy, sound energy, thermal energy, and so on. However, we'll limit our focus in this section to include only the *mechanical* energy concepts described above.

Formulas

Kinetic energy

An object of mass m moving at velocity $\vec{v}$ has a *kinetic energy* of

$$K = \frac{1}{2}m\|\vec{v}\|^2 \qquad [\text{J}].$$

Note the kinetic energy depends on the speed $\|\vec{v}\|$ of the object and not on the direction of motion.

Work

When an external force $\vec{F}$ acts on an object during a displacement $\vec{d}$, the *work* done by this force is

$$W = \vec{F}\cdot\vec{d} = \|\vec{F}\|\|\vec{d}\|\cos\theta \qquad [\text{J}].$$

The second equality follows from the geometric interpretation of the dot product $\vec{u}\cdot\vec{v} = \|\vec{u}\|\|\vec{v}\|\cos\theta$, where θ is the angle between $\vec{u}$ and $\vec{v}$.

If the force $\vec{F}$ acts in the same direction as the displacement $\vec{d}$, then the force will do positive work ($\cos(0°) = +1$) by adding energy to the system. If the force acts in the opposite direction to the direction of the displacement, the force will do negative work ($\cos(180°) = -1$)—it withdraws energy from the system.

Gravitational potential energy

An object raised to a height h above the ground has a *gravitational potential energy* given by

$$U_g(h) = mgh \qquad [\text{J}],$$

where m is the mass of the object and $g = 9.81[\text{m/s}^2]$ is the gravitational acceleration on the surface of the Earth.

Spring potential energy

The potential energy stored in a spring when it is displaced by $\vec{x}$[m] from its relaxed position is given by

$$U_s = \frac{1}{2}k\|\vec{x}\|^2 \qquad [\text{J}],$$

where k[N/m] is the spring constant.

Note, it is irrelevant whether the spring is stretched or compressed: only the magnitude of the displacement matters $\|\vec{x}\|$.

Conservation of energy

Consider a system that starts from an initial state (i), undergoes some motion, and arrives at a final state (f). The law of conservation of energy states that **energy cannot be created or destroyed in any physical process.** The initial energy of the system plus the work that is *in*put into the system must equal the final energy of the system plus any work that is *out*put:

$$\sum E_i \; + W_{\text{in}} \;=\; \sum E_f \; + W_{\text{out}}. \tag{4.10}$$

The expression $\sum E_i$ corresponds to the sum of all the different types of energy the system contains in its initial state. Similarly, $\sum E_f$ corresponds to the sum of the final energies of the system. In mechanics, we consider three types of energy: kinetic energy, gravitational potential energy, and spring potential energy. Thus the conservation of energy equation in mechanics is

$$K_i + U_{gi} + U_{si} \; + W_{\text{in}} \;=\; K_f + U_{gf} + U_{sf} \; + W_{\text{out}}.$$

Usually, we're able to drop some of the terms in this lengthy expression. For example, we do not need to consider the spring potential energy U_s in physics problems that do not involve springs.

Explanations

Work and energy are measured in Joules [J]. Joules can be expressed in terms of other fundamental units:

$$[\text{J}] = [\text{N m}] = [\text{kg m}^2/\text{s}^2].$$

The first equality follows from the definition of work as force times displacement. The second equality comes from the definition of the Newton: $[\text{N}] = [\text{kg m/s}^2]$, which comes from $F = ma$.

Kinetic energy

A moving object has energy $K = \frac{1}{2}m\|\vec{v}\|^2$[J], called *kinetic* energy from the Greek word for motion, *kinema*.

Note that velocity $\vec{v}$ and speed $\|\vec{v}\|$ are not the same as energy. Suppose you have two objects of the same mass, and one is moving two times faster than the other. The faster object will have twice the velocity of the slower object, and four times more kinetic energy.

Work

When hiring movers to help you move, you must pay them for the *work* they do. Work is the product of the amount of force needed for the move and the distance of the move. When the move requires a lot of force, more work will be done. And the bigger the displacement (think moving to a different city versus moving next door), the more money the movers will ask for.

The amount of *work* done by a force $\vec{F}$ on an object that moves along some path p is given by

$$W = \int_p \vec{F}(x) \cdot d\vec{x}.$$

The integral accounts for the fact that the force's magnitude and direction might change along the path of motion.

If the force is constant and the displacement path is a straight line, the formula for work simplifies to

$$W = \int_0^d \vec{F} \cdot d\vec{x} = \vec{F} \cdot \int_0^d d\vec{x} = \vec{F} \cdot \vec{d} = \|\vec{F}\|\|\vec{d}\| \cos\theta. \tag{4.11}$$

Note the use of the dot product to obtain only the part of $\vec{F}$ that is pushing in the direction of the displacement $\vec{d}$. A force that acts perpendicular to the displacement produces no work, since it neither speeds nor slows the object's motion.

Potential energy is stored work

Some kinds of work are just a waste of time, like working at a job you despise. You work and you get your paycheque, but you don't learn anything useful at the end of the day. Other kinds of work leave you with some useful resource at the end of the work day—they grow your human potential.

In physics, we make a similar distinction. Some types of work, like work against friction, are called *dissipative* since they simply waste energy. Other kinds of work are called *conservative* since the work performed isn't lost but converted into *potential energy*.

The gravitational force and the spring force are *conservative forces*. Any work you do lifting an object into the air against the force of gravity is not lost but *stored* in the height of the object. By letting go of the object, you will get a full return on all the work performed while lifting the object. The energy will return in the form of kinetic energy since the object picks up speed during the fall.

The negative of the work done against a conservative force is called *potential energy*. For any conservative force $\vec{F}_?$, we can define the associated potential energy $U_?$ through the formula,

$$U_?(d) = -W_{\text{done}} = -\int_0^d \vec{F}_? \cdot d\vec{x}.$$

We'll discuss two specific examples of this general formula below: gravitational potential energy and spring potential energy. An object high in the air has a great potential to fall; similarly, compressing a spring by a certain distance gives it the potential to spring back to its normal position. Let's look at the exact formulas for these two cases.

Gravitational potential energy

The force of gravity is given by $\vec{F}_g = -mg\hat{\jmath}$. The direction of the gravitational force is downward, toward the centre of the Earth.

The gravitational potential energy of lifting an object from a height of $y = 0$ to a height of $y = h$ is given by

$$\begin{aligned} U_g(h) \equiv -W_{\text{done}} &= -\int_0^h \vec{F}_g \cdot d\vec{y} = -\int_0^h (-mg\hat{\jmath}) \cdot \hat{\jmath}\, dy \\ &= mg\int_0^h 1\, dy = mgy\Big|_{y=0}^{y=h} \\ &= mgh \qquad [\text{J}]. \end{aligned}$$

Spring potential energy

The force of a spring when displaced by $\vec{x}$[m] from its natural position is given by $\vec{F}_s(\vec{x}) = -k\vec{x}$. The potential energy stored in a spring as it is stretched from $y = 0$ to $y = x$[m] is given by

$$\begin{aligned} U_s(x) \equiv -W_{\text{done}} &= -\int_0^x \vec{F}_s(y) \cdot d\vec{y} \\ &= -\int_0^x (-ky)\, dy = k\int_0^x y\, dy = k\frac{1}{2}y^2\Big|_{y=0}^{y=x} \\ &= \frac{1}{2}kx^2 \qquad [\text{J}]. \end{aligned}$$

Note the formula applies when $x > 0$ (spring stretched by length $|x|$) and when $x < 0$ (spring compressed by length $|x|$).

Conservation of energy

Energy cannot be created or destroyed. It can only be transformed from one form to another. If no external forces act on the system, then the system obeys the *conservation of energy* equation:

$$\sum E_i = \sum E_f.$$

If external forces like friction do work on the system, we must account for their energy contributions:

$$\sum E_i + W_{\text{in}} = \sum E_f, \quad \text{or} \quad \sum E_i = \sum E_f + W_{\text{out}}.$$

The conservation of energy is one of the most important equations you will find in this book. It allows you to solve complicated problems by simply accounting for all the different kinds of energy involved in a system.

Examples

Banker dropped

An investment banker is dropped (from rest) from a building of height 100[m]. What is his speed when he hits the ground?

We start from

$$\begin{aligned} \sum E_i &= \sum E_f, \\ K_i + U_i &= K_f + U_f, \end{aligned}$$

and plug in the numbers to get

$$0 + m \times 9.81 \times 100 = \frac{1}{2}mv^2 + 0.$$

We cancel the mass m from both sides of the equation and are left with

$$9.81 \times 100 = \frac{1}{2}v_f^2.$$

Solving for v_f in the above equation, we find the banker will be falling at $v_f = \sqrt{2 \times 9.81 \times 100} = 44.2945$[m/s] when he hits the ground. This is about 160[km/h]. Ouch! That will definitely hurt.

Bullet speedometer

An incoming bullet at speed v hits a block of mass M which is suspended in the air. Use conservation of momentum and conservation of energy principles to find the speed v of the bullet if the block rises to a height h after being hit by the bullet.

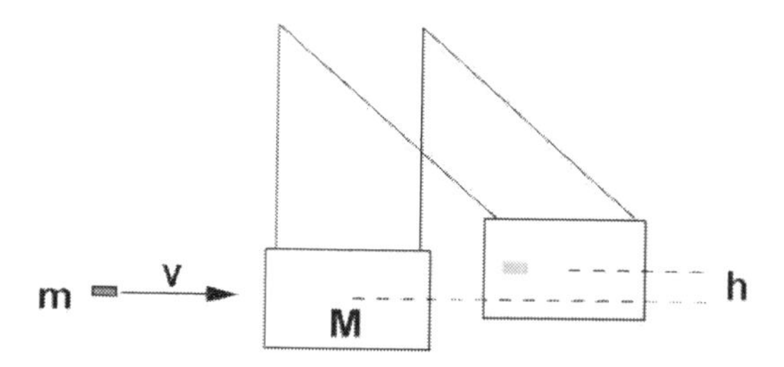

Figure 4.13: A bullet of mass m hits a block of mass M and causes the mass to swing up and to the right. Find the incoming velocity of the bullet v if the block-plus-bullet system rises by a height h after the impact.

First we apply the conservation of momentum principle to find the block's horizontal speed and its mass just after the bullet hits:

$$\vec{p}_{\text{in},m} + \vec{p}_{\text{in},M} = \vec{p}_{\text{out}},$$
$$mv + 0 = (m + M)v_{\text{out}}.$$

Thus, the block's velocity just after the bullet's impact is $v_{\text{out}} = \frac{mv}{M+m}$.

Next, we go to the conservation of energy principle to relate the initial kinetic energy of the block-plus-bullet to the height h by which the block rises:

$$K_i + U_i = K_f + U_f,$$
$$\frac{1}{2}(M + m)v_{\text{out}}^2 + 0 = 0 + (m + M)gh.$$

Isolate v_{out} in the above equation and set it equal to the v_{out} we obtained from the momentum calculation:

$$v_{\text{out}} = \frac{mv}{M + m} = \sqrt{2gh} = v_{\text{out}}.$$

We can use this equation to find the speed of the incoming bullet:

$$v = \frac{M + m}{m}\sqrt{2gh}.$$

Incline and spring

A block of mass m is released from rest at point (A), located on top of an incline at coordinate $y = y_i$. The block slides down the frictionless incline to the point (B) $y = 0$. The coordinate $y = 0$ corresponds to the relaxed length of a spring with spring constant k. The block then compresses the spring all the way to point (C), corresponding to $y = y_f$, where the block momentarily comes to rest. The angle of the incline's slope is θ.

What is the speed of the block at $y = 0$? Find the value of y_f, the compression of the spring when the block stops. Bonus points if you can express your answer for y_f in terms of Δh, the difference in height between points (A) and (C).

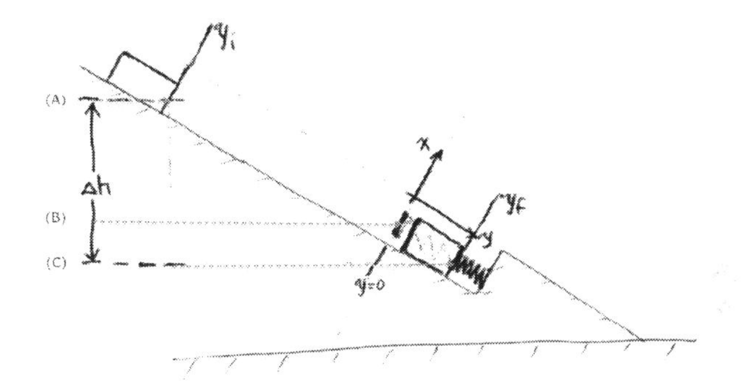

Figure 4.14: A block is released from the point (A) and slides down a frictionless incline to the point (B). The motion of the block is then slowed by a spring at the bottom of the incline. The block comes to rest at the point (C), after the spring is compressed by a length y_f.

Essentially, we have two problems: the block's motion from (A) to (B) in which its gravitational potential energy is converted into kinetic energy; and the block's motion from (B) to (C), in which all its energy is converted into spring potential energy.

There is no friction in either movement, so we can use the conservation of energy formula:

$$\sum E_i = \sum E_f.$$

For the block's motion from (A) to (B), we have

$$K_i + U_i = K_f + U_f.$$

The block starts from rest, so $K_i = 0$. The difference in potential energy is equal to mgh, and in this case the block is $|y_i| \sin\theta$ [m] higher at (A) than it is at (B), so we write

$$0 + mg|y_i| \sin\theta = \frac{1}{2} m v_B^2 + 0.$$

In the formula above, we assume the block has zero gravitational potential energy at point (B). The potential energy at point (A) is $U_i =$

$mgh = mg|y_i - 0|\sin\theta$ *relative* to point (B), since point (A) is $h = |y_i - 0|\sin\theta$ metres higher than point (B).

Solving for v_B in this equation answers the first part of our question:

$$v_B = \sqrt{2g|y_i|\sin\theta}.$$

Now for the second part of the block's motion. The law of conservation of energy dictates that

$$K_i + U_{gi} + U_{si} = K_f + U_{gf} + U_{sf},$$

where i now refers to the moment (B), and f refers to the moment (C). Initially the spring is uncompressed, so $U_{si} = 0$. By the end of the motion, the spring is compressed by a total of $\Delta y = |y_f - 0|$[m], so its spring potential energy is $U_{sf} = \frac{1}{2}k|y_f|^2$. We choose the height of (C) as the reference potential energy; thus $U_{gf} = 0$. Since the difference in gravitational potential energy is $U_{gi} - U_{gf} = mgh = |y_f - 0|\sin\theta$, we can complete the entire energy equation:

$$\frac{1}{2}mv_B^2 + mg|y_f|\sin\theta + 0 = 0 + 0 + \frac{1}{2}k|y_f|^2.$$

Assuming the values of k and m are given, and knowing v_B from the first part of the question, we can solve for $|y_f|$ in the above equation.

To obtain the answer $|y_f|$ in terms of Δh, we'll use $\sum E_i = \sum E_f$ again, but this time i will refer to moment (A) and f to moment (C). The conservation of energy equation tells us $mg\Delta h = \frac{1}{2}k|y_f|^2$, from which we obtain $|y_f| = \sqrt{\frac{2mg\Delta h}{k}}$.

Energy lost to friction

You place a block of mass 50[kg] on an incline. The force of friction between the block and the incline is 30[N]. The block slides for 200[m] down the incline. The incline's slope is $\theta = 30°$ making the block's total vertical displacement $200\sin 30° = 100$[m]. What is the block's speed after sliding for 200[m] down the incline?

This is a problem in which initial energies are converted into a combination of final energies and *lost* work:

$$\sum E_i = \sum E_f + W_{\text{lost}}.$$

The term W_{lost} represents energy lost due to friction.

A better way of describing this situation is that **a negative amount of work is done on the block**:

$$\sum E_i + \underbrace{W_{\text{done}}}_{\text{negative}} = \sum E_f.$$

The quantity W_{done} is negative because the friction force acts on the object in the opposite direction of the object's motion:

$$W_{\text{done}} = \vec{F} \cdot \vec{d} = \|\vec{F}_f\| \|\vec{d}\| \cos(180^\circ) = -F_f \|\vec{d}\|,$$

where $\|\vec{d}\|$ is the sliding distance of 200[m] over which the friction acts.

We substitute the value of W_{done} into the conservation of energy equation:

$$K_i + U_i + W_{\text{done}} = K_f + U_f,$$
$$0 + mgh + (-F_f|d|) = \frac{1}{2}mv_f^2 + 0.$$

Note we used the formula $mgh = U_i - U_f$ for the difference in gravitational potential energy.

Since we're told $F_f = 30$[N], we can calculate $W_{\text{done}} = W_{\text{friction}} = -30[\text{N}] \times 200[\text{m}] = -6000[\text{J}]$. Substituting all known values, we find

$$0 + 50 \times 9.81 \times 100 - 6000 = \frac{1}{2}(50)v_f^2 + 0,$$

which we can solve for v_f.

Discussion

It's useful to describe physical situations in terms of the energies involved. The law of conservation of energy allows us to use simple "energy accounting" principles to calculate the values of unknown quantities.

Exercise

E4.2 You and your friend are playing frisbee. Your friend throws the 175[g] frisbee at you with a speed $v = 15$[m/s]. The frisbee flies horizontally with a constant speed until you catch it (ignore air resistance and gravity). How much energy does the frisbee lose when you stop it with your hand?

4.7 Uniform circular motion

This section covers the circular motion of objects. Circular motion differs from linear motion, and we'll need to learn new techniques and concepts specifically used to describe circular motion.

Imagine a rock of mass m attached to the end of a rope and swinging around in a horizontal circle. The rock flies through the air at a constant speed of v_t[m/s], along a circular path of radius R[m], at a height h[m] above the ground. What is the tension T in the rope?

Consider a coordinate system with its x and y axes placed on the ground. At the centre of the circle of motion is the z-axis, which measures the height above the ground. In this (x, y, z) coordinate system, the rock's trajectory is described by the equation

$$\vec{r}(t) = (x(t), y(t), z(t)) = \left(R\cos\left(\frac{v_t}{R}t\right), \ R\sin\left(\frac{v_t}{R}t\right), \ h\right).$$

Do you agree with me that this expression looks somewhat complicated? Its complexity stems from the fact that the (x, y, z) coordinate system is not well-adapted for describing circular paths.

A new coordinate system

Instead of the usual coordinate system $\hat{x}, \hat{y}, \hat{z}$, which is static, we can choose a new coordinate system $\hat{t}, \hat{r}, \hat{z}$ that is "attached" to the rotating object. The new coordinate system consists of:

- $\hat{t}$: the *tangential* direction is the object's instantaneous direction of motion. The name comes from the Greek word for "touch" (imagine a straight line "touching" the circle).
- $\hat{r}$: the *radial* direction always points toward the centre of the circle of rotation.
- $\hat{z}$: the usual $\hat{z}$-direction

From a static observer's point of view, the tangential and radial directions constantly change their orientation as the object rotates around in a circle. From the rotating object's point of view, the tangential and radial directions are fixed. The tangential direction is always "forward" and the radial direction is always "to the side."

We can use the new coordinate system to describe the position, velocity, and acceleration of an object undergoing circular motion:

- $\vec{v} = (v_r, v_t)_{\hat{r}\hat{t}}$: the object's *velocity* expressed with respect to the $\hat{r}\hat{t}$-coordinate system
- $\vec{a} = (a_r, a_t)_{\hat{r}\hat{t}}$: the object's *acceleration*

The most important motion parameters are the tangential velocity v_t, the radial acceleration a_r, and the radius of the circle of motion R. We have $v_r = 0$ since the motion is entirely in the $\hat{t}$-direction, and $a_t = 0$ because in this case we assume the tangential velocity v_t remains constant (*uniform* circular motion).

Radial acceleration

The defining feature of circular motion is the presence of an acceleration that acts perpendicularly to direction of motion. At each instant, the object wants to continue moving along the tangential direction, but the radial acceleration causes the object's velocity to change direction. This constant inward acceleration causes the object to follow a circular path.

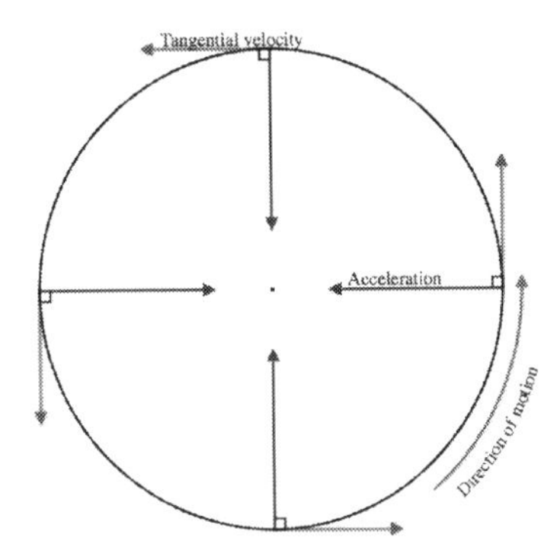

Figure 4.15: An object moving in circular motion experiences a constant acceleration towards the centre of the circle of rotation.

The *radial acceleration* a_r of an object moving in a circle of radius R with a tangential velocity v_t is given by

$$a_r = \frac{v_t^2}{R}. \tag{4.12}$$

This important equation relates the three key parameters of circular motion.

According to Newton's second law $\vec{F} = m\vec{a}$, an object's radial acceleration must be caused by a *radial force*. We can calculate the magnitude of this radial force F_r as follows:

$$F_r = ma_r = m\frac{v_t^2}{R}.$$

This formula connects the observable aspects of a circular motion v_t and R with the motion's cause: the force F_r, which always acts toward the centre of rotation.

To phrase it another way, we can say circular motion *requires* a radial force. From now on, when you see an object in circular motion, you can try to visualize the radial force that is causing the circular motion.

In the rock-on-a-rope example introduced in the beginning of the section (page 229), circular motion is caused by the tension in the rope that always acts in the radial direction (toward the centre of rotation). We're now in a position to calculate the value of the tension T in the rope using the equation

$$F_r = T = ma_r \qquad \Rightarrow \qquad T = m\frac{v_t^2}{R}.$$

The heavier the rock and the faster it goes, the higher the tension in the rope. Inversely, the bigger the circle's radius, the less tension is required for the same v_t.

Example

During a student protest, a young activist named David is stationed on the rooftop of a building of height 12[m]. A mob of blood-thirsty neoconservatives is slowly approaching his position, determined to lynch him because of his leftist views. David has assembled a makeshift weapon by attaching a 0.3[kg] rock to the end of a shoelace of length 1.5[m]. The maximum tension the shoelace can support is 500[N]. What is the maximum tangential velocity $\max\{v_t\}$ the shoelace can support? What is the projectile's maximum *range* when it is launched from the roof?

The first part of the question can be answered using the formula $T = m\frac{v_t^2}{R}$:

$$\max\{v_t\} = \sqrt{\frac{RT}{m}} = \sqrt{\frac{1.5 \times 500}{0.3}} = 50[\text{m/s}].$$

To answer the second question, we must solve for the distance travelled by a projectile with initial velocity $\vec{v}_i = (v_{ix}, v_{iy}) = (50, 0)[\text{m/s}]$, launched from $\vec{r}_i = (x_i, y_i) = (0, 12)[\text{m}]$. First, solve for the total time of flight $t_f = \sqrt{2 \times 12/9.81} = 1.56[\text{s}]$. Then find the range of the rock by multiplying the projectile's horizontal speed by the time of flight $x(t_f) = 0 + v_{ix}t_f = 50 \times 1.56 = 78.20[\text{m}]$.

After carrying out these calculations on a piece of paper, David starts to spin-up the rock and waits for the neocons to come into range.

Circular motion parameters

It's time to introduce some further terminology that will help us describe circular motion:

- $C = 2\pi R[\text{m}]$: the *circumference* of the circle of motion

- T: the *period* of the motion. The time T is how long it takes for the object to complete one full circle. This period is measured in seconds [s].
- $f = \frac{1}{T}$: the frequency of rotation. The frequency describes the number of turns the object completes in one second. Frequency is measured in Hertz [Hz]=[1/s]. We sometimes describe the frequency of rotation in *revolutions per minute* (RPM).
- $\omega \equiv \frac{v_t}{R} = 2\pi f$: the *angular velocity* describes how fast the object is rotating. Angular velocity is measured in [rad/s].

Recall that a circle of radius R has a circumference $C = 2\pi R$. The *period* T is defined as how long it takes the object to complete one full turn around the circle:

$$T = \frac{\text{distance}}{\text{speed}} = \frac{C}{v_t} = \frac{2\pi R}{v_t},$$

where $C = 2\pi R$ is the total distance travelled to compete one turn, and v_t is the velocity of the object along the curve. The object completes one full turn every T seconds.

There is another way to describe circular motion by referencing an object's *frequency* of rotation:

$$f = \frac{1}{T} = [\text{Hz}].$$

The frequency of an object in circular motion tells you how many turns the object completes in one second. If the object completes one turn in $T = 0.2$[s], then the motion's frequency is $f = \frac{1}{0.2} = 5$[Hz], or $f = 60 \times 5 = 300$[RPM].

The most natural parameter for describing rotation is in terms of *angular velocity* ω[rad/s]. We know one full turn corresponds to an angle of rotation of 2π[rad], so angular velocity is obtained by dividing 2π by the time it takes to complete one turn:

$$\omega = \frac{2\pi}{T} = 2\pi f = \frac{v_t}{R}.$$

The angular velocity ω is useful because it describes the speed of a circular motion without any reference to the radius. If we know the angular velocity of an object is ω, we can obtain the tangential velocity by multiplying angular velocity times the radius: $v_t = R\omega$[m/s].

You'll be asked to compute some angular velocities in the upcoming examples.

Bicycle odometer

Imagine you place a small speed detector gadget on one of the spokes of your bicycle's front wheel. Your bike's wheels have a radius $R = 14[\text{in}]$, and the gadget is attached at a distance $\frac{3}{4}R[\text{m}]$ from the wheel's centre. Find the wheel's angular velocity ω, period T, and frequency f of rotation when the bicycle's speed relative to the ground is 40[km/h]. What is the tangential velocity v_t of the detector gadget?

The bicycle's velocity relative to the ground $v_{\text{bike}} = 40[\text{km/h}]$ is equal to the tangential velocity of the rim of the wheel:

$$v_{\text{bike}} = v_{\text{rim}} = 40[\cancel{\text{km}}/\cancel{\text{h}}] \times \frac{1000[\text{m}]}{1[\cancel{\text{km}}]} \times \frac{1[\cancel{\text{h}}]}{3600[\text{s}]} = 11.11[\text{m/s}].$$

We can find the wheel's angular velocity using $\omega = \frac{v_{\text{rim}}}{R}$ and the radius of the wheel $R = 14[\text{in}] = 0.355[\text{m}]$. We obtain $\omega = \frac{11.11}{0.355} = 31.24[\text{rad/s}]$. From here we calculate $T = \frac{2\pi}{\omega} = 0.20[\text{s}]$ and $f = \frac{1}{0.20} = 5[\text{Hz}]$. Finally, to compute the gadget's tangential velocity, multiply the wheel's angular velocity ω by its radius of rotation: $v_{\text{det}} = \omega \times \frac{3}{4}R = 8.333[\text{m/s}]$.

Rotation of the Earth

It takes exactly 23 hours, 56 minutes and 4.09 seconds for the Earth to compete one full turn (2π radians) around its axis of rotation. What is the Earth's angular velocity? What is the tangential speed of a person standing in Montreal, at a latitude of 45°?

We can find ω by carrying out a simple conversion:

$$\frac{2\pi[\text{rad}]}{1[\cancel{\text{day}}]} \cdot \frac{1[\cancel{\text{day}}]}{23.93447[\cancel{\text{h}}]} \cdot \frac{1[\cancel{\text{h}}]}{3600[\text{s}]} = 7.2921 \times 10^{-5}[\text{rad/s}].$$

The radius of the trajectory traced by someone located at a latitude of 45° is given by $r = R\cos(45°) = 4.5025 \times 10^6[\text{m}]$, where $R = 6.3675 \times 10^6[\text{m}]$ is the radius of the Earth. Though it may not feel like you're moving, you are actually hurtling through space at a speed of

$$v_t = r\omega = 4.5025 \times 10^6 \times 7.2921 \times 10^{-5} = 328.32[\text{m/s}],$$

which is equal to 1181.95[km/h]. Imagine that! You can attempt to present this fact if you are ever stopped by the cops for a speeding infraction: "Yes officer, I was doing 130[km/h], but this is really a negligible speed relative to the 1200[km/h] the Earth is doing around its axis of rotation."

Three dimensions

For some problems involving circular motion, we'll need to consider the z-direction in the force diagram. In these cases, the best approach is to draw the force diagram as a cross section that is perpendicular to the tangential direction. Your diagram should show the $\hat{r}$ and $\hat{z}$ axes.

Using the force diagram, you can find all forces in the radial and vertical directions, as well as solve for accelerations a_r, a_z. Remember, you can always use the relation $a_r = \frac{v_t^2}{R}$, which connects the value of a_r with the tangential velocity v_t and the radius of rotation R.

Example Japanese people of the future design a giant racetrack for retired superconducting speed trains. The shape of the race track is a big circle with radius $R = 3[\text{km}]$. Because the trains are magnetically levitated, there is no friction between the track and the train $\mu_s = 0, \mu_k = 0$. What is the bank angle required for the racetrack so trains moving at a speed of exactly 400[km/h] will stay on the track without moving laterally?

We begin by drawing a force diagram that shows a cross section of the train in the $\hat{r}$ and $\hat{z}$ directions (see Figure 4.16). The bank angle of the racetrack is θ. This is the unknown we're looking for. Because of the frictionless-ness of levitated superconducting suspension, there cannot be any force of friction F_f. Therefore, the only forces acting on the train are its weight $\vec{W}$ and the normal force $\vec{N}$.

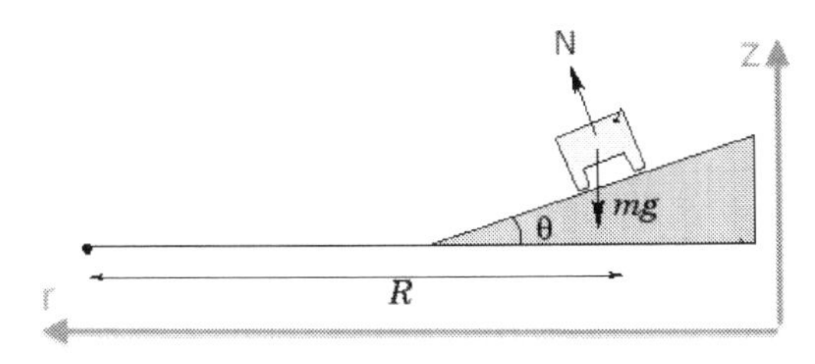

Figure 4.16: Force diagram showing the forces acting on a magnetically levitating train travelling on a circular racetrack of radius R and bank angle θ.

The next step is to write two force equations that represent the $\hat{r}$ and $\hat{z}$ directions:

$$\sum F_r = N\sin\theta = ma_r = m\frac{v_t^2}{R} \quad \Rightarrow \quad N\sin\theta = m\frac{v_t^2}{R},$$
$$\sum F_z = N\cos\theta - mg = 0 \quad \Rightarrow \quad N\cos\theta = mg.$$

Note how the normal force $\vec{N}$ is split into two parts. The vertical component counterbalances the train's weight so it doesn't slide down the track. The component of $\vec{N}$ in the $\hat{r}$-direction is the force that causes the train's rotational motion.

We want to solve for θ in the above equations. It's a common trick to solve equations containing multiple trigonometric functions by dividing one equation by the other. Doing this, we obtain

$$\frac{N\sin\theta}{N\cos\theta} = \frac{m\frac{v_t^2}{R}}{mg} \quad \Rightarrow \quad \tan\theta = \frac{v_t^2}{Rg}.$$

The final answer is $\theta = \tan^{-1}\left(\frac{v_t^2}{gR}\right) = \tan^{-1}\left(\frac{(400\times\frac{1000}{3600})^2}{9.81\times 3000}\right) = 22.76^\circ$. If the angle were any steeper, the trains would fall toward the track's centre. If the bank angle were any shallower, the trains would fly off to the side. The angle 22.76° is just right.

Discussion

Radial acceleration

In the kinematics section (page 136) we studied problems involving *linear acceleration*, in which an acceleration $\vec{a}$ acted in the direction of the velocity, causing a change in the magnitude of the velocity $\vec{v}$.

Circular motion deals with a different situation in which the object's speed $\|\vec{v}\|$ remains constant while its velocity $\vec{v}$ changes direction. At each point along the circle, the object's velocity points along the tangential direction; simultaneously, the radial acceleration pulls the object inwards, causing it to rotate.

Another term for radial acceleration is *centripetal* acceleration, which literally means "tending toward the centre."

Nonexistence of the centrifugal force

When a car makes a left turn, the passenger riding shotgun will feel pushed toward the right, into the passenger door. It would be erroneous to attribute this effect to a *centrifugal force* that acts away from the centre of rotation. In fact, no force is directly responsible for the feeling of being flung out of a car during a sharp turn.

The passenger is pushed into the door because of Newton's first law, which says that in the absence of external forces, an object will continue moving in a straight line. Since the initial motion occurs in the forward direction, the passenger's body naturally wants to continue moving in that direction. The force that the passenger feels from the car's door is necessary to cause the circular trajectory. If it weren't for the force from the door, the passenger would fly straight out!

Radial forces do no work

An interesting property of radial forces is that they perform zero work. Recall that the work done by a force $\vec{F}$ during a displacement $\vec{d}$ is computed using the dot product $W = \vec{F} \cdot \vec{d}$. For circular motion, displacement is always in the $\hat{t}$-direction, while radial force acts in the $\hat{r}$-direction, making the dot product of the two vectors zero. Thus, the effects of radial forces do not increase the object's speed—they only act to change the direction of the velocity.

Example

Staying in touch

A racetrack features a vertical loop of radius 6.6[m] as illustrated in Figure 4.17. A motorcyclist is about to attempt a loop-de-loop. What is the minimum speed v_{in} the motorcyclist needs in order to enter the ramp and drive all the way around the vertical loop? Bear in mind, the motorcyclist will lose contact with the track at the top of the ramp if the magnitude of the normal force drops to zero.

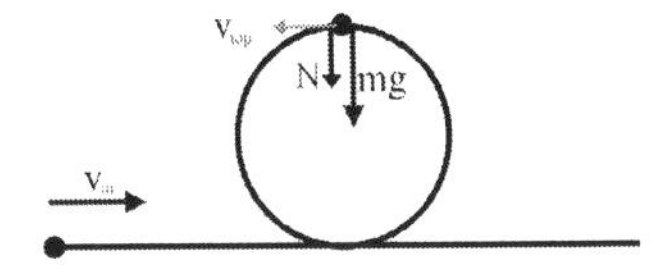

Figure 4.17: A racetrack with a loop-de-loop section. The motorcyclist will start to fall if the normal force becomes zero at the top of the loop.

A radial force equal to $F_r = m\frac{v_{\text{top}}^2}{6.6}$ is required to keep the motorcycle in the loop. Assuming $N = 0$ at the top of the loop, the radial force at the top is given by $F_r = mg + N = mg + 0 = m\frac{v_{\text{top}}^2}{6.6}$, which we solve to find $v_{\text{top}} = \sqrt{6.6g}$. Next, we use conservation of energy $\frac{1}{2}mv_{\text{in}}^2 = m \times g \times 2 \times 6.6 + \frac{1}{2}mv_{\text{top}}^2$ to find $v_{\text{in}} = \sqrt{4 \times g \times 6.6 + 6.6 \times g} = \sqrt{5 \times 6.6 \times g} = 18[\text{m/s}]$.

Links

[Loop-de-loop with a car]
`http://www.youtube.com/watch?v=wiZoVAZGgsw`

4.8 Angular motion

We'll now study the physics of objects in rotation. Rotational motion is exemplified by spinning disks, rotating bicycle wheels, spinning footballs, and spinning figure skaters, among other spinning things.

As you'll see shortly, the basic concepts we'll use to describe angular motion are directly analogous to the concepts of linear motion: position, velocity, acceleration, force, momentum, and energy.

Review of linear motion

It will be helpful to begin with a quick review of the concepts and formulas used to describe the linear motion of objects.

The linear motion of an object is described by its position $x(t)$, velocity $v(t)$, and acceleration $a(t)$ as functions of time. The position function tells you where the object is, the velocity tells you how fast it is moving, and the acceleration measures the change in the object's velocity.

The motion of objects is governed by Newton's first and second laws. In the absence of external forces, objects will maintain a uniform velocity (UVM), which corresponds to the equations of motion $x(t) = x_i + v_i t$ and $v(t) = v_i$. If a net force $\vec{F}$ acts on the object, the force will cause the object to accelerate. We obtain the magnitude of this acceleration with the formula $F = ma$. A constant force acting on an object will produce a constant acceleration (UAM), which corresponds to the equations of motion $x(t) = x_i + v_i t + \frac{1}{2}at^2$ and $v(t) = v_i + at$.

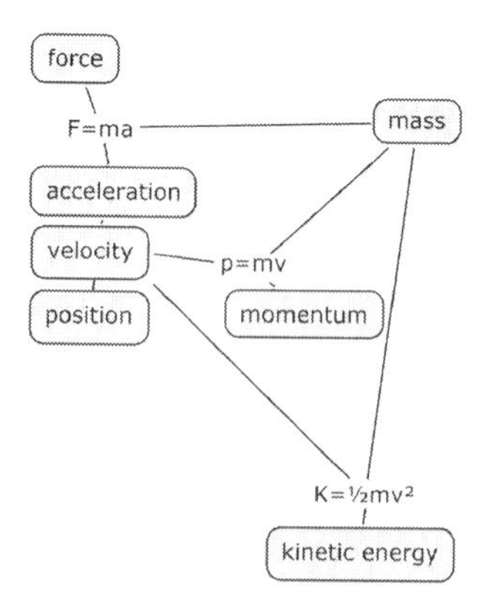

Figure 4.18: The main concepts used to describe linear motion.

We also learned how to quantify the *momentum* $\vec{p} = m\vec{v}$ and the *kinetic energy* $K = \frac{1}{2}mv^2$ of moving objects. The momentum vector is the natural measure of the "quantity of motion," which plays a key role in collisions. The kinetic energy measures the energy stored in the object by virtue of its motion.

An object's mass m is also an important factor in many physics equations. In the equation $F = ma$, the mass m measures the object's *inertia*—the object's resistance to being moved. The object's mass also appears in the formulas for momentum and kinetic energy; the heavier the object, the larger its momentum and its kinetic energy will be.

Concepts

We're ready to introduce the new concepts for describing the angular motion of objects.

- The kinematics of rotating objects is described in terms of angular quantities:
  - ▷ $\theta(t)$[rad]: the object's angular position
  - ▷ $\omega(t)$[rad/s]: the object's angular velocity
  - ▷ $\alpha(t)$[rad/s^2]: the object's angular acceleration
- I[kg m^2]: the *moment of inertia* tells you how difficult it is to make the object turn. The quantity I plays the same role in angular motion as the mass m plays in linear motion.
- $\mathcal{T}$[N m]: *torque* measures angular force. Torque is the cause of angular acceleration. The angular equivalent of Newton's second law $\sum F = ma$ is given by the equation $\sum \mathcal{T} = I\alpha$. This law states that applying an angular force (torque) $\mathcal{T}$ will produce an amount of angular acceleration α that is inversely proportional to the object's moment of inertia I.
- $L = I\omega$[kg m^2/s]: the *angular momentum* of a rotating object describes the "quantity of rotational motion."
- $K_r = \frac{1}{2}I\omega^2$[J]: the *rotational* kinetic energy quantifies the amount of energy an object has by virtue of its rotational motion.

Formulas

Angular kinematics

Instead of talking about position x, velocity v, and acceleration a, for angular motion we use the angular position θ, angular velocity ω, and angular acceleration α. Except for this change of ingredients, the "recipe" for finding the equations of motion remains the same:

$$\alpha(t) \overset{\omega_i+\int dt}{\longrightarrow} \omega(t) \overset{\theta_i+\int dt}{\longrightarrow} \theta(t).$$

Given the knowledge of an object's angular acceleration $\alpha(t)$, its initial angular velocity ω_i, and its initial angular position θ_i, we can use integration to find the equation of motion $\theta(t)$ that describes the angular position of the rotating object at all times.

Though this recipe can be applied to any form of angular acceleration function, you are only *required* to know the equations of motion for two special cases: the case of constant angular acceleration $\alpha(t) = \alpha$, and the case of zero angular acceleration $\alpha(t) = 0$. These are the angular analogues of *uniform acceleration motion* and *uniform velocity motion* we studied in the kinematics section.

The equations that describe *uniformly accelerated angular motion* are

$$\begin{aligned}
\alpha(t) &= \alpha, \\
\omega(t) &= \alpha t + \omega_i, \\
\theta(t) &= \frac{1}{2}\alpha t^2 + \omega_i t + \theta_i, \\
\omega_f^2 &= \omega_i^2 + 2\alpha(\theta_f - \theta_i).
\end{aligned}$$

Note how the form of the equations is *identical* to the linear UAM equations. This should come as no surprise since both sets of equations are obtained using the same integration procedure.

The equations of motion for *uniform velocity angular motion* are

$$\begin{aligned}
\alpha(t) &= 0, \\
\omega(t) &= \omega_i, \\
\theta(t) &= \omega_i t + \theta_i.
\end{aligned}$$

Relation to linear quantities

The angular quantities θ, ω, and α are the natural parameters for describing the motion of rotating objects. In certain situations, however, we may want to relate these angular quantities to linear quantities like distance, velocity, and linear acceleration. The connection between angular and linear quantities can be established by multiplying the angular quantity by the radius of motion:

$$d = R\theta, \qquad v = R\omega, \qquad a = R\alpha.$$

For example, suppose you have a spool of network cable with radius 20[cm], and you need to measure a length of 20[m] to connect your computer to your neighbour's computer. How many turns of the spool are needed to unwind 20[m] of cable? To find out, we can solve for θ in the formula $d = R\theta$ and obtain $\theta = 20/0.2 = 100$[rad], which corresponds to 15.9 turns.

Torque

Torque is angular force. In order to make an object rotate, you must exert a torque on it. Torque is measured in Newton metres [N m].

The *torque* produced by a force $\vec{F}$ is given by

$$\mathcal{T} = F_{\perp} r = \|\vec{F}\| \sin\theta \, r,$$

where r is the distance from the centre of rotation where the force is applied. Note that only the $F_{\perp}$ component of the force creates a torque. You can think of the distance r as *leverage*; even a small amount of force can produce a lot of torque if it acts far away from the centre.

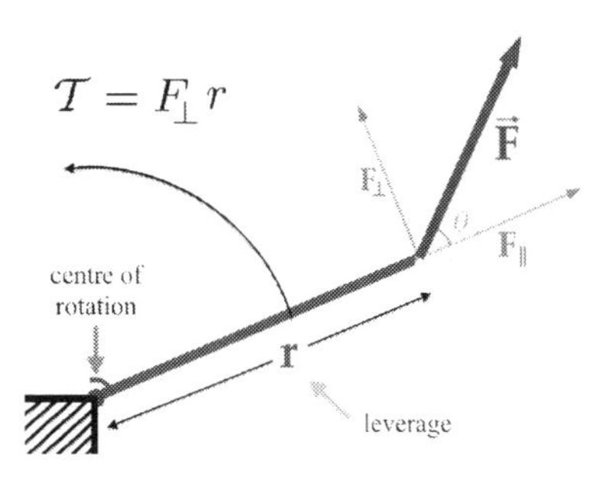

Figure 4.19: The force $\vec{F}$ acting at the distance r from the centre of rotation produces the torque $\mathcal{T} = F_{\perp} r$.

To understand the meaning of the torque equation, you should stop reading for a moment and go experiment with a door. When you push on the door near the hinges, it takes a lot more force to make it move than when you push the edge of the door farthest from the hinges. The more leverage r you have, the more torque you'll produce. Also, if you pull the door's handle away from its hinges (as if trying to pull the door out of the wall), your force will have an $F_{||}$ component, but no $F_{\perp}$ component, so no matter how hard you pull, you will not cause the door to move.

As a standard convention, we use positive numbers to describe torques that produce counter-clockwise rotation, and negative numbers to describe torques that cause clockwise rotation.

The relationship between torque and force can also be used in the other direction. If a motor produces a torque of $\mathcal{T}$[N m] and is attached to a chain wheel of radius R, then the tension in the chain will be

$$T = F_{\perp} = \mathcal{T}/R \qquad [\text{N}].$$

With this equation you can compute the maximum pulling force produced by a car. You'll need to look up the value of the maximum torque produced by the car at the drive wheels, then divide by the radius of the wheels.

Moment of inertia

An object's *moment of inertia* describes how difficult it is to cause the object to rotate:

$$I = \{ \text{ how difficult it is to make an object turn } \}.$$

The calculation describing the moment of inertia accounts for the mass distribution of the object. An object with most of its mass close to its centre will have a smaller moment of inertia, whereas objects with masses far from their centres will have larger moments of inertia.

The formula for calculating the moment of inertia is

$$I = \sum m_i r_i^2 = \int_{\text{obj}} r^2 \, dm \qquad [\text{kg m}^2].$$

The contribution of each piece of the object's mass dm to the total moment of inertia is multiplied by the squared distance of that piece from the object's centre, hence the units [kg m^2].

We rarely use the integral formula to calculate objects' moments of inertia. Most physics problems you'll be asked to solve will involve geometric shapes for which the moment of inertia is given by simple formulas:

$$I_{\text{disk}} = \frac{1}{2}mR^2, \; I_{\text{ring}} = mR^2, \; I_{\text{sphere}} = \frac{2}{5}mR^2, \; I_{\text{sph.shell}} = \frac{2}{3}mR^2.$$

When you learn more about calculus (Chapter 5), you will be able to derive each of the above formulas on your own. For now, just try to remember the formulas for the moment of inertia of a disk and a ring, as they are likely to show up in problems.

The quantity I plays the same role in the equations of angular motion as the mass m plays in the equations of linear motion.

Torques cause angular acceleration

Recall Newton's second law $F = ma$, which describes the amount of acceleration produced by a given force acting on an object. The angular analogue of Newton's second law is expressed as

$$\mathcal{T} = I\alpha. \tag{4.13}$$

This equation indicates that the angular acceleration produced by the torque $\mathcal{T}$ is inversely proportional to the object's moment of inertia. Torque is the cause of angular acceleration.

Angular momentum

The angular momentum of a spinning object measures the "amount of rotational motion." The formula for the angular momentum of an object with moment of inertia I rotating at an angular velocity ω is

$$L = I\omega \qquad [\text{kg m}^2/\text{s}].$$

In the absence of external torques, an object's angular momentum is a conserved quantity:

$$L_{\text{in}} = L_{\text{out}}. \tag{4.14}$$

This property is similar to the way momentum $\vec{p}$ is a conserved quantity in the absence of external forces.

Rotational kinetic energy

The kinetic energy of a rotating object is calculated as

$$K_r = \frac{1}{2}I\omega^2 \qquad [\text{J}].$$

This expression is the rotational analogue to the linear kinetic energy formula $K = \frac{1}{2}mv^2$.

The amount of work produced by a torque $\mathcal{T}$ applied during an angular displacement of θ is given by

$$W = \mathcal{T}\theta \qquad [\text{J}].$$

With the equations above, we can now include the energy and work of rotating objects in our conservation-of-energy calculations.

Examples

Rotational UVM

A disk is spinning at a constant angular velocity of 12[rad/s]. How many turns will the disk complete in one minute?

Since the angular velocity is constant, we can use the equation $\theta(t) = \omega t + \theta_i$ to find the disk's total angular displacement after one minute. We obtain $\theta(60) = 12 \times 60 = 720$[rad]. To find the number of turns, divide this number by 2π and obtain 114.6[turns].

Rotational UAM

A solid disk of mass 20[kg] and radius 30[cm] is initially spinning with an angular velocity of 20[rad/s]. A brake pad applied to the edge of the disk produces a friction force of 60[N]. How much time does it take for the disk to stop?

To solve this kinematics problem, we must first find the angular acceleration produced by the brake. We can find it with the equation $\mathcal{T} = I\alpha$. We need to find $\mathcal{T}$ and I_{disk} and solve for α. The torque produced by the brake is calculated using the force-times-leverage formula: $\mathcal{T} = F_{\perp} r = 60 \times 0.3 = 18$[N m]. The moment of inertia of a disk is given by $I_{\text{disk}} = \frac{1}{2}mR^2 = \frac{1}{2}(20)(0.3)^2 = 0.9$[kg m^2]. Thus we have $\alpha = -\frac{18}{0.9} = -20$[rad/s^2]. Now we can use the UAM formula for angular velocity $\omega(t) = \alpha t + \omega_i$ and solve for the time when the object's motion will stop: $0 = \alpha t + \omega_i$. The disk will come to a stop after $t = -\omega_i/\alpha = 1$[s].

Combined motion

A pulley of radius R and moment of inertia I has a rope wound around it. At the end of the rope is attached a rock of mass m. What will be the angular acceleration of the pulley if we let the rock drop to the ground while unwinding the rope?

A force diagram of the rock tells us that $mg - T = ma_y$ (where $\hat{y}$ points downward). A torque diagram of the disk tells us that $TR = I\alpha$. Taking the product of R times the first equation and adding it to the second equation gives us

$$R(mg - T) + TR = Rma_y + I\alpha,$$

and after simplification we're left with

$$Rmg = Rma_y + I\alpha.$$

Additionally, since we know the rope forms a solid connection between the pulley and the rock, this means that the angular acceleration of the pulley is related to the linear acceleration of the rock:

$R\alpha = a_y$. We can use this relationship between the variables a_y and α to obtain an equation with only one unknown. We substitute $R\alpha$ for a_y in the above equation to obtain

$$Rmg = Rm(R\alpha) + I\alpha = (R^2m + I)\alpha.$$

Solving for α we find

$$\alpha = \frac{Rmg}{R^2m + I}.$$

This answer makes sense intuitively. From the rotating disk's point of view, the cause of rotation is the torque produced by the falling mass, while the denominator represents the total moment of inertia for the mass-pulley system as a whole.

The vertical acceleration of the falling mass is obtained via $a_y = R\alpha$:

$$a_y = \frac{R^2mg}{R^2m + I} = \frac{mg}{m + \frac{I}{R^2}}.$$

From the point of view of the falling mass, the cause of the motion is the weight of the object $W = mg$, while the denominator represents the total inertia of the system. Recall that *inertia* in this case refers to the notion of "resistance to motion." The effective inertia of the system is the combination of the mass m and the moment of inertia of the disk I divided by R^2.

Conservation of angular momentum

A spinning figure skater starts from an initial angular velocity of $\omega_i = 12$[rad/s] with her arms extending away from her body. In this position, her body's moment of inertia is $I_i = 3$[kg m^2]. The skater then brings her arms close to her body, and in the process her moment of inertia changes to $I_f = 0.5$[kg m^2]. What is her new angular velocity?

This is a job for the law of conservation of angular momentum:

$$L_i = L_f \qquad \Rightarrow \qquad I_i\omega_i = I_f\omega_f.$$

We know I_i, ω_i, and I_f, so we can solve for the final angular velocity ω_f. The answer is $\omega_f = I_i\omega_i/I_f = 3 \times 12/0.5 = 72$[rad/s], which corresponds to 11.46 turns per second.

Conservation of energy

You have a 14[in] bicycle wheel with mass $m = 4$[kg], with nearly all of its mass concentrated near the outside rim. The wheel is set in rolling motion up an incline at a velocity of 20[m/s]. How far up the incline will the wheel reach before it stops?

We can solve this problem with the principle of conservation of energy $\sum E_i = \sum E_f$. We must account for both the linear and rotational kinetic energies of the wheel:

$$\begin{aligned} K_i \ + \ K_{ri} \ + U_i &= K_f + K_{rf} + U_f\,, \\ \frac{1}{2}mv^2 + \frac{1}{2}I\omega^2 + 0 &= \ 0 \ + \ 0 \ + mgh. \end{aligned}$$

First, calculate I_{wheel} using the formula $I_{\text{ring}} = mR^2 = 4 \times (0.355)^2 = 0.5[\text{kg m}^2]$. If the wheel's linear velocity is 20[m/s], then its angular velocity is $\omega = v_t/R = 20/0.355 = 56.34[\text{rad/s}]$. We can now use these values in the conservation of energy equation:

$$\frac{1}{2}(4)(20)^2 + \frac{1}{2}(0.5)(56.34)^2 + 0 = 800.0 + 793.55 = (4)(9.81)h.$$

The wheel will reach a maximum height of $h = 40.61[\text{m}]$.

Note that roughly half the wheel's kinetic energy is stored in its rotational motion. This demonstrates the importance of accounting for K_r when solving energy problems involving rotating objects.

Static equilibrium

We say a system is in *equilibrium* when all forces and torques acting on the system "balance each other out." If an object is not moving, we say the object is in *static equilibrium*. Basically, zero motion implies zero net force. If you see an object that is completely still, then the forces and torques acting on it must be in equilibrium:

$$\sum F_x = 0, \quad \sum F_y = 0, \quad \sum \mathcal{T} = 0. \tag{4.15}$$

Equilibrium means there is zero net force in the x-direction, zero net force in the y-direction, and zero net torque acting on the object.

Example: Walking the plank

A heavy wooden plank is placed so one-third of its length protrudes from the side of a pirate ship as illustrated in Figure 4.20. The plank has a total length of 12[m] and a total weight of 120[kg]. How far onto the plank can a person weighing 100[kg] walk before the plank tips into the ocean?

We'll use the torque equilibrium equation $\sum \mathcal{T}_E = 0$, where we calculate the torques relative to the edge of the ship, the point around which the plank will pivot. There are two torques involved: the

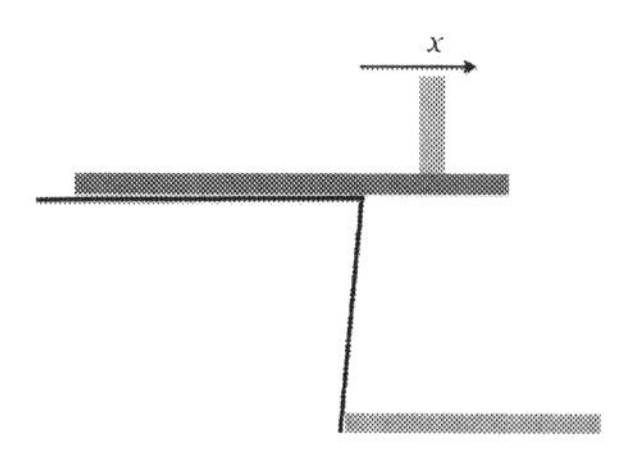

Figure 4.20: How far can the person walk on the plank before it tips over?

torque produced by the plank's weight and the torque produced by the person's weight. The plank's weight acts in its centre of mass, which is located 2[m] from the edge of the ship. The torque produced by the weight of the plank is therefore given by $\mathcal{T}_2 = 120g \times 2 = 240g$[N m]. The torque produced by the person when he reaches a distance of x[m] from the edge of the ship is $\mathcal{T}_1 = -100gx$[N m]. Thus, the maximum distance the person can walk before the plank tips is $x = \frac{240g}{100g} = 2.4$[m].

Discussion

In this section, we applied the techniques and ideas from linear motion in order to describe the rotational motion of objects. Our coverage of rotational motion has been relatively brief because there were no new notions of physics to be learned.

Calling upon our prior knowledge of physics, we explored the parallels between the new rotational concepts and their linear counterparts. It is important you understand these parallels. To help you connect the notions of rotational motion with the notions of linear motion, you can revisit the diagram on page 238 in the beginning of this section.

Let's summarize. If you know the torque acting on an object, and the object's moment of inertia, you can calculate its angular acceleration α. If you know the object's angular acceleration $\alpha(t)$, its initial angular position θ_i, and its initial angular velocity ω_i, you can calculate its equation of motion $\theta(t)$, which tells you the object's angular position at all times.

Furthermore, a rotating object's angular velocity ω is related to its *angular momentum* $L = I\omega$ and its *rotational kinetic energy* $K_r = \frac{1}{2}I\omega^2$. Angular momentum measures the "quantity of rotational motion," while rotational kinetic energy measures how much energy the object has by virtue of its rotational motion.

In rotational equations, the moment of inertia I plays the role of the mass m. In the equation $\mathcal{T} = I\alpha$, the moment of inertia I measures how difficult it is to make the object turn. The moment of

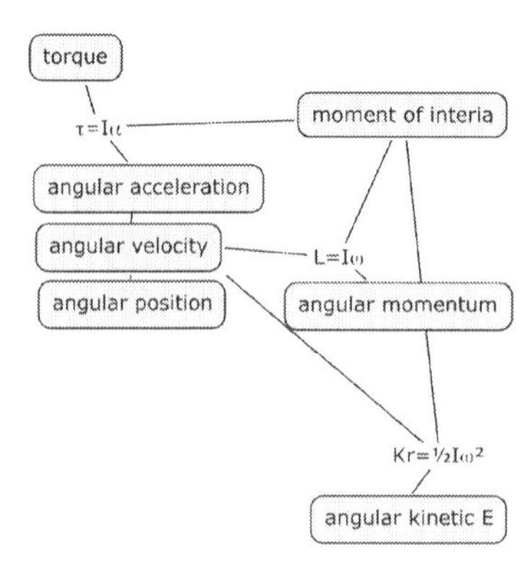

Figure 4.21: The main concepts used to describe angular motion.

inertia also appears in the formulas for finding a spinning object's angular momentum and its rotational kinetic energy.

4.9 Simple harmonic motion

Vibrations, oscillations, and waves are everywhere around us. For example, what appears to our eyes as white light is actually made of many different oscillations of the electromagnetic field. These oscillations vibrate at a range of frequencies, which correspond to the colours we perceive. Sounds are also made of combined air vibrations with various frequencies and strengths. In this section, we'll learn about *simple harmonic motion*, which describes the oscillation of a mechanical system at a fixed frequency and with a constant amplitude. As its name suggests, simple harmonic motion is the simplest form of oscillatory motion. By studying oscillations in their simplest form, you'll gather important intuition that applies to all types of oscillations and wave phenomena.

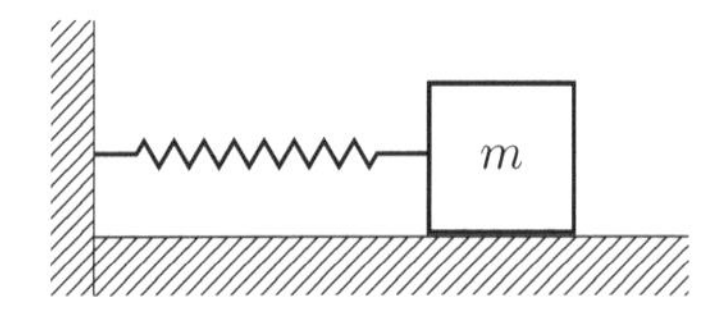

Figure 4.22: A block of mass m attached to a spring.

The canonical example of simple harmonic motion is the motion of a mass-spring system, as illustrated in Figure 4.22. The block is free to slide along the horizontal frictionless surface. If the system is disturbed from its equilibrium position, it will start to oscillate back and forth at a certain *natural* frequency, which depends on the mass of the block and the stiffness of the spring.

We'll focus our attention on two mechanical systems: the mass-spring system and the simple pendulum. We'll follow the usual approach by describing the positions, velocities, accelerations, and energies associated with these two kinds of motion. The notion of *simple harmonic motion* (SHM) reaches further than these two systems. The equations and intuition developed while analyzing the oscillations within these simple mechanical systems can be applied more generally to sound oscillations, electric current oscillations, and even quantum oscillations. Pay attention, is all I'm saying.

Concepts

- A: The *amplitude* of the movement is how far the object moves back and forth relative to its centre position.
- $x(t)[\text{m}]$, $v(t)[\text{m/s}]$, $a(t)[\text{m/s}^2]$: position, velocity, and acceleration of the object as functions of time
- $T[\text{s}]$: the *period* of the object's motion. The period is how long it takes for the motion to repeat.
- $f[\text{Hz}]$: the *frequency* of the motion
- $\omega[\text{rad/s}]$: *angular frequency*
- $\phi[\text{rad}]$: the phase shift denoted by the Greek letter *phee*

Simple harmonic motion

Figure 4.23 illustrates a mass-spring system undergoing simple harmonic motion. The position of the mass as a function of time oscillates like the cosine function. From the diagram, we can identify two important parameters of the system's motion: the amplitude A, which describes the maximum displacement of the mass from the centre position, and the period T, which describes how long it takes the mass to return to its initial position.

The equation that describes the object's position as a function of time is

$$x(t) = A\cos(\omega t + \phi).$$

The constant ω (omega) represents the *angular frequency* of the motion. Angular frequency is related to the period T by the equation $\omega = \frac{2\pi}{T}$. The additive constant ϕ (*phee*) is called the *phase shift*. Its value depends on the initial condition for the motion $x_i \equiv x(0)$.

I don't want you to be scared by the formula for simple harmonic motion. I know there are a lot of Greek letters in there, but it is actually pretty simple. In order to understand the purpose of the three

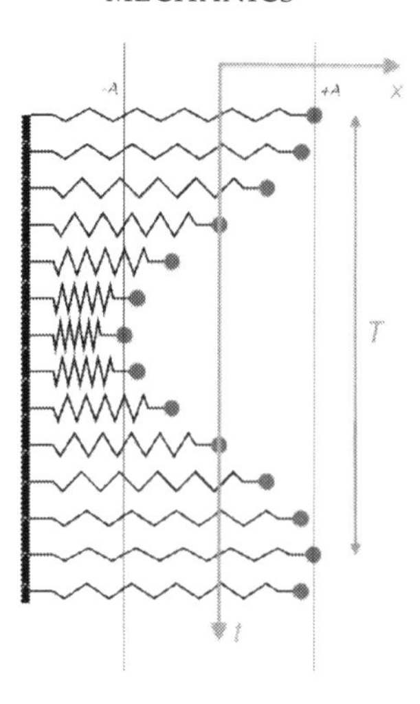

Figure 4.23: A mass-spring system undergoing simple harmonic motion.

parameters A, ω, and ϕ, let's quickly review the properties of the cos function.

Review of sin and cos functions

The functions $f(t) = \sin(t)$ and $f(t) = \cos(t)$ are periodic functions that oscillate between -1 and 1 with a period of 2π. Previously we used the functions cos and sin to find the horizontal and vertical components of vectors, and we called the input variable θ (theta). However, in this section the input variable is the time t measured in seconds. Look carefully at the plot of the function $\cos(t)$ in Figure 4.24. As t goes from $t = 0$ to $t = 2\pi$, the function $\cos(t)$ completes one full cycle. We say the *period* of $\cos(t)$ is $T = 2\pi$.

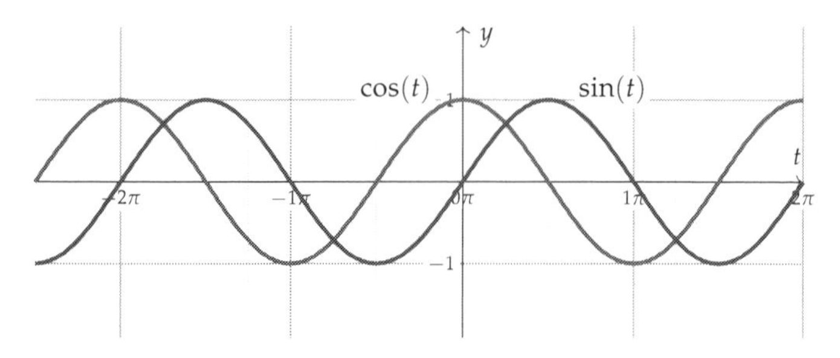

Figure 4.24: Graphs of the periodic functions $\sin t$ and $\cos t$.

Input-scaling

If we want to describe a periodic motion with a different period, we can still use the cos function, but inside the cos function we must include a multiplier before the variable t. This multiplier describes the *angular frequency* and is denoted ω (*omega*). The input-scaled cos function

$$f(t) = \cos(\omega t)$$

has a period of $T = \frac{2\pi}{\omega}$.

Scaling the input of the cos function by the constant $\omega = \frac{2\pi}{T}$ produces a periodic function with period T. When you vary t from 0 to T, the quantity ωt goes from 0 to 2π, so the function $\cos(\omega t)$ completes one cycle. You shouldn't just take my word for this; try it yourself by drawing a cos function with a period of 3 units.

The *frequency* of periodic motion describes the number of times per second the motion repeats. The frequency is equal to the inverse of the period:

$$f = \frac{1}{T} = \frac{\omega}{2\pi} \text{ [Hz]}.$$

Frequency f and angular frequency ω are related by a factor of 2π. We need this multiplier since the natural cycle length of the cos function is 2π radians.

Output-scaling

We can scale the output of the cos function by a constant A, called the *amplitude*. The function

$$f(t) = A\cos(\omega t)$$

will oscillate between A and $-A$.

Time-shifting

The motion described by the function $A\cos(\omega t)$ starts from its maximum value at $t = 0$. A mass-spring system described by the position function $x(t) = A\cos(\omega t)$ begins its motion with the spring maximally stretched $x_i \equiv x(0) = A$.

If we want to describe other starting positions for the motion, it may be necessary to introduce a *phase shift* inside the cos function:

$$x(t) = A\cos(\omega t + \phi).$$

The constant ϕ must be chosen so that at $t = 0$, the function $x(t)$ correctly describes the initial position of the system.

For example, if the harmonic motion starts from the system's centre $x_i \equiv x(0) = 0$ and initially moves in the positive direction, then the motion is described by the function $A\sin(\omega t)$. Or, since $\sin(\theta) = \cos(\theta - \frac{\pi}{2})$, we can describe the same motion in terms of a shifted cos function:

$$x(t) = A\cos\left(\omega t - \frac{\pi}{2}\right) = A\sin(\omega t).$$

Note, the function $x(t)$ correctly describes the system's initial position $x(0) = 0$.

By now, the meaning of all the parameters in the simple harmonic motion equation should be clear to you. The constant in front of the cos tells us the motion's amplitude A, and the multiplicative constant ω inside the cos is related to the motion's period/frequency: $\omega = \frac{2\pi}{T} = 2\pi f$. Finally, the additive constant ϕ is chosen depending on the initial conditions.

Mass and spring

Okay, it's time to apply all this math to a physical system which exhibits simple harmonic motion: the mass-spring system.

An object of mass m attached to a spring with spring constant k, when disturbed from rest, will undergo simple harmonic motion with angular frequency

$$\omega = \sqrt{\frac{k}{m}}. \tag{4.16}$$

A stiff spring attached to a small mass will result in very rapid oscillations. A weak spring or a heavy mass will result in slow oscillations.

A typical exam question may tell you k and m and ask about the period T. If you remember the definition of T, you can easily calculate the answer:

$$T = \frac{2\pi}{\omega} = 2\pi\sqrt{\frac{m}{k}}.$$

Equations of motion

The general equations of motion for the mass-spring system are

$$x(t) = A\cos(\omega t + \phi), \tag{4.17}$$

$$v(t) = -A\omega\sin(\omega t + \phi), \tag{4.18}$$

$$a(t) = -A\omega^2\cos(\omega t + \phi). \tag{4.19}$$

The general shape of the function $x(t)$ is similar to that of a cos function. The *angular frequency* ω parameter is governed by the physical properties of the system. The parameters A and ϕ describe the specifics of the motion, namely, the *amplitude* of the oscillation and its starting position.

The function $v(t)$ is obtained, as usual, by taking the derivative of $x(t)$. The function $a(t)$ is obtained by taking the derivative of $v(t)$, which corresponds to the second derivative of $x(t)$. The velocity and acceleration are also periodic functions.

Motion parameters

The key motion parameter of SHM is how far the mass swings back and forth through the *centre position*. The amplitude A describes the maximum distance the mass will travel in the positive x-direction.

We can also find the maximum values of an object's velocity and acceleration by reading the coefficient located in front of sin and cos in the functions $v(t)$ and $a(t)$.

- The object's maximum velocity is $v_{\max} = A\omega$.
- The object's maximum acceleration is $a_{\max} = A\omega^2$.

The velocity function reaches its maximum as the object passes through the centre position. The acceleration is maximum when the spring is maximally stretched or compressed—these are the locations where the pull of the spring is the strongest.

You'll definitely be asked to solve for the quantities $v_{\max}$ and $a_{\max}$ in exercises and exams. This is an easy task if you remember the above formulas and you know the values of the amplitude A and the angular frequency ω. Note the term *amplitude* applies more generally to the constant in front of *any* sin or cos function. Thus, we say that A is the amplitude of the position, $v_{\max} = A\omega$ is the amplitude of the velocity, and $a_{\max} = A\omega^2$ is the amplitude of the acceleration.

Energy

The potential energy stored in a spring that is stretched or compressed by a length x is given by the formula $U_s = \frac{1}{2}kx^2$. Since we know $x(t)$, we can obtain the potential energy of the mass-spring system as a function of time:

$$U_s(t) = \frac{1}{2}k[x(t)]^2 = \frac{1}{2}kA^2\cos^2(\omega t + \phi).$$

The potential energy reaches its maximum value $U_{s,\max} = \frac{1}{2}kA^2$ when the spring is fully stretched or fully compressed.

The kinetic energy of the mass as a function of time is given by

$$K(t) = \frac{1}{2}m[v(t)]^2 = \frac{1}{2}m\omega^2 A^2 \sin^2(\omega t + \phi).$$

The kinetic energy is maximum when the mass passes through the centre position. The maximum kinetic energy is given by $K_{\max} = \frac{1}{2}mv_{\max}^2 = \frac{1}{2}mA^2\omega^2$.

Conservation of energy

Since the mass-spring system does not experience any dissipative forces (friction), the total energy of the system $E_T(t) = U_s(t) + K(t)$ must be *conserved*. The conservation of energy principle says that the sum of the system's potential energy and its kinetic energy must be the same at any two instants t_1 and t_2:

$$E_T(t_1) = U_s(t_1) + K(t_1) = U_s(t_2) + K(t_2) = E_T(t_2).$$

According to this equation, even if $U_s(t)$ and $K(t)$ change over time, the system's total energy $E_T(t)$ always remains constant.

Let us convince ourselves the system's total energy is indeed a constant. We can use the identity $\cos^2\theta + \sin^2\theta = 1$ to find the value of this constant:

$$\begin{aligned}
E_T(t) &= U_s(t) + K(t) \\
&= \frac{1}{2}kA^2\cos^2(\omega t) + \frac{1}{2}m\omega^2 A^2 \sin^2(\omega t) \\
&= \frac{1}{2}m\omega^2 A^2\cos^2(\omega t) + \frac{1}{2}m\omega^2 A^2 \sin^2(\omega t) \quad (\text{since } k = m\omega^2) \\
&= \frac{1}{2}m\underbrace{\omega^2 A^2}_{v_{\max}^2}\underbrace{\left[\cos^2(\omega t) + \sin^2(\omega t)\right]}_{=1} = \frac{1}{2}mv_{\max}^2 = K_{\max} \\
&= \frac{1}{2}m\omega^2 A^2 = \frac{1}{2}(m\omega^2)A^2 = \frac{1}{2}kA^2 = U_{s,\max}.
\end{aligned}$$

The system's total energy is equal to $U_{s,\max}$ and to $K_{\max}$.

The best way to understand simple harmonic motion is to visualize how the system's energy shifts between the spring's potential energy and the kinetic energy of the moving mass. When the spring is maximally stretched $x = \pm A$, the mass will have zero velocity and thus zero kinetic energy $K = 0$. At this moment of maximal displacement, all the system's energy is stored in the potential energy of the spring $E_T = U_{s,\max}$.

The other important moment happens when the mass has zero displacement. In this moment the position $x = 0$ implies there is zero potential energy in the spring $U_s = 0$. This is when the velocity is maximum $v = \pm A\omega$ and all the system's energy is stored entirely in its kinetic energy $E_T = K_{\text{max}}$.

Pendulum motion

We now turn our attention to another simple mechanical system in which motion is described by the simple harmonic motion equations: the pendulum.

A pendulum is a mass suspended at the end of a string of length ℓ. Imagine pulling the mass so it is positioned a certain angle θ_{max} away from the pendulum's vertical resting position. When you release the mass, the pendulum swings back and forth undergoing simple harmonic motion.

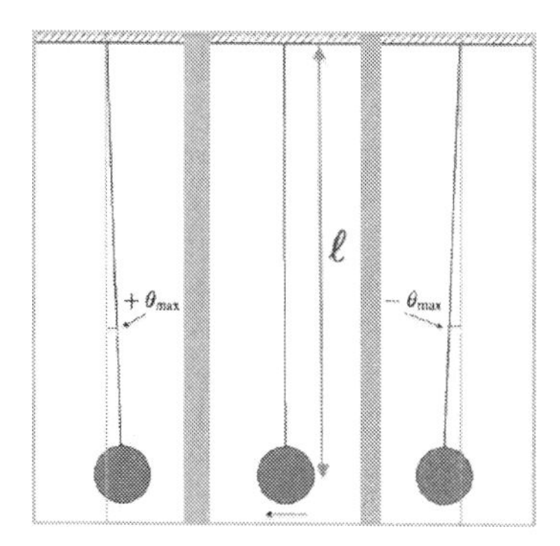

Figure 4.25: The motion of a pendulum started from the initial angle θ_{max}.

In a gravitational field of strength g, the pendulum's period of oscillation is given by the formula

$$T = 2\pi\sqrt{\frac{\ell}{g}}.$$

Note, the period does not depend on the amplitude of the oscillation (how far the pendulum swings), nor does the period depend on the pendulum's mass. The only factors that play a role in determining the period of oscillation are the length of the string ℓ and the strength of the gravitational field g. Recall that angular frequency is defined as $\omega = \frac{2\pi}{T}$, so the angular frequency for the pendulum is

$$\omega \equiv \frac{2\pi}{T} = \sqrt{\frac{g}{\ell}}. \tag{4.20}$$

Instead of describing the pendulum's position x with respect to the xy-coordinate system, we describe its position in terms of the angle

θ it makes with the vertical line that passes through the centre of the motion. The equations of motion are described in terms of *angular quantities*: the angular position θ, the angular velocity ω_θ, and the angular acceleration α_θ of the pendulum:

$$\begin{aligned}
\theta(t) &= \theta_{\max} \cos\left(\sqrt{\frac{g}{\ell}}t + \phi\right), \\
\omega_\theta(t) &= -\theta_{\max}\sqrt{\frac{g}{\ell}} \sin\left(\sqrt{\frac{g}{\ell}}t + \phi\right), \\
\alpha_\theta(t) &= -\theta_{\max}\frac{g}{\ell} \cos\left(\sqrt{\frac{g}{\ell}}t + \phi\right).
\end{aligned}$$

The angle $\theta_{\max}$ describes the maximum angle to which the pendulum swings. Notice the new variable name ω_θ we use for the pendulum's angular velocity $\omega_\theta(t) = \frac{d}{dt}(\theta(t))$. The angular velocity ω_θ of the pendulum should not be confused with the *angular frequency* $\omega = \sqrt{\frac{g}{\ell}}$ of the periodic motion, which is the constant inside the cos function.

Energy

A pendulum's motion is best understood by imagining how the energy in the system shifts between gravitational potential energy and kinetic energy.

The pendulum reaches its maximum potential energy when it swings sideways to reach angle $\theta_{\max}$. At this angle, the mass's vertical position is increased by a height h above the mass's lowest point, as illustrated in Figure 4.26. We can calculate h as follows:

$$h = \ell - \ell\cos\theta_{\max}.$$

The maximum gravitational potential energy of the mass is therefore

$$U_{g,\max} = mgh = mg\ell(1 - \cos\theta_{\max}).$$

By the conservation of energy principle, the pendulum's maximum kinetic energy must equal its maximum gravitational potential energy:

$$mg\ell(1 - \cos\theta_{\max}) = U_{g,\max} = K_{\max} = \frac{1}{2}mv_{\max}^2,$$

where $v_{\max} = \ell\omega_\theta$ is the linear velocity of the mass as it swings through the centre position.

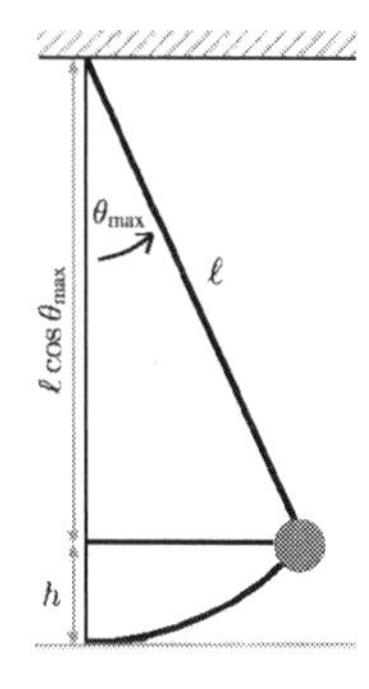

Figure 4.26: The height h of the mass relative to its lowest point.

Explanations

It's worthwhile to understand where the simple harmonic motion equation comes from. In this subsection, we'll discuss how the equation $x(t) = A\cos(\omega t + \phi)$ is derived from Newton's second law $F = ma$ and the equation for the force of a spring $F_s = -kx$.

Trigonometric derivatives

The slope (derivative) of the function $\sin(t)$ varies between -1 and 1. The slope is largest when sin passes through the x-axis, and the slope is zero when the function reaches its maximum and minimum values. A careful examination of the graphs of the bare functions sin and cos reveals that the derivative of the function $\sin(t)$ is described by the function $\cos(t)$, and vice versa:

$$f(t) = \sin(t) \qquad \Rightarrow \qquad f'(t) = \cos(t),$$

$$f(t) = \cos(t) \qquad \Rightarrow \qquad f'(t) = -\sin(t).$$

When you learn more about calculus, you'll know how to find the derivative of any function you want; for now, you can take my word that the above two formulas are true.

The chain rule for derivatives (page 309) dictates that a composite function $f(g(x))$ has derivative $f'(g(x)) \cdot g'(x)$. First we take the derivative of the outer function, then we multiply by the derivative of the inner function. We can find the derivative of the position function $x(t) = A\cos(\omega t + \phi)$ using the chain rule:

$$v(t) \equiv x'(t) = -A\sin(\omega t + \phi) \cdot \omega = -A\omega \sin(\omega t + \phi),$$

where the outer function is $f(x) = A\cos(x)$ with derivative $f'(x) = -A\sin(x)$, and the inner function is $g(x) = \omega x + \phi$ with derivative $g'(x) = \omega$.

The same reasoning is applied to obtain the second derivative:

$$a(t) \equiv \frac{d}{dt}\{v(t)\} = -A\omega^2 \cos(\omega t + \phi) = -\omega^2 x(t).$$

Note the function $a(t) \equiv x''(t)$ has the same form as the function $x(t)$; the two functions differ only by the factor $-\omega^2$.

Derivation of the mass-spring SHM equation

You may be wondering where the equation $x(t) = A\cos(\omega t + \phi)$ comes from. This formula looks very different from the kinematics equation for linear motion $x(t) = x_i + v_i t + \frac{1}{2}at^2$, which we obtained starting with Newton's second law $F = ma$ and completing two steps of integration.

In this section, I've seemingly pulled the $x(t) = A\cos(\omega t + \phi)$ formula out of thin air, as if by revelation. Why did we suddenly start talking about cos functions and Greek letters with dubious names like "phase"? Are you fazed by all of this? When I was first learning about simple harmonic motion, I was totally fazed because I didn't see where the sin and cos were coming from.

The cos also comes from $F = ma$, but the story is a little more complicated this time. The force exerted by a spring is $F_s = -kx$. Since we assume the surface the mass slides along is frictionless, the only force acting on the mass is the force of the spring:

$$\sum F = F_s = ma \qquad \Rightarrow \qquad -kx = ma.$$

Recall that the acceleration function is the second derivative of the position function:

$$a(t) \equiv \frac{dv(t)}{dt} \equiv \frac{d^2x(t)}{dt^2} \equiv x''(t).$$

We can rewrite the equation $-kx = ma$ in terms of the function $x(t)$ and its second derivative:

$$-kx(t) = m\frac{d^2x(t)}{dt^2}$$

$$-\frac{k}{m}x(t) = \frac{d^2x(t)}{dt^2},$$

which can be rewritten as

$$0 = \frac{d^2x(t)}{dt^2} + \frac{k}{m}x(t).$$

This is called a *differential equation*. Instead of looking for an *unknown number* as in normal equations, in differential equations we are looking for an *unknown function* $x(t)$. We do not know what the function $x(t)$ is, but the differential equation tells us one of its properties: the second derivative of $x(t)$ is equal to the negative of $x(t)$ multiplied by some constant.

To solve a differential equation you must guess which function $x(t)$ satisfies this property. Engineering and physics students must take a differential equations course to learn to do this guessing thing. Can you think of a function that, when multiplied by $\frac{k}{m}$, is equal to its second derivative?

Okay, I thought of one:

$$x_1(t) = A_1 \cos\left(\sqrt{\frac{k}{m}}t\right).$$

Come to think of it, there is also a second function that works:

$$x_2(t) = A_2 \sin\left(\sqrt{\frac{k}{m}}t\right).$$

You should try this for yourself. Verify that $x_1''(t) + \frac{k}{m}x_1(t) = 0$ and $x_2''(t) + \frac{k}{m}x_2(t) = 0$, which means these functions are *both* solutions to the differential equation $x''(t) + \frac{k}{m}x(t) = 0$. Since both $x_1(t)$ and $x_2(t)$ are solutions, their sum must also be a solution:

$$x(t) = A_1 \cos(\omega t) + A_2 \sin(\omega t).$$

This is *kind of* the answer we're looking for: an expression that describes the object's position as a function of time. I say *kind of* because the solution we obtained is not specified as a cos function with amplitude A and a phase ϕ, but instead in terms of the coefficients A_1 and A_2, which describe the cos and sin components of the motion.

Lo and behold, using the trigonometric identity $\cos(a+b) = \cos(a)\cos(b) - \sin(a)\sin(b)$ (see page 89), we can rewrite the above expression for $x(t)$ as a time-shifted cos function:

$$x(t) = A\cos(\omega t + \phi) = A_1 \cos(\omega t) + A_2 \sin(\omega t),$$

where $A_1 = A\cos(\phi)$ and $A_2 = -A\sin(\phi)$. The expression on the left is the preferred way of describing simple harmonic motion because the parameters A and ϕ correspond to observable aspects of the motion. If we know the coefficients A_1 and A_2, we can find the canonical parameters A and ϕ using $A = \sqrt{A_1^2 + A_2^2}$ and $\phi = \tan^{-1}(A_2/A_1)$.

Let's review one more time: we are looking for the equation of motion that predicts an object's position as a function of time $x(t)$. We can draw an analogy to a situation we've seen before. In linear kinematics, uniform accelerated motion with $a(t) = a$ is described by the equation $x(t) = x_i + v_i t + \frac{1}{2}at^2$ in terms of parameters x_i and v_i. Depending on the object's initial position and initial velocity, we obtain different trajectories. Simple harmonic motion with angular frequency ω is described by the equation $x(t) = A\cos(\omega t + \phi)$ in terms of the parameters A and ϕ. Depending on the values of the amplitude A and the phase ϕ, we obtain different simple harmonic motion trajectories.

Derivation of the pendulum SHM equation

To see how the simple harmonic motion equation for the pendulum is derived, we need to start from the torque equation $\mathcal{T} = I\alpha$.

Figure 4.27 illustrates how we can calculate the torque on the pendulum, which is caused by the force of gravity on the mass as a function of the displacement angle θ. Recall the torque calculation only accounts for the $F_\perp$ component of any force, since this is the only part of the force that causes rotation:

$$\mathcal{T}_\theta = F_\perp \ell = -mg\sin\theta\ell.$$

The torque is negative because it acts in the opposite direction to the displacement angle θ.

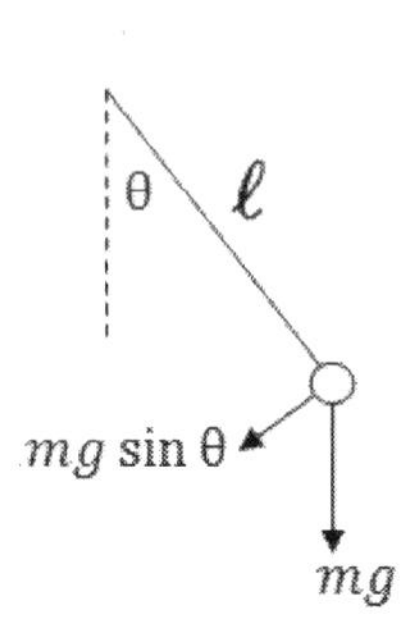

Figure 4.27: Force diagram of a pendulum showing the weight component $mg\sin\theta$ that causes the torque $\mathcal{T}$.

Now we substitute this expression for $\mathcal{T}_\theta$ into the angular version of Newton's second law $\mathcal{T} = I\alpha$ to obtain

$$\begin{aligned}\mathcal{T} &= I\alpha \\ -mg\sin\theta(t)\ell &= m\ell^2\frac{d^2\theta(t)}{dt^2} \\ -g\sin\theta(t) &= \ell\frac{d^2\theta(t)}{dt^2}.\end{aligned}$$

To continue with the derivation, we must make an approximation. When θ is a small angle, we can use the following approximation:

$$\sin(\theta) \approx \theta, \qquad \text{for } \theta \ll 1.$$

This is known as a *small angle approximation*. You'll see where it comes from later when you learn about Taylor series approximations to functions (page 396). For now, you can convince yourself of the above formula by zooming in near the origin on the graph of the function $\sin x$ until you realize $y = \sin(x)$ looks very much like $y = x$.

Using the small angle approximation $\sin\theta \approx \theta$, we rewrite the equation involving $\theta(t)$ and its second derivative as

$$\begin{aligned}-g\sin\theta(t) &= \ell\frac{d^2\theta(t)}{dt^2} \\ -g\theta(t) &\approx \ell\frac{d^2\theta(t)}{dt^2} \\ 0 &= \frac{d^2\theta(t)}{dt^2} + \frac{g}{\ell}\theta(t).\end{aligned}$$

Now we can recognize that we're dealing with the same differential equation as in the case of the mass-spring system: $\theta''(t) + \omega^2\theta(t) = 0$, which has the solution

$$\theta(t) = \theta_{\max}\cos(\omega t + \phi),$$

where the constant inside the cos function is $\omega = \sqrt{\frac{g}{\ell}}$.

Examples

Most word problems will usually tell you the initial amplitude $x_i = A$ or the initial velocity $v_i = \omega A$ of the SHM and ask you to calculate some other quantity. Answering these problems shouldn't be too difficult if you write down the general equations for $x(t)$, $v(t)$, and $a(t)$, fill-in the known quantities, and then solve for the unknowns.

Example

You are observing a mass-spring system built from a 1[kg] mass and a 250[N/m] spring. The amplitude of the mass's oscillation is 10[cm]. Determine (a) the mass's maximum speed, (b) the maximum acceleration, and (c) the total mechanical energy in the system.

First we must find this system's angular frequency: $\omega = \sqrt{k/m} = \sqrt{250/1} = 15.81$[rad/s]. To find (a) we use the equation $v_{\max} = \omega A = 15.81 \times 0.1 = 1.58$[m/s]. Similarly, we can find the maximum acceleration using $a_{\max} = \omega^2 A = 15.81^2 \times 0.1 = 25$[m/s^2]. There are two equivalent ways to solve for (c). We can obtain the system's total energy by considering the spring's potential energy when it is maximally stretched or maximally compressed: $E_T = U_s(A) = \frac{1}{2}kA^2 = 1.25$[J]. Or, we can obtain the total energy from the maximum kinetic energy $E_T = K = \frac{1}{2}mv_{\max}^2 = 1.25$[J].

Discussion

In this section we learned about simple harmonic motion, which is described by the equation $x(t) = A\cos(\omega t + \phi)$. You may be wondering what *non-simple* harmonic motion is. You could extend what we've learned by studying oscillating systems where the energy is slowly dissipating. This is known as *damped harmonic motion*, for which the equation of motion looks like $x(t) = Ae^{-\gamma t}\cos(\omega t + \phi)$. This equation describes an oscillation with an amplitude that slowly decreases. The coefficient γ is known as the damping coefficient, and indicates how quickly the system's energy dissipates.

The concept of simple harmonic motion arises in many other areas of physics. When you learn about electric circuits, capacitors, and inductors, you'll run into equations of the form $v''(t) + \omega^2 v(t) = 0$, which indicates that a circuit's *voltage* is undergoing simple harmonic motion. Guess what—the same equation that describes the mechanical motion of the mass-spring system is used to describe the voltage in an oscillating circuit!

Links

[Plot of the simple harmonic motion using a can of spray-paint]
`http://www.youtube.com/watch?v=p9uhmjbZn-c`

[Slow motion movie clip of a mass-spring system]
`http://bit.ly/QTRse3`

[15 pendulums with different lengths]
`http://www.youtube.com/watch?v=yVkdfJ9PkRQ`

4.10 Conclusion

The fundamental purpose of mechanics is to predict the motion of objects using equations. In the beginning of the chapter, I claimed there are only 20 equations you need to know in order to solve any physics problem. Let us verify this claim and review the material we've covered.

Our goal was to find $x(t)$ for all times t. However, none of the equations of physics tell us $x(t)$ directly. Instead, we have Newton's second law $F = ma$, which tells us that the acceleration of the object $a(t)$ equals the *net force* acting on the object divided by the object's mass. To find $x(t)$ starting from $a(t)$, we use integration twice:

$$\frac{1}{m}\left(\sum \vec{F} \equiv \vec{F}_{\text{net}}\right) = a(t) \overset{v_i+\int dt}{\longrightarrow} v(t) \overset{x_i+\int dt}{\longrightarrow} x(t).$$

We studied kinematics in several different contexts. We originally looked at kinematics problems in one dimension, and derived the UAM and UVM equations. We also studied the problem of projectile motion by deconstructing it into two separate kinematics subproblems: one in the x-direction (UVM), and one in the y-direction (UAM). Later, we studied the circular motion of objects and stated equation $a_r = \frac{v_t^2}{r}$, which describes an important relationship between the radial acceleration, the tangential velocity, and the radius of the circle of rotation. We also studied rotational motion using angular kinematics quantities $\theta(t)$, $\omega(t)$, and $\alpha(t)$. We defined the concept of *torque* and saw the role it plays in the angular equivalent of Newton's second law $\mathcal{T} = I\alpha$. We studied the equation that describes simple harmonic motion, $x(t) = A\cos(\omega t + \phi)$, and showed the formula $\omega = \sqrt{\frac{k}{m}}$, which gives the angular frequency of a mass-spring system.

We also discussed three conservation laws: the conservation of linear momentum law $\sum \vec{p}_i = \sum \vec{p}_f$, the conservation of angular momentum law $L_i = L_f$, and the conservation of energy law $\sum E_i = \sum E_f$. Each of these three fundamental quantities is conserved overall and can neither be created nor destroyed. Momentum calculations are used to analyze collisions, while energy formulas like equations $K = \frac{1}{2}mv^2$, $U_g = mgh$, and $U_s = \frac{1}{2}kx^2$ can be used to analyze the motion of objects in terms of energy principles.

Now you can see how 20 equations truly are enough to master all of mechanics. Nice work! Your next step should be to practice solving some problems in order to solidify your understanding.

4.11 Mechanics problems

It's now time for you to verify experimentally how well you've understood the material from this chapter. Try solving the physics problems presented in this section. Go ahead, dig in! And don't be discouraged if you find some of the problems difficult—they are meant to be challenging in order to force you to think hard and reinforce the connections between the concepts in your head.

When solving physics problems, I recommend you follow this five-step procedure:

1. Figure out what **type of problem** you are dealing with. Is it a kinematics problem? A momentum problem? An energy problem? A problem about angular motion?

2. Draw a **diagram** that describes the physical situation. If the problem involves vectors, draw a coordinate system. Label the known and the unknown quantities in the diagram.

3. Write down the physics **formulas** that are usually used for the type of problem you're solving. You can copy the necessary formulas from the table on page 484.

4. Substitute the **known quantities** into the equations and determine which unknown(s) you need to find. Visualize the steps you'll take to solve for the unknown(s).

5. Do the math.

Note that math appears only in the last step. If you want to solve a physics problem and the first thing you do is manipulate equations and numbers, you're shooting yourself in the foot. Physics is not about solving equations; rather, the focus of physics is thinking abstractly about the "moving parts" in the problem: positions, velocities, energies, etc. As far as I'm concerned, if you complete Steps 1, 2, 3, and 4 correctly and make a mistake in Step 5, you're good in my books. Manipulating math equations fluently and errorlessly is a skill that takes time to hone. If you're still new to the techniques covered in Chapters 1–3, it's normal to make mistakes. Don't worry about it; just practice.

Make sure you attempt each of the exercises on your own before looking at the answers and the solutions. If you want to practice Step 1 of the "solving physics problems" procedure, don't look at the hints. The first step, determining the type of problem, is very strategic and you need to practice it. The problems are intentionally presented out of order, to force you to think about Step 1. Knowing what type of problem you're dealing with is the part that most closely resembles what physics research is like. Given a physics question, physicists try to visualize the situation, label the variables of the problem, and then ask "What can I use here?" Earlier, I likened working with physics equations to playing with LEGOs. You must find the physics equation (or principle) that "fits" the problem. Once you've identified the type of problem, writing the equations and doing the math become comparatively easier tasks. The cool part about learning physics in the "controlled environment" of this problem set is that one of the equations you learned is guaranteed to work.[1]

P4.1 You throw a water balloon from ground level with initial velocity $\vec{v}_i$ at an angle θ above the horizontal.

1. Find $v_y(t)$, the vertical velocity of the balloon as a function of time: (a) when the y-axis points up and (b) when the y-axis points down.
2. A cat starts running away from you just as the you throw the balloon. If the cat's horizontal velocity v_{cat} is equal to v_{ix} of the balloon, will the cat get splashed by the balloon?

Hint: When y is upward, a_y is negative. The balloon's v_x is constant.

P4.2 The four vectors in the diagram below have the same magnitude. Place $\vec{F}_4$ properly (you can change its direction) to achieve the following cases: (1) $\vec{a}_{\text{block}} = 0$, (2) $\vec{a}_{\text{block}}$ has an upward component, and (3) $\vec{a}_{\text{block}}$ has a single component directed to the left.
Hint: Use the equation $\vec{F}_{\text{net}} = m\vec{a}$.

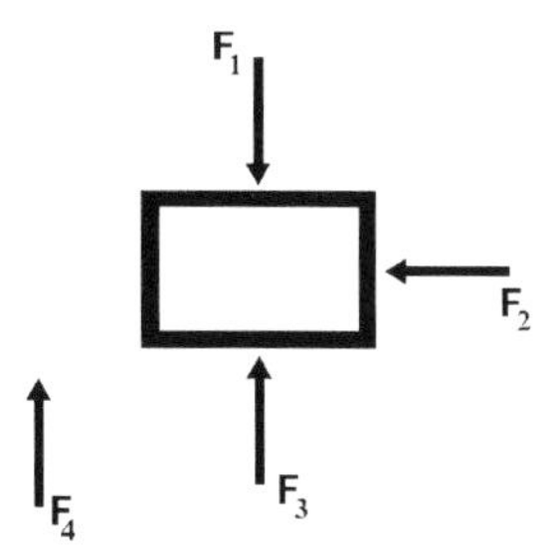

P4.3 Two particles: the first has mass m and speed $2v$, the second has mass $2m$ and speed v. Compare the magnitudes of their momenta and their kinetic energies.
Hint: Recall $\|\vec{p}\| = m\|\vec{v}\|$ and $K = \frac{1}{2}m\|\vec{v}\|^2$.

P4.4 A space station has two identical compartments A and B and is moving with velocity $\vec{v}$ in space. An explosive charge separates the two compartments and they continue with velocities $\vec{v}_A$ and $\vec{v}_B$. Find $\vec{v}_B$ in the following three cases: (1) $\vec{v}_A = \vec{v}$, (2) $\vec{v}_A = -\vec{v}$, and (3) $\vec{v}_A = 0$.
Hint: Use conservation of momentum.

[1] In research, this isn't always the case; sometimes there is no "known" strategy to follow and a new approach is needed to solve the problem.

P4.5 A 10[cm] spring is suspended vertically and a mass m hangs from it. What are the types of energies in the system when the mass m is in positions 1 and 2 below? Measure U_g relative to the height $y = 0$.

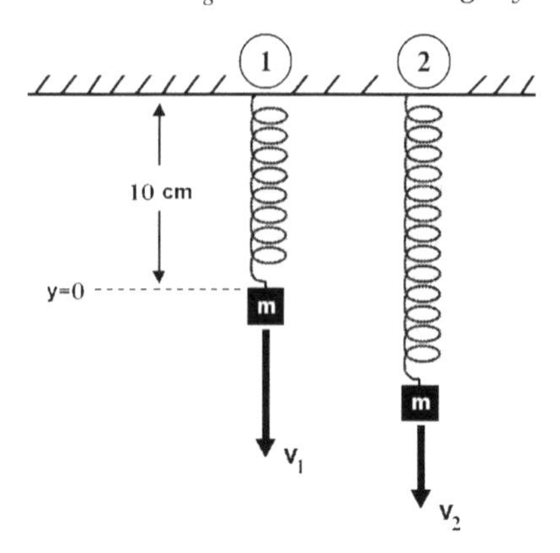

P4.6 You throw a ball from the ground vertically at speed v and measure its speed when it falls back to the ground. You first carry out this experiment on Earth, then repeat it on the Moon. Does the ball have a greater speed as it hits the ground on Earth or on the Moon?
Hint: Use conservation of energy.

P4.7 In the previous problem, assume there is a pit that allows the ball to fall 10[m] below the level from which it was thrown. Will the ball have a greater speed on Earth or on the Moon when it hits the bottom of the 10[m]-deep pit?
Hint: Use conservation of energy.

P4.8 A rod of mass m is rotating horizontally about one of its ends. An additional mass M is attached at the other end. Assume the system rotates at a constant angular velocity ω. What is the torque on the mass M? If the mass M is detached from the rod without any intervention of an external force, what will the new angular velocity of the rod be?

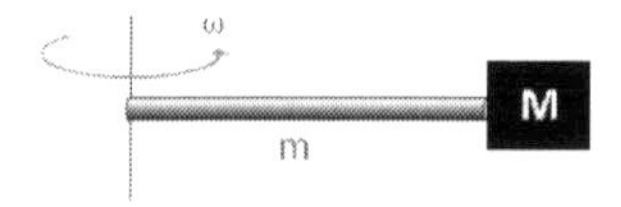

Hint: Use $\mathcal{T} = I\alpha$. Use conservation of angular momentum.

P4.9 A car is driving inside a vertical circular loop-de-loop. Assume the car passes the top and the bottom of the loop at the same speed. Will the normal force exerted by the loop on the car be greater at the top or at the bottom?
Hint: The car requires a centripetal force to maintain its circular path.

P4.10 Two balls of mass m are thrown from the top of a building with equal velocity $\vec{v}$ as shown in the diagram. Which ball has the greatest speed at the moment it hits the ground (ignore air resistance)?

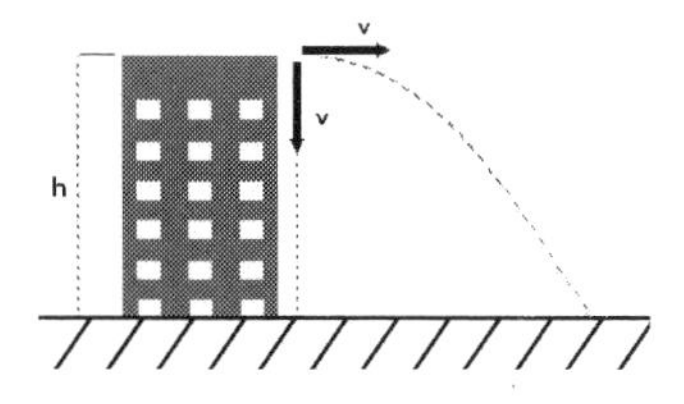

Hint: Use conservation of energy.

P4.11 Three pendulum clocks are made using strings of the same length, but each clock has a different swinging amplitude: $\theta_{\max,1} = 5°$, $\theta_{\max,2} = 7.5°$, and $\theta_{\max,3} = 10°$. Will the clocks measure time consistently?
Hint: Remember that $T = 2\pi\sqrt{\frac{\ell}{g}}$.

P4.12 Three pendulum clocks are made using pendulums of the same mass but different lengths: $\ell_1 = 50$[cm], $\ell_2 = 75$[cm], and $\ell_3 = 100$[cm]. Find the period T of each pendulum on Earth.

P4.13 You start a pendulum from an initial angle $\theta_{\max}$ on Earth. The pendulum consists of a mass m suspended on a string of length ℓ. You repeat the experiment on the Moon. Will the mass have greater speed as it passes through $\theta = 0$ on Earth or on the Moon?
Hint: Use conservation of energy.

P4.14 A diver jumps into a swimming pool from a platform that is 10 [m] above the water and performs several flips in midair. What types of energy exist while the diver is in the air? What kinds of momenta are present?
Hint: Remember the diver is rotating in midair.

P4.15 A pendulum is made from a mass m suspended on a long string. The string is being wound at a certain rate by a motor, thus making the pendulum shorter. What effect does this have on the pendulum's period?
Hint: Remember that $T = 2\pi\sqrt{\frac{\ell}{g}}$.

P4.16 You're pushing a 15[kg] box of stuff. The kinetic coefficient of friction between the box and the floor is $\mu_k = 0.032$. How much force should you apply on the box to keep it moving with constant velocity?
Hint: Constant velocity implies zero acceleration.

P4.17 Two identical pulleys with the same moment of inertia but different radii have strings wound around them. The first pulley has radius R, while the second pulley has a smaller radius $r < R$. The same force F is applied to pull the string and rotate the pulleys. After a fixed time t, which pulley has the faster rotational speed? Which pulley has the greater rotational kinetic energy?
Hint: This is an angular motion question.

P4.18 Two football players collide head on, then fall on the ground at the same place without moving further. Their masses are $m_1 = 90$[kg] and $m_2 = 75$[kg]. Their velocities before the impact are $v_1 = 4.5$[m/s] and v_2. Consider

the players to be point masses on a frictionless field. (1) What is v_2? (2) Is this an elastic collision?
Hint: Use conservation of momentum.

P4.19 The sliding blackboard in your classroom has two panels of mass $m = 20$[kg] balanced on a pulley. See Figure 4.28. Each of the blackboard panels is 1.5[m] in height. You notice that your professor switches the boards by pulling board A down with a constant force for 0.5[m] until it reaches a speed of 1[m/s], then he allows the panel to slide down freely for another 0.5[m]. In the last 0.5[m] he exerts an upward force on the panel to decrease its speed to zero by the end of the motion. In the end, the upper board A is lowered by 1.5[m] and board B is raised by 1.5[m]. Assume the system is frictionless, with massless pulley and ropes.

1. Draw a force diagram of the two boards during each of the three stages of the motion.
2. Calculate the acceleration of board A during each of the three stages.
3. Calculate the force exerted by the professor on board A during the first stage.

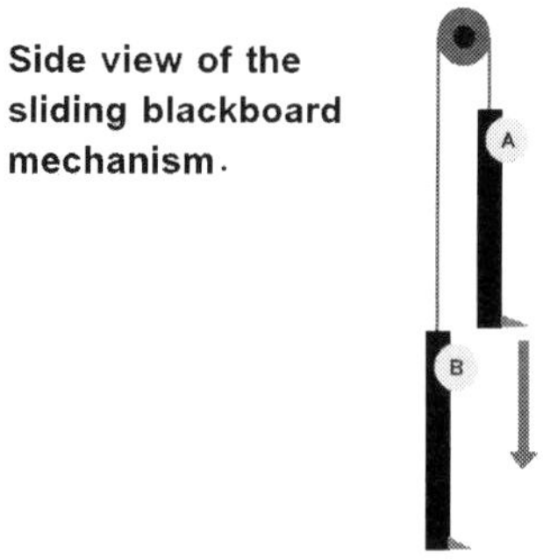

Figure 4.28: The sliding blackboard mechanism discussed in **P4.19**.

Hint: Pay attention to the tension force connecting the two panels and use Newton's 2nd law of motion.

P4.20 Define W_a[J] to be the work required to get an object of mass m[kg] moving at speed v[m/s] by starting from rest and pushing the object in a straight line on a frictionless surface. Suppose you now perform double the amount of work $W = 2W_a$[J] to compress a spring from its normal length to a certain shorter length. You then fix one side of the compressed spring, put the same object in front of the spring and release the spring. What is the velocity of the object after it is pushed by the spring?
Hint: Use conservation of energy.

P4.21 The moment of inertia of a door is $I_{door} = 11.4[\text{kg m}^2]$. You want to make the door accelerate from rest to an angular velocity of $\omega = 1.3$[rad/s] in 3 seconds using uniform angular acceleration.

1. Calculate the torque you need to apply on the door.
2. How much work will you do during this process?

Hint: Use kinematics and $\mathcal{T} = I\alpha$.

P4.22 A spring with stiffness $k = 115[\text{N/m}]$ is compressed by $\Delta x = 40[\text{cm}]$ then released to push a ball of radius $R = 10[\text{cm}]$ placed in front of it. When the ball leaves the spring, it rolls without skidding at an angular velocity of $\omega = 30[\text{rad/s}]$. What is the mass of the ball?
Hint: Use the angular velocity and the radius to find the linear velocity of the ball. Recall that $I_{\text{ball}} = \frac{2}{5}mR^2$.

P4.23 Two blocks are stacked on top of each other and resting on a frictionless surface. The upper block has mass $m_1 = 0.25[\text{kg}]$, the lower block has mass $m_2 = 1.00[\text{kg}]$, and the static coefficient of friction between the two blocks is $\mu_s = 0.24$. You push the lower block with a constant force $\vec{F}[\text{N}]$ as shown in the figure. Find the maximum force you can apply for which the upper block will not slip.

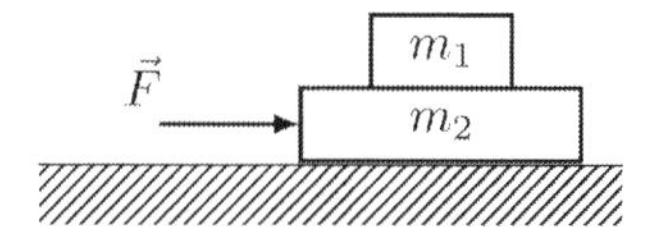

Hint: To remain connected, both blocks must have the same acceleration.

P4.24 A ball is released from rest at coordinates (d, h) as in Figure 4.29. At the same moment, a cannon placed at the origin fires a shell with initial velocity $v_i\angle 45°$.

1. Find the relation between h and d such that the shell hits the ball at a height $\frac{h}{2}$.
2. If $h = 20.0[\text{m}]$, what is v_i? Find the time $t = t_{\text{hit}}$ when the shell hits the ball.

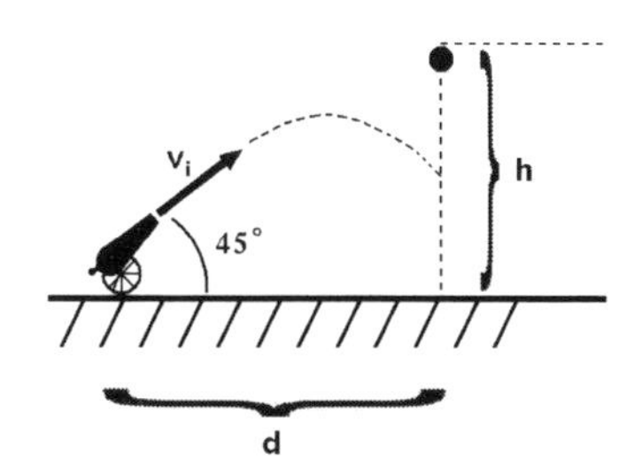

Figure 4.29: Hitting a falling target. A situation is analyzed in **P4.24**.

Hint: Construct the equations of motion for the ball and the shell.

P4.25 In Figure 4.30, all surfaces have the same friction coefficient μ_s and the system is in equilibrium (no block is moving). Assume massless, frictionless ropes and pulleys.

1. Find the friction coefficient μ_s in terms of m_1, m_2, and M.
2. Calculate the friction coefficient μ_s if $m_1 = 3.50[\text{kg}]$, $m_2 = 6.00[\text{kg}]$, and $M = 4.00[\text{kg}]$.
3. If there were no friction ($\mu_s = 0$, $\mu_k = 0$), what would the acceleration of mass the M be, in terms of m_1, m_2, M, and g?

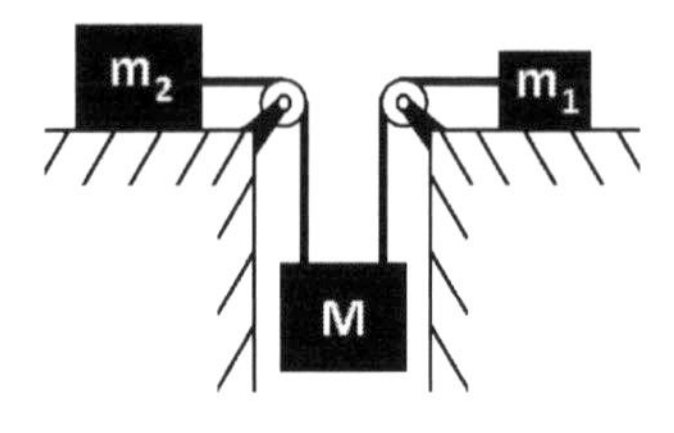

Figure 4.30: The three-mass system analyzed in **P4.25**.

Hint: Draw a force diagram for each block. The blocks have the same a.

P4.26 A ball is fired with $v_{1i} = 10[\text{m/s}]$ at an angle $\theta = 30^\circ$ with the horizontal. You need to fire a second ball vertically from the same height such that it hits the first ball as it reaches its maximum height.

1. Find the horizontal distance d from the first ball's firing position, from where you should fire the second ball.
2. Find the initial velocity required for the second ball.

Hint: Find the maximum height and the half-range of the first ball.

P4.27 A 14 000[kg] F-16 fighter jet is in a dogfight. The pilot needs to make a turn with a radius of 5[km] while maintaining a speed of 605.5[km/h]. The plane executes a banked turn at an angle $\theta = 30^\circ$ and follows a horizontal circular path.

1. How much lift does the pilot need to perform this maneuver? The lift force is perpendicular to the wings and the fuselage of the plane.
2. Will the altitude of the fighter change during this maneuver?

Hint: Find the lift force needed to produce the centripetal acceleration.

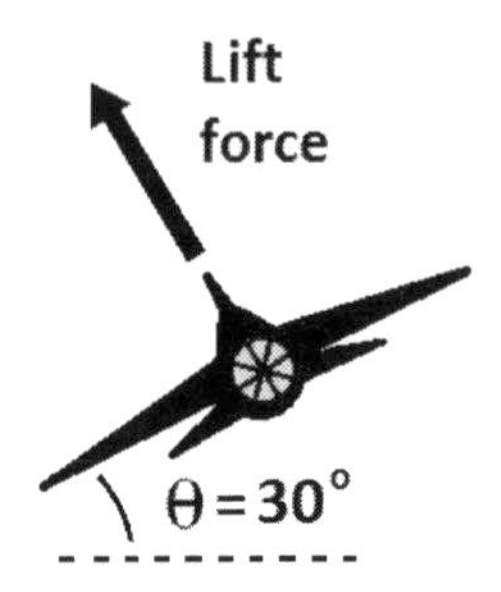

P4.28 You're in a subway car moving at $v = 12.5[\text{m/s}]$ when you drop a water bottle on the floor. The bottle comes to rest with respect to the subway car. The subway then starts braking and comes to a stop. The bottle starts rolling forward without slipping on the floor of the subway car. Find the linear velocity of the bottle as it rolls forward. The bottle's moment of inertia is $I = \frac{1}{2}mr^2$ and its mass is m.
Hint: The kinetic energy of the bottle is conserved.

P4.29 You're playing with two hockey pucks on a pool table as shown in Figure 4.31. The coefficient of friction between the pucks and the table is μ_k. Puck 2 is at rest before the collision and at a distance d from the corner pocket. Puck 1 hits Puck 2 ($m_1 = m_2$) with velocity v_i. After the collision, Puck 1 has velocity v_1 and Puck 2 has velocity v_2.

1. What is the minimum v_i in terms of the variables provided such that Puck 2 enters the pocket?
2. Calculate v_i, v_1, and v_2 if $\mu_k = 0.273$ and $d = 0.70[\text{m}]$.
3. How far does Puck 1 move after the collision if v_i is chosen as in part 2 of the question?
4. Is the collision elastic?

Hint: Use conservation of momentum and $K_i = K_f + W_{\text{lost}}$.

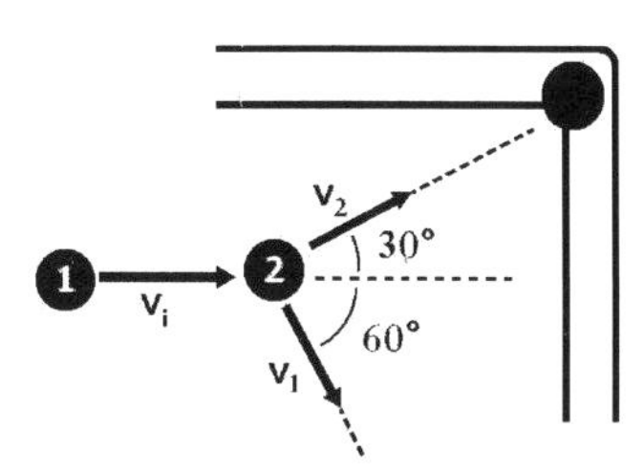

Figure 4.31: The collision of two pucks analyzed in **P4.29**.

P4.30 A car accelerates at $a = 4[\text{m/s}^2]$. Each tire has radius $r = 30[\text{cm}]$ and moment of inertia $I = 0.27[\text{kg m}^2]$. The car doesn't skid.

1. What is the torque applied on each tire?
2. If $\theta_i = 0$ and $\omega_i = 3[\text{rad/s}]$, how many revolutions did the tire complete from $t = 0[\text{s}]$ until $t = 4[\text{s}]$?

Hint: Use the relation between a and α.

P4.31 A solid cylinder and a hollow cylinder of identical mass are placed side by side on an incline. If both cylinders are released from rest and start rolling, which cylinder will reach the bottom of the incline first?
Hint: Think about $\mathcal{T} = I\alpha$.

P4.32 A ball is thrown from ground level with upward initial velocity $20[\text{m/s}]$. How long will the ball be in the air before it returns to the ground?

P4.33 A pendulum of mass M is released from rest when the string is perfectly horizontal and swings down to hit the box of mass m. The pendulum string is vertical when the collision occurs and the pendulum stops after it hits the box (it doesn't bounce back). If the box slides a distance d along the horizontal surface after the collision, what is the coefficient of kinetic friction μ_k between the box and the surface? State your answer in terms of the quantities M, m, L, d, and g.

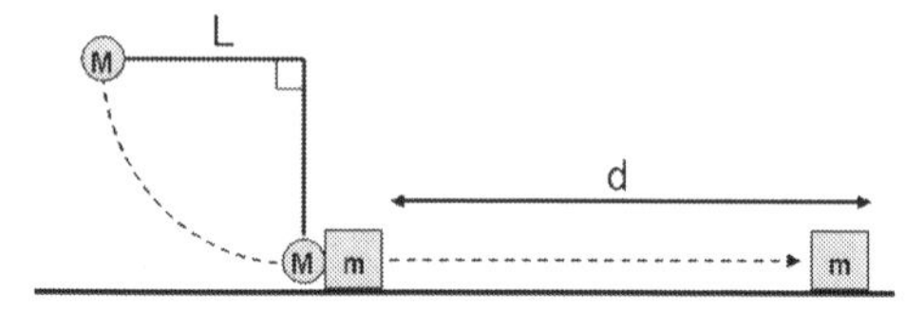

Hint: Use an energy calculation, then momentum, then energy again.

P4.34 The gravitational acceleration on Earth is not the same everywhere. The weakest gravitational acceleration is at the top of the Nevado Huascarán summit in Peru $g_{\text{min}} = 9.76[\text{m/s}^2]$. The strongest g is on the North Pole where it is $g_{\text{max}} = 9.83[\text{m/s}^2]$. Ignoring the effects of air frictions, how much further will a football travel if kicked with initial velocity $30\angle 45°[\text{m/s}]$ on the top of Nevado Huascarán compared to the North Pole?
Hint: This problem requires two range calculations for projectile motion.

P4.35 Given $a(t) = 4[\text{m/s}^2]$, $v_i = 10[\text{m/s}]$, and $x_i = 20[\text{m}]$, find $x(t)$, the position as a function of time $t[\text{s}]$.

P4.36 A disk is rotating with angular velocity $\omega = 5[\text{rad/s}]$. A slug is sliding along the surface of the disk in the radial direction. The slug starts from the disk's centre and is moving outward. If the coefficient of friction between the slug and the disk is $\mu_s = 0.4$, how far can the slug slide before it flies off the surface of the disk?

P4.37 You have loaded a fridge into an elevator. Due to the static force of friction, the refrigerator needs a strong push to start it sliding across the elevator floor. From smallest to largest, rank the magnitude of the static force of friction in these three situations: a stationary elevator, an upward accelerating elevator, and a downward accelerating elevator.

P4.38 Three coins are placed on a turntable. One coin is placed 5[cm] from the turntable's centre, another is placed 10[cm] from the centre, and the third is placed 15[cm] from the centre. The turntable is powered on and begins to spin. Initially, due to static friction, the coins move together with the turntable as it starts rotating. The angular speed ω of the turntable then increases slowly. Assuming all the coins have the same coefficient of friction with the turntable surface, which coin begins to slide first?
Hint: This is a circular motion question.

The following exercises require a mix of techniques from different sections.

P4.39 Each wheel of your bicycle is equipped with a disk brake that consists of a disk squeezed by two brake pads. The normal force between each brake

pad and the disk is 5000[N]. The coefficient of friction is $\mu_k = 0.3$. A brake disk has radius $r = 6$[cm] and a wheel's radius is $R = 20$[cm].
1. What is the total friction force exerted by each brake (two break pads)?
2. What is the torque exerted by each brake?
3. Suppose you're moving at 10[m/s] when you apply both brakes. The combined mass of you and your bicycle is 100[kg]. The mass of the wheels is negligible. How many times will the wheels turn before the bike stops?
4. What will the braking distance be?

P4.40 Tarzan A half-naked dude swings from a long rope 6[m] in length, that hangs six metres above the ground. The dude swings from an initial angle of $-50°$ ($50°$ to the left of the rope's vertical line), almost grazes the ground, then swings all the way to the angle $+10°$, at which point he lets go of the rope. See Figure 4.32. How far will Tarzan fall, as measured from the centre position of the swing motion? Find $x_f = 6\sin(10) + d$ where d is the distance travelled by Tarzan after he lets go.

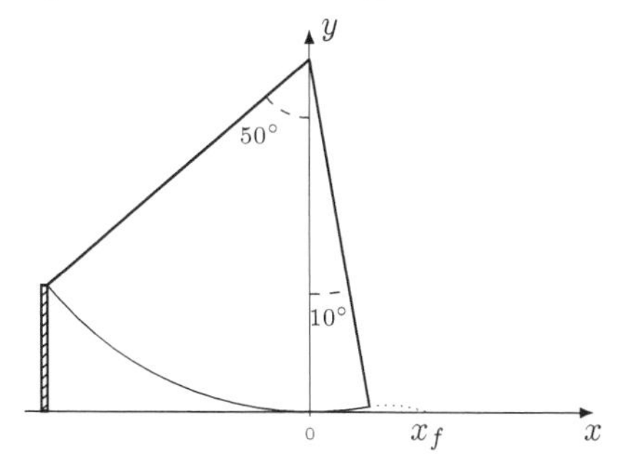

Figure 4.32: Diagram describing Tarzan's swing and jump in **P4.40**.

Hint: This is an energy problem followed by a projectile motion problem.

P4.41 A disgruntled airport employee decides to vandalize a moving walkway by suspending a leaking-paint-bucket pendulum above it. The pendulum is composed of a long cable (considered massless) and a paint bucket with a hole in the bottom. The pendulum's oscillations are small, and perpendicular to the direction of the walkway's motion. Find the equation $y(x)$ of the pattern of paint that forms on the moving walkway in terms of the pendulum's maximum angular displacement $\theta_{\max}$, its length ℓ, and the speed of the walkway v. Assume x measures distance along the walkway and y denotes the bucket's transversal displacement, measured from the centre of the walkway.
Hint: This is a simple harmonic motion question involving a pendulum.

Links

[Lots of interesting worked examples]
`http://farside.ph.utexas.edu/teaching/301/lectures/lectures.html`

Chapter 5

Calculus

Calculus is *useful* math. We use calculus to solve problems in physics, chemistry, computing, biology, and many other areas of science. You need calculus to perform the quantitative analysis of how functions change over time (derivatives), and to calculate the total amount of a quantity that accumulates over a time period (integrals).

The language of calculus will allow you to speak precisely about the properties of functions and better understand their behaviour. You will learn how to calculate the slopes of functions, how to find their maximum and minimum values, how to compute their integrals, and other tasks of practical importance.

5.1 Introduction

In Chapter 2, we developed an intuitive understanding of integrals. Starting with the knowledge of an object's acceleration function over time, we used the integration operation to calculate the object's velocity function and its position function. We'll now take a closer look at the techniques of calculus using precise mathematical statements, and study how these techniques apply to other problems in science.

A strong knowledge of functions is essential for your understanding of the new calculus concepts. I recommend revisiting Section 1.12 (page 58) to remind yourself of the functions introduced therein. I insist on this. Go! Seriously, there is no point in learning that the derivative of the function $\sin(x)$ is the function $\cos(x)$ if you don't have a clue what $\sin(x)$ and $\cos(x)$ are.

Before we introduce any formal definitions, formulas or derivations, let's demonstrate how calculus is used in a real-world example.

Download example

Suppose you're downloading a large file to your computer. At $t = 0$ you click "save as" in your browser and the download starts. Let $f(t)$ represent the size of the downloaded data. At any time t, the function $f(t)$ tells you the amount of disk space taken by the partially-downloaded file. You are downloading a 720[MB] file, so the download progress at time t corresponds to the fraction $\frac{f(t)}{720[\text{MB}]}$.

Download rate

The derivative function $f'(t)$, pronounced "f prime," describes how the function $f(t)$ changes over time. In our example $f'(t)$ is the download speed. If your downloading speed is $f'(t) = 100[\text{kB/s}]$, then the file size $f(t)$ must increase by 100[kB] each second. If you maintain this download speed, the file size will grow at a constant rate: $f(0) = 0[\text{kB}]$, $f(1) = 100[\text{kB}]$, $f(2) = 200[\text{kB}]$, $\ldots$, $f(100) = 10[\text{MB}]$.

To calculate the "estimated time remaining" until the download's completion, we divide the amount of data that remains to be downloaded by the current download speed:

$$\text{time remaining} = \frac{720 - f(t)}{f'(t)} \quad [\text{s}].$$

The bigger the derivative, the faster the download will finish. If your internet connection were 10 times faster, the download would finish 10 times more quickly.

Inverse problem

Let's consider this situation from the point of view of the modem that connects your computer to the internet. Any data you download comes through the modem. The modem knows the download rate $f'(t)[\text{kB/s}]$ at all times during the download.

However, since the modem is separate from your computer, it does not know the file size $f(t)$ as the download progresses. Nevertheless, the modem can infer the file size at time t from knowing the transmission rate $f'(t)$. The integral of the download rate between $t = 0$ and $t = \tau$ corresponds to the total amount of downloaded data stored on your computer. During this download period, the change in file size is described by the integral

$$\Delta f = f(\tau) - f(0) = \int_0^{\tau} f'(t)\, dt\,.$$

Assuming the file size starts from zero $f(0) = 0$[kB] at $t = 0$, the modem can use the integration procedure to find $f(\tau)$, the file size on your computer at $t = \tau$:

$$f(\tau) = \int_0^\tau f'(t)dt.$$

The download rate $f'(t)$ is measured in [kB/s], and each time step dt is 1[s] long, so the data downloaded during one second is $f'(t)dt$[kB]. The file size at time $t = \tau$ is equal to the sum of the data downloaded during each second from $t = 0$ until $t = \tau$.

The integral $\int_a^b q(t)\,dt$ is the calculation of the *total* of some quantity $q(t)$ that accumulates during the time period from $t = a$ to $t = b$. Integrals are necessary any time you want to calculate the total of a quantity that changes over time.

As demonstrated above, calculus is much more than the theoretical activity reserved for math specialists. Calculus relates to everyday notions you're already familiar with. Indeed, we carry out calculus-like operations in our head every day—we just don't necessarily use calculus terminology when we do so.

Learning the language of calculus will help you think more clearly about certain types of problems. Understanding the language of calculus is *essential* for learning science because many laws of nature are best described in terms of derivatives and integrals.

Usually, differential calculus and integral calculus are taught as two separate subjects. Perhaps teachers and university administrators are worried the undergraduates' little heads will explode from sudden exposure to *all* of calculus. However, this separation actually makes calculus more difficult, and prevents students from discovering the connections between differential and integral calculus. We'll have no such split in this book, because I believe you can handle the material in one go. Understanding calculus involves figuring out new mathematical concepts like infinity, limits, and summations, but these ideas are not *that* complicated. By getting this far, you've proven you're more than ready to learn the theory, techniques, and applications of derivatives, integrals, sequences, and series.

Let's begin with an overview of the material.

5.2 Overview

This section presents a bird's-eye view of the core concepts of calculus. We'll define more precisely the operations of differentiation and integration, which were introduced in Chapter 2 (see page 143).

We'll also discuss the other parts of calculus: *limits*, *sequences*, and *series*. We'll briefly touch upon some applications for each of these concepts; after all, you should know *why* you want to learn all this stuff.

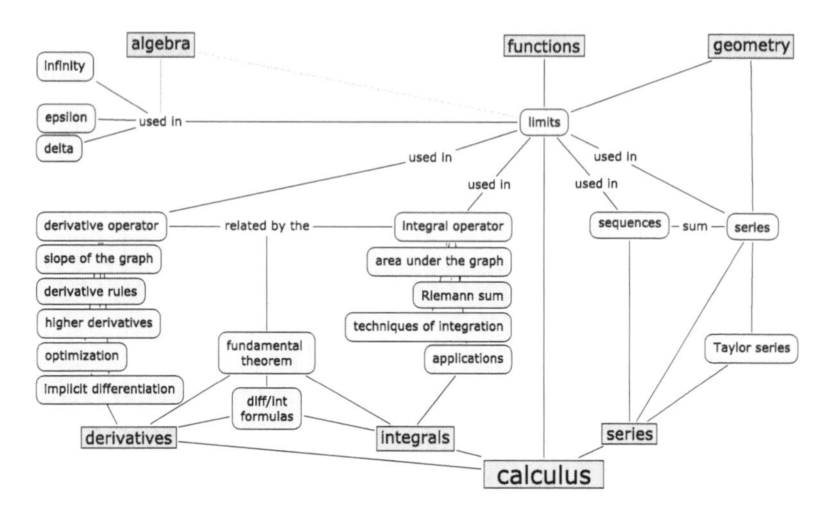

Figure 5.1: The main topics in calculus are limits, derivatives, integrals, sequences, and series. Understanding these notions and how they relate will equip you with many practical problem-solving skills.

Calculus requires a higher level of abstraction than the mathematical topics discussed in Chapter 1. We began our journey through "Math Land" with the study of *numbers*. Then we learned about *functions*, which are transformations that take real numbers as inputs and produce real numbers as outputs, $f : \mathbb{R} \to \mathbb{R}$. In calculus, the derivative and integral *operators* are procedures that take functions as inputs and produce functions as outputs. Let $\{\mathbb{R} \to \mathbb{R}\}$ denote the set of all functions that take real numbers as inputs and produce real numbers as outputs. The derivative operator takes functions as inputs and produces functions as outputs:

$$\frac{d}{dx} : \{\mathbb{R} \to \mathbb{R}\} \quad \to \quad \{\mathbb{R} \to \mathbb{R}\}.$$

More specifically, the derivative operator $\frac{d}{dx}$ acts on a function $f(x)$ to produce its derivative function: $\frac{d}{dx}[f(x)] = f'(x)$.

Differential calculus

Consider the function $f(x)$, which takes real numbers as inputs and produces real numbers as outputs, $f : \mathbb{R} \to \mathbb{R}$. The input variable for the function f is usually denoted x, but we will sometimes also use the variables u, t, and τ to denote the inputs. The function's output is denoted $f(x)$ and is usually identified with the y-coordinate in graphs.

The *derivative* function, denoted $f'(x)$, $\frac{d}{dx}f(x)$, $\frac{df}{dx}$, or $\frac{dy}{dx}$, describes the *rate of change* of the function $f(x)$. For example, the constant function $f(x) = c$ has derivative $f'(x) = 0$ since the function $f(x)$ does not change at all.

The derivative function describes the *slope* of the graph of the function $f(x)$. The derivative of a line $f(x) = mx + b$ is $f'(x) = m$ since the slope of this line is equal to m. In general, the slope of a function is different at different values of x. For a given choice of input $x = x_0$, the value of the derivative function $f'(x_0)$ is equal to the slope of $f(x)$ as it passes through the point $(x_0, f(x_0))$.

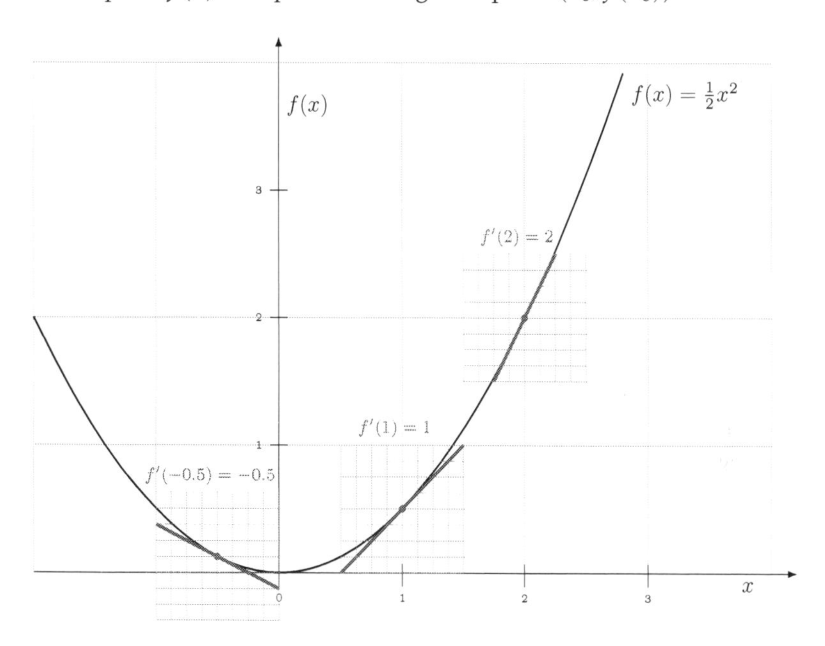

Figure 5.2: The diagram illustrates how to compute the derivative of the function $f(x) = \frac{1}{2}x^2$ at three different points on the graph of the function. To calculate the derivative of $f(x)$ at $x = 1$, we can "zoom in" near the point $(1, \frac{1}{2})$ and draw a line that has the same slope as the function. We can then calculate the slope of the line using a rise-over-run calculation, aided by the mini coordinate system that is provided. The derivative calculations for $x = -\frac{1}{2}$ and $x = 2$ are also shown. Note that the slope of the function is different for each value of x. What is the value of the derivative at $x = 0$? Can you find the general pattern?

The derivative function $f'(x)$ describes the slope of the graph of the function $f(x)$ for all inputs $x \in \mathbb{R}$. The derivative function is a function of the form $f' : \mathbb{R} \to \mathbb{R}$. In our study of mechanics, we learned about the position function $x(t)$ and the velocity function $v(t)$, which describe the motion of an object over time. The velocity is the derivative of the object's position with respect to time $v(t) = \frac{dx}{dt} = x'(t)$.

The derivative function $f'(x)$ is a property of the original function $f(x)$. Indeed, this is where the name *derivative* comes from: $f'(x)$ is not an independent function—it is *derived* from the original function $f(x)$. In mechanics, the function $x(t)$ describes an object's position as a function of time, and the velocity function $v(t)$ describes one property of the position function, namely, how fast the object's position is changing. Similarly, the acceleration function $a(t)$ describes the rate of change of the function $v(t)$.

The *derivative operator*, denoted $\frac{d}{dx}$ or simply D, takes as input a function $f(x)$ and produces as output the derivative function $f'(x)$. The derivative operator notation is useful because it show the derivative is an operation you do to a function:

$$f'(x) \equiv \frac{d}{dx} f(x).$$

The derivative operator acts on the original function $f(x)$ to produce the derivative function $f'(x)$, which describes the rate of change of f for all x. Applying the derivative operator to a function is also called "taking the derivative" of a function.

For example, the derivative of the function $f(x) = \frac{1}{2}x^2$ is the function $f'(x) = x$. We can describe this relationship as $(\frac{1}{2}x^2)' = x$ or as $\frac{d}{dx}(\frac{1}{2}x^2) = x$. You should flip back to Figure 5.2 and use the graph to prove to yourself that the slope of $f(x) = \frac{1}{2}x^2$ is described by $f'(x) = x$ everywhere on the graph.

Differentiation techniques

Section 5.6 will formally define the derivative operation. Afterward, we'll develop techniques for computing derivatives, or *taking* derivatives. Computing derivatives is not a complicated task once you learn how to use the derivative formulas. If you flip ahead to Section 5.7 (page 308), you'll find a table of formulas for taking the derivatives of common functions. In Section 5.8, we'll learn the basic rules for computing derivatives of sums, products, and compositions of the basic functions.

Applications of derivatives

Once you develop your ability to find derivatives, you'll be able to use this skill to perform several useful tasks.

Optimization The most prominent application of differential calculus is *optimization*: the process of finding a function's maximum and minimum values. When a function reaches its maximum value, its derivative momentarily becomes zero. The function increases just before it reaches its maximum, and the function decreases just after its maximum. At its maximum value, the function is horizontal, and $f'(x) = 0$ at this point.

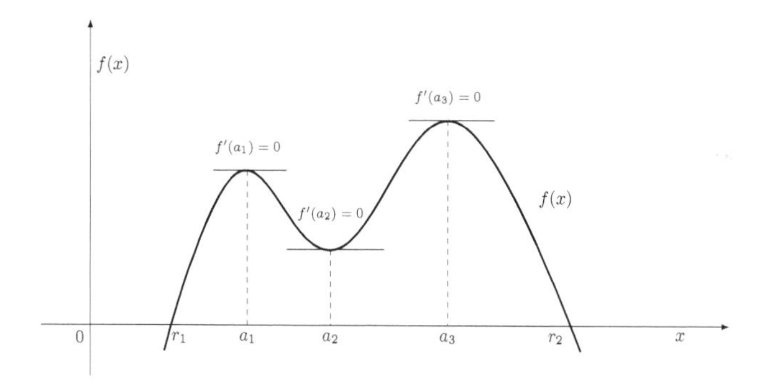

Figure 5.3: The *critical points* of a function occur where the function's derivative equals zero. The critical points of the illustrated function $f(x)$ are $x = a_1$, $x = a_2$, and $x = a_3$. You can use the critical points to find the location of a function's maxima and minima. The point $(a_1, f(a_1))$ is called a *local maximum* of the function, the point at $x = a_2$ is a *local minimum*, while the point at $x = a_3$ is the function's *global maximum*.

The values of x for which $f'(x) = 0$ are called the *critical points* of the function $f(x)$. To find the maximum of a function, we start by compiling a list of its critical points, then go through the list to find the point where the function takes on its largest value. We will discuss the details of this optimization algorithm in Section 5.10.

Tangent lines The *tangent line* to the function $f(x)$ at $x = x_0$ corresponds to the line that passes through the point $(x_0, f(x_0))$ and has the same slope as the function at that point. The word *tangent* comes from the Latin *tangere*, meaning "to touch."

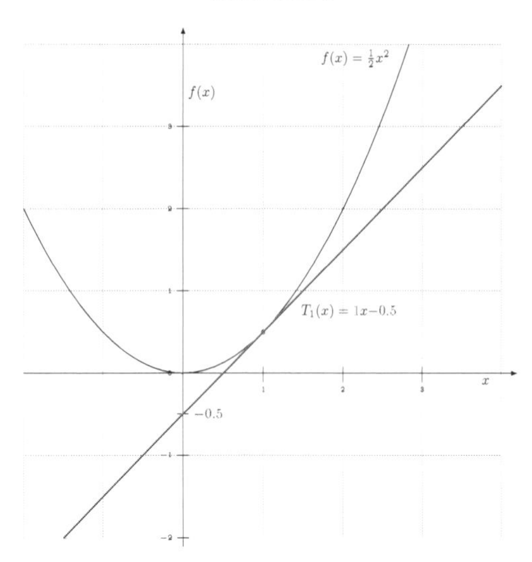

Figure 5.4: An illustration of the tangent line to the function $f(x) = \frac{1}{2}x^2$ at the point $x_0 = 1$. The equation of the tangent line is $T_1(x) = 1x - 0.5$.

The tangent line to the function $f(x)$ at the point $x = x_0$ is described by the equation

$$T_1(x) = \underbrace{f'(x_0)}_{m}\, x \; + \; \underbrace{(f(x_0) - f'(x_0)x_0)}_{b} = f(x_0) \; + \; f'(x_0)(x - x_0).$$

The tangent line $T_1(x)$ is an approximation to the function $f(x)$ near the coordinate $x = x_0$. The approximation $T_1(x)$ is equal to the function $f(x)$ at $x = x_0$ since the tangent line passes through the point $(x_0, f(x_0))$. For coordinates near $x = x_0$, the approximation is also accurate since $T_1(x)$ has the same slope as the function $f(x)$. As the input value x moves farther from x_0, the tangent becomes less accurate at approximating the function $f(x)$.

Integral calculus

The *integral* of $f(x)$ corresponds to the computation of the area under the graph of $f(x)$. The area under $f(x)$ between the points $x = a$ and $x = b$ is denoted as follows:

$$A(a, b) = \int_a^b f(x)\, dx.$$

The area $A(a, b)$ is bounded by the function $f(x)$ from above, by the x-axis from below, and by two vertical lines at $x = a$ and $x = b$. The points $x = a$ and $x = b$ are called the limits of integration. The $\int$ sign comes from the Latin word *summa*. The integral is the "sum" of the values of $f(x)$ between the two limits of integration.

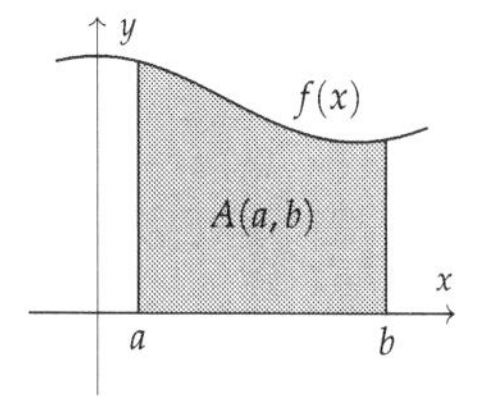

Figure 5.5: The integral of the function $f(x)$ between $x = a$ and $x = b$ corresponds to the area $A(a,b)$.

The *integral function* $F(c)$ corresponds to the area calculation as a function of the upper limit of integration:

$$F(c) \equiv \int_0^c f(x)\, dx\,.$$

There are two variables and one constant in this formula. The input variable c describes the upper limit of integration. The *integration variable* x performs a sweep from $x = 0$ until $x = c$. The constant 0 describes the lower limit of integration. Note that choosing $x = 0$ for the starting point of the integral function was an arbitrary choice.

The integral function $F(c)$ contains the "precomputed" information about the area under the graph of $f(x)$. Recall the derivative function $f'(x)$, which tells us the "slope of the graph" property of the function $f(x)$ for all values of x. Similarly, the integral function $F(c)$ tells us the "area under the graph" property of the function $f(x)$ for *all* possible limits of integration.

The area under $f(x)$ between $x = a$ and $x = b$ is obtained by calculating the *change* in the integral function as follows:

$$A(a,b) = \int_a^b f(x)\, dx = F(b) - F(a).$$

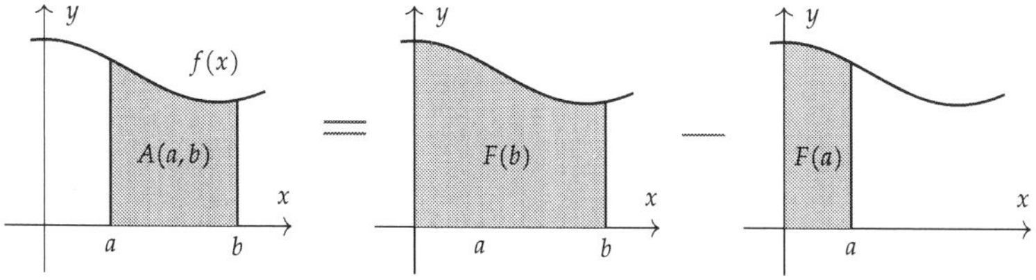

Figure 5.6: The integral function $F(x)$ computes the area under the curve $f(x)$ starting from $x = 0$. The area under $f(x)$ between $x = a$ and $x = b$ is computed using the formula $A(a,b) = F(b) - F(a)$.

Integration techniques

The bulk of the new material needed to understand integral calculus lies in learning various techniques for calculating integrals of functions. Computing integrals is not as easy as computing derivatives, because there are no general rules to follow.

In Section 5.15, we'll describe a number of common techniques for integration. These techniques will enable you to compute the integrals of polynomial functions, exponential functions, logarithmic functions, and trigonometric functions. While these techniques will help you compute integrals in many situations, the process of computing integrals remains somewhat of an art. In art, there are no rules to follow—as an artist, you must be creative and test different approaches until you find one that works.

Applications of integration

Integral calculations have widespread applications to more areas of science than are practical to list here. Let's explore a few examples to gain a general idea of how integrals are applied in the real world.

Computing totals Integral calculations are needed every time we want to compute the total of some quantity that changes over time. If the quantity in question remains constant over time, we can multiply this quantity by the time to find the total quantity. For example, if your monthly rent is \$720, your annual rent is $R = \$720 \times 12$.

But what if your rent changes over time? Imagine a crazy landlord who demands you pay on a daily basis and changes the daily rent $r(t)$ each day. Some days rent is \$20/day, some days \$23/day, and some days he lets you stay for only \$15/day. In this situation, computing your annual rent involves the integral $R = \int_0^{365} r(t)\,dt$, which describes the calculation of the daily rate $r(t)$ times the duration of each day dt summed over all the days in the year.

Computing potentials In Section 4.6 we defined the notion of potential energy as the negative of the work done when moving an object against a conservative force. We studied two specific cases: gravitational potential energy $U_g(h) \equiv -\int_0^h \vec{F}_g \cdot d\vec{y} = mgh$, and spring potential energy $U_s(x) \equiv -\int_0^x \vec{F}_s(y) \cdot d\vec{y} = \frac{1}{2}kx^2$. Understanding integrals will allow you to solidify your understanding of the connection between each force $\vec{F}_?(x)$ and its associated potential energy $U_?(x)$.

Computing moments of inertia An object's moment of inertia describes how difficult it is to make the object turn. The moment of inertia is computed as the following integral:

$$I = \int_{\text{obj}} r^2 \, dm.$$

In the mechanics chapter, I asked you to memorize the formulas for $I_{\text{disk}} = \frac{1}{2}mR^2$ and $I_{\text{sphere}} = \frac{2}{5}mR^2$ because it was not yet time to explain the details of integral calculations. After learning about integrals, you'll be able to derive the formulas for I_{disk} and I_{sphere} on your own.

Solving differential equations One of the most important applications of integrals is their ability to "undo" the derivative operation. Recall Newton's second law $F_{\text{net}}(t) = ma(t)$, which can also be written as

$$\frac{F_{\text{net}}(t)}{m} = a(t) = x''(t) = \frac{d}{dx}\left(\frac{d}{dx}x(t)\right).$$

In Chapter 2 we learned how to use integration to solve for $x(t)$ in special cases where the net force is constant $F_{\text{net}}(t) = F_{\text{net}}$. In this chapter, we'll revisit the procedure for finding $x(t)$, and learn how to calculate the motion of an object affected by an external force that varies over time $F_{\text{net}}(t)$.

Limits

The main new tool we'll use in calculus is the notion of a *limit*. In calculus we use limits to describe what happens to mathematical expressions when one variable becomes very large, or alternately becomes very small.

For example, to describe a situation where a number n becomes bigger and bigger, we can say,

$$\lim_{n\to\infty} (\text{expression involving } n).$$

This expression is read, "In the limit as n goes to infinity, expression involving n."

Another type of limit occurs when a small, positive number—for example $\delta > 0$, the Greek letter *delta*—becomes progressively smaller and smaller. The precise mathematical statement that describes what happens when the number δ tends to 0 is

$$\lim_{\delta\to 0} (\text{expression involving } \delta),$$

which reads, "In the limit as δ goes to zero, expression involving δ."

Derivative and integral operations are both defined in terms of limits, so understanding limits is essential for calculus. We'll explore limits in more detail and discuss their properties in Section 5.4.

Sequences

So far, we've studied functions defined for real-valued inputs $x \in \mathbb{R}$. We can also study functions defined for natural number inputs $n \in \mathbb{N}$. These functions are called *sequences*.

A sequence is a function of the form $a : \mathbb{N} \to \mathbb{R}$. The sequence's input variable is usually denoted n or k, and it corresponds to the *index* or number in the sequence. We describe sequences either by specifying the formula for the nth term in the sequence or by listing all the values of the sequence:

$$a_n, n \in \mathbb{N} \quad \Leftrightarrow \quad (a_0, a_1, a_2, a_3, a_4, \ldots).$$

Note the new notation for the input variable as a subscript. This is the standard notation for describing sequences. Also note the sequence continues indefinitely.

An example of a sequence is

$$a_n = \frac{1}{n^2}, \, n \in \mathbb{N}_+ \quad \Leftrightarrow \quad \left(\frac{1}{1}, \frac{1}{4}, \frac{1}{9}, \frac{1}{16}, \frac{1}{25}, \ldots\right).$$

This sequence is only defined for strictly positive natural numbers $\mathbb{N}_+ = \{1, 2, 3, 4, \ldots\}$ as the input $n = 0$ yields a divide-by-zero error.

The fundamental question we can ask about sequences is whether they *converge* in the limit when n goes to infinity. For instance, the sequence $a_n = \frac{1}{n^2}$ converges to 0 as n goes to infinity. We can express this fact with the limit expression $\lim\limits_{n\to\infty} \frac{1}{n^2} = 0$.

We'll discuss sequences in more detail in Section 5.18.

Series

Suppose we're given a sequence a_n and we want to compute the sum of all the values in this sequence.

To describe the sum of 3rd, 4th, and 5th elements of the sequence a_n, we turn to summation notation:

$$a_3 + a_4 + a_5 \equiv \sum_{3 \leqslant n \leqslant 5} a_n \equiv \sum_{n=3}^{5} a_n \,.$$

The capital Greek letter *sigma* stands in for the word *sum*, and the range of index values included in this sum is denoted below and above the summation sign.

The partial sum of the sequence values a_n ranging from $n = 0$ until $n = N$ is denoted as

$$S_N = \sum_{n=0}^{N} a_n = a_0 + a_1 + a_2 + \cdots + a_{N-1} + a_N.$$

The *series* $\sum a_n$ is the sum of *all* the values in the sequence a_n:

$$\sum a_n \equiv S_\infty = \lim_{N\to\infty} S_N = \sum_{n=0}^{\infty} a_n = a_0 + a_1 + a_2 + a_3 + a_4 + \cdots.$$

Note this is an infinite sum.

Series techniques

The main mathematical question we'll study with series is the question of their convergence. We say a series $\sum a_n$ *converges* if the infinite sum $S_\infty \equiv \sum_{n\in\mathbb{N}} a_n$ equals some finite number $L \in \mathbb{R}$.

$$S_\infty = \sum_{n=0}^{\infty} a_n = L \quad \Rightarrow \quad \text{the series } \sum a_n \text{ converges.}$$

We call L the *limit* of the series $\sum a_n$.

If the infinite sum $S_\infty \equiv \sum_{n\in\mathbb{N}} a_n$ grows to infinity, we say the series $\sum a_n$ *diverges*.

$$S_\infty = \sum_{n=0}^{\infty} a_n = \pm\infty \quad \Rightarrow \quad \text{the series } \sum a_n \text{ diverges.}$$

The main series technique you need to learn is how to spot the differences between series that converge and series that diverge. You'll learn how to perform different *convergence tests* on the terms in the series, which will indicate whether the infinite sum converges or diverges.

Applications

Series are a powerful computational tool. We can use series to compute approximations to numbers and functions.

For example, the number e can be computed as the following series:

$$e = \sum_{n=0}^{\infty} \frac{1}{n!} = 1 + 1 + \frac{1}{2\cdot 1} + \frac{1}{3\cdot 2} + \frac{1}{4\cdot 3\cdot 2} + \frac{1}{5\cdot 4\cdot 3\cdot 2} + \cdots.$$

The factorial operation $n!$ is the product of n times all integers smaller than n: $n! = n(n-1)(n-2)\cdots 3\cdot 2\cdot 1$. As we compute more terms from the series, our estimate of the number e becomes more accurate. The partial sum of the first six terms (as shown above) gives us an approximation of e that is accurate to three decimals.

The partial sum of the first 12 terms gives us e to an accuracy of nine decimals.

Another useful thing you can do with series is approximate functions by infinitely long polynomials. The *power series* approximation for a function $f(x)$ is defined as the series

$$f(x) = \sum_{n=0}^{\infty} c_n x^n = c_0 + c_1 x + c_2 x^2 + c_3 x^3 + c_4 x^4 + \cdots .$$

Each term in the series is of the form $a_n = c_n x^n$, where c_n is a constant that depends on the function $f(x)$.

For example, the power series of $\sin(x)$ is

$$\sin(x) = \underbrace{\overbrace{x}^{T_1(x)} - \frac{x^3}{3!} + \frac{x^5}{5!}}_{T_5(x)} - \frac{x^7}{7!} + \frac{x^9}{9!} - \frac{x^{11}}{11!} + \cdots .$$

We can truncate the infinite series anywhere to obtain an approximation to the function. The function $T_5(x) = x - \frac{x^3}{3!} + \frac{x^5}{5!}$ is the best approximation to the function $\sin(x)$ by a polynomial of degree 5. The equation of the tangent line $T_1(x)$ at $x = 0$ is a special case of the power series approximation procedure, which approximates the function as a first-degree polynomial. We will continue the discussion on series, their properties, and their applications in Section 5.19.

If you haven't noticed yet from glancing at the examples so far, the common theme underpinning all the topics of calculus is the notion of *infinity*. We now turn our attention to the infinite.

5.3 Infinity

Working with infinitely small quantities and infinitely large quantities can be tricky business. It's important that we develop the appropriate language for describing these concepts as soon as possible. Like, now.

Infinitely large

The number ∞ is *really* large. How large? Larger than any number you can think of. Think of any number n. It is true that $n < \infty$. Now think of a bigger number N. It will still hold true that $N < \infty$. In fact, any finite number you can think of, no matter how large, will always be less than ∞.

Technically speaking, ∞ is not a number; infinity is a *process*. You can think of ∞ as the answer you obtain by starting from 0 and continuously adding 1 *forever*.

To see why $N < \infty$ for any finite number N, consider the following reasoning. When we add 1 to a number, we obtain a larger number. The operation $+1$ is equivalent to taking one unit step to the right on the number line. For any n, it is true that $n < n+1$. To get to infinity we start from $n = 0$ and keep adding 1. After N steps, we'll arrive at $n = N$. But then we must continue adding 1 and obtain $N+1$, $N+2$, $N+3$, and so on. Since adding 1 always creates a larger number, the following chain of inequalities is true:

$$N < N+1 < N+2 < N+3 < \cdots < \infty.$$

Therefore $N < \infty$ for any finite N.

When we say a number n "goes to" infinity, we're saying n becomes increasingly larger and larger. No number ever actually arrives at infinity since infinity is obtained by adding 1 forever. There is no number $n \in \mathbb{R}$ such that $n = \infty$. Nevertheless, sometimes we can write $N = \infty$, which is an informal way of saying $N = \lim_{n\to\infty} n$.

Infinitely small

The opposite of an infinitely large number is an infinitely small number. As a mathematical convention, infinitely small numbers are denoted by the Greek letters ϵ (*epsilon*) and δ (*delta*). The infinitely small number $\epsilon > 0$ is a nonzero number smaller than any number you can think of. The number 0.00001 is pretty small, but it's true that $\epsilon < 0.00001$. The number 10^{-16} extends for 15 zeros after the decimal point, but still ϵ is smaller than it: $\epsilon < 10^{-16}$. Most often, the variable ϵ appears in limit expressions as a quantity that tends toward 0. The expression $\lim_{\epsilon\to 0}$ describes the process of ϵ becoming smaller and smaller, but never actually reaching zero, since by definition $\epsilon > 0$.

Infinitely many

The interval $[0,1]$ of the number line contains infinitely many numbers. Think of the sequence 1, $\frac{1}{2}$, $\frac{1}{4}$, $\frac{1}{8}$, $\frac{1}{16}$, and so forth. There is an infinite number of such fractions, and they all lie in the interval $[0,1]$.

The ancient Greek philosopher Zeno was confused by this fact. He reasoned as follows. Suppose an archer shoots an arrow and sends it flying toward a target. After some time, the arrow will have travelled half the distance to the target. At some later time, the arrow will have travelled half of the remaining distance and so on, always getting closer and closer to the target. Zeno observed that no matter how little distance remains between the arrow and the target, there will always remain some distance to travel. To reach the target, the arrow would need to pass through an infinite number of points, which is impossible. "How could an infinite number of points fit inside a finite interval?" he figured.

Zeno's argument is not quite right. It is true that the arrow must pass through infinitely many points before it hits the target, but these points "fit" fine in the interval $[0, 1]$. These are mathematical points—they don't take up any space at all. We can commend Zeno for thinking about limits centuries before calculus was invented, but we shouldn't repeat his mistake. You must learn how to make limit arguments, because limits are important. Imagine if Zeno had tried to verify his theory experimentally by placing himself in front of an arrow. A wrong argument about limits could get you killed!

Interlude

If the concept of infinity were a person, it would have several problematic character traits. Let's see what we know about infinity so far. The bit about the infinitely large shows signs of megalomania. There is enough of this whole "more, more, more" mentality in the world already, so the last thing you want is someone like this as a friend. Conversely, the obsession with the infinitely small ϵ could be a sign of abnormal altruism: the willingness to give up all and leave less and less for oneself. You don't want someone *that* altruistic in your group. And that last part about how infinitely many numbers can fit in a finite interval of the number line sounds infinitely theoretical—definitely not someone to invite to a party.

Let's learn about one redeeming, practical quality of the concept of infinity. Who knows, you might become friends after all.

Infinitely precise

A computer science (CS) student and a math student are chatting over lunch. The CS student recently learned how to write code that computes mathematical functions as infinitely long series:

$$f(x) = e^x = \sum_{n=0}^{\infty} \frac{x^n}{n!} = 1 + x + \frac{x^2}{2 \cdot 1} + \frac{x^3}{3 \cdot 2} + \frac{x^4}{4 \cdot 3 \cdot 2} + \cdots$$

She wants to tell her friend about her newly acquired powers.

The math student is also learning cool stuff about numbers. For example the number e can be defined as $e \equiv \lim_{n\to\infty}(1+\frac{1}{n})^n$, but can never be computed exactly—it can only be approximated.

"You know, math is *soooo* much better than CS," says the math student, baiting her friend into an argument about the relative merits of their fields of study.

"What? No way. I can do *anything* on a computer," replies the incredulous scholar of code.

"But can you find exact answers?" the mathematician asks. "Can you compute the number *e exactly*?"

"Sure," says the computer scientist, opening her laptop and typing in a few commands. "The answer is $e = 2.718281828459045$."

"That is not exact," the mathematician points out, "it is just an approximation."

"Whatever—I gave you an approximation to fifteen digits after the decimal. If you're not satisfied with this, then I don't know what your problem is."

"Well, I asked for the *exact* value of e and you only gave me an approximation. Can you find e to 25 digits of precision?" asks the mathematician.

The computer scientist goes back to her laptop.

"Okay, $e = 2.7182818284590452353602875$," she says.

"What about computing e to 50 digits of precision?"

"$e = 2.71828182845904523536028747135266249775724709369995$," says the computer scientist a few seconds later.

"What about—"

"Listen,—" says her friend, "I have this code here that computes e in terms of its power series. The more terms I add in this series, the better my approximation will become. **I can achieve any precision you could possibly ask for**," she explains.

"Then you really know e!" exclaims the mathematician, convinced.

The computer scientist and the mathematician are discussing how to compute approximations to the number e. The mathematician thinks of the number e as the limit $e \equiv \lim_{n\to\infty}(1+\frac{1}{n})^n$. The computer scientist thinks of the number e as the infinite series

$$e = e^1 = \lim_{N\to\infty} \sum_{n=0}^{N} \frac{1}{n!} = 1 + 1 + \frac{1}{2!} + \frac{1}{3!} + \frac{1}{4!} + \frac{1}{5!} + \cdots .$$

Both formulas for e are correct. Observe that we can never compute the value of e exactly, since the formulas for e involve limits to infinity. Because no number ever arrives at infinity, we can never arrive at e either. The number e is a limit. We can only compute numbers that *approach e*.

The computer scientist can obtain approximations to e by computing the partial sum of the first N terms in the series:

$$e_N = \sum_{n=0}^{N} \frac{1}{n!} = 1 + 1 + \frac{1}{2!} + \frac{1}{3!} + \frac{1}{4!} + \cdots + \frac{1}{N!}.$$

Let us denote as ϵ the required precision of the approximation. The more terms she adds, the more accurate the approximation e_N will become. She can always choose a value for N such that the approximation e_N satisfies $|e_N - e| < \epsilon$.

The computer scientist's first answer has a precision of $\epsilon = 10^{-15}$. To obtain an approximation to e with this precision, it is sufficient to compute $N = 19$ terms in the series:

$$e_{19} = \sum_{n=0}^{19} \frac{1}{n!} = 1 + 1 + \frac{1}{2!} + \frac{1}{3!} + \cdots + \frac{1}{19!}.$$

The resulting approximation e_{19} is a number somewhere in the interval $(e - 10^{-15}, e + 10^{-15})$. We can also say the absolute value of the difference between e_{19} and the true value of e is smaller than ϵ: $|e_{19} - e| \leqslant 10^{-15}$.

When the mathematician asks for a precision of $\epsilon' = 10^{-25}$, the computer scientists takes $N = 26$ terms in the series to produce

$$e_{26} = \sum_{n=0}^{26} \frac{1}{n!} = 1 + 1 + \frac{1}{2!} + \frac{1}{3!} + \cdots + \frac{1}{19!} + \cdots + \frac{1}{26!},$$

which satisfies $|e_{26} - e| \leqslant \epsilon'$. In the third step, the mathematician demands a precision $\epsilon'' = 10^{-50}$, and the CS student computes $N = 42$ terms in the series, to produce an approximation satisfying $|e_{42} - e| \leqslant \epsilon''$. In principle, the game can continue indefinitely because the computer scientist has figured out a *process* for computing increasingly accurate approximations.

This scenario embodies precisely how mathematicians think about limits. It's a bit like a game: the ϵ,N-game. The object of the game is for the CS student to convince the mathematician she knows the number e. The mathematician chooses the precision ϵ. To prove she knows e to precision ϵ, the CS student computes the appropriate number of terms in the series such that her approximation e_N comes ϵ-close to the true answer $|e_N - e| < \epsilon$. If she can produce an approximation which satisfies $|e_N - e| < \epsilon$ **for all** $\epsilon > 0$, then the mathematician will be convinced.

Knowing the value of any finite approximation e_N, no matter how precise, does not constitute a mathematical proof that you can compute e. The mathematician is convinced because the computer scientist has found a *process* for computing approximations with arbitrary precision. In the words of the band Rage Against The Machine,

> "⟨EXPLETIVE⟩ the G-rides,
> I want the machines that are making them."

Calculus proofs are not about the approximations e_{19}, e_{26}, e_{42}, but about the machines that are making them.

The scenarios presented in this section illustrate the need for a precise mathematical language for talking about infinitely large numbers, infinitely small steps, and mathematical procedures with infinite numbers of steps. In the next section we'll learn how to talk about these concepts in terms of *limits*.

5.4 Limits

Limits are the mathematically precise way to talk about infinity. You must understand the language of limits to truly understand the infinitely small, the infinitely large, and the infinitely precise. Once you become comfortable with limits, you'll be able to understand the formal definitions of the derivative and integral operations.

Example

Let's begin with a simple example. Say you have a string of length ℓ and you want to divide it into infinitely many, infinitely short segments. There are infinitely many segments, and they are infinitely short, so together the segments add to the string's total length ℓ.

It's easy enough to describe this process in words. Now let's describe the same process using the notion of a limit. If we divide the length of the string ℓ into N equal pieces then each piece will have a length of

$$\delta \equiv \frac{\ell}{N}.$$

Let's make sure that N pieces of length δ added together equal the string's total length:

$$N\delta = N\frac{\ell}{N} = \ell.$$

Now imagine what happens when the variable N becomes larger and larger. The larger N becomes, the shorter the pieces of string will become. In fact, if N goes to infinity (written $N \to \infty$), then the pieces of string will have zero length:

$$\lim_{N\to\infty} \delta = \lim_{N\to\infty} \frac{\ell}{N} = 0.$$

In the limit as $N \to \infty$, the pieces of string are *infinitely small.*

Note we can still add the pieces of string together to obtain the whole length:

$$\lim_{N\to\infty} (N\delta) = \lim_{N\to\infty} \left(N\frac{\ell}{N}\right) = \ell.$$

Even if the pieces of string are *infinitely small*, because there are *infinitely many* of them, they still add to ℓ.

The take-home message is that as long as you clearly define your limits, you can use infinitely small numbers in your calculations. The notion of a limit is one of the central ideas in this course.

Limits at infinity

In math, we're often interested in describing what happens to a certain function when its input variable tends to infinity. This information helps us draw the function's graph. Does $f(x)$ approach a finite number, or does it keep on growing to ∞?

As an example of this type of calculation, consider the limit of the function $f(x) = \frac{1}{x}$ as x goes to infinity:

$$\lim_{x\to\infty} f(x) = \lim_{x\to\infty} \frac{1}{x} = 0.$$

This statement is true, even though the function $\frac{1}{x}$ never *actually* reaches zero. The function gets closer and closer to the x-axis but never touches it. This is why the concept of a limit is useful: it allows us to write $\lim\limits_{x\to\infty} f(x) = 0$ even though $f(x) \neq 0$ for any $x \in \mathbb{R}$.

The function $f(x)$ is said to *converge* to the number L if the function approaches the value L for large values of x:

$$\lim_{x\to\infty} f(x) = L.$$

We say "The limit of $f(x)$ as x goes to infinity is the number L." See Figure 5.7 for an illustration. The limit expression is a concise way of saying the following precise mathematical statement: for *any* precision $\epsilon > 0$, there exists a starting point S, after which $f(x)$ equals L within a precision ϵ.

The precise mathematical meaning of $\lim\limits_{x\to\infty} f(x) = L$ is

$$\forall \epsilon > 0 \ \exists S \in \mathbb{R} \text{ such that } \forall x \geqslant S \ \ |f(x) - L| < \epsilon.$$

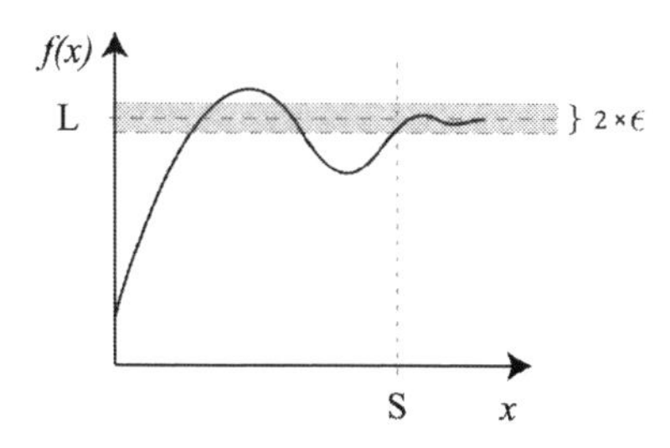

Figure 5.7: A function $f(x)$ whose oscillations around the value L are smaller than ϵ for all $x \geqslant S$. The starting point S depends on the choice of precision ϵ.

I know what you are thinking. Whoa! What just happened here? Chill. I know we saw that upside-down-A and backward-E business all the way back in Chapter 1 (see page 110), so let me rewrite the expression for you in plain English:

For all $\epsilon > 0$,
there exists a number S such that
$|f(x) - L| < \epsilon$ for all x greater than or equal to S.

The limit equation $\lim_{x\to\infty} f(x) = L$ states that the "limit at infinity" of the function $f(x)$ is equal to the number L. This statement is true if and only if there exists a winning strategy for an ϵ,S-game, similar to the ϵ,N-game played by the computer scientist and the mathematician. In the new ϵ,S-game, the mathematician specifies the precision ϵ, and the computer scientists must find a starting point S after which $f(x)$ becomes (and stays) ϵ-close to the limit L. If the computer scientist can succeed for all levels of precision ϵ, then the mathematician will be convinced the equation $\lim_{x\to\infty} f(x) = L$ is true.

Example 2 Calculate $\lim_{x\to\infty} \frac{2x+1}{x}$.

You are given the function $f(x) = \frac{2x+1}{x}$ and must determine what the function looks like for very large values of x. We can rewrite the function as $\frac{2x+1}{x} = 2 + \frac{1}{x}$ to more easily see what is going on:

$$\lim_{x\to\infty} \frac{2x+1}{x} = \lim_{x\to\infty}\left(2 + \frac{1}{x}\right) = 2 + \lim_{x\to\infty}\left(\frac{1}{x}\right) = 2 + 0,$$

since $\frac{1}{x}$ tends toward zero for large values of x.

In an introductory calculus course, you will not be required to give formal proofs for statements like $\lim_{x\to\infty} \frac{1}{x} = 0$; instead, you can assume the result is obvious and needs no proof. As the denominator x becomes larger and larger, the fraction $\frac{1}{x}$ becomes smaller and smaller.

Limits to a number

The limit of $f(x)$ approaching $x = a$ *from the right* is defined as

$$\lim_{x \to a^+} f(x) = \lim_{\delta \to 0} f(a + \delta).$$

To find the limit from the right at a, we let x take on values like $a + 0.1$, $a + 0.01$, $a + 0.001$, $a + 0.0001$, etc. Figure 5.8 shows the graph of a function $f(x)$ near the point $(a, f(a))$. To prove the statement

$$\lim_{x \to a^+} f(x) = L,$$

you must show that

$$\forall \epsilon > 0,$$
$$\exists \delta > 0 \text{ such that}$$
$$\forall x \in (a, a + \delta) \quad |f(x) - L| < \epsilon.$$

In other words, the limit from the right corresponds to an ϵ,δ-game in which the mathematician specifies the precision $\epsilon > 0$, and the computer scientist must find a distance $\delta > 0$, such that $|f(x) - L| < \epsilon$, for all x in the range $(a, a + \delta)$.

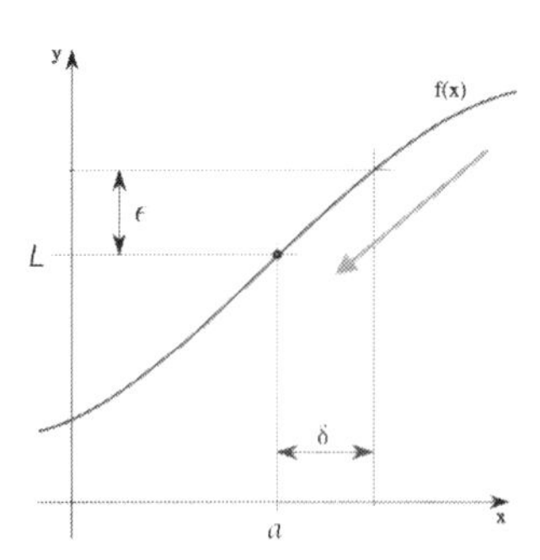

Figure 5.8: A function $f(x)$ whose variation around the value L is smaller than ϵ for all x in the interval $(a, a + \delta)$. The value δ depends the choice of ϵ.

The limit of $f(x)$ when x approaches *from the left* is defined analogously,

$$\lim_{x \to a^-} f(x) = \lim_{\delta \to 0} f(a - \delta).$$

If both limits from the left and from the right of some number exist and are equal to each other, we can talk about the limit as $x \to a$ without specifying the direction of approach:

$$\lim_{x \to a} f(x) = \lim_{x \to a^+} f(x) = \lim_{x \to a^-} f(x).$$

For the two-sided limit of a function to exist at a point, both the limit from the left and the limit from the right must converge to the same number. If the function $f(x)$ obeys, $f(a) = L$ and $\lim_{x \to a} f(x) = L$, we say the function $f(x)$ is continuous at $x = a$.

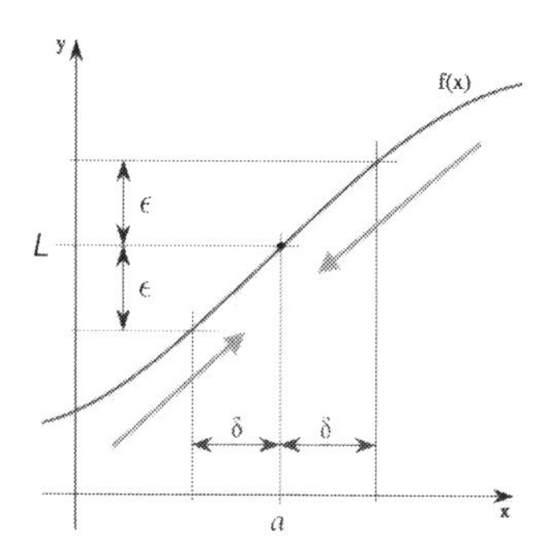

Figure 5.9: The two-sided limit $\lim_{x \to a} f(x) = L$ exists if both the limit from the left and the limit from the right exist and are equal to L.

Continuity

A function is said to be *continuous* if its graph looks like a smooth curve that doesn't make any sudden jumps and contains no gaps. If you can draw the graph of the function on a piece of paper without lifting your pen, the function is continuous.

A more mathematically precise way to define continuity is to say the function is equal to its limit for all x. We say a function $f(x)$ is *continuous* at a if the limit of f as $x \to a$ converges to $f(a)$:

$$\lim_{x \to a} f(x) = f(a).$$

Remember, the two-sided limit $\lim_{x \to a}$ requires both the left and the right limit to exist and to be equal. Thus, the definition of continuity implies the following equality:

$$\lim_{x \to a^-} f(x) = f(a) = \lim_{x \to a^+} f(x).$$

Consider the mathematical definition of continuity given in the equation above. Can you see how it connects to the intuitive idea of continuous functions as functions that can be drawn without lifting the pen?

Most functions we'll study in calculus are continuous, but not all functions are. Functions that are not defined for some value, as well as functions that make sudden jumps, are not continuous. For example, consider the function

$$f(x) = \frac{|x-3|}{x-3} = \begin{cases} 1 & \text{if } x \geqslant 3, \\ -1 & \text{if } x < 3. \end{cases}$$

This function is *continuous from the right* at the point $x = 3$, since $\lim_{x\to 3^+} f(x) = 1 = f(3)$. However, taking the limit from the left, we find $\lim_{x\to 3^-} f(x) = -1 \neq f(3)$. Therefore, the function is not continuous. The function $f(x)$ is continuous everywhere on the real line except at $x = 3$.

Example 3 We can calculate the limit $\lim\limits_{x\to 5} \dfrac{2x+1}{x}$ as follows:

$$\lim_{x\to 5} \frac{2x+1}{x} = \frac{2(5)+1}{5} = \frac{11}{5}.$$

There is nothing tricky going on here—we plug the number 5 into the equation, and voila. The function $f(x) = \frac{2x+1}{x}$ is continuous at the value $x = 5$, so the limit of the function as $x \to 5$ is equal to the value of the function $\lim\limits_{x\to 5} f(x) = f(5)$.

Asymptotes

An *asymptote* of the function $f(x)$ is a line the function approaches but never touches. The word asymptote comes from the Greek *asumptotos*, which means "not falling together." For example, the line $y = 0$ (the x-axis) is an asymptote of the function $f(x) = \frac{1}{x}$ as x goes to infinity.

A *vertical asymptote* is a vertical line that the function approaches. For example, the function $f(x) = \frac{1}{3-x}$ has a vertical asymptote at $x = 3$. When the function approaches $x = 3$ from the left, the function increases to infinity:

$$\lim_{x\to 3^-} \frac{1}{3-x} = \infty.$$

The limit describes x taking on values like 2.9, 2.99, 2.999, and so on. The number in the denominator gets smaller and smaller, thus the fraction grows larger and larger. Note, the function is not defined at the exact value $x = 3$. Nevertheless, the above limit allows us to describe what happens to the function near that point.

Example 4 Find $\lim_{x\to 0} \frac{2x+1}{x}$.

Plugging $x = 0$ into the fraction yields a divide-by-zero error $\frac{2(0)+1}{0}$, so a more careful treatment is required.

First we'll consider the limit from the right $\lim_{x\to 0+} \frac{2x+1}{x}$. We want to approach the value $x = 0$ with small positive numbers. First we'll define a small positive number $\delta > 0$, then choose $x = \delta$, and then compute the limit:

$$\lim_{\delta\to 0} \frac{2(\delta)+1}{\delta} = 2 + \lim_{\delta\to 0} \frac{1}{\delta} = 2 + \infty = \infty.$$

In this instance, we take it for granted that $\lim_{\delta\to 0} \frac{1}{\delta} = \infty$. Intuitively, let's imagine what happens in the limit as δ approaches 0. When $\delta = 10^{-3}$, the function value will be $\frac{1}{\delta} = 10^3$. When $\delta = 10^{-6}$, $\frac{1}{\delta} = 10^6$. As $\delta \to 0$, the expression $\frac{1}{\delta}$ becomes larger and larger all the way to infinity.

If we take the limit from the left, letting x take on small negative values, we obtain

$$\lim_{\delta\to 0} f(-\delta) = \frac{2(-\delta)+1}{-\delta} = -\infty.$$

Since $\lim\limits_{x\to 0+} f(x)$ does not equal $\lim\limits_{x\to 0-} f(x)$, we say $\lim\limits_{x\to 0} f(x)$ does not exist.

Limits are fundamentally important for calculus. Indeed, the three main calculus topics we'll discuss in the remainder of this chapter are derivatives, integrals, and series—all of which are defined using limits.

Limits for derivatives

The formal definition of a function's derivative is expressed in terms of the rise-over-run formula for an infinitely short run:

$$f'(x) = \lim_{\text{run}\to 0} \frac{\text{rise}}{\text{run}} = \lim_{\delta\to 0} \frac{f(x+\delta) - f(x)}{x+\delta - x}.$$

We'll continue the discussion of this formula in Section 5.6.

Limit for integrals

One way to approximate the area under the curve $f(x)$ between $x = a$ and $x = b$ is to split the area into N little rectangles of width $\epsilon =$

$\frac{b-a}{N}$ and height $f(x)$, and then calculate the sum of the areas of the rectangles:

$$A(a,b) \approx \underbrace{\epsilon f(a) + \epsilon f(a+\epsilon) + \epsilon f(a+2\epsilon) + \cdots + \epsilon f(b-\epsilon)}_{N \text{ terms}}.$$

We obtain the exact value of the area in the limit where we split the area into an infinite number of rectangles with infinitely small width:

$$\int_a^b f(x)\,dx = A(a,b) = \lim_{N\to\infty} \left[\epsilon f(a) + \epsilon f(a+\epsilon) + \epsilon f(a+2\epsilon) + \cdots + \epsilon f(b-\epsilon)\right].$$

Computing the area under a function by splitting the area into infinitely many rectangles is an approach known as a *Riemann sum*, which we'll discuss in Section 5.13.

Limits for series

We use limits to describe the convergence properties of series. For example, the partial sum of the first N terms of the geometric series $a_n = r^n$ corresponds to the following expression:

$$S_N = \sum_{n=0}^{N} r^n = 1 + r + r^2 + r^3 + \cdots + r^N.$$

The *series* a_n is defined as the limit $N \to \infty$ of the above expression. For values of r that obey $|r| < 1$, the series converges:

$$S_\infty = \lim_{N\to\infty} S_N = \sum_{n=0}^{\infty} r^n = 1 + r + r^2 + r^3 + \cdots = \frac{1}{1-r}.$$

To convince yourself the above formula is correct, observe how the infinite sum S_∞ is similar to a shifted version of itself: $S_\infty = 1 + rS_\infty$. Now solve for S_∞ in the equation $S_\infty = 1 + rS_\infty$.

You'll find more about series in Section 5.19.

5.5 Limit formulas

We now switch gears into *reference* mode, where we'll describe a whole bunch of known formulas for limits of various kinds of functions. You do not need to know *why* these limit formulas are true; your mission is to understand what they mean.

Ratios of functions

The following statements tell you about the *relative sizes* of functions. If the limit of the ratio of two functions is equal to 1, then these functions must behave similarly in the limit. If the limit of the ratio goes to zero, then the function in the denominator must be much larger than the function in the numerator.
Limits of trigonometric functions:

$$\lim_{x\to 0}\frac{\sin(x)}{x}=1,\ \lim_{x\to 0}\cos(x)=1,\ \lim_{x\to 0}\frac{1-\cos x}{x}=0,\ \lim_{x\to 0}\frac{\tan(x)}{x}=1.$$

A polynomial of degree n and the exponential function e^x both go to infinity as x goes to infinity:

$$\lim_{x\to\infty} x^n=\infty, \qquad \lim_{x\to\infty} e^x=\infty.$$

Though both functions grow to infinity, the exponential function grows much faster. The limit of the ratio of the exponential function divided by any polynomial function is

$$\lim_{x\to\infty}\frac{e^x}{x^n}=\infty, \qquad \text{for all } n\in\mathbb{N}.$$

In computer science, this distinction is a big deal when comparing the running times of algorithms. Imagine x represents the *size* of the problem we want to solve. A *polynomial-time algorithm* will take fewer than Cx^n steps to compute the answer, for some constants C and n. An *exponential-time algorithm* takes an exponential number of steps to compute the answer—the number of steps is described by the expression De^x, for some constant D. Exponential-time algorithms are kind of useless because their running time becomes prohibitively long for large problems. With a large enough input x, an exponential-time algorithm with running time De^x will take longer than the age of the universe to finish! The above results hold true not only for the exponential function base e, but for all exponential functions with base a, so long as $a > 1$:

$$\lim_{x\to\infty}\frac{a^x}{x^n}=\infty, \qquad \text{for all } n\in\mathbb{N},\ \text{for all } a>1.$$

The exponential function a^x with base $a > 1$ grows faster than any polynomial function.

We'll now look at some limit formulas involving logarithms. The logarithmic function is weaker than any polynomial function:

$$\lim_{x\to\infty}\frac{\ln(x)}{x^n}=0, \qquad \forall n\in\mathbb{N}_+.$$

Both $\ln(x)$ and x^n go to infinity as x becomes very large, but logarithmic functions grow more slowly than any polynomial function, so the ratio goes to zero. In fact, even a logarithmic function raised to the power p is weaker than any polynomial:

$$\lim_{x\to\infty} \frac{\ln^p(x)}{x^n} = 0, \qquad \forall n \in \mathbb{N}_+ \text{ and } p < \infty.$$

Also of interest is the behaviour of the logarithmic function as x approaches zero from the right:

$$\lim_{x\to 0^+} x^n \ln(x) = 0, \qquad \forall n \in \mathbb{N}_+.$$

The two factors in this limit expression pull in different directions. The logarithmic function goes to $-\infty$ as x approaches zero, but the polynomial factor x^n goes to zero as x goes to zero. Since the limit is equal to zero, we know the polynomial factor wins, because near $x = 0^+$, the polynomial function x^n goes to zero faster than the logarithmic function $\ln(x)$ goes to negative infinity.

A third point of interest for the logarithmic function occurs near the value $x = 1$, where the following limit holds:

$$\lim_{x\to 1} \frac{\ln(x)}{x-1} = 1.$$

In other words, the shape of $\ln(x)$ near $x = 1$ resembles the function $x - 1$, which is a line with slope one passing through the point $(1, 0)$.

Euler's number

The number e is defined as the following limit:

$$e \equiv \lim_{n\to\infty}\left(1+\frac{1}{n}\right)^n \quad \text{or alternately as} \quad e \equiv \lim_{\epsilon\to 0}(1+\epsilon)^{1/\epsilon}.$$

The first expression corresponds to a compound interest calculation with an annual interest rate of 100% where compounding is performed infinitely often.

The exponential function e^x can be obtained through similar limit expressions:

$$\lim_{n\to\infty}\left(1+\frac{x}{n}\right)^n = e^x \qquad \text{or} \qquad \lim_{\epsilon\to 0}(1+\epsilon x)^{1/\epsilon} = e^x.$$

For future reference, here is another limit formula involving the exponential function:

$$\lim_{x\to 0}\frac{e^x - 1}{x} = 1,$$

which tells us $e^x - 1$ is similar to the function x near $x = 0$.

Properties

The calculation of the limit of the sum, difference, product, and quotient of two functions is computed as follows, respectively:

$$\lim_{x\to a}(f(x)+g(x)) = \lim_{x\to a} f(x) + \lim_{x\to a} g(x),$$
$$\lim_{x\to a}(f(x)-g(x)) = \lim_{x\to a} f(x) - \lim_{x\to a} g(x),$$
$$\lim_{x\to a} f(x)g(x) = \lim_{x\to a} f(x) \cdot \lim_{x\to a} g(x),$$
$$\lim_{x\to a} \frac{f(x)}{g(x)} = \frac{\lim_{x\to a} f(x)}{\lim_{x\to a} g(x)}.$$

The above formulas indicate we are allowed to *take the limit inside* of the basic arithmetic operations.

L'Hopital's rule

If you are taking the limit of a fraction of two functions $\frac{f(x)}{g(x)}$ that obey $\lim_{x\to\infty} f(x) = 0$ and $\lim_{x\to\infty} g(x) = \infty$, the limit of their ratio is

$$\lim_{x\to\infty} \frac{f(x)}{g(x)} = \frac{\lim_{x\to\infty} f(x)}{\lim_{x\to\infty} g(x)} = \frac{0}{\infty} = 0.$$

Both the numerator and the denominator help drive the ratio to zero. Alternately, if you ever obtain a fraction of the form $\frac{\infty}{0}$ as a limit, where both the large numerator and the small denominator make the fraction grow to infinity, you can write $\frac{\infty}{0} = \infty$.

Sometimes, when evaluating limits of fractions $\frac{f(x)}{g(x)}$, you might end up with a fraction like

$$\frac{0}{0} \quad \text{or} \quad \frac{\infty}{\infty}.$$

These are called *undecidable* conditions. They are undecidable because we cannot tell whether the function in the numerator or the denominator is bigger. One way to compute limits with undecidable conditions is to compare the ratio of the derivatives of the numerator and the denominator. This is called *L'Hopital's rule*:

$$\lim_{x\to a} \frac{f(x)}{g(x)} \overset{\text{H.R.}}{=} \lim_{x\to a} \frac{f'(x)}{g'(x)}.$$

You can find the derivative formulas you'll need for using L'Hopital's rule in the table of derivative formulas on page 308.

Example Consider the calculation of the limit of the ratio $\frac{x^3}{e^x}$ as x goes to infinity. Both functions grow to infinity. We can calculate the limit of their ratio by using L'Hopital's rule three times:

$$\lim_{x\to\infty}\frac{x^3}{e^x}\overset{\text{H.R.}}{=}\lim_{x\to\infty}\frac{3x^2}{e^x}\overset{\text{H.R.}}{=}\lim_{x\to\infty}\frac{6x}{e^x}\overset{\text{H.R.}}{=}\lim_{x\to\infty}\frac{6}{e^x}=\frac{6}{\infty}=0.$$

Example 2 Calculate the limit $\lim_{x\to 0}\frac{\sin^{-1}(x)}{x}$. Both the numerator and the denominator go to zero as x goes to zero. We can find the derivative formula for $\sin^{-1}(x)$ in the table on page 308, then apply L'Hopital's rule:

$$\lim_{x\to 0}\frac{\sin^{-1}(x)}{x}\overset{\text{H.R.}}{=}\lim_{x\to 0}\frac{\frac{1}{\sqrt{1-x^2}}}{1}=\lim_{x\to 0}\frac{1}{\sqrt{1-x^2}}=\frac{1}{\sqrt{1-0}}=1.$$

Links

[See the Wikipedia page for more examples of limits]
`https://en.wikipedia.org/wiki/Limit_of_a_function`

Exercises

E5.1 Calculate the following limit expressions and explain what limit expression means in words:

(a) $\lim_{x\to\infty}\frac{1}{x+4}$ (b) $\lim_{x\to\infty}\frac{2x+2}{x+4}$ (c) $\lim_{x\to\infty}\frac{x^2+2}{x+4}$

Hint: Use L'Hopital's rule for (b) and (c).

E5.2 Calculate the limits:

(a) $\lim_{x\to\infty}\frac{22}{11}$ (b) $\lim_{x\to 3^+}\frac{4}{x-3}$ (c) $\lim_{x\to 3^-}\frac{4}{x-3}$

(d) $\lim_{x\to\infty}\frac{22+3x^3}{11+4x^3}$ (e) $\lim_{x\to\infty}\frac{4}{x-3}$ (f) $\lim_{x\to-\infty}\frac{4}{x-3}$

Use the information from your answers in (b), (c), (e), and (f) to draw the graph of the function $f(x)=\frac{4}{x-3}$.

5.6 Derivatives

In the beginning of the chapter we introduced the derivative concept by identifying the derivative with the slope of the function's graph. This graphical representation of derivatives and the intuition that comes with it are very important: this is how mathematicians and physicists usually "think" about derivatives. It is equally important to understand the formal definition of the derivative operation, so this is what we will cover next. Afterward, we'll build some practical skills for calculating derivatives of functions.

Definition

The *derivative* of a function is defined as

$$f'(x) \equiv \lim_{\delta \to 0} \frac{f(x+\delta) - f(x)}{\delta}.$$

The definition of the derivative comes from the rise-over-run formula for calculating the slope of a line:

$$\frac{\text{rise}}{\text{run}} = \frac{\Delta y}{\Delta x} = \frac{y_f - y_i}{x_f - x_i} = \frac{f(x+\delta) \; - \; f(x)}{x + \delta \; - \; x}.$$

By making δ tend to zero in the above expression, we are able to obtain the slope of the function $f(x)$ at the point x.

Derivatives occur so often in math that people have devised many ways to denote them. Don't be fooled by this multitude of notations—all of them refer to the same concept:

$$Df(x) \equiv f'(x) \equiv \frac{d}{dx} f(x) \equiv \frac{df}{dx} \equiv \nabla f.$$

Example Let's calculate the derivative of $f(x) = 2x^2 + 3$ to illustrate how the complicated-looking derivative formula works:

$$f'(x) = \lim_{\delta \to 0} \frac{f(x+\delta) - f(x)}{\delta} = \lim_{\delta \to 0} \frac{2(x+\delta)^2 + 3 \; - \; (2x^2+3)}{\delta}.$$

We can simplify the fraction inside the limit:

$$\frac{2x^2 + 4x\delta + \delta^2 - 2x^2}{\delta} = \frac{4x\delta + \delta^2}{\delta} = \frac{4x\delta}{\delta} + \frac{\delta^2}{\delta} = 4x + \delta.$$

The second term of this expression disappears when we take the limit to obtain the final answer:

$$f'(x) = \lim_{\delta \to 0} (4x + \delta) = 4x + 0 = 4x.$$

Congratulations, you have just calculated your first derivative! The calculation wasn't that complicated, but the process was pretty long and tedious. The good news is you only need to calculate the derivative from first principles once. Once you obtain a *derivative formula* for a particular function, you can use the formula every time you see a function of that form.

The power rule

The derivative formula we obtained in the last example is a special case of the general formula for computing derivatives of powers of x. The *power rule* formula states:

$$\text{if} \quad f(x) = x^n \quad \text{then} \quad f'(x) = nx^{n-1}.$$

The proof of this formula proceeds by steps analogous to the steps used in the example above.

Example 2 Use the power rule to compute the derivatives of the following functions:

$$f(x) = x^{10}, \qquad g(x) = \sqrt{x^3}, \qquad h(x) = \frac{1}{x^3}.$$

In the first case, we apply the formula directly to find the derivative $f'(x) = 10x^9$. In the second case, we begin with the fact that square root is equivalent to an exponent of $\frac{1}{2}$, thus we rewrite the function as $g(x) = x^{\frac{3}{2}}$. After rewriting, we find $g'(x) = \frac{3}{2}x^{\frac{1}{2}} = \frac{3}{2}\sqrt{x}$. We can rewrite the third function as $h(x) = x^{-3}$, then use the power rule to compute the derivative $h'(x) = -3x^{-4} = -\frac{3}{x^4}$.

Applications of derivatives

Optimization

Consider some real-world problem in which a quantity is described by the function $f(x)$. The derivative function $f'(x)$ describes how the quantity $f(x)$ *changes* as x changes. Often, we don't actually care about the value of $f'(x)$ and only need to find the sign of the derivative. If the derivative is positive $f'(x) > 0$, the function is *increasing*. If $f'(x) < 0$, the function is *decreasing*. If the function is horizontal at a certain point $x = x_0$, then $f'(x_0) = 0$. The points where $f'(x) = 0$ are important for finding the maximum and minimum values of $f(x)$.

Recall we previously used the rule "the max is where the derivative is zero" to calculate the maximum height h reached by a ball thrown in the air. We identified the top of the ball's trajectory as the location when its velocity in the y-direction equals zero. The ball moves upward initially ($v_y > 0$), stops momentarily at its maximum height ($v_y = 0$), then moves downward ($v_y < 0$) until it comes back to the ground. We can find the time t_{top} it takes for the ball to reach its top height by solving the equation $v_y(t_{\text{top}}) = 0$, which is the same as $y'(t_{\text{top}}) = 0$. Once we know the time t_{top}, we substitute this value into the equation for $y(t)$ to obtain $h = \max\{y(t)\} = y(t_{\text{top}})$.

We'll discuss the details of the *optimization algorithm* in Section 5.10.

Tangent lines

The *tangent line* to the function $f(x)$ at $x = x_0$ is the line with slope $f'(x_0)$ that passes through the point $(x_0, f(x_0))$. The tangent line is special because it only "touches" the function at a single point. This is in contrast with *secant* lines (from the Latin *secare*), which *cut* through the function at more than one point. There are infinitely many secant lines that cut through the point $(x_0, f(x_0))$, but only a single tangent line—denoted $T_1(x)$.

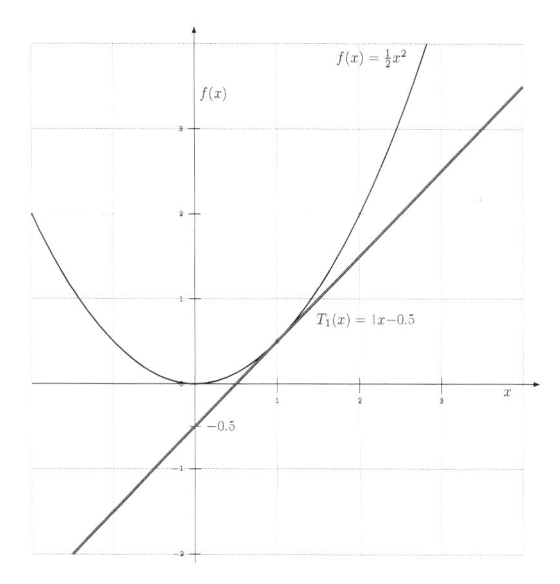

Figure 5.10: The tangent line to the function $f(x) = \frac{1}{2}x^2$ at the point $x = 1$ is $T_1(x) = 1x - 0.5$. Note how the tangent line touches the function *only* at the point $(1, 1)$ and the slope of the tangent line is the same as the slope of $f(x)$ at that point.

Let's calculate the equation of the tangent line at $x = x_0$. We are looking for the equation of the line $T_1(x) = mx + b$ that passes through the point $(x_0, f(x_0))$ and has slope equal to $f'(x_0)$. Since m represents the slope of the line, we can conclude that $m = f'(x_0)$. Since the tangent line passes through the point $(x_0, f(x_0))$, we can find the initial value b by solving the equation

$$f(x_0) = T_1(x_0) = f'(x_0)x_0 + b.$$

Solving for b, we find $b = f(x_0) - f'(x_0)x_0$.

The equation of a tangent line can be written as

$$T_1(x) = \underbrace{f(x_0)}_{(c)} + \underbrace{f'(x_0)(x - x_0)}_{(\ell)}.$$

The above expression describes the tangent line as the sum of a constant term (c) and a second term (ℓ) proportional to the shifted coordinate $(x - x_0)^1$ centred at x_0.

The tangent line $T_1(x)$ is the best linear approximation to the function $f(x)$ near the coordinate $x = x_0$. Written informally, this statement says,

$$f(x) \approx T_1(x) \quad \text{for } x \text{ near } x_0.$$

We previously used this type of linear approximation to derive the simple harmonic motion equation for a pendulum on page 261. The *small angle* approximation states that

$$f(\theta) = \sin\theta \approx \theta = T_1(\theta), \qquad \text{for } \theta \text{ near } 0.$$

Discussion

Now that you know what derivatives are and what they are used for, it's time to learn how to compute them.

5.7 Derivative formulas

The table below shows the derivative formulas for a number of commonly used functions. You'll be using these derivative formulas a lot in the remainder of this chapter so it's a good idea to memorize them.

$$\begin{array}{rcl} f(x) & \text{– derivative} \rightarrow & f'(x) \\ a & -\tfrac{d}{dx} \rightarrow & 0 \\ \alpha f(x) + \beta g(x) & -\tfrac{d}{dx} \rightarrow & \alpha f'(x) + \beta g'(x) \\ x & -\tfrac{d}{dx} \rightarrow & 1 \end{array}$$

$$x^n \quad -\tfrac{d}{dx}\rightarrow \quad nx^{n-1}$$
$$\frac{1}{x} \equiv x^{-1} \quad -\tfrac{d}{dx}\rightarrow \quad \frac{-1}{x^2} \equiv -x^{-2}$$
$$\sqrt{x} \equiv x^{\frac{1}{2}} \quad -\tfrac{d}{dx}\rightarrow \quad \frac{1}{2\sqrt{x}} \equiv \frac{1}{2}x^{-\frac{1}{2}}$$
$$e^x \quad -\tfrac{d}{dx}\rightarrow \quad e^x$$
$$a^x \quad -\tfrac{d}{dx}\rightarrow \quad a^x \ln(a)$$
$$\ln(x) \quad -\tfrac{d}{dx}\rightarrow \quad \frac{1}{x}$$
$$\log_a(x) \quad -\tfrac{d}{dx}\rightarrow \quad (x\ln(a))^{-1}$$
$$\sin(x) \quad -\tfrac{d}{dx}\rightarrow \quad \cos(x)$$
$$\cos(x) \quad -\tfrac{d}{dx}\rightarrow \quad -\sin(x)$$
$$\tan(x) \quad -\tfrac{d}{dx}\rightarrow \quad \sec^2(x) \equiv \cos^{-2}(x)$$
$$\sin^{-1}(x) \quad -\tfrac{d}{dx}\rightarrow \quad \frac{1}{\sqrt{1-x^2}}$$
$$\cos^{-1}(x) \quad -\tfrac{d}{dx}\rightarrow \quad \frac{-1}{\sqrt{1-x^2}}$$
$$\tan^{-1}(x) \quad -\tfrac{d}{dx}\rightarrow \quad \frac{1}{1+x^2}$$
$$\sinh(x) \quad -\tfrac{d}{dx}\rightarrow \quad \cosh(x)$$
$$\cosh(x) \quad -\tfrac{d}{dx}\rightarrow \quad \sinh(x)$$

You can find a complete table of derivative formulas on page 481 in the back of the book.

5.8 Derivative rules

Taking derivatives is a simple task: find the appropriate formula in the table of derivative formulas and apply the formula to the specific problem at hand. Derivative tables come in handy, but they usually do not list formulas for *composite* functions. This section covers some important derivatives rules that will allow you to find derivatives of more complicated functions.

Linearity

The derivative of a sum of two functions is the sum of the derivatives:

$$[f(x)+g(x)]' = f'(x) + g'(x),$$

and for any constant α, we have

$$[\alpha f(x)]' = \alpha f'(x).$$

The derivative of a linear combination of functions $\alpha f(x) + \beta g(x)$ is equal to the linear combination of the derivatives $\alpha f'(x) + \beta g'(x)$.

Product rule

The derivative of a product of two functions is obtained as follows:

$$[f(x)g(x)]' = f'(x)g(x) + f(x)g'(x).$$

Quotient rule

The *quotient rule* tells us how to obtain the derivative of a fraction of two functions:

$$\left[\frac{f(x)}{g(x)}\right]' = \frac{f'(x)g(x) - f(x)g'(x)}{g(x)^2}.$$

Chain rule

If you encounter a situation that includes an inner function and an outer function, like $f(g(x))$, you can obtain the derivative by a two-step process:

$$[f(g(x))]' = f'(g(x))g'(x).$$

In the first step, leave the inner function $g(x)$ alone, and focus on taking the derivative of the outer function $f(x)$. This step gives us $f'(g(x))$, the value of f' evaluated at $g(x)$. As the second step, we multiply the resulting expression by the derivative of the *inner* function $g'(x)$.

The chain rule tells us the derivative of a composite function is calculated as the product of the derivative of the outer function and the derivative of the inner function.

Simple example Consider the following derivative calculation:

$$\left[\sin(x^2)\right]' = \cos(x^2)\left[x^2\right]' = \cos(x^2)2x.$$

The chain rule also applies to functions of functions of functions $f(g(h(x)))$. To take the derivative, start from the outermost function and work your way toward x.

$$[f(g(h(x)))]' = f'(g(h(x)))g'(h(x))h'(x).$$

More complicated example Compute the following derivative:

$$\begin{aligned}\left[\sin(\ln(x^3))\right]' &= \cos(\ln(x^3))\left[\ln(x^3)\right]' \\ &= \cos(\ln(x^3))\tfrac{1}{x^3}\left[x^3\right]' \\ &= \cos(\ln(x^3))\tfrac{3}{x}.\end{aligned}$$

Simple, right?

Examples

The above rules define *all* you need to know to take the derivative of any function, no matter how complicated. To convince you, I'll show you some examples of really hairy functions. Don't be scared by complexity: as long as you follow the rules, you'll find the right answer in the end.

Example Calculate the derivative of

$$f(x) = e^{x^2}.$$

We need the chain rule for this one:

$$f'(x) = e^{x^2}[x^2]' = e^{x^2}2x.$$

Example 2 Find the derivative of

$$f(x) = \sin(x)e^{x^2}.$$

We'll need the product rule for this one:

$$f'(x) = \cos(x)e^{x^2} + \sin(x)2xe^{x^2}.$$

Example 3 Compute the derivative of

$$f(x) = \sin(x)e^{x^2}\ln(x).$$

This situation again calls for the product rule, but this time we'll have three terms. For each term, take the derivative of one of the functions and multiply this derivative by the other two functions:

$$f'(x) = \cos(x)e^{x^2}\ln(x) + \sin(x)2xe^{x^2}\ln(x) + \sin(x)e^{x^2}\frac{1}{x}.$$

Example 4 Take the derivative of

$$f(x) = \sin(\cos(\tan(x))).$$

We need a triple chain rule for this one:

$$\begin{aligned} f'(x) &= \cos(\cos(\tan(x)))\,[\cos(\tan(x))]' \\ &= -\cos(\cos(\tan(x)))\sin(\tan(x))\,[\tan(x)]' \\ &= -\cos(\cos(\tan(x)))\sin(\tan(x))\sec^2(x). \end{aligned}$$

Explanations

Derivation of the product rule

By definition, the derivative of $f(x)g(x)$ is

$$[f(x)g(x)]' = \lim_{\delta\to 0}\frac{f(x+\delta)g(x+\delta) - f(x)g(x)}{\delta}.$$

Consider the numerator of the fraction. If we add and subtract $f(x)g(x+\delta)$, we can factor the expression into two terms, like this:

$$\begin{aligned} & f(x+\delta)g(x+\delta)\ \overbrace{-f(x)g(x+\delta) + f(x)g(x+\delta)}^{=0}\ -f(x)g(x) \\ &= [f(x+\delta) - f(x)]g(x+\delta) + f(x)[g(x+\delta) - g(x)]. \end{aligned}$$

The expression for the derivative of the product becomes

$$[f(x)g(x)]' = \lim_{\delta\to 0}\left\{\frac{[f(x+\delta) - f(x)]}{\delta}g(x+\delta) + f(x)\frac{[g(x+\delta) - g(x)]}{\delta}\right\}.$$

This looks almost exactly like the product rule formula, except here we have $g(x+\delta)$ instead of $g(x)$. This difference is okay since we assume $g(x)$ is a continuous function. Recall that a continuous function $g(x)$ obeys $\lim_{\delta\to 0} g(x+\delta) = g(x)$ for all x. Using the continuity property of $g(x)$, we obtain the final form of the product rule:

$$[f(x)g(x)]' = f'(x)g(x) + f(x)g'(x).$$

Proving the correctness of the chain rule for derivatives is a bit more complicated. Actually, it is *a lot* more complicated. The argument presented in the next section is the most technical part of this book, and it's totally fine if you're not able to follow all the details. It's my duty as your calculus teacher to prove to you that the formula $[f(g(x))]' = f'(g(x))g'(x)$ is correct, but the proof is included only for readers who insist on seeing the full, excruciating details. Other readers should feel free to skip the next section and continue reading on page 316.

Derivation of the chain rule

Assume $f(x)$ and $g(x)$ are differentiable functions. We want to show that the derivative of $f(g(x))$ equals $f'(g(x))g'(x)$, which is the chain rule for derivatives:

$$[f(g(x))]' = f'(g(x))g'(x).$$

Before we begin, I'd like to comment on the notation used to define derivatives. I happen to like the Greek letter δ (lowercase *delta*), so I defined the derivative of $f(x)$ as

$$f'(x) = \lim_{\delta\to 0} \frac{f(x+\delta) - f(x)}{\delta}.$$

Instead, we could also use the variable Δ (uppercase *delta*) and write

$$f'(x) \equiv \lim_{\Delta\to 0} \frac{f(x+\Delta) - f(x)}{\Delta}.$$

In fact, we can use *any* variable for the limit expression. All that matters is that we divide by the *same* non-zero quantity as the quantity added to x inside the function, and that this quantity goes to zero. If we're not careful with our choice of limit variable we could run into trouble. Specifically, the definition of a limit depends on a "small, nonzero number Δ," which is then used in the limit $\Delta \to 0$. The condition $\Delta \neq 0$ is essential because the expression $\frac{f(x+\Delta)-f(x)}{\Delta}$ is not well defined when $\Delta = 0$, since it leads to a divide-by-zero error.

In order to avoid any possibility of such errors, we define the following piecewise function:

$$R(y,b) \equiv \begin{cases} \frac{f(y)-f(b)}{y-b} & \text{if } y \neq b, \\ f'(b) & \text{if } y = b. \end{cases}$$

Observe the function $R(y,b)$ is continuous in y, when we treat b as a constant. This follows from the definition of the derivative formula and the assumption that $f(x)$ is differentiable. Using the function $R(y,b)$, we can write the formula for the derivative of $f(x)$ as $f'(x) = \lim_{\Delta \to 0} R(x+\Delta, x)$. Note this formula is valid even in the case $\Delta = 0$.

To prove the chain rule, we'll need the function $R\big(g(x+\delta), g(x)\big)$, which is defined as follows:

$$R\big(g(x+\delta), g(x)\big) \equiv \begin{cases} \frac{f(g(x+\delta))-f(g(x))}{g(x+\delta)-g(x)} & \text{if } g(x+\delta) \neq g(x), \\ f'(g(x)) & \text{if } g(x+\delta) = g(x). \end{cases}$$

Okay, we're done with the preliminaries, so we can get back to proving the chain rule, $[f(g(x))]' = f'(g(x))g'(x)$. We start with the limit expression for the left-hand side of the equation:

$$[f(g(x))]' = \lim_{\delta \to 0} \frac{f(g(x+\delta)) - f(g(x))}{\delta}.$$

Observe that the fraction inside the limit can be written as

$$\frac{f(g(x+\delta)) - f(g(x))}{\delta} = R\big(g(x+\delta), g(x)\big) \frac{g(x+\delta) - g(x)}{\delta}.$$

This is the trickiest part of the proof, so let's analyze carefully why this equation holds. We must check that the equation holds in the two special cases in the definition of $R\big(g(x+\delta), g(x)\big)$.

Case A Whenever $g(x+\delta) \neq g(x)$, we have:

$$\begin{aligned} \frac{f(g(x+\delta)) - f(g(x))}{\delta} &= \frac{f(g(x+\delta)) - f(g(x))}{\delta} \frac{g(x+\delta) - g(x)}{g(x+\delta) - g(x)} \\ &= \frac{f(g(x+\delta)) - f(g(x))}{g(x+\delta) - g(x)} \frac{g(x+\delta) - g(x)}{\delta} \\ &= R\big(g(x+\delta), g(x)\big) \frac{g(x+\delta) - g(x)}{\delta}. \end{aligned}$$

Case B For points where $g(x+\delta) = g(x)$, we have:

$$\frac{f(g(x+\delta)) - f(g(x))}{\delta} = \frac{0}{\delta} = 0,$$

and

$$R\big(g(x+\delta), g(x)\big)\frac{g(x+\delta)-g(x)}{\delta} = f'(g(x))\frac{0}{\delta} = 0.$$

Thus, the equation $\frac{f(g(x+\delta))-f(g(x))}{\delta} = R\big(g(x+\delta), g(x)\big)\frac{g(x+\delta)-g(x)}{\delta}$ holds in both cases.

We can now rewrite the limit expression for $[f(g(x))]'$ using the equation established above:

$$\begin{aligned}
[f(g(x))]' &= \lim_{\delta\to 0}\frac{f(g(x+\delta))-f(g(x))}{\delta} \\
&= \lim_{\delta\to 0}\left(\underbrace{R\big(g(x+\delta), g(x)\big)}_{F_1}\underbrace{\frac{g(x+\delta)-g(x)}{\delta}}_{F_2}\right).
\end{aligned}$$

We're trying to evaluate a limit expression that is the product of two factors; $\lim_{\delta\to 0} F_1 F_2$. The limit of a product exists if the limits of both factors—$\lim_{\delta\to 0} F_1$ and $\lim_{\delta\to 0} F_2$—exist. Before we proceed, we must evaluate the limit $\delta \to 0$ for both factors to ensure the limits exist.

To obtain the limit of the first factor, we'll rely on the continuity of the functions $g(x)$ and $R(y,b)$:

$$\lim_{\delta\to 0} g(x+\delta) = g(x) \;\text{ and }\; \lim_{\Delta\to 0} R\big(b+\Delta, b\big) = R\big(b,b\big) = f'(b).$$

We define the quantity $\Delta \equiv g(x+\delta) - g(x)$ and using the continuity of $g(x)$, we can establish $\Delta \to 0$ as $\delta \to 0$. We are therefore allowed to change the limit variable from δ to Δ, and evaluate the limit of the first factor as follows:

$$\begin{aligned}
\lim_{\delta\to 0} F_1 &= \lim_{\delta\to 0} R\big(g(x+\delta), g(x)\big) \\
&= \lim_{\Delta\to 0} R\big(g(x)+\Delta, g(x)\big) \\
&= R\big(g(x), g(x)\big) = f'(g(x)).
\end{aligned}$$

We also know the limit of the second factor exists because it corresponds to the derivative of $g(x)$:

$$\lim_{\delta\to 0} F_2 = \lim_{\delta\to 0}\frac{g(x+\delta)-g(x)}{\delta} = g'(x),$$

and, since we assumed $g(x)$ is differentiable, its derivative must exist.

Since the limits of both factors—$\lim_{\delta\to 0} F_1$ and $\lim_{\delta\to 0} F_2$—exist and are well defined, we can now complete the proof:

$$\begin{aligned}
[f(g(x))]' &= \lim_{\delta\to 0}\left(R(g(x+\delta), g(x))\frac{g(x+\delta)-g(x)}{\delta}\right) \\
&= \left(\lim_{\delta\to 0} R(g(x+\delta), g(x))\right)\left(\lim_{\delta\to 0}\frac{g(x+\delta)-g(x)}{\delta}\right) \\
&= f'(g(x))g'(x).
\end{aligned}$$

This establishes the validity of the chain rule $[f(g(x))]' = f'(g(x))g'(x)$.

Alternate notation

The presence of so many primes and brackets can make derivative formulas difficult to read. As an alternative, we sometimes use the *Leibniz notation* for derivatives. The three rules of derivatives in Leibniz notation are written as follows:

- Linearity: $\frac{d}{dx}(\alpha f(x) + \beta g(x)) = \alpha\frac{df}{dx} + \beta\frac{dg}{dx}$
- Product rule: $\frac{d}{dx}(f(x)g(x)) = \frac{df}{dx}g(x) + f(x)\frac{dg}{dx}$
- Chain rule: $\frac{d}{dx}(f(g(x))) = \frac{df}{dg}\frac{dg}{dx}$

Some authors prefer the notation $\frac{df}{dx}$ for the derivative of $f(x)$ because it is more evocative of a rise-over-run calculation.

5.9 Higher derivatives

In the previous section we learned how to calculate the derivative $f'(x)$ of any function $f(x)$. The second derivative of $f(x)$ is the derivative of the derivative of $f(x)$, and is denoted

$$f''(x) \equiv [f'(x)]' \equiv \frac{d}{dx}f'(x) \equiv \frac{d^2}{dx^2}f(x).$$

This process can be continued to calculate higher derivatives of $f(x)$.

In practice, the first and second derivatives are most important because they have a geometric interpretation. The first derivative of $f(x)$ describes the *slope* of $f(x)$ while the second derivative describes the *curvature* of $f(x)$.

Definitions

- $f(x)$: the original function
- $f'(x)$: the first derivative of the function $f(x)$. The first derivative contains information about the *slope* of the function $f(x)$.
- $f''(x)$: the second derivative of the function $f(x)$. The second derivative contains information about the *curvature* of the function $f(x)$.
  - ▷ If $f''(x) > 0$ for all x, the function $f(x)$ is *convex*. Convex functions open upward, like $f(x) = x^2$.
  - ▷ If $f''(x) < 0$ for all x, the function $f(x)$ is *concave*. Concave functions open downward, like $f(x) = -x^2$.
- $f'''(x) \equiv f^{(3)}(x)$: the third derivative of $f(x)$
- $f^{(n)}(x)$: the nth derivative of $f(x)$

Second derivative

The second derivative describes the change in the value of the first derivative. To obtain $f''(x)$ we compute the derivative of $f'(x)$.

The second derivative tells us about the *curvature* of the function $f(x)$. If the curvature of a function is positive ($f''(x) > 0$), this means the function's slope is increasing, so the function must curve upward. Negative curvature means the function curves downward.

Example Calculate the second derivatives of the functions $u(x) = x^2$ and $d(x) = -x^2$ and comment on the *shape* of these functions.

To solve this problem, we calculate the first derivatives $u'(x) = 2x$ and $d'(x) = -2x$. We obtain a function's second derivative by taking the derivative of its first derivative: $u''(x) = 2$ and $d''(x) = -2$. Since the second derivative of the function $u(x)$ is always positive, the curvature of the function $u(x)$ is always positive. We say the function $u(x)$ is *convex*; it opens upward. On the other hand $d(x)$ is *concave*; it opens downward.

The functions $u(x)$ and $d(x)$ are canonical examples of functions with positive and negative curvature. If a function $f(x)$ has positive curvature at a point x^* ($f''(x^*) > 0$), then the function locally *resembles* $u(x - x^*) = (x - x^*)^2$. On the other hand, if the second derivative of $f(x)$ is negative at x^*, the function will locally resemble $d(x - x^*) = -(x - x^*)^2$. In other words, the terms *convex* and *concave* refer to the u-likeness vs. d-likeness property of functions.

Higher derivatives

If we take the derivative of the derivative of the derivative of $f(x)$, we obtain the *third* derivative of the function. This process can be continued further to obtain the nth derivative of the function:

$$f^{(n)}(x) \equiv \frac{d^n}{dx^n} f(x) \equiv \underbrace{\frac{d}{dx}\frac{d}{dx}\cdots\frac{d}{dx}}_{n} f(x).$$

Higher derivatives do not have an obvious geometric interpretation. However, if you are given a function $f(x)$ such that $f'''(x) > 0$, then the function $f(x)$ must be $+x^3$-like. Alternately, if $f'''(x) < 0$, then the function must resemble $-x^3$.

Later in this chapter, we will learn how to compute the Taylor series of a function, which is a procedure used to find polynomial approximations to any function $f(x)$:

$$f(x) \;\approx\; c_0 + c_1 x + c_2 x^2 + c_3 x^3 + c_4 x^4 + \cdots + c_n x^n.$$

The values of the coefficients $c_0, c_1, \ldots, c_n$ in the approximation require us to compute higher derivatives of $f(x)$. The coefficient c_n tells us whether $f(x)$ is more similar to $+x^n$ ($c_n > 0$), or to $-x^n$ ($c_n < 0$), or to neither of the two ($c_n = 0$).

Example Compute the third derivative of $f(x) = \sin(x)$.

The first derivative is $f'(x) = \cos(x)$. The second derivative will be $f''(x) = -\sin(x)$ so the third derivative must be $f'''(x) = -\cos(x)$. Note that $f^{(4)}(x) = f(x)$.

Optimization: the killer app of calculus

Knowing your derivatives will allow you to *optimize* any function—a crucial calculus skill. Suppose you can choose the input of $f(x)$ and you want to pick the *best* value of x. The best value usually means the *maximum* value (if the function measures something desirable like profits) or the *minimum* value (if the function describes something undesirable like costs). We'll discuss the *optimization algorithm* in more detail in the next section, but first let us look at an example.

Example

The boss of a large drug organization has recently run into problems with the authorities. The more drugs he sells, the more money he makes; but if he sells too much, the authorities will start to regulate his operations and he loses money. When you're in the drug business, the last thing you want is to attract undue attention!

Fed up with this situation, he decides to find the *optimal* amount of drugs to push: as much as possible, but not enough to run into trouble with the law. One day he tells all his advisors and underbosses to leave the room, he picks up a pencil and a piece of paper, takes a deep breath, and sits down to do some calculus.

If x is the amount of drugs his organization sells every day, then the amount of money he makes is given by the function

$$f(x) = 3000xe^{-0.25x},$$

where the linear factor $3000x$ represents his profits and the factor $e^{-0.25x}$ represents the effects of the authorities stepping up their actions as more drugs are released.

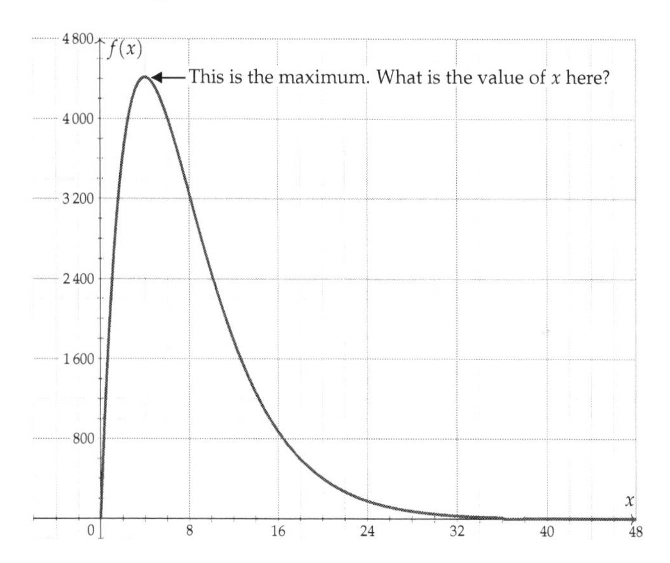

Figure 5.11: The graph of profit as a function of quantity sold.

Looking at the function, the drug boss asks, "What is the value of x that will give me the most profit?" Stated mathematically, he is asking,

$$\underset{x}{\operatorname{argmax}}\ 3000xe^{-0.25x} = ?$$

which means, "Find the value of the argument x that gives the *maximum* value of $f(x)$."

Remembering a conversation with a crooked financial analyst, the drug boss recalls the steps required to find the maximum of a function. First he must take the function's derivative. Because the function is a product of two functions, he applies the product rule, $[g(x)h(x)]' = g'(x)h(x) + g(x)h'(x)$. Taking the derivative of $f(x)$, he obtains

$$f'(x) = 3000e^{-0.25x} + 3000x(-0.25)e^{-0.25x}.$$

Whenever $f'(x) = 0$, the function $f(x)$ has zero slope. A maximum is exactly the kind of place where you'll find zero slope—think of a mountain peak with steep slopes on all sides; the mountain is momentarily horizontal at its peak.

So when is the derivative zero? We set up the equation,

$$f'(x) = 3000e^{-0.25x} + 3000x(-0.25)e^{-0.25x} = 0.$$

We factor out the 3000 and the exponential function to obtain

$$3000e^{-0.25x}(1 - 0.25x) = 0.$$

Since $3000 \neq 0$ and $e^{-0.25x} \neq 0$, the term in the bracket must be equal to zero:

$$(1 - 0.25x) = 0,$$

or $x = 4$. The slope of $f(x)$ is equal to zero when $x = 4$. This x value corresponds to the peak of the curve.

The boss calls his posse back into the room and proudly announces that from then on, his organization will release exactly four kilograms of drugs per day.

"Boss, how much money will we make per day if we sell four kilograms?" asks one of the underbosses, dressed in a slick suit.

"We'll make the *maximum* possible!" replies the boss.

"Yes I know Boss, but how much money is the maximum?"

The dude in the suit is asking a good question. It's one thing to know where the maximum occurs, and it's another to know the *value* of the function at this point. The dude is asking the following math question:

$$\max_x \ 3000xe^{-0.25x} = ?$$

Since we already know the maximum occurs at $x^* = 4$, we can plug this number into the function $f(x)$ to find

$$\max_x f(x) = f(4) = 3000(4)e^{-0.25(4)} = \frac{12000}{e} \approx 4414.55.$$

After the meeting, the boss feels exceptionally good about himself, and is convinced he's doing his job really well. As the CEO of a pharmaceutical corporation, his job is to maximize corporate profits, irrespective of possible negative outcomes and side effects.

A word of caution

The System is obsessed with this whole optimization thing. Optimize to make more profits, optimize to minimize costs, optimize stealing of natural resources from Third World countries, optimize anything that moves, basically. Therefore, the System wants *you*—the young and powerful generation of the future—to learn this important skill and become faithful employees of corporations. The corporates want you to learn calculus so you can help them optimize things, ensuring the smooth continuation of the whole enterprise.

Mathematical knowledge does not come with an ethics manual to help you decide what should and should not be optimized; this responsibility falls on you. If, like me, you don't want to become a corporate sellout, you can always choose to use calculus for science. It doesn't matter whether it will be physics, medicine, or running your own company, it is all good. Just stay away from the System. Please do this for yourself and our future, will you?

Having said these words of warning, let's now proceed so I can show you the powerful optimization algorithm.

5.10 Optimization algorithm

This section shows and explains the details of the algorithm for finding the maximum of a function. This is called *optimization*, as in finding the optimal solution to a problem.

Say you have the function $f(x)$, which represents a real-world phenomenon. For example, $f(x)$ could represent how much *fun* you have as a function of alcohol consumed during one evening. We all know that with too much x, the fun stops and you find yourself, as the Irish say, "talking to God on the big white phone." Too little x and you might not have enough Dutch courage to chat up that girl/guy from the table across the room. To have as much fun as possible, you want to find the alcohol consumption x^* where f takes on its maximum value.

This is one of the prominent applications of calculus (I'm talking about optimization, not alcohol consumption). This is why you've been learning about all those limits, derivative formulas, and differentiation rules in previous sections.

Definitions

- x: the *variable* we can control

- $[x_i, x_f]$: the interval of values from which x can be chosen. The values of x must obey $x_i \leqslant x \leqslant x_f$. These are the *constraints* of the optimization problem. For the drinking optimization problem, $x \geqslant 0$ since you can't drink negative alcohol, and probably $x < 2$ (in litres of hard booze) because roughly at this point a person will die from alcohol poisoning. So we are searching for the optimal amount of alcohol x in the interval $[0, 2]$.
- $f(x)$: the *function* we want to optimize. This function must be *differentiable*, meaning we can take its derivative.
- $f'(x)$: the *derivative* of $f(x)$. The derivative contains information about the slope of $f(x)$.
- *maximum*: a place where the function reaches a peak. When there are multiple peaks, we call the highest peak the *global maximum*, while all other peaks are *local maxima*.
- *minimum*: a place where the function reaches a low point at the bottom of a valley. The *global minimum* is the lowest point overall, whereas a *local minimum* is the minimum in some neighbourhood.
- *extremum*: a general term to describe both maximum and minimum points.
- *saddle point*: a place where $f'(x) = 0$ at a point that is neither a max nor a min. For example, the function $f(x) = x^3$ has a saddle point at $x = 0$.

Suppose some function $f(x)$ has a global maximum at x^*, and the value of that maximum is $f(x^*) = M$. The following mathematical notations apply:

- $\max_x f(x) = M$: the maximum value of $f(x)$
- $\text{argmax}_x f(x) = x^*$: the argmax operator tells you the location (the *argument* of the function) where the maximum occurs

Algorithm for finding extrema

Input: a function $f(x)$ and a constraint region $C = [x_i, x_f]$
Output: the locations and values of all maxima and minima of $f(x)$

Follow this algorithm step-by-step to find the extrema of a function:

1. First, *look* at $f(x)$. If you can plot it, plot it. If not, try to imagine what the function looks like.

2. Find the derivative $f'(x)$.

3. Solve the equation $f'(x) = 0$. Usually, there will be multiple solutions. Make a list of them. We'll call this the list of *candidates*.

4. For each candidate x^* in the list, check to see whether it is a maximum, a minimum, or a saddle point:

   - If $f'(x^* - 0.1)$ is positive and $f'(x^* + 0.1)$ is negative, then the point x^* is a maximum. The function goes up, flattens at x^*, then goes down after x^*. Therefore, x^* must be a peak.
   - If $f'(x^* - 0.1)$ is negative and $f'(x^* + 0.1)$ is positive, the point x^* is a minimum. The function goes down, flattens, then goes up, so the point must be a minimum.
   - If $f'(x^* - 0.1)$ and $f'(x^* + 0.1)$ have the same sign, the point x^* is a saddle point. Remove it from the list of candidates.

5. Now go through the list one more time and reject all candidates x^* that do not satisfy the constraints C. In other words, if $x \in [x_i, x_f]$, the candidate stays; but if $x \notin [x_i, x_f]$, we remove it since this solution is not *feasible*. Returning to the alcohol consumption example, if you have a candidate solution that says you should drink 5[L] of booze, you must reject it because otherwise you would die.

6. Add x_i and x_f to the list of candidates. These are the boundaries of the constraint region and should also be considered. If no constraint was specified, use the *default* constraint region $-\infty < x < \infty$ and add $-\infty$ and ∞ to the list of candidates.

7. For each candidate x^*, calculate the function value $f(x^*)$.

The resulting list is a collection of *local* extrema: maxima, minima, and endpoints. The *global maximum* is the largest value from the list of local maxima. The *global minimum* is the smallest of the local minima.

When dealing with points at infinity such as $x^* = \infty$, we don't actually calculate a value; rather, we calculate the limit $\lim_{x\to\infty} f(x)$. The function either blows up $\lim_{x\to\infty} f(x) = \infty$ (like x, x^2, e^x), drops down indefinitely $\lim_{x\to\infty} f(x) = -\infty$ (like $-x, -x^2, -e^x$), or tends to some finite value (like $\lim_{x\to\infty} \frac{1}{x} = 0$, $\lim_{x\to\infty} e^{-x} = 0$). If a function goes to positive ∞, it doesn't have a global maximum and instead continues growing indefinitely. Similarly, functions that go toward negative ∞ don't have a global minimum.

Example 1 Find all the maxima and minima of the function

$$f(x) = x^4 - 8x^2 + 356.$$

Since no interval is specified, we'll use the default interval $x \in \mathbb{R}$. Let's go through the steps of the algorithm.

1. We don't know what the function x^4 looks like, but it's probably similar to the x^2—it goes up to infinity on the far left and the far right.

2. Using the power rule for derivatives, we find

$$f'(x) = 4x^3 - 16x.$$

3. Now we must solve

$$4x^3 - 16x = 0,$$

which is the same as

$$4x(x^2 - 4) = 0,$$

which is the same as

$$4x(x-2)(x+2) = 0.$$

The list of candidate points is $\{x = 0, x = 2, x = -2\}$.

4. For each of these points, we'll check to see if it is a max, a min, or a saddle point.

   (a) For $x = -2$, we check $f'(-2.1) = 4(-2.1)(-2.1-2)(-2.1+2) < 0$ and $f'(-1.9) = 4(-1.9)(-1.9-2)(-1.9+2) > 0$ to conclude $x = -2$ must be a minimum.

   (b) For $x = 0$ we try $f'(-0.1) = 4(-0.1)(-0.1-2)(-0.1+2) > 0$ and $f'(0.1) = 4(0.1)(0.1-2)(0.1+2) < 0$, which reveals we have a maximum at $x = 0$.

   (c) For $x = 2$, we check $f'(1.9) = 4(1.9)(1.9-2)(1.9+2) < 0$ and $f'(2.1) = 4(2.1)(2.1-2)(2.1+2) > 0$, so $x = 2$ must be a minimum.

5. We don't have any constraint region, so all of the above candidates make the cut.

6. We add the default boundaries $-\infty$ and ∞ to the list of candidates. At this point, our final shortlist of candidates contains $\{x = -\infty, x = -2, x = 0, x = 2, x = \infty\}$.

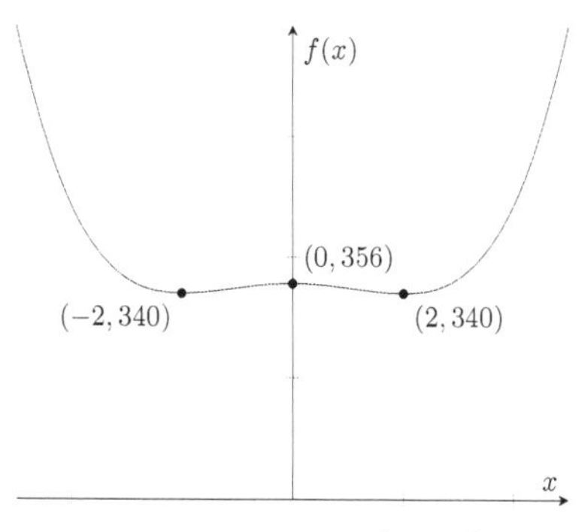

Figure 5.12: Graph of the function $f(x) = x^4 - 8x^2 + 356$ indicating the three critical points of the function located at $x = -2$, $x = 0$, and $x = 2$.

7. We now evaluate the function $f(x)$ for each of the values to obtain location-value pairs $(x, f(x))$, like so: $\{(-\infty, \infty), (-2, 340), (0, 356), (2, 340), (\infty, \infty)\}$. Note that $f(\infty) = \lim_{x\to\infty} f(x) = \infty^4 - 8\infty^2 + 356 = \infty$ and the same is true for $f(-\infty) = \infty$.

We are done. The function has no global maximum since it increases to infinity. It has a local maximum at $x = 0$ with value 356. It also has two global minima at $x = -2$ and $x = 2$, both of which have value 340. Thank you, come again.

Alternate algorithm

Instead of checking nearby points to the left and right of each critical point, we can modify the algorithm with an alternate Step 4 known as the *second derivative test*. Recall the second derivative tells us the function's *curvature*. If the second derivative is positive at a critical point x^*, then the point x^* must be a minimum. If, on the other hand, the second derivative at a critical point is negative, the function must be maximum at x^*. If the second derivative is zero, the test is inconclusive.

Alternate Step 4

- For each candidate x^*, see if it's a max, a min, or a saddle point:
  - ▷ If $f''(x^*) < 0$ then x^* is a max.
  - ▷ If $f''(x^*) > 0$ then x^* is a min.
  - ▷ If $f''(x^*) = 0$, the second derivative test fails. We must revert back to checking nearby values $f'(x^* - \delta)$ and $f'(x^* + \delta)$ to determine if x^* is a max, a min, or a saddle point.

Limitations

The optimization algorithm described above applies to *differentiable* functions of a single variable. Not all functions are differentiable. Functions with sharp corners in their graphs like the absolute value function $|x|$ are not differentiable everywhere, and therefore cannot be analyzed using the optimization algorithm. Functions with jumps in them, like the *Heaviside function*, are not continuous and therefore not differentiable—the algorithm cannot be used on them either.

We can generalize the optimization procedure to optimize multivariable functions like $f(x,y)$. You'll learn how to do this in a *multivariable calculus* course. Multivariable optimization techniques are similar to the steps above, but with more variables and with more intricate constraint regions.

At last, I want to comment on the fact that **we can only maximize *one* function at a time**. Say the CEO of the pharmaceutical corporation wanted to maximize the company's profits $f(x)$ *and* the company's growth $g(x)$. This is not a well-posed problem; either you maximize $f(x)$ or you maximize $g(x)$, but you can't do both at the same time. There is no reason why a single x would give the highest value for both $f(x)$ and $g(x)$. If both functions are important, we can make a new function that combines the original two $F(x) = f(x) + g(x)$ and maximize $F(x)$. If company growth is three times more important than profits, then the function to optimize is $F(x) = f(x) + 3g(x)$, but it is mathematically and logically impossible to maximize both $f(x)$ and $g(x)$ at the same time.

Exercises

E5.3 The function $f(x) = x^3 - 2x^2 + x$ has a local maximum on the interval $x \in [0,1]$. Find where this maximum occurs, and find the value of f at that point.

5.11 Implicit differentiation

Thus far, we discussed how to compute derivatives of functions $f(x)$. We identified the function's output with the variable y and wrote $y = f(x)$ to show the output y depends on the input x through the function $f(x)$. The slope of this function is the rise in the y-direction divided by the run in the x-direction and is equal to the value of the derivative function $\frac{dy}{dx} \equiv f'(x)$ at that point.

We can also use the derivative operation to compute the slope of graphs describing *mathematical relations* that are not expressed in the form $f(x) =$ something. For example, consider the equation that describes a circle of radius R:

$$x^2 + y^2 = R^2.$$

The equation of a circle describes a *relation* between the variables x and y without specifying one variable as a function of the other. Nevertheless, we can still treat y as a function of x. We say the function $y(x)$ is *implicit*.

If we want to make the functional relationship between y and x *explicit*, we can rewrite the equation as $x^2 + (y(x))^2 = R^2$ and then solve for $y(x)$ to obtain

$$y(x) = \pm\sqrt{R^2 - x^2},$$

which shows explicitly how y depends on the variable x. Note there are actually two ys for each x: the top half and the bottom half of the circle.

Example

Consider the point $P = (x_P, y_P)$ that lies on the circle $x^2 + y^2 = R^2$. Find the *slope* of the tangent line to the circle at P.

This problem is asking us to find $y'(x_P)$. Using the explicit function $y(x)$, we would first compute the derivative function $y'(x) = \pm\frac{1}{2}\frac{1}{\sqrt{R^2-x^2}}(-2x)$ and then substitute the value x_P into $y'(x)$. The slope of the tangent line to the circle at the point $P = (x_P, y_P)$ is

$$y'(x_P) = \frac{-x_P}{\sqrt{R^2 - x_P^2}} = -\frac{x_P}{y_P}.$$

But do we really need to go through the explicit equation? Let me show you a faster way to solve the problem, without the need to compute the function $y(x)$ explicitly. Apply the derivative operator $\frac{d}{dx}$ on the equation that describes the circle:

$$\begin{aligned}\frac{d}{dx}[\,x^2 + y^2\,] &= \frac{d}{dx}[\,R^2\,],\\ 2x + 2y\frac{dy}{dx} &= 0,\\ \frac{dy}{dx} &= -\frac{x}{y}.\end{aligned}$$

The slope at $P = (x_P, y_P)$ is therefore $\dfrac{dy}{dx} = -\dfrac{x_P}{y_P}$.

Note how we used the chain rule for the implicit function $y(x)$.

Definitions

- $g(x,y)$: a function that takes as inputs two variables
- $g(x,y) = 0$: a *relation* between the variables x and y
- $\frac{d}{dx}[g(x,y)] = 0$: the derivative of the relation $g(x,y) = 0$ with respect to the variable x
- $dg = \frac{dg}{dx}dx + \frac{dg}{dy}dy$: the *total derivative* of the function $g(x,y)$

Explanations

The equation of a circle can be written as a relation $g(x,y) = 0$:

$$g(x,y) \equiv x^2 + y^2 - R^2 = 0.$$

The *implicit* derivative of this equation with respect to x is

$$\begin{aligned} \frac{d}{dx}[g(x,y)] = \frac{d}{dx}\left[x^2 + y^2 - R^2\right] &= \frac{d}{dx}[0] \\ \frac{dg}{dx} + \frac{dg}{dy}\frac{dy}{dx} &= 0 \\ 2x + 2y\frac{dy}{dx} &= 0 \qquad \Rightarrow \qquad \frac{dy}{dx} = -\frac{x}{y}. \end{aligned}$$

What is *implicit* in this derivative calculation is the assumption that y is a function of x. The expression $\frac{dy}{dx}$ refers to the derivative of this implicit function $y(x)$. After isolating $\frac{dy}{dx}$, we obtain an expression that describes the slope of the circle at any point $P = (x_P, y_P)$. You can check that the slope predicted for the point at top of the circle $(0,R)$ is zero. Also note the slope is infinite at $(R,0)$ since the tangent to the circle is vertical at that point.

Let's now look at an example involving implicit differentiation.

Example In the corporate world, an executive officer's ego E is related to the executive's salary S by the following equation:

$$E^2 = S^3.$$

Suppose both E and S are functions of time. What is the rate of change of the executive's ego when the executive's salary is 60k and the salary increases at a rate of 5k per year?

This is called a *related rates* problem. We know the relation $E^2 = S^3$ and the rate $\frac{dS}{dt} = 5000$ and we're asked to find the rate of change

$\frac{dE}{dt}$ when $S = 60000$. First, take the implicit derivative of the salary-to-ego relation:

$$\frac{d}{dt}\left[E^2 \right] = \frac{d}{dt}\left[S^3 \right],$$
$$2E\frac{dE}{dt} = 3S^2\frac{dS}{dt}.$$

We're interested in the point where $S = 60000$. To find the ego points, solve for E in the relation $E^2 = S^3$; $E = \sqrt{60000^3} = 14696938.46$ ego points when $S = 60000$. Substituting all known values into the derivative of the relation, we find

$$2(14696938.46)\frac{dE}{dt} = 3(60000)^2(5000).$$

The executive's ego is growing at $\frac{dE}{dt} = \frac{3(60000)^2(5000)}{2(14696938.46)} = 1837117.31$ ego points per year. Yay, ego points! I wonder what you can redeem these for.

Total derivative

Consider again a relation $g(x,y) = 0$, but this time assume that both x and y are implicit functions of a third variable t. To compute the derivative of the expression $g(x,y)$ with respect to t we must trace g's dependence on t through both x and y:

$$\frac{dg}{dt} = \frac{dg}{dx}\frac{dx}{dt} + \frac{dg}{dy}\frac{dy}{dt}.$$

We call this the *total derivative* of g because it represents the total dependence between g and t through both functions $x(t)$ and $y(t)$.

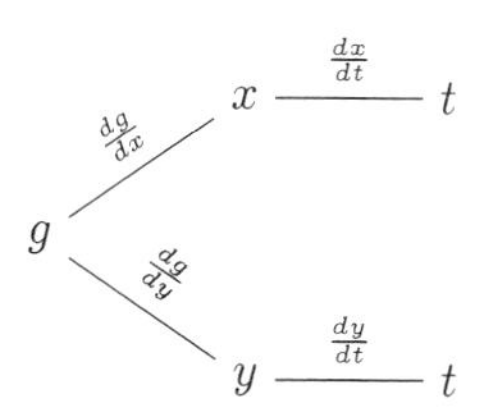

Figure 5.13: Helper diagram for computing the total derivative of the function $g(x(t), y(t))$ with respect to t.

The reasoning behind the total derivative is similar to the reasoning behind the product rule. The derivative of $g(t) = f(t)h(t)$ is $\frac{dg}{dt} = f'(t)h(t) + f(t)h'(t)$ and consists of two terms. In the first term, we take the derivative of $f(t)$ while keeping $h(t)$ constant. In the second term we keep $f(t)$ constant and take the derivative of $h(t)$. Similarly, we compute each term in the total derivative by taking the derivative of g with respect to t through one of the intermediary variables, treating the other variable as constant. Each term is obtained through the chain rule:

$$\frac{d}{dt}g(x(t),y) = \frac{dg}{dx}\frac{dx}{dt} \quad \text{and} \quad \frac{d}{dt}g(x,y(t)) = \frac{dg}{dy}\frac{dy}{dt}.$$

Let's now look at an example that uses the total derivative.

Example The distance r of the point (x, y) from the origin is given by the formula $r(x,y) = \sqrt{x^2+y^2}$. Suppose the horizontal and vertical coordinates of a projectile are described by the functions $x(t) = 1 + 20t$ and $y(t) = 3 + 4t + 5t^2$, where t is the time. Calculate the rate of change $\frac{dr}{dt}$ of the projectile's distance from the origin when $t = 6$.

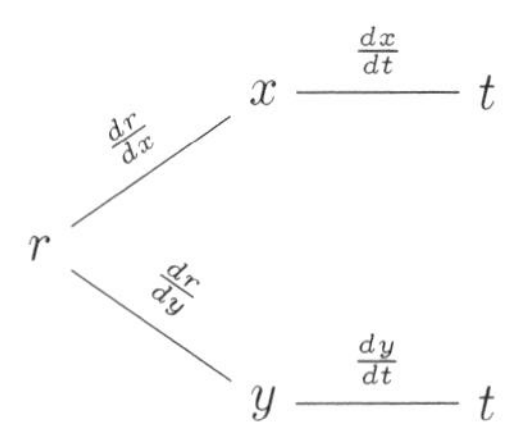

Figure 5.14: Computing the total derivative of $r(x(t), y(t))$ with respect to t.

To compute $\frac{dr}{dt}$, the total derivative of r with respect to t, we must differentiate along both "branches" that connect the variable r to the variable t, as illustrated in Figure 5.14:

$$\begin{aligned}\frac{dr}{dt} &= \frac{dr}{dx}\frac{dx}{dt} + \frac{dr}{dy}\frac{dy}{dt} \\ &= \frac{x}{\sqrt{x^2+y^2}}(20) + \frac{y}{\sqrt{x^2+y^2}}(4+10t).\end{aligned}$$

When $t = 6$, $x = 13$ and $y = 207$, and the answer is $\frac{dr}{dt} = 65.346$.

Differentials

The *differential* of a quantity Q is the same as the derivative but without specifying the "with respect to" variable. The differential dQ represents the change in Q that will result for a given change in the variable (or variables) that Q depends on. The rules for computing differentials are analogous to the rules for computing derivatives:

$$Q = ax^n \qquad \Rightarrow \qquad dQ = nx^{n-1}dx.$$

You can think of differentials as incomplete derivatives: if we later discover that x depends on t, we can divide both sides of the above equation by dt to obtain the derivative expression $\frac{dQ}{dt} = nx^{n-1}\frac{dx}{dt}$.

Application of differentials to computing error bars

In science, when we report the results of an experimental measurement of some quantity Q, we write $Q \pm dQ$, where dQ is an estimate of the error of the measurement. The measurement error dQ is represented graphically as an "error bar" as shown in Figure 5.15. The *precision* of a measurement is defined as the *ratio* of the error of the measurement divided by the size of the quantity being measured $\frac{dQ}{Q}$, or as a percentage.

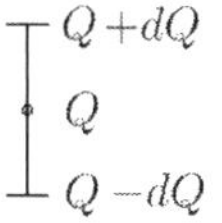

$Q+dQ$

Q

$Q-dQ$

Figure 5.15: The error bars dQ are a visual representation of the uncertainty of the quantity Q.

Suppose the quantity Q depends on the variables x and y. We can express the dependence between the error in the measurement of Q and the error in the measurement of x and y as the formula:

$$dQ = \frac{dQ}{dx}dx + \frac{dQ}{dy}dy.$$

This is the *total differential* of Q. Note the similarity of the total differential formula to the total derivative formula.

Example You want to calculate the kinetic energy of a particle using the formula $K = \frac{1}{2}mv^2$. You measure the particle's mass m with precision 3%, and the particle's velocity with precision 2%. What is the precision of your kinetic energy calculation?

We want to find $\frac{dK}{K}$ and we're told $\frac{dm}{m} = 0.03$ and $\frac{dv}{v} = 0.02$. The first step is to calculate the *total differential* of the kinetic energy:

$$dK = d\left(\frac{1}{2}mv^2\right) = \frac{dK}{dm}dm + \frac{dK}{dv}dv = \frac{1}{2}v^2(dm) + mv(dv),$$

in which we used the product rule and the chain rule for derivatives. To obtain the relative error, divide both sides by K to obtain

$$\frac{dK}{K} = \frac{\frac{1}{2}v^2\,dm + mv\,dv}{\frac{1}{2}mv^2} = \frac{dm}{m} + 2\frac{dv}{v}.$$

The precision of the kinetic energy calculation in your experiment is $\frac{dK}{K} = 0.03 + 2(0.02) = 0.07$ or 7%. Note the error in the velocity measurement dv contributes twice as much as the error in the mass measurement dm, since it appears with exponent two in the formula.

Discussion

We have reached the half-point of the calculus chapter. We learned about derivatives and described applications of derivatives to optimization problems, finding tangent lines, related rates, etc.

Before you continue reading about integrals in the second half of the chapter, I highly recommend you attempt to solve some of the derivative problems starting on page 403.

5.12 Integrals

We now begin our discussion of integrals, the second topic in calculus. An integral is a fancy way of computing the area under the graph of a function. Integral calculus is usually taught as a separate course after differential calculus, but this separation can be counterproductive. The easiest way to understand integration is to think of it as the inverse of the derivative operation. Integrals are antiderivatives. Once you realize this fundamental fact, you'll be able to apply all your differential calculus knowledge to the domain of integral calculus. In differential calculus, we learned how to take a function $f(x)$ and find its derivative $f'(x)$. In integral calculus, we'll be given a function $f(x)$ and we'll be asked to find its *antiderivative* function $F(x)$. The antiderivative of $f(x)$ is a function $F(x)$ whose derivative equals $f(x)$.

In this section, we'll learn about two tasks: how to compute antiderivatives, and how to compute the area under the graph of $f(x)$. Confusingly, both of these operations are called *integration*. To avoid any possibility of confusion, we'll define the two concepts right away:

- The *indefinite integral* of $f(x)$ is denoted $\int f(x)dx = F(x) + C$. To compute the indefinite integral of $f(x)$, you must find a function $F : \mathbb{R} \to \mathbb{R}$, such that $F'(x) = f(x)$. The indefinite integral is the antiderivative function.
- The *definite integral* of $f(x)$ between $x = a$ and $x = b$ is denoted $\int_a^b f(x)dx = A(a,b)$. Definite integrals correspond to the computation of the area under the function $f(x)$ between $x = a$ and $x = b$. The definite integral is a number $A(a,b) \in \mathbb{R}$.

The two integration operations are related. The area under the curve $A(a,b)$ can be computed as the *change* in the antiderivative function, using to the formula $A(a,b) = \left[F(x) + C\right]_a^b = F(b) - F(a)$.

Definitions

You should already be familiar with these concepts:

- $\mathbb{R}$: the set of real numbers
- $f(x)$: a function of the form $f : \mathbb{R} \to \mathbb{R}$, which means f takes real numbers as inputs and produces real numbers as outputs
- $\lim_{\delta\to 0}$: a limit expression in which the number δ tends to zero
- $f'(x)$: the derivative of $f(x)$ is the rate of change of f at x:

$$f'(x) = \lim_{\delta\to 0} \frac{f(x+\delta) - f(x)}{\delta}.$$

  The derivative is a function of the form $f' : \mathbb{R} \to \mathbb{R}$.

These are the new concepts, which we will learn about in integral calculus:

- $A(a,b)$: the value of the *area* under the curve $f(x)$ from $x = a$ until $x = b$. The area $A(a,b)$ is computed as the following integral

$$A(a,b) = \int_a^b f(x)\,dx.$$

  The $\int$ sign stands for *sum*. Indeed, the integral is the "sum" of $f(x)$ for all values of x between a and b.

- $A_0(x)$: the *integral function* of $f(x)$. The integral function corresponds to the computation of the area under $f(x)$ as a function of the upper limit of integration:

$$A_0(x) \equiv A(0,x) = \int_0^x f(u)\,du.$$

The choice of $x = 0$ as the lower limit of integration is arbitrary.

- $F(x) + C$: The *antiderivative* function of the function $f(x)$. An antiderivative function is defined as a function whose derivative equals to $f(x)$. The antiderivative function always includes an additive constant C. If the function $F(x)$ is an antiderivative (obeys $F'(x) = f(x)$) then the function $F(x) + C$ is also an antiderivative since

$$\frac{d}{dx}[F(x) + C] = f(x),$$

for any constant C.

- The fundamental theorem of calculus (FTC) states that the integral function $A_0(x)$ is equal to the antiderivative function $F(x)$ up to an additive constant C:

$$A(0, x) \equiv A_0(x) \overset{\text{FTC}}{=} F(x) + C.$$

The fundamental theorem leads us to the following formula for computing the area $A(a, b)$:

$$A(a, b) = A(0, b) - A(0, a) = A_0(b) - A_0(a) = F(b) - F(a).$$

The area under the curve, $A(a, b)$, is equal to the change in the antiderivative function $F(x)$ between $x = a$ and $x = b$.

The area under the curve

An integral describes the computation of the area under the curve $f(x)$ between $x = a$ and $x = b$:

$$A(a, b) \equiv \int_a^b f(x)\, dx.$$

We refer to the numbers a and b as the *limits of integration*. The location where the integral starts, $x = a$, is called the *lower limit* of integration. The location where the integral stops, $x = b$, is called the *upper limit* of integration.

The integral as a function

The *integral function* of $f(x)$ describes the "running total" of the area under the curve $f(x)$ as a function of the upper limit of integration:

$$A_0(x) \equiv A(0, x) \equiv \int_0^x f(u)\, du.$$

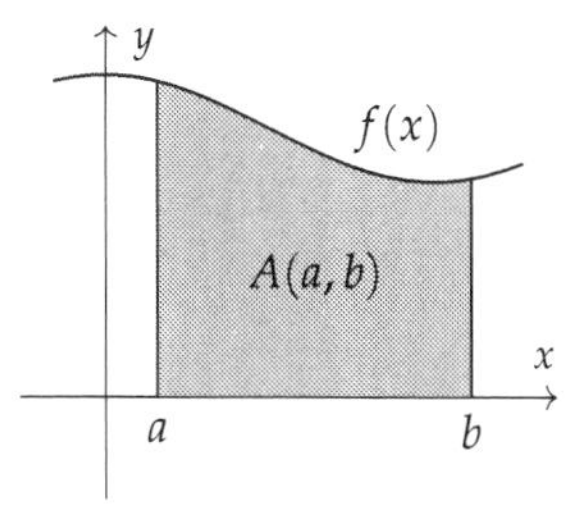

Figure 5.16: The integral of the function $f(x)$ between $x = a$ and $x = b$ corresponds to the area $A(a,b)$.

The variable x represents the upper limit of integration. The variable u inside the integral is called the *integration variable* and its value varies between $u = 0$ and $u = x$. The name of the integration variable u is not important; we can write $\int_0^x f(y)dy$ or $\int_0^x f(z)dz$ or even $\int_0^x f(\xi)d\xi$ and all of these represent the same function $A_0(x)$.

The choice of the lower limit of integration is also not important. For the sake of concreteness, we define the integral function to start at $x = 0$. A different choice for the lower limit of integration would lead to a different integral function. For example, the integral function that describes the area under $f(x)$ starting from $x = a$ is defined as $A_a(x) \equiv A(a,x) \equiv \int_a^x f(u)du$. The functions $A_0(x)$ and $A_a(x)$ differ only by the constant factor $A(0,a) = A_0(a)$:

$$\begin{aligned} \int_0^x f(u)\,du &= \int_0^a f(v)\,dv + \int_a^x f(w)\,dw \\ A(0,x) &= A(0,a) \quad + \; A(a,x) \\ A_0(x) &= A_0(a) \quad\;\; + \; A_a(x). \end{aligned}$$

The area $A(a,b) \equiv A_a(b)$ can be computed as the *change* in the value of $A_0(x)$ between $x = a$ and $x = b$:

$$A(a,b) \equiv \int_a^b f(x)\,dx = A_0(b) - A_0(a).$$

Note the formula $A(a,b) = A_c(b) - A_c(a)$ applies for all $c \in \mathbb{R}$.

The antiderivative function

The *antiderivative* function $F(x)$ of $f(x)$ is a function whose derivative equals $f(x)$:

$$\frac{d}{dx}[\,F(x)\,] = f(x).$$

The antiderivative function is not unique: any function $F(x) + C$ also obeys $\frac{d}{dx}[F(x) + C] = f(x)$, since the derivative of a constant is zero.

The fundamental theorem of calculus

The fundamental theorem of calculus states that the integral function $A_c(x)$ is an antiderivative of $f(x)$:

$$\frac{d}{dx}\left[A_c(x)\right] = \frac{d}{dx}\int_c^x f(u)\,du = f(x).$$

Thus far, we spoke of integral functions $A_c(x)$ and antiderivative functions $F(x)+C$ as different mathematical objects, but the fundamental theorem of calculus implies the equation

$$A_c(x) = F(x) + C.$$

Every integral function $A_c(x)$ is also an antiderivative function, and every antiderivative function $F(x)+C$ corresponds to the integral function $A_c(x)$, for some $c \in \mathbb{R}$. From this point on, we will use the notation $F(x)$ to refer to the integral function.

We'll discuss the fundamental theorem of calculus in more detail when we reach Section 5.14. For now, let's focus on the task of computing integrals by performing reverse-differentiation.

Indefinite integrals

The function $F(x)$ is the result of applying the integral *operator* $\int \cdot\, dx$ to the function $f(x)$. Let's denote by $\{\mathbb{R} \to \mathbb{R}\}$ the set of functions that take real numbers as inputs and produce real numbers as outputs. The integral operator $\int \cdot\, dx$ takes functions as inputs and produces functions as outputs:

$$\int \cdot\, dx : \{\mathbb{R} \to \mathbb{R}\} \quad \to \quad \{\mathbb{R} \to \mathbb{R}\}.$$

The integral operator takes a function $f(x)$ as an input and produces its antiderivative function $F(x)$ as output. Like the derivative function $f'(x)$, the integral function $\int f(x)\,dx$ computes a *property* of the original function $f(x)$. We use the derivative operator to find the "slope of the graph" property of a function. We use the integral operator to find the "area under the graph" property of a function.

In an *indefinite* integral problem, we are given a function $f(x)$ and asked to find its integral function $F(x)$:

$$F(x) = \int f(x)\,dx.$$

The integral is *indefinite* because we're performing an integral calculation but haven't defined the limits of integration $x = a$ and $x = b$.

As a consequence of the fundamental theorem of calculus, we know the derivative of the function $F(x)$ is equal to $f(x)$:

$$F'(x) = f(x).$$

Thus, to find an integral function of the function $f(x)$, we must find a function $F(x)$ such that $F'(x) = f(x)$.

Example Suppose you want to find the indefinite integral $\int x^2\,dx$. Using the fundamental theorem, we can rephrase this problem as the search for some function $F(x)$ such that

$$F'(x) = x^2.$$

Since you remember your derivative formulas (page 308), you can guess right away that $F(x)$ must contain an x^3 term. From the power rule for derivatives, you know that taking the derivative of a cubic term results in a quadratic term. Therefore, the function you are looking for has the form $F(x) = cx^3$, for some constant c. Pick the constant c that makes this equation true:

$$F'(x) = 3cx^2 = x^2.$$

Solving $3c = 1$, we find $c = \frac{1}{3}$ and so the answer to this indefinite integral problem is

$$\int x^2\,dx = \frac{1}{3}x^3 + C.$$

You can verify that $\frac{d}{dx}\left[\frac{1}{3}x^3 + C\right] = x^2$.

Did you see what just happened? We were able to take an integral using only derivative formulas and "reverse engineering."

Example 2 Since we know

$$F(x) = x^4 \quad \xrightarrow{\frac{d}{dx}} \quad F'(x) = 4x^3 \equiv f(x),$$

then it must be that

$$f(x) = 4x^3 \quad \xrightarrow{\int dx} \quad F(x) = \int 4x^3\,dx = x^4 + C.$$

Example 3 Let's look at some more integrals:

- The indefinite integral of $f(x) = \cos\theta$ is

$$F(x) = \int \cos\theta\,d\theta = \sin\theta + C,$$

since $\frac{d}{d\theta}\sin\theta = \cos\theta$.

- Similarly, the integral of $f(x) = \sin\theta$ is

$$F(x) = \int \sin\theta \, d\theta = -\cos\theta + C,$$

since $\frac{d}{d\theta}[-\cos\theta] = \sin\theta$.

- The integral of $f(x) = x^n$ for any number $n \neq -1$ is

$$F(x) = \int x^n \, dx = \frac{1}{n+1}x^{n+1} + C,$$

since $\frac{d}{d\theta}x^n = nx^{n-1}$.

- The integral of $f(x) = x^{-1} = \frac{1}{x}$ is

$$F(x) = \int \frac{1}{x} \, dx = \ln x + C,$$

since $\frac{d}{dx}\ln x = \frac{1}{x}$.

I could go on but I think you get the point: all the derivative formulas you learned (see page 308) can be used in the opposite direction as integral formulas.

Remember to always add a constant term $+C$ to your answer. The answer to the indefinite integral question $\int f(x)\,dx$ is not a single function $F(x)$, but a whole family of functions $F(x) + C$ that differ by an additive constant C.

Definite integrals

A *definite* integral specifies the function to integrate as well as the limits of integration $x = a$ and $x = b$. The area under $f(x)$ between $x = a$ and $x = b$ is

$$A(a,b) \equiv \int_a^b f(x)\,dx.$$

To find the value of the definite integral, we will proceed in two steps. The first step is to calculate the antiderivative function $\int f(x)\,dx = F(x) + C$. In other words, you must solve the indefinite integral before you solve the definite integral.

The second step is to compute the area $A(a,b)$ as the change in the antiderivative function between $x = a$ and $x = b$:

$$A(a,b) = \big[F(x) + C\big]\Big|_{x=a}^{x=b} = [F(b) + C] - [F(a) + C] = F(b) - F(a).$$

Note the new "vertical bar" notation: $g(x)\big|_\alpha^\beta \equiv g(\beta) - g(\alpha)$. This is a useful shorthand for denoting the change in the function $g(x)$

between two points. Figure 5.17 illustrates the meaning of this procedure.

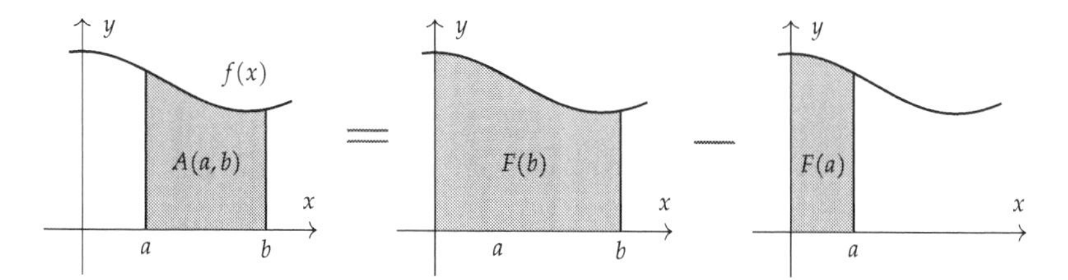

Figure 5.17: The function $F(x)$ measures the area under the curve $f(x)$. The area under $f(x)$ from $x=a$ to $x=b$ is $A(a,b)=F(x)\big|_a^b \equiv F(b)-F(a)$.

You can also try rearranging the plots in Figure 5.17 to visualize the equation $A(0,b) = A(0,a) + A(a,b)$. The "running total" of the area under $f(x)$ until $x = b$ is equal to the "running total" of the area under $f(x)$ until $x = a$, plus the area $A(a,b)$. The formula $A(a,b) = F(b) - F(a)$ follows from combining the equation $A(0,b) = A(0,a) + A(a,b)$ with the result of the fundamental theorem of calculus: $A(0,x) \equiv A_0(x) \stackrel{\text{FTC}}{=} F(x)$.

Example 4 The antiderivative of $f(x) = x^2$ is $F(x) = \frac{1}{3}x^3 + C$. Use this fact to find the value of the definite integral $\int_a^b x^2\,dx$.

The definite integral is computed by evaluating the value of the antiderivative function at the upper limit and subtracting the value of the antiderivative function at the lower limit:

$$\int_a^b x^2\,dx = \left[\tfrac{1}{3}x^3 + C\right]_{x=a}^{x=b} = \left[\tfrac{1}{3}b^3 + C\right] - \left[\tfrac{1}{3}a^3 + C\right] = \frac{1}{3}(b^3 - a^3).$$

Example 5 What is the area under the curve $f(x) = \sin(x)$, between $x = 0$ and $x = \pi$? First we take the antiderivative

$$F(x) = \int \sin(x)\,dx = -\cos(x) + C.$$

Now we calculate the difference between $F(x)$ at the upper limit minus $F(x)$ at the lower limit:

$$\begin{aligned} A(0,\pi) &= \int_0^\pi \sin(x)\,dx \\ &= \underbrace{\left[-\cos(x) + C\right]}_{F(x)}\Big|_0^\pi \end{aligned}$$

$$= [-\cos\pi + C] - [-\cos(0) + C]$$
$$= \cos(0) - \cos\pi \quad = \quad 1 - (-1) = 2.$$

The final answer does not depend on the constant C because we evaluate the *change* in $F(x) + C$.

In case you are wondering what the "area under the curve" calculation is used for in practice, you should recall how we derived the kinematics equations in Chapter 2. The velocity $v(t)$ measures change in position $x(t)$ over time. The total change in position between $t = 0$ and $t = \tau$ is obtained by calculating the integral of $v(t)$ as follows:

$$x(\tau) - x(0) = \int_0^{\tau} v(t)\, dt.$$

Note how the dimensions work in this equation. Time is measured in seconds [s], and $v(t)$ is measured in [m/s], so the area under $v(t)$ has dimensions of [m/s]×[s] = [m].

Properties of integrals

Signed area

The value of a definite integral can be either positive or negative. If the limits of integration a and b satisfy $a < b$ (b is to the right of a on the number line), and if $f(x) > 0$ (meaning $f(x)$ is a positive function), then the area under the curve will be positive:

$$A(a,b) = \int_a^b f(x)\, dx \;>\; 0.$$

For a function $g(x) < 0$, the integral from a to b corresponds to a negative area. In general, if $f(x)$ is above the x-axis in some places, these zones contribute positively to the total area under the curve; places where $f(x)$ is below the x-axis contribute negatively to the total area $A(a,b)$.

We can also obtain a negative area if we swap the limits of integration. Suppose we have $f(x) > 0$, and limits of integration a and b such that $a < b$. If we start integrating at $x = b$ and stop integrating at $x = a$, the area under the curve will be negative:

$$A(b,a) = \int_b^a f(x)\, dx \;<\; 0.$$

The function $f(x)$ is positive but each integration step dx is *negative*, since we're moving from right to left.

Integrals are *signed* areas. Changing the direction of integration changes the sign of the integral:

$$A(b,a) = \int_b^a f(x)\,dx = -\int_a^b f(x)\,dx = -A(a,b).$$

Additivity

The integral from a to b plus the integral from b to c is equal to the integral from a to c:

$$A(a,b) + A(b,c) = \int_a^b f(x)\,dx + \int_b^c f(x)\,dx = \int_a^c f(x)\,dx = A(a,c).$$

Linearity

Integration is a *linear* operation, meaning

$$\int [\alpha f(x) + \beta g(x)]\,dx = \alpha \int f(x)\,dx + \beta \int g(x)\,dx$$

for arbitrary constants α, β. Recall the derivative is also a linear operation:

$$[\alpha f(x) + \beta g(x)]' = \alpha f'(x) + \beta g'(x).$$

Thus, we can say the operations of calculus as a whole are *linear* operations. This property is really cool, because it allows us to break down complicated problems into smaller chunks.

Explanations

In this section, we introduced several new concepts: the area under the curve $A(a,b)$, the integral function $A_c(x)$, and the antiderivative function $F(x) + C$. We also stated the fundamental theorem of calculus, which relates these three concepts:

$$A(c,x) \equiv A_c(x) \overset{\text{FTC}}{=} F(x) + C,$$

for some choice of the constants c and C. Let's define more precisely the equivalence between these concepts.

The set of antiderivative functions

The antiderivative function $F(x) + C$ always includes an arbitrary additive constant C. Thus it would be wrong to talk about *the* antiderivative as a single function; there is a whole set of functions that are antiderivatives of $f(x)$.

Let $\{\mathbb{R} \to \mathbb{R}\}$ denote the set of all functions that take real numbers as inputs and produce real numbers as outputs. The *set* of antiderivative functions for a function $f(x)$ is defined as

$$\left\{ F \in \{\mathbb{R} \to \mathbb{R}\} \;\middle|\; F'(x) = f(x) \right\}.$$

In words, the set of antiderivatives of the function $f(x)$ is the subset of all functions $\{\mathbb{R} \to \mathbb{R}\}$ such that $F'(x) = f(x)$.

Similarly, there is a whole set of integral functions, which differ by the choice of the starting point of integration:

$$\left\{ A_c \in \{\mathbb{R} \to \mathbb{R}\}, c \in \mathbb{R} \;\middle|\; A_c(x) = \int_c^x f(u)\, du \right\}.$$

The fundamental theorem of calculus states that the *set* of antiderivative functions is equal to the *set* of integral functions.

Observe that *any* function from the set of integral functions (antiderivatives) can be used for the area calculation:

$$A(a,b) \equiv \int_a^b f(x)\, dx = A_c(b) - A_c(a) = F(b) - F(a).$$

Integration is the inverse operation of differentiation

You are already familiar with the inverse relationship between *functions* from Chapter 1. You know that to solve for x in the equation $f(x) = c$, you must apply the inverse function f^{-1} to both sides of the equation. The function f^{-1} will undo the effects of f, leaving $x = f^{-1}(c)$.

There exists an analogous inverse relationship between the derivative operator $\frac{d}{dx}$ and the integral operator $\int \cdot \, dx$:

$$\text{int}(\text{diff}(F(x))) = \int_0^x \left(\frac{d}{du} F(u) \right) du = \int_0^x f(u)\, du \overset{\text{FTC}}{=} F(x) + C.$$

The integral operator $\int \cdot \, dx$ is the "undo button" for the derivative operator.

Applications

Suppose you want to find the function $f(t)$ that satisfies the differential equation

$$\frac{d}{dt}\Big[f(t) \Big] = 100.$$

To find $f(t)$ you must *undo* the $\frac{d}{dt}$ operation. After applying the integration operation to both sides of the equation, we obtain

$$\int \left(\frac{d}{dt} f(t) \right) dt = \int (100)\, dt$$
$$f(t) = 100t + C.$$

The solution to the equation $f'(t) = 100$ is $f(t) = 100t + C$, where C is called the *integration constant*.

5.13 Riemann sums

Our discussion in the previous section focussed on the inverse relationship between the integral operator $\int f(x)dx$ and the derivative operator $\frac{d}{dx}$. We learned the antiderivative function $F(x)$ can be used to compute the area under a curve $f(x)$ using the formula $\int_a^b f(x)\, dx = F(b) - F(a)$. Thus, with your differentiation skills and some reverse engineering, you can now handle integrals too.

Is there a way to compute integrals without referring to the derivative operation? No course on calculus would be complete without telling the classic "rectangles story" for computing definite integrals, which goes by the name *Riemann sum*. The Riemann sum is a procedure for computing the area under a curve by breaking up the area into many, little, rectangular strips with heights that vary according to $f(x)$. To obtain the total area under the curve, we sum all the areas of these little rectangles.

First, like a cast of characters, we'll introduce some definitions.

Definitions

- $f(x)$: a function $f\colon \mathbb{R} \to \mathbb{R}$
- a: where the sum starts
- b: where the sum stops
- $A(a,b)$: the exact value of the area under the curve $f(x)$ from $x = a$ until $x = b$
- $S_n(a,b)$: an approximation to the area A in terms of n rectangles
- s_k: the area of the kth rectangle when counting from the left

In this section we will consider the calculation of the area under the curve $f(x) = x^3 - 5x^2 + x + 10$ between $x = -1$ and $x = 4$. Figure 5.18 shows the graph of $f(x)$ and an approximation of the area under the curve as the sum of the areas of 12 rectangles.

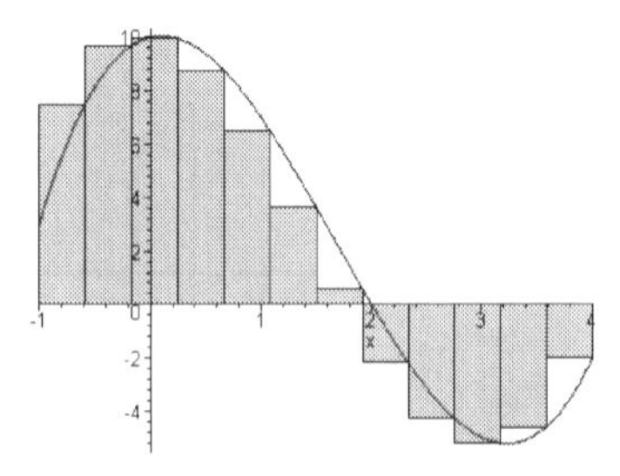

Figure 5.18: An approximation of the area under the function $f(x) = x^3 - 5x^2 + x + 10$ between $x = -1$ and $x = 4$ using $n = 12$ rectangles.

Formulas

The combined-area approximation is given by the *sum* of the areas of the little rectangles:

$$S_n(a,b) = \sum_{k=1}^{n} s_k.$$

Each of the little rectangles has an area s_k given by the rectangle's *height* multiplied by its *width*. The height of each rectangle will vary, but the width is constant. Why constant? Riemann figured that having each rectangle with a constant width Δx would make it easy to calculate the approximation. The total length of the interval from $x = a$ to $x = b$ is $(b - a)$. When we divide this length into n equally spaced segments, each segment will have width Δx given by

$$\Delta x = \frac{b - a}{n}.$$

Okay, we have the width formula; now let's find the height of the kth rectangle in the sequence of rectangles. For the rectangles, we pick isolated "samples" of $f(x)$ for the following values:

$$x_k = a + k\Delta x, \text{ for } k \in \{1, 2, 3, \ldots, n\},$$

with all rectangles equally spaced $\Delta x = \frac{b-a}{n}$ apart.

The function's height varies as we move along the x-axis. The area of each rectangle is equal to its height $f(x_k)$ times its width:

$$s_k = f(a + k\Delta x)\Delta x.$$

Now, my dear students, I want you to stare at the above equation and do some simple calculations to check that you understand. There is no point in continuing if you are just taking my word for it. **Verify** that when $k = 1$, the formula gives the area of the first little rectangle.

Verify also that when $k = n$, the formula $x_k = a + k\Delta x$ reaches the upper limit b.

Let's put our formula for s_k in the sum where it belongs. The Riemann sum approximation using n rectangles is given by

$$S_n(a,b) = \sum_{k=1}^{n} f(a + k\Delta x)\Delta x,$$

where $\Delta x = \frac{b-a}{n}$.

The integral is defined as the limit of the Riemann sum as n goes to infinity: $\int_a^b f(x)\,dx \equiv \lim_{n\to\infty} S_n(a,b) \equiv \lim_{n\to\infty} \sum_{k=1}^{n} f(a + k\Delta x)\Delta x$.

Example

Let's apply the Riemann sum formula in the case of the 12-rectangle approximation to the function $f(x) = x^3 - 5x^2 + x + 10$ illustrated in Figure 5.18. The width of each rectangle is $\Delta x = \frac{4-(-1)}{12} = \frac{5}{12}$. The location of the right endpoint of the kth rectangle is given by the formula

$$x_k = -1 + k\Delta x = -1 + k\frac{5}{12}.$$

The area of the kth rectangle is equal to the height of the function $f(x_k)$ times the width Δx:

$$s_k = f(x_k)\Delta x = (x_k^3 - 5x_k^2 + x_k + 10)\frac{5}{12}.$$

The value for the 12-rectangle approximation to the area under the curve is

$$S_{12}(a,b) = \sum_{k=1}^{12} f(a + k\Delta x)\Delta x = \sum_{k=1}^{12} (x_k^3 - 5x_k^2 + x_k + 10)\frac{5}{12}.$$

Relax, we won't be doing the calculation by hand! We'll get the computer to calculate this summation for us. Go to `live.sympy.org` and type in the following expressions:

```
>>> n = 12
>>> xk = -1 + k*5/n
>>> sk = (xk**3-5*xk**2+xk+10)*(5/n)
>>> summation( sk, (k,1,n) ).evalf()
11.802662...                              # the value of S_12(a,b)
```

The actual value of the area under the curve is given by

$$A(-1,4) = 12.91666\ldots.$$

Comparing our approximation $S_{12}(-1,4)$ with the true value $A(-1,4)$ we see that it is not very accurate. At least we got the first digit right! Let's see if we can do better.

More is better

The 12-rectangle approximation is very low fidelity. You can *clearly* see some rectangles lie outside of the curve (overestimates), and some are too far inside the curve (underestimates). You might be wondering why we are wasting so much time to achieve such a lousy approximation. We have not been wasting our time. You see, the Riemann sum formula $S_n(a,b)$ gets better and better as you cut the region into smaller and smaller rectangles.

Using $n = 25$ rectangles, we obtain a better approximation:

$$S_{25}(a,b) = \sum_{k=1}^{25} f(a + k\Delta x)\Delta x = 12.4.$$

For $n = 50$, we obtain an even closer approximation:

$$S_{50}(a,b) = \sum_{k=1}^{50} f(a + k\Delta x)\Delta x = 12.6625.$$

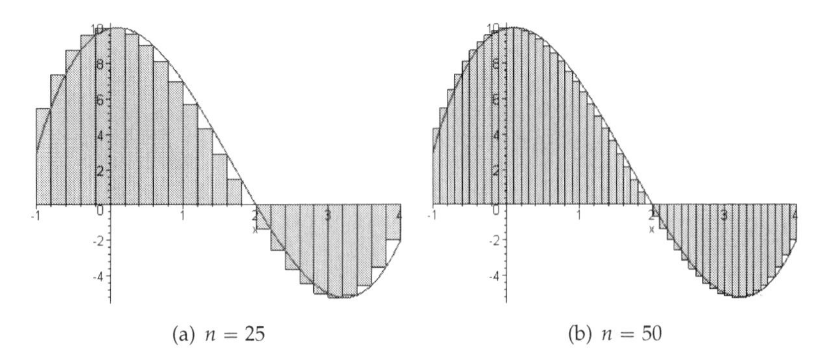

(a) $n = 25$ (b) $n = 50$

Figure 5.19: An approximation to the area under the graph of the function $f(x) = x^3 - 5x^2 + x + 10$ using $n = 25$ and $n = 50$ rectangles.

For $n = 100$, the sum of the rectangles' areas starts to look prettttty much like the function. The calculation gives us $S_{100}(a,b) = 12.7906$.

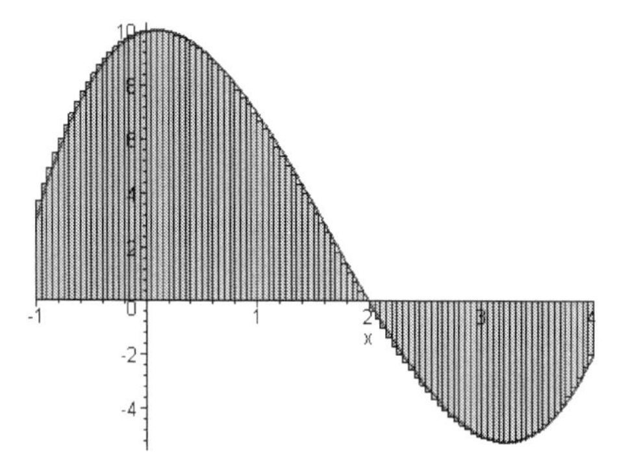

Figure 5.20: An approximation of the area under the function $f(x) = x^3 - 5x^2 + x + 10$ between $x = -1$ and $x = 4$ using $n = 100$ rectangles.

Using $n = 1000$ rectangles, we obtain an approximation to the area $S_{1000}(-1,4) = 12.9041562$, which is accurate to the first decimal.

In the long run, when n grows really large, the Riemann sum approximations will get better and better and approach the true value of the area under the curve. Imagine cutting the region into $n = 10000$ rectangles; isn't $S_{10000}(-1,4)$ a pretty accurate approximation of the actual area $A(-1,4)$?

The integral as a limit

In the limit as the number of rectangles n approaches ∞, the Riemann sum approximation to the area under the curve becomes *arbitrarily close* to the true area:

$$\lim_{n\to\infty} \sum_{k=1}^{n} f(a + k\Delta x)\Delta x = A(a,b).$$

The definite integral between $x = a$ and $x = b$ is *defined* as the limit of a Riemann sum as n goes to infinity:

$$\int_a^b f(x)\,dx \equiv \lim_{n\to\infty} \sum_{k=1}^{n} f(a + k\Delta x)\Delta x \equiv A(a,b).$$

Perhaps now the weird notation we use for integrals will start to make more sense to you. An integral is, literally, the sum of the function at the different sample points! In the limit as $n \to \infty$, the summation sign $\sum$ becomes an integral sign $\int$, and the step size Δx becomes an infinitely small step dx.

It is not computationally practical to make $n \to \infty$; we can simply stop at some finite n which produces the desired accuracy of approximation. The approximation using 1 million rectangles is accurate to the fourth decimal place, which you can verify by entering the following commands on `live.sympy.org`:

```
>>> n = 1000000
>>> xk = -1 + k*5/n
>>> sk = (xk**3-5*xk**2+xk+10)*(5/n)
>>> summation( sk, (k,1,n) ).evalf()
12.9166 541666563
>>> integrate( x**3-5*x**2+x+10, (x,-1,4) ).evalf()
12.9166 666666667
```

Formal definition of the integral

We rarely compute integrals using Riemann sums. The Riemann sum is a *theoretical construct* like the rise-over-run calculation that we use to define the derivative operation:

$$f'(x) = \lim_{\delta \to 0} \frac{f(x+\delta) - f(x)}{\delta}.$$

The integral is defined as the approximation of the area under the curve with infinitely many rectangles:

$$\int_a^b f(x)\,dx \equiv \lim_{n\to\infty} \sum_{k=1}^{n} f(a + k\Delta x)\Delta x, \quad \Delta x = \frac{b-a}{n}.$$

It is usually much easier to refer to a table of derivative formulas (see page 308) rather than compute a derivative starting from the formal definition and taking the limit $\delta \to 0$. Similarly, it is easier to refer to a table of integral formulas (also see page 308), rather than computing the integral by taking the limit as $n \to \infty$ of a Riemann sum.

Now that we have established a formal definition of the integral, we'll be able to understand why integral formulas are equivalent to derivative formulas applied in the opposite direction. In the next section we'll give a formal proof of the inverse relationship between the derivative operation and the integral operation.

Links

[A Riemann sum demonstration]
`http://www.geogebratube.org/student/m68523`

[Riemann sum wizard]
`http://mathworld.wolfram.com/RiemannSum.html`

5.14 The fundamental theorem of calculus

In Section 5.12 we defined the integral function $A_0(x)$ that corresponds to the calculation of the area under $f(x)$ starting from $x = 0$:

$$A_0(x) \equiv \int_0^x f(t)\,dt.$$

We also discussed the notion of an antiderivative function: the function $F(x)$ is an antiderivative of $f(x)$ if $F'(x) = f(x)$.

A priori, there is no reason to suspect the integral function would be related to the derivative operation. The integral corresponds to the computation of an area, whereas the derivative operation computes the slope of a function. The fundamental theorem of calculus describes the relationship between derivatives and integrals.

Theorem (fundamental theorem of calculus). *Let $f(x)$ be a continuous function on the interval $[a, b]$, and let $c \in \mathbb{R}$ be a constant. Define the function $A_c(x)$ as follows:*

$$A_c(x) \equiv \int_c^x f(u)\,du.$$

Then, the derivative of $A_c(x)$ is equal to $f(x)$:

$$\frac{d}{dx}[A_c(x)] = f(x),$$

for any $x \in (a, b)$.

The fundamental theorem of calculus establishes an equivalence between the set of integral functions and the set of antiderivative functions:

$$A_c(x) = F(x) + C.$$

All integral functions $A_c(x)$ are antiderivatives of $f(x)$.

Differential calculus and integral calculus are two sides of the same coin. If you understand why the theorem is true, you will understand something very deep about calculus. Differentiation is the inverse operation of integration. Given a function $G(x) = \int g(x)dx$, we can obtain the function $g(x)$ by taking the derivative of $G(x)$: $G'(x) = g(x)$. The inverse relationship works in the other direction as well. If you're given the derivative $h'(x)$ of some unknown function $h(x)$, you can find the function $h(x)$ (up to a constant), using integration: $h(x) + C = \int h'(x)dx$.

Got proof?

There is an unspoken rule in mathematics: when the word *theorem* appears in writing, it must be followed by the word *proof.* We therefore need to look into the proof of the fundamental theorem of calculus (FTC). It is not so important you understand the details of the proof, but I still recommend you read this subsection for your general math knowledge. If you are in a rush though, feel free to skip ahead.

Before we get to the proof of the FTC, we'll first introduce the *squeezing principle*, which we'll use in the proof. Suppose you have three functions, f, ℓ, and u, such that

$$\ell(x) \leqslant f(x) \leqslant u(x) \qquad \text{for all } x.$$

We say $\ell(x)$ is a *lower bound* on $f(x)$ since its graph is always below that of $f(x)$. Similarly, $u(x)$ is an *upper bound* on $f(x)$. We know the value of $f(x)$ is between $\ell(x)$ and $u(x)$.

Suppose $u(x)$ and $\ell(x)$ both converge to the same limit L:

$$\lim_{x \to a} \ell(x) = L, \quad \text{and} \quad \lim_{x \to a} u(x) = L.$$

Then it must be true that $f(x)$ also converges to the same limit:

$$\lim_{x \to a} f(x) = L.$$

This is true because the function f is *squeezed* between ℓ and u; it has no other choice than to converge to the same limit.

Proof of the fundamental theorem of calculus

For the sake of concreteness, let's use a fixed lower limit of integration $c = 0$. Our starting point is the graph of the function $f(x)$ and the definition of the integral function

$$A_0(x) \equiv \int_0^x f(u)\, du.$$

Our goal is to show that the derivative of the function $A_0(x)$ with respect to x is the function $f(x)$.

Recall the definition of the derivative $g'(x) = \lim_{\epsilon \to 0} \frac{g(x+\epsilon)-g(x)}{\epsilon}$. If we want to find the derivative of $A_0(x)$, we must compute the difference $A_0(x+\epsilon) - A_0(x)$ and then divide by ϵ. Using the definition of the integral function $A_0(x)$, we obtain

$$\begin{aligned} A_0(x+\epsilon) - A_0(x) &= \int_0^{x+\epsilon} f(t)\,dt - \int_0^{x} f(t)\,dt \\ &= \int_x^{x+\epsilon} f(t)\,dt. \end{aligned}$$

Figure 5.21 illustrates the region corresponding to this difference $A_0(x+\epsilon) - A_0(x)$. The region is a long, vertical strip of width ϵ, and a height that varies according to $f(x)$:

$$\int_x^{x+\epsilon} f(t)\,dt \approx \underbrace{\text{width}}_{\epsilon} \times \underbrace{\text{height}}_{?}.$$

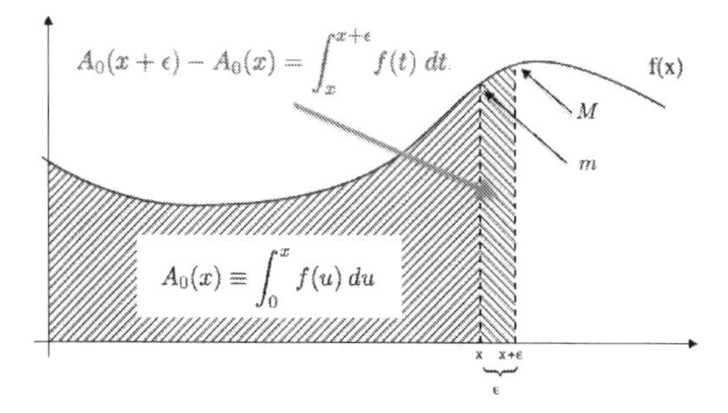

Figure 5.21: The difference $A_0(x+\epsilon) - A_0(x)$ corresponds to the integral of $f(x)$ between x and $x+\epsilon$.

Define the numbers M and m that correspond to the maximum and minimum values of the function $f(x)$ on the interval $[x, x+\epsilon]$:

$$M \equiv \max_{t\in[x,x+\epsilon]} f(t) \qquad \text{and} \qquad m \equiv \min_{t\in[x,x+\epsilon]} f(t).$$

By definition, the quantities ϵm and ϵM provide a lower and an upper bound on the quantity we're trying to study:

$$\epsilon m \leqslant \int_x^{x+\epsilon} f(t)\,dt \leqslant \epsilon M.$$

Recall from the theorem statement that we assume f is *continuous*. If f is continuous, then as $\epsilon \to 0$, we'll have

$$\lim_{\epsilon\to 0} f(x+\epsilon) = f(x).$$

In fact, as $\epsilon \to 0$, all the values of f on the shortening interval $[x, x + \epsilon]$ will approach $f(x)$. In particular, both the minimum value m and the maximum value M will approach $f(x)$:

$$\lim_{\epsilon \to 0} f(x+\epsilon) = f(x) = \lim_{\epsilon \to 0} m = \lim_{\epsilon \to 0} M.$$

So, starting from the inequality

$$\epsilon m \leqslant \int_x^{x+\epsilon} f(t)\,dt \leqslant \epsilon M,$$

and taking the limit as $\epsilon \to 0$, we obtain

$$\begin{aligned} \lim_{\epsilon \to 0} \epsilon m &\leqslant \lim_{\epsilon \to 0} \int_x^{x+\epsilon} f(t)\,dt \leqslant \lim_{\epsilon \to 0} \epsilon M, \\ \lim_{\epsilon \to 0} \epsilon f(x) &\leqslant \lim_{\epsilon \to 0} \int_x^{x+\epsilon} f(t)\,dt \leqslant \lim_{\epsilon \to 0} \epsilon f(x). \end{aligned}$$

Then applying the squeezing principle, we obtain

$$\lim_{\epsilon \to 0} \int_x^{x+\epsilon} f(t)\,dt = \lim_{\epsilon \to 0} \epsilon f(x). \qquad (\dagger)$$

Let's see how this expression fits into the formula for the derivative of $A_0(x)$:

$$\begin{aligned} A_0'(x) &= \lim_{\epsilon \to 0} \frac{A_0(x+\epsilon) - A_0(x)}{\epsilon} \\ &= \lim_{\epsilon \to 0} \frac{\int_x^{x+\epsilon} f(t)\,dt}{\epsilon} \\ &= \lim_{\epsilon \to 0} \frac{\epsilon f(t)}{\epsilon} && \text{(by using equation } (\dagger) \text{)} \\ &= f(x) \lim_{\epsilon \to 0} \frac{\epsilon}{\epsilon} \\ &= f(x). \end{aligned}$$

Thus we have proved that $A_0'(x) = f(x)$. The argument presented did not depend on the choice $c = 0$ we made in the beginning, so the statement $A_c'(x) = f(x)$ is true for all $c \in \mathbb{R}$. □

Applications

You can use the fundamental theorem of calculus to check your answers to indefinite integral questions.

Integral verification Suppose a friend tells you that

$$\int \ln(x)dx = x\ln(x) - x + C,$$

but he's a shady character and you don't trust him. How can you check his answer? If you had a smartphone handy, you could check the answer on `live.sympy.org`. What if you just have some old-school pen and paper? If $x\ln(x) - x$ is really the integral of $\ln(x)$, then by the fundamental theorem of calculus, we should obtain $\ln(x)$ if we take the derivative. Let's check:

$$\begin{aligned}\frac{d}{dx}[x\ln(x) - x] &= \overbrace{\frac{d}{dx}[x]\ln(x) + x\left[\frac{d}{dx}\ln(x)\right]}^{\text{product rule}} - \frac{d}{dx}[x] \\ &= 1\ln(x) + x\frac{1}{x} - 1 = \ln(x).\end{aligned}$$

This time, your shady friend is correct.

Discussion

Integration and differentiation are inverse operations

You previously studied the inverse relationship for functions. Recall that for any *bijective* function f (a one-to-one relationship) there exists an *inverse function* f^{-1} that *undoes* the effects of f:

$$(f^{-1} \circ f)(x) \equiv f^{-1}(f(x)) = 1x$$

and also

$$(f \circ f^{-1})(y) \equiv f(f^{-1}(y)) = 1y.$$

The integral is the "inverse operation" of the derivative. If you perform the integral operation followed by the derivative operation on some function, you'll obtain the same function:

$$\left(\frac{d}{dx} \circ \int dx\right) f(x) \equiv \frac{d}{dx}\int_c^x f(u)\, du = f(x).$$

Note we need a new variable u inside the integral since x is already used to denote the upper limit of integration.

Alternately, if you compute the derivative followed by the integral, you will obtain the original function $f(x)$ (up to a constant):

$$\left(\int dx \circ \frac{d}{dx}\right) f(x) \equiv \int_c^x f'(u)\, du = f(x) + C.$$

What next?

If integration is nothing more than backward differentiation, and if you already know differentiation inside out from differential calculus, you might be wondering what you are going to do during an entire semester of integral calculus. For all intents and purposes, if you understand the conceptual material in this section, you understand integral calculus. Give yourself a pat on the back—you are done.

The Establishment, however, not only wants you to know the concepts of integral calculus; you must also become proficient in computing integrals of functions. Thus, you'll need to practice the techniques of integration presented in the next section. There are a bunch of techniques that allow you to integrate complicated functions. For example, if I asked you to integrate $f(x) = \sin^2(x) = (\sin(x))^2$ from 0 to π and you look at the formula sheet, you won't find a function $F(x)$ with a derivative that equals $f(x)$. So how do we solve

$$\int_0^{\pi} \sin^2(x)\,dx = ?$$

One way to approach this problem is with the double-angle trigonometric identity (page 90), which states that $\sin^2(x) = \frac{1-\cos(2x)}{2}$. Using this identity, we can proceed as follows:

$$\int_0^{\pi} \sin^2(x)dx = \int_0^{\pi} \left[\frac{1}{2} - \frac{1}{2}\cos(2x)\right]dx = \underbrace{\frac{1}{2}\int_0^{\pi} 1\,dx}_{T_1} - \underbrace{\frac{1}{2}\int_0^{\pi} \cos(2x)\,dx}_{T_2}.$$

We are allowed to split the integral into two parts and take the constants $\frac{1}{2}$ out of the integrals because integration is a *linear* operation.

The integral we want to calculate can be computed as the difference of two terms:

$$\int_0^{\pi} \sin^2(x)\,dx \quad = \quad T_1 \; - \; T_2.$$

Let's compute the terms one by one.

The value of the integral in the first term is

$$T_1 = \frac{1}{2}\int_0^{\pi} 1\,dx = \frac{1}{2}x\bigg|_0^{\pi} = \frac{\pi - 0}{2} = \frac{\pi}{2}.$$

The value of the second term is

$$T_2 = \frac{1}{2}\int_0^{\pi} \cos(2x)\,dx = \frac{1}{4}\sin(2x)\bigg|_0^{\pi} = \frac{\sin(2\pi) - \sin(0)}{4} = \frac{0-0}{4} = 0.$$

We find the final answer for the integral is

$$\int_0^{\pi} \sin^2(x)\, dx = T_1 - T_2 = \frac{\pi}{2} - 0 = \frac{\pi}{2}.$$

Do you see how integration can quickly become tricky? You need to learn all kinds of tricks to solve integrals. I can teach you all the necessary tricks, but to become proficient you can't solely read—you need to *practice* the techniques. Promise me you will practice! As my student, I expect nothing less than total ass-kicking of the questions you'll face on the final exam.

5.15 Techniques of integration

The operation of "taking the integral" of some function is usually much more complicated than that of taking the derivative. You can take the derivative of *any* function—no matter how complex—by using the product rule, the chain rule, and the derivative formulas. This is not true for integrals.

Plenty of integrals have no *closed-form solution*, meaning the function has no antiderivative. There is no simple procedure to follow such that you input a function and "turn the crank" until the integral comes out. Integration is a bit of an art.

Which functions *can* we integrate, and how? Back in the day, scientists collected big tables with integral formulas for various complicated functions. We can use these tables to *look up* a specific integral formula. Such table is given on page 481 in the back of the book.

We can also learn some *integration techniques* to help make complicated integrals simpler. Think of the techniques presented in this section as *adapters*. You can reach for these adapters when the function you need to integrate doesn't appear in your table of integrals, but a similar one is found in the table.

A note to all our students in the audience who are taking an integral calculus course. These integration techniques are exactly the skills you'll be expected to demonstrate on the final. Instead of using the table of integrals to look up complicated integrals, you'll need to know how to fill in the table.

For people interested in learning physics, I'll honestly tell you that if you skip this next section you won't miss much. You should read the important section on *substitution*, but there's no need to read the details of all the recipes for integrating things. For most intents and purposes, once you understand what an integral is, you can use a computer to calculate it. A good tool for calculating integrals is the computer algebra system at `live.sympy.org`.

```
>>> integrate( sin(x) )
-cos(x)
>>> integrate( x**2*exp(x) )
x**2*exp(x) - 2*x*exp(x) + 2*exp(x)
```

You can use SymPy for all your integration needs.

A comment to those of you reading this book for fun, without the added stress of homework and exams. Consider the next dozen pages as an ethnographic snapshot of the daily life of the undergraduate experience in science. Try to visualize the life of first-year science students, busy integrating things they don't want to integrate for many, long hours. Picture some unlucky science student locked in her room, crunching calculus while hundreds of dangling integrals scream for attention, keeping her from hanging with friends.

Actually, it is not that bad. There are, like, four tricks to learn. If you **practice**, you can learn all of them in a week or so. Mastering these four tricks is essentially the purpose of the entire integral calculus course. If you understand the material in this section, you'll be done with integral calculus and you'll have two months to chill.

Substitution

Say you're integrating some complicated function that contains a square root $\sqrt{x}$. You wonder how to compute this integral:

$$\int \frac{1}{x - \sqrt{x}}\, dx \;= ?$$

Sometimes you can simplify an integral by *substituting* a new variable into the expression. Let $u = \sqrt{x}$. Substitution is like search-and-replace in a word processor. Every time you see the expression $\sqrt{x}$, replace it with u:

$$\int \frac{1}{x - \sqrt{x}}\, dx = \int \frac{1}{u^2 - u}\, dx.$$

Note we also replaced $x = (\sqrt{x})^2$ with u^2.

We're not done yet. To change from the x variable to the u variable, we must also change dx to du. Can we simply replace dx with du? Unfortunately no, otherwise it would be like saying the "short step" du is equal in length to the "short step" dx, which is only true for the trivial substitution $u = x$.

To find the relation between the small step du and the small step dx, we take the derivative:

$$u(x) = \sqrt{x} \quad \Rightarrow \quad u'(x) = \frac{du}{dx} = \frac{1}{2\sqrt{x}}.$$

For the next step, I need you to stop thinking about the expression $\frac{du}{dx}$ as a whole, and instead think about it as a rise-over-run fraction that can be split. Let's move the *run* dx to the other side of the equation:

$$du = \frac{1}{2\sqrt{x}}\,dx.$$

Next, to isolate dx, multiply both sides by $2\sqrt{x}$:

$$dx = 2\sqrt{x}\,du = 2u\,du,$$

where we use the fact that $u = \sqrt{x}$ in the last step.

We now have an expression for dx expressed entirely in terms of the variable u. After the substitution, the integral looks like

$$\int \frac{1}{x-\sqrt{x}}\,dx = \int \frac{1}{u^2-u}\,2u\,du = \int \frac{2}{u-1}\,du.$$

We can recognize the general form of the function inside the integral, $f(u) = \frac{2}{u-1}$, to be similar to the function $f(u) = \frac{1}{u}$. Recall that the integral of $\frac{1}{u}$ is $\ln(u)$. Accounting for the -1 horizontal shift and the factor of 2 in the numerator, we obtain the answer:

$$\int \frac{1}{x-\sqrt{x}}\,dx = \int \frac{2}{u-1}\,du = 2\ln(u-1) = 2\ln(\sqrt{x}-1).$$

Note in the last step, we changed back to the x variable to give the final answer. The variable u exists only in our calculation. We invented it out of thin air when we said, "Let $u = \sqrt{x}$" in the beginning.

Thanks to the substitution, the integral became simpler: we were able to eliminate the square roots. The extra u that came from the expression $dx = 2u\,du$ canceled with one of the us in the denominator, thus making the expression even simpler. In practice, substituting x with u inside f is the easy part. The hard part is making sure our choice of substitution leads to a replacement for dx that helps to simplify the integral.

For definite integrals—that is, integrals with limits of integration—there is an extra step we need to take when changing variables: we must change the x-limits of integration to u-limits. In our expression, when changing to the u variable, we write

$$\int_a^b \frac{1}{x-\sqrt{x}}\,dx = \int_{u(a)}^{u(b)} \frac{2}{u-1}\,du.$$

Say we are asked to compute the definite integral between $x = 4$ and $x = 9$ for the same expression. In this case, the new limits are $u = \sqrt{4} = 2$ and $u = \sqrt{9} = 3$, and we have

$$\int_4^9 \frac{1}{x - \sqrt{x}}\, dx = \int_2^3 \frac{2}{u-1}\, du = 2\ln(u-1)\Big|_2^3 = 2(\ln(2) - \ln(1)) = 2\ln(2).$$

Let's recap. Substitution involves three steps:

1. Replace all occurrences of $u(x)$ with u.
2. Replace dx with $\frac{1}{u'(x)}du$.
3. If there are limits, replace the x-limits with u-limits.

If the resulting integral is simpler to solve, then good for you!

Example Find $\int \tan(x)\, dx$. We know $\tan(x) = \frac{\sin(x)}{\cos(x)}$, so we can use the substitution $u = \cos(x)$, $du = -\sin(x)dx$ as follows:

$$\begin{aligned} \int \tan(x)dx &= \int \frac{\sin(x)}{\cos(x)}dx \\ &= \int \frac{-1}{u}du \\ &= -\ln|u| + C \\ &= -\ln|\cos(x)| + C. \end{aligned}$$

Integrals of trig functions

Because sin, cos, tan, and the other trig functions are related, we can often express one function in terms of another in order to simplify integrals.

Recall the trigonometric identity,

$$\cos^2(x) + \sin^2(x) = 1,$$

which is the statement of Pythagoras' theorem.

If we choose to make the substitution $u = \sin(x)$, we can replace all kinds of trigonometric terms with the new variable u:

$$\begin{aligned} &\sin^2(x) = u^2, \\ &\cos^2(x) = 1 - \sin^2(x) = 1 - u^2, \\ &\tan^2(x) = \frac{\sin^2(x)}{\cos^2(x)} = \frac{u^2}{1-u^2}. \end{aligned}$$

Of course the change of variable $u = \sin(x)$ means you must also change the integration step $du = \cos(x)dx \Rightarrow dx = \frac{1}{\cos(x)}du$—so there better be an extra $\cos(x)$ factor in the integral to cancel this $\frac{1}{\cos(x)}$.

Let me show you one example where things work perfectly. Suppose m is some arbitrary number and you need to integrate:

$$\int (\sin(x))^m \cos^3(x)\, dx \equiv \int \sin^m(x) \cos^3(x)\, dx.$$

This integral contains m powers of the sin function and three powers of the cos function. Let us split the cos term into two parts:

$$\int \sin^m(x) \cos^3(x)\, dx = \int \sin^m(x) \cos^2(x) \cos(x)\, dx.$$

Making the change of variables ($u = \sin(x)$ and $du = \cos(x)dx$) means we can replace $\sin^m(x)$ by u^m, and $\cos^2(x) = 1 - u^2$ in the above expression to obtain

$$\int \sin^m(x) \cos^2(x) \cos(x)\, dx = \int u^m \left(1 - u^2\right) \cos(x)\, dx.$$

Conveniently, we happen to have $dx = \frac{1}{\cos(x)}\, du$, so the complete change-of-variable step is

$$\int \sin^m(x) \cos^2(x) \cos(x)\, dx = \int u^m \left(1 - u^2\right)\, du.$$

This is what I was talking about earlier when I mentioned "having an extra $\cos(x)$" to cancel the one that appears as a result of the $dx \to du$ change.

What is the answer then? It is a simple integral of a polynomial:

$$\begin{aligned}\int u^m \left(1 - u^2\right)\, du &= \int \left(u^m - u^{m+2}\right)\, du \\ &= \frac{1}{m+1}u^{m+1} - \frac{1}{m+3}u^{m+3} \\ &= \frac{1}{m+1}\sin^{m+1}(x) - \frac{1}{m+3}\sin^{m+3}(x).\end{aligned}$$

You might be wondering how useful this substitution technique actually is. I mean, how often will you need to integrate such particular combinations of sin and cos powers, where substitution works perfectly? You might be surprised! Sin and cos functions are used often in this thing called the *Fourier transform*, which is a way of expressing a sound wave $f(t)$ in terms of the frequencies it contains.

Also, integrals with trig functions are known favourites of teachers to ask on exams. A trig substitution question will test if you can perform substitutions, *and* teachers use them to check whether you remember all the trigonometric identities (page 89), which you are supposed to have learned in high school.

Are there other trig substitution tricks you should know about? On an exam, you should try any possible substitution you can think of, combined with any trigonometric identity that seems to simplify things. Some common substitutions are described below.

Cos

Just as we can substitute sin, we can also substitute $u = \cos(x)$ and use $\sin^2(x) = 1 - u^2$. Again, this substitution only makes sense when there is a leftover sin somewhere in the integral that can cancel with the sin in $dx = \frac{-1}{\sin x}\, du$.

Tan and sec

We can get some more mileage out of the trigonometric identity $\cos^2(x) + \sin^2(x) = 1$. Dividing both sides of this identity by $\cos^2(x)$ gives us

$$1 + \tan^2(x) = \sec^2(x) \equiv \frac{1}{\cos^2(x)}.$$

This is useful since $u = \tan(x)$ gives $du = \sec^2(x)dx$, allowing us to "kill" even powers of $\sec^2(x)$ in integrals of the form

$$\int \tan^m(x) \sec^n(x)\, dx.$$

Even powers of sin and cos

There are other trigonometric identities, called half-angle and double-angle formulas, which give us formulas such as

$$\sin^2(x) = \frac{1}{2}(1 - \cos(2x)), \qquad \cos^2(x) = \frac{1}{2}(1 + \cos(2x)).$$

These identities are useful if you need to integrate even powers of sin and cos.

Example How can we find $I = \int \sin^2(x)\cos^4(x)\, dx$? Let's find out:

$$I = \int \sin^2(x) \cos^4(x)\, dx$$

$$
\begin{aligned}
&= \int \left(\frac{1}{2}(1-\cos(2x))\right)\left(\frac{1}{2}(1+\cos(2x))\right)^2 dx \\
&= \frac{1}{8}\int \left(1-\cos^2(2x)+\cos(2x)-\cos^3(2x)\right) dx \\
&= \frac{1}{8}\int \left(1-\cos^2(2x)+\cos(2x)-\cos^2(2x)\cos(2x)\right) dx \\
&= \frac{1}{8}\int \left(1-\frac{1}{2}(1+\cos(4x))+\cancel{\cos(2x)}-(\cancel{1}-\sin^2(2x))\underline{\cos(2x)}\right) dx \\
&= \frac{1}{16}\int (1-\cos(4x))dx \;+\; \frac{1}{8}\int \underbrace{\sin^2(2x)}_{u^2}\,\underbrace{\cos(2x)dx}_{du/2} \quad (\text{let } u=\sin(2x)) \\
&= \frac{1}{16}\left(x-\frac{\sin(4x)}{4}\right) \;+\; \frac{1}{8}\left(\frac{\sin^3(2x)}{6}\right) \;+\; C \\
&= \frac{x}{16}-\frac{\sin(4x)}{64}+\frac{\sin^3(2x)}{48}+C.
\end{aligned}
$$

There is no limit to the number of combinations of simplification steps you can try. On a homework question or an exam, the teacher will ask for something simple. Your job is to find the correct substitution.

Sneaky example Sometimes, the required substitution is not obvious at all, as in the case of $\int \sec(x)dx$. To find the integral, you need the following trick: multiply and divide by $\tan(x)+\sec(x)$:

$$
\begin{aligned}
\int \sec(x)\,dx &= \int \sec(x)\,1\,dx \\
&= \int \sec(x)\frac{\tan(x)+\sec(x)}{\tan(x)+\sec(x)}\,dx \\
&= \int \frac{\sec^2(x)+\sec(x)\tan(x)}{\tan(x)+\sec(x)}\,dx \\
&= \int \frac{1}{u}du \\
&= \ln|u|+C = \ln|\tan(x)+\sec(x)|+C,
\end{aligned}
$$

where, in the fourth line of solving, we use the substitution $u = \tan(x)+\sec(x)$ and $du = (\sec^2(x)+\tan(x)\sec(x))dx$.

I highly recommend you practice all the examples you can get your hands on. Don't bother memorizing any recipes though; you can do just as well with trial and error.

Trig substitution

Often when calculating integrals for physics, we run into terms of the form $\sqrt{a^2 - x^2}$, $\sqrt{a^2 + x^2}$, or $\sqrt{x^2 - a^2}$, which can be difficult to handle directly. In each of these three instances, we can perform a *trig substitution*, replacing x with one of the trigonometric functions $a\sin(\theta)$, $a\tan(\theta)$, or $a\sec(\theta)$ to obtain a simpler integral.

Sine substitution

Consider an integral that contains an expression of the form $\sqrt{a^2 - x^2}$. By applying the substitution $x = a\sin\theta$, the complicated square-root expression is simplified:

$$\sqrt{a^2 - x^2} = \sqrt{a^2 - a^2\sin^2\theta} = a\sqrt{1 - \sin^2\theta} = a\cos\theta.$$

The simplification is possible because of the identity $\cos^2\theta = 1 - \sin^2\theta$. The transformed integral now involves a trigonometric function that we know how to integrate.

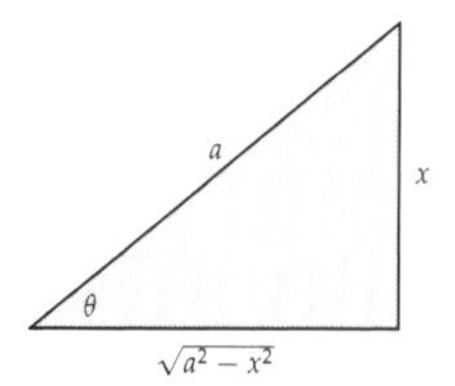

Figure 5.22: Triangle associated with the substitution $x = a\sin\theta$.

Once we find the integral in terms of θ, we need to look at the answer and convert the various θ expressions therein back to the original variables x and a:

$$\sin\theta = \frac{x}{a}, \quad \cos\theta = \frac{\sqrt{a^2 - x^2}}{a}, \quad \tan\theta = \frac{x}{\sqrt{a^2 - x^2}},$$

$$\csc\theta = \frac{a}{x}, \quad \sec\theta = \frac{a}{\sqrt{a^2 - x^2}}, \quad \cot\theta = \frac{\sqrt{a^2 - x^2}}{x}.$$

Example 1 Calculate $\int \sqrt{1 - x^2}\, dx$.

We can approach the problem by making the sin substitution with $a = 1$:

$$x = \sin\theta, \qquad dx = \cos\theta\, d\theta.$$

We proceed:

$$\begin{aligned}
\int \sqrt{1-x^2}\,dx &= \int \sqrt{1-\sin^2\theta}\cos\theta\,d\theta \\
&= \int \cos^2\theta\,d\theta \\
&= \frac{1}{2}\int [1+\cos 2\theta]\;d\theta \\
&= \frac{1}{2}\theta + \frac{1}{4}\sin 2\theta \\
&= \frac{1}{2}\theta + \frac{1}{2}\sin\theta\cos\theta \\
&= \frac{1}{2}\sin^{-1}(x) + \frac{1}{2}\frac{x}{1}\frac{\sqrt{1-x^2}}{1}.
\end{aligned}$$

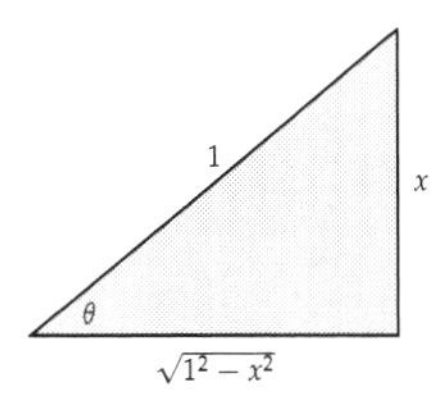

Figure 5.23: Triangle associated with the substitution $x = \sin\theta$.

In the last step, we use the triangle shown in Figure 5.23 to "read" the values of θ, $\sin\theta$, and $\cos\theta$. The substitution $x = \sin\theta$ means the hypotenuse in the triangle is of length 1, and the opposite side is of length x.

Example 2 Compute $\int \sqrt{\frac{a+x}{a-x}}\,dx$.

We can rewrite this fraction as

$$\sqrt{\frac{a+x}{a-x}} = \sqrt{\frac{a+x}{a-x}\frac{1}{1}} = \sqrt{\frac{a+x}{a-x}\frac{a+x}{a+x}} = \frac{a+x}{\sqrt{a^2-x^2}}.$$

We make the substitution $x = a\sin\theta$, and $dx = a\cos\theta d\theta$ and proceed as follows:

$$\begin{aligned}
\int \frac{a+x}{\sqrt{a^2-x^2}}dx &= \int \frac{a+a\sin\theta}{\cancel{a\cos\theta}}\cancel{a\cos\theta}\,d\theta \\
&= a\int [1+\sin\theta]\,d\theta \\
&= a\,[\theta - \cos\theta] \\
&= a\sin^{-1}\left(\frac{x}{a}\right) - a\frac{\sqrt{a^2-x^2}}{a}
\end{aligned}$$

$$= a \sin^{-1}\left(\frac{x}{a}\right) - \sqrt{a^2 - x^2}.$$

We use the triangle from Figure 5.22 to obtain the fourth equation.

Tan substitution

When an integral contains $\sqrt{a^2 + x^2}$, use the substitution,

$$x = a \tan\theta, \qquad dx = a \sec^2\theta d\theta.$$

Because of the identity $1 + \tan^2\theta = \sec^2\theta$, the square root expression will simplify to

$$\sqrt{a^2 + x^2} = \sqrt{a^2 + a^2 \tan^2\theta} = a\sqrt{1 + \tan^2\theta} = a \sec\theta.$$

Simplification is a good thing. Simplification makes it much easier to find the integral in terms of θ than in terms of $\sqrt{a^2 + x^2}$.

Once you calculate the integral in terms of θ, you can convert the answer back into x coordinates. To do this, you need to draw a triangle labelled according to your substitution:

$$\tan\theta = \frac{x}{a} = \frac{\text{opp}}{\text{adj}},$$

as show in Figure 5.24. The equivalent of $\sin\theta$ in terms of x is $\sin\theta \equiv \frac{\text{opp}}{\text{hyp}} = \frac{x}{\sqrt{a^2+x^2}}$. Similarly, the other trigonometric functions are defined as various ratios of a, x, and $\sqrt{a^2 + x^2}$.

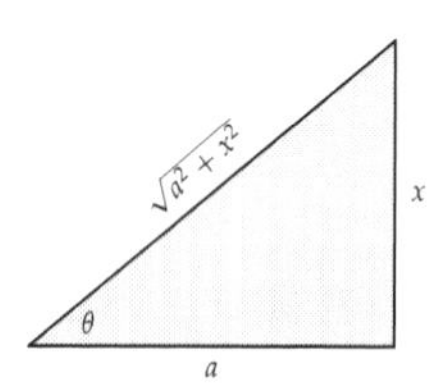

Figure 5.24: Triangle associated with the substitution $x = a \tan\theta$.

Example Calculate $\int \frac{1}{x^2+1}\, dx$.

The denominator of this function is equal to $\left(\sqrt{1 + x^2}\right)^2$. The form $1 + x^2$ suggests we can probably substitute $x = \tan\theta$, then use the identity $1 + \tan^2\theta = \sec^2\theta$. Testing this substitution, we obtain

$dx = \sec^2\theta\, d\theta$. Thus,

$$\begin{aligned}\int \frac{1}{x^2+1}\,dx &= \int \frac{1}{\tan^2\theta+1}\sec^2\theta\,d\theta \\ &= \int \frac{1}{\sec^2\theta}\sec^2\theta\,d\theta \\ &= \int 1\,d\theta \\ &= \theta \\ &= \tan^{-1}(x) + C.\end{aligned}$$

Obfuscated example What if the denominator doesn't look like x^2+1? What if, instead, we have a general second-degree polynomial, such as

$$\frac{1}{y^2-6y+10}?$$

How do we integrate a this function? If there were no $-2y$ term, we'd be able to use the tan substitution. Or perhaps you could look up the formula $\int \frac{1}{x^2+1}dx = \tan^{-1}(x)$ in the table of integrals. Alas, there is no formula to be found in the table for

$$\int \frac{1}{y^2-6y+10}\,dy.$$

We'll need another route, and we'll start by following the good old substitution technique $u = \ldots$, along with a high school algebra trick called "completing the square." This route will help us rewrite the fraction inside the integral so the integral looks like $(y-h)^2+k$ with no linear term.

First, find "by inspection" the values of h and k such that:

$$\frac{1}{y^2-6y+10} = \frac{1}{(y-h)^2+k} = \frac{1}{(y-3)^2+1}.$$

The "square completed" quadratic expression has no linear term. Now we'll use the substitution $x = y-3$ and $dx = dy$ to obtain an integral we know how to solve:

$$\int \frac{1}{(y-3)^2+1}\,dy = \int \frac{1}{x^2+1}\,dx = \tan^{-1}(x) = \tan^{-1}(y-3).$$

Sec substitution

In the previous two sections, we learned how to handle $\sqrt{a^2-x^2}$ and $\sqrt{x^2+a^2}$. One more option remains: $\sqrt{x^2-a^2}$, which we approach using the secant substitution.

Recall the trigonometric identity $1 + \tan^2\theta = \sec^2\theta$ or, rewritten differently,

$$\sec^2\theta - 1 = \tan^2\theta.$$

The appropriate substitution for terms like $\sqrt{x^2 - a^2}$ is

$$x = a\sec\theta, \qquad dx = a\tan\theta\sec\theta\, d\theta.$$

The substitution procedure is the same as in previous cases of the sin substitution and the tan substitution we discussed, so we won't elaborate here in detail. We can label the sides of the triangle accordingly, as

$$\sec\theta = \frac{x}{a} = \frac{\text{hyp}}{\text{adj}},$$

as shown in Figure 5.25. We'll use this triangle when converting back from θ to x in the final steps of the integral calculation.

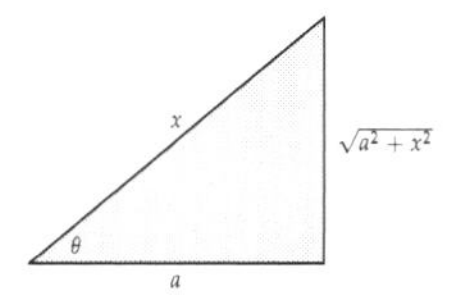

Figure 5.25: Triangle associated with the substitution $x = a\sec\theta$.

Interlude

By now, things are starting to get pretty tight for your calculus teacher. You are beginning to understand how to "handle" any kind of integral he can throw at you: polynomials, fractions with x^2, plus or minus a^2, and square roots. He can't even fool you with dirty trigonometric tricks involving sin, cos, and tan, since you know about these, too. Are there any integrals left that he can drop on the exam to trick you up?

Substitution is the most important integration technique. Recall the steps involved: (1) the choice of substitution $u = \ldots$, (2) the associated dx to du change, and (3) the change in the limits of integration required for definite integrals. With medium to advanced substitution skills, you'll score at least an 80% on your integral calculus final.

What will the remaining 20% of the exam depend on? How many more techniques could there possibly be? I know all these integration techniques that I've been throwing at you during the last 10 pages may seem arduous and difficult to understand, but this is what you got yourself into when you signed up for the course "integral calculus." In this course, there are lots of *integrals* and you *calculate* them.

The good news is that we are almost done. Only one more "trick" remains, and afterward, I'll finally tell you about the *integration by parts* procedure, which is very useful.

Don't bother memorizing the steps in each of the examples discussed: the correct substitution of $u = \ldots$ will be different in each problem. Think of integration techniques as general recipe guidelines you must adapt based on the ingredients available to you at the moment of cooking. When faced with a complicated integral problem, you can always return to this section, find the example that is most similar to your problem, and use the same approach.

Partial fractions

Suppose you need to integrate a rational function $\frac{P(x)}{Q(x)}$, where P and Q are polynomials.

For example, you could be asked to integrate

$$\frac{P(x)}{Q(x)} = \frac{ax+b}{cx^2+dx+e},$$

where a, b, c, d, and e are arbitrary constants. To get even more specific, let's say you are asked to calculate

$$\int \frac{3x+1}{x^2+x}\,dx.$$

By magical powers, I can transform the function in this integral into two *simple fractions*:

$$\int \frac{3x+1}{x^2+x}\,dx \quad = \quad \int \frac{1}{x}\,dx \quad + \quad \int \frac{2}{x+1}\,dx.$$

We split the complicated-looking rational expression into two partial fractions.

Now that the hard part is done, all that remains is to compute the two integrals. Recall that $\frac{d}{dx}\ln(x) = \frac{1}{x}$, so the integrals will give ln-like terms. The final answer is

$$\int \frac{3x+1}{x^2+x}\,dx = \ln|x| + 2\ln|x+1| + C.$$

How did I split the problem into partial fractions? Is it really magic or is there a method? The answer is, a little of both. My method was to *assume* the existence of constants A and B such that

$$\frac{3x+1}{x^2+x} = \frac{3x+1}{x(x+1)} = \frac{A}{x} + \frac{B}{x+1}.$$

Then I solved the above equation for A and B by computing the sum of the two fractions:

$$\frac{3x+1}{x(x+1)} = \frac{A(x+1)+Bx}{x(x+1)}.$$

The magic involves the fact that we can solve for *two* unknowns in *one* equation. The relevant part of the equation is the numerator, because both sides have the same denominator. To find A and B, we must solve

$$3x+1 = (3)x + (1)1 = A(x+1) + Bx = (A+B)x + (A)1.$$

We solve by grouping the unknown constants into two terms: a term involving x (the linear term) and a constant term. On the left-hand side of the equation, the constant term is equal to 1, and on the right-hand side the constant coefficient is A, so $A = 1$. Similarly, we can deduce that $B = 2$ from the equality of the coefficients of the linear terms $3 = A + B$, having found $A = 1$ in the first step.

Another way of finding the values of the unknowns A and B is by evaluating the numerator equation

$$3x+1 = A(x+1) + Bx$$

at different values of x. This equation must hold true for all values of the variable x. The input $x = 0$ gives us $1 = A$, and inputting $x = -1$ gives $-2 = -B$, so $B = 2$.

The above problem highlights the power of the *partial fractions* method for attacking integrals of polynomial fractions $\frac{P(x)}{Q(x)}$. Most of the work involves factoring the denominator and finding the unknowns. Then, once you've split the problem into partial fractions, some simple calculus steps finish the job. Some people call this method *separation of quotients*, but whatever you call it, it's clear that being able to split a fraction into multiple parts is very helpful:

$$\frac{3x+1}{x^2+x} = \frac{A}{x} + \frac{B}{x+1}.$$

How many parts will the fraction $\frac{P(x)}{Q(x)}$ split into? What will each part look like? The answer is that there will be as many parts as the degree of the polynomial $Q(x)$, which is located in the fraction's denominator. Each part will consist of one of the factors of $Q(x)$.

1. Factor the denominator $Q(x)$ as a product of factors. For example, $Q(x) = x^3 + 4x^2 + 5x + 2$ can be factored as $Q(x) = (x+1)^2(x+2)$. For each factor of $Q(x)$, *assume* an appropriate partial fraction term on the right-hand side of the equation. There are three types of factors to consider:

- Simple factors, like $(x-\alpha)^1$. For each simple factor, you should *assume* a partial fraction of the form

$$\frac{A}{x-\alpha}.$$

- Repeated factors, like $(x-\beta)^n$, for which we assume the existence of n different terms on the right-hand side:

$$\frac{B}{x-\beta}+\frac{C}{(x-\beta)^2}+\cdots+\frac{F}{(x-\beta)^n}.$$

- If one of the factors is a polynomial ax^2+bx+c that cannot be factored, such as x^2+1, we must preserve this portion as a whole and assume that a term of the form

$$\frac{Gx+H}{ax^2+bx+c}$$

exists on the right-hand side.

2. Add all the parts on the equation's right-hand side by first cross-multiplying each part in order to bring all fractions to a common denominator, and then adding the fractions together. If you followed the steps correctly in Part 1, the common denominator will turn out to be $Q(x)$, and both sides will have the same denominator. Solve for the unknown coefficients $A, B, C, \ldots$ in the numerators. Find the coefficients of each power of x on the right-hand side and set them equal to the corresponding coefficient in the numerator $P(x)$ of the left-hand side.

3. Use the appropriate integral formula for each kind of term:

- For simple factors, use

$$\int \frac{1}{x-\alpha}\,dx = A\ln|x-\alpha|+C.$$

- For higher powers in the denominator, use

$$\int \frac{1}{(x-\beta)^m}\,dx = \frac{-1}{(m-1)(x-\beta)^{m-1}}+C.$$

- For the quadratic denominator terms with "matching" numerator terms, use

$$\int \frac{2ax+b}{ax^2+bx+c}\,dx = \ln|ax^2+bx+c|+C.$$

For quadratic terms with only a constant in the numerator, use a two-step substitution process. First, change x to the complete-the-square variable $y = x - h$:

$$\int \frac{1}{ax^2 + bx + c}\,dx = \int \frac{1/a}{(x-h)^2 + k}\,dx = \frac{1}{a}\int \frac{1}{y^2 + k}\,dy.$$

Then apply a trig substitution $y = \sqrt{k}\tan\theta$ to obtain

$$\frac{1}{a}\int \frac{1}{y^2 + k}\,dy = \frac{1}{a\sqrt{k}}\tan^{-1}\left(\frac{y}{\sqrt{k}}\right) = \frac{1}{a\sqrt{k}}\tan^{-1}\left(\frac{x-h}{\sqrt{k}}\right).$$

Example Find $\int \frac{1}{(x+1)(x+2)^2}dx$.

Here, $P(x) = 1$ and $Q(x) = (x+1)(x+2)^2$. If I wanted to be sneaky, I could have asked for $\int \frac{1}{x^3+5x^2+8x+4}dx$ instead—which is the same question, but you'd need to do the factoring yourself.

According to the recipe outlined above, we must look for a split fraction of the form

$$\frac{1}{(x+1)(x+2)^2} = \frac{A}{x+1} + \frac{B}{x+2} + \frac{C}{(x+2)^2}.$$

To make the equation more explicit, let's add the fractions on the right. Set all of them to the least common denominator and add:

$$\begin{aligned}\frac{1}{(x+1)(x+2)^2} &= \frac{A}{x+1} + \frac{B}{x+2} + \frac{C}{(x+2)^2} \\ &= \frac{A(x+2)^2}{(x+1)(x+2)^2} + \frac{B(x+1)(x+2)}{(x+1)(x+2)^2} + \frac{C(x+1)}{(x+1)(x+2)^2} \\ &= \frac{A(x+2)^2 + B(x+1)(x+2) + C(x+1)}{(x+1)(x+2)^2}.\end{aligned}$$

The denominators are the same on both sides of the above equation, so we can focus our attention on the numerator:

$$A(x+2)^2 + B(x+1)(x+2) + C(x+1) = 1.$$

We can evaluate this equation for three different values of x to find the values of A, B, and C:

$$\begin{aligned} x &= 0 & 1 &= 2^2A + 2B + C \\ x &= -1 & 1 &= A \\ x &= -2 & 1 &= -C \end{aligned}$$

so $A = 1$, $B = -1$, and $C = -1$. Thus,

$$\frac{1}{(x+1)(x+2)^2} = \frac{1}{x+1} - \frac{1}{x+2} - \frac{1}{(x+2)^2}.$$

We can now calculate the integral by integrating each of the terms:

$$\int \frac{1}{(x+1)(x+2)^2} dx = \ln(x+1) - \ln(x+2) + \frac{1}{x+2} + C.$$

The partial fractions technique for integrating rational functions is best understood using using a hands-on approach. Try solving the following exercises to see if you can apply the techniques.

Exercises

E5.4 Split the expressions into partial fractions and compute their indefinite integrals.

(a) $\frac{3x+5}{(x-3)(x+4)}$ (b) $\frac{3x-4}{(x-1)(x-2)}$ (c) $\frac{x}{(x^2-1)(x+1)}$

Integration by parts

There is no general formula for finding the integral of the product of two functions $f(x)g(x)$. However, if one of the two functions in the product happens to look like the *derivative* of a function that we recognize, we can perform the following trick:

$$\int f(x)\, g'(x)\, dx = f(x)g(x) - \int f'(x)g(x)\, dx.$$

This trick is called "integration by parts" and comes from the product rule for derivatives. We'll discuss how the formula is derived on page 375. First, let's see *why* we might want to use this trick.

The integration by parts procedure aims to simplify your task of integration. Both sides of the above equation involve an integral of the product of two functions: on the left we have $\int f(x)g'(x)dx$, while on the right we have $\int f'(x)g(x)dx$. The function $f(x)$ is replaced by its derivative $f'(x)$, while the function $g'(x)$ is replaced by its antiderivative function $g(x)$. Derivatives tend to simplify functions, whereas antiderivatives make functions more complicated. Thus, using integration by parts changes the integral calculation to one with a simplified $f(x)$.

It is easier to remember the integration by parts formula in its shorthand notation,

$$\int u\, dv = uv - \int v\, du.$$

You can think of integration by parts as a form of "double substitution," where you simultaneously replace u and dv. To be clear about what's happening during this substitution, I recommend you always make a little table like this:

$$\begin{aligned} u &= & dv &= \\ du &= & v &= . \end{aligned}$$

It's up to you to fill in the blanks. In the top row of this table, write the two factors from the original integral. Once you differentiate in the left column and integrate in the right column, the bottom row will contain the factors required for the integral on the right-hand side of the integration by parts formula.

Example 1 Find $\int xe^x\,dx$. We identify the good candidates for u and dv in the original expression, and follow the steps to apply the substitution:

$$\begin{aligned} u &= x & dv &= e^x\,dx, \\ du &= dx & v &= e^x. \end{aligned}$$

Next, apply the integration by parts formula,

$$\int u\,dv = uv - \int v\,du,$$

to obtain

$$\begin{aligned} \int xe^x\,dx &= xe^x - \int e^x\,dx \\ &= xe^x - e^x + C. \end{aligned}$$

Example 2 Find $\int x \sin x\,dx$. We choose the substitutions $u = x$ and $dv = \sin x dx$. With these choices, we have $du = dx$ and $v = -\cos x$. Integrating by parts gives us

$$\begin{aligned} \int x \sin x\,dx &= -x \cos x - \int (-\cos x)\ dx \\ &= -x \cos x + \int \cos x\,dx \\ &= -x \cos x + \sin x + C. \end{aligned}$$

Example 3 Often, you'll need to integrate by parts *multiple* times. To calculate $\int x^2 e^x\,dx$, we start by choosing the following substitutions:

$$\begin{aligned} u &= x^2 & dv &= e^x\,dx \\ du &= 2x\,dx & v &= e^x. \end{aligned}$$

After integration by parts, we have

$$\int x^2e^x\,dx = x^2e^x \;-\; 2\int xe^x\,dx.$$

We apply integration by parts *again* to the remaining integral. This time, we use $u = x$ and $dv = e^x\,dx$, which gives $du = dx$ and $v = e^x$.

$$\begin{aligned}\int x^2e^x\,dx &= x^2e^x - 2\int xe^x\,dx \\ &= x^2e^x - 2\left(xe^x - \int e^x\,dx\right) \\ &= x^2e^x - 2xe^x + 2e^x + C.\end{aligned}$$

By now I hope you're starting to see why this integration by parts thing is good. If you remember to clearly write down the substitutions (indicating what is what in $\int udv$), and if you apply the formula correctly ($= uv - \int vdu$), you can break down any integral. Careful you don't make the wrong choice for your u and dv substitutions; if the integral $\int vdu$ is no simpler than the original $\int udv$, you are missing the point of integrating by parts, which is to make your life easier.

Sometimes, you might find yourself in a weird, self-referential loop when performing integration by parts. After a couple of integration by parts steps, it's possible to arrive at the very integral you started with! The way out of this loop is best shown by example.

Example 4 Evaluate the integral $\int \sin(x)e^x\,dx$. First, let $u = \sin(x)$ and $dv = e^x\,dx$, which gives $du = \cos(x)dx$ and $v = e^x$. Using integration by parts,

$$\int \sin(x)e^x\,dx = e^x\sin(x) - \int \cos(x)e^x\,dx.$$

We integrate by parts again. This time, set $u = \cos(x)$, $dv = e^x dx$, and $du = -\sin(x)dx$, $v = e^x$. We obtain

$$\underbrace{\int \sin(x)e^x\,dx}_{I} \;=\; e^x\sin(x) - e^x\cos(x) \;-\; \underbrace{\int e^x\sin(x)\,dx}_{I}.$$

Do you see the Ouroboros? We could continue integrating by parts indefinitely in this way.

Let us clearly define what we are doing here. The question asks us to find I where

$$I = \int \sin(x)e^x\,dx,$$

and after completing two integration by parts steps, we obtain the equation

$$I = e^x \sin(x) - e^x \cos(x) - I.$$

Okay, good. Now move all the Is to one side:

$$2I = e^x \sin(x) - e^x \cos(x).$$

After factoring out e^x and dividing by 2 we finally obtain

$$\int \sin(x)e^x \, dx = I = \tfrac{1}{2}e^x \left(\sin(x) - \cos(x)\right) + C.$$

Integration by parts for integrals with limits

For definite integrals, the integration by parts rule must account for evaluation at the function's limits:

$$\int_a^b u \, dv = (uv)\Big|_a^b - \int_a^b v \, du.$$

This expression tells us to evaluate the change in the product uv at the limits of integration.

Example 5 Find $\int_0^5 xe^x \, dx$. We've already seen this example, but this time it includes limits of integration. The first part of the procedure is the same. We apply the substitution

$$u = x \qquad dv = e^x \, dx,$$
$$du = dx \qquad v = e^x.$$

Then use the formula for integration by parts with limits:

$$\begin{aligned}
\int_0^5 xe^x \, dx &= (xe^x)\Big|_0^5 - \int_0^5 e^x \, dx \\
&= (xe^x)\Big|_0^5 - e^x\Big|_0^5 \\
&= \left[5e^5 - 0e^0\right] - \left[e^5 - e^0\right] \\
&= 5e^5 - e^5 + 1 \\
&= 4e^5 + 1.
\end{aligned}$$

Derivation of the Integration by parts formula

Remember the product rule for derivatives?

$$\frac{d}{dx}(f(x)g(x)) = \frac{df}{dx}g(x) + f(x)\frac{dg}{dx}.$$

We can rewrite it as

$$f(x)\frac{dg}{dx} = \frac{d}{dx}(f(x)g(x)) - \frac{df}{dx}g(x).$$

Take the integral on both sides of the equation:

$$\begin{aligned}\int \left[f(x)\frac{dg}{dx}\right] dx &= \int \left[\frac{d}{dx}(f(x)g(x)) - \frac{df}{dx}g(x)\right] dx \\ \int f(x)\frac{dg}{dx}\, dx &= \int \left[\frac{d}{dx}(f(x)g(x))\right] dx - \int \frac{df}{dx}g(x)dx.\end{aligned}$$

At this point, think back to the fundamental theorem of calculus (see page 349), which says the derivative and the integral are inverse operations, $\int \left(\frac{d}{dx}h(x)\right) dx = h(x)$.

We apply this logic to simplify the first term on the right-hand side of the above equation and obtain

$$\int f(x)\frac{dg}{dx}\, dx = f(x)g(x) - \int \frac{df}{dx}g(x)\, dx,$$

which is the integration by parts formula.

Outro

We are done. You know all the integration techniques. I know it took a while, but we had to discuss a lot of tricks. In any case, my job of teaching you is done. Now *your* job begins. Practice all the examples you can find. Try solving all the problems in the end of the chapter. You must practice the tricks until you become comfortable with them.

Here's a suggestion for you. Make your own trophy case for formulas. As you cover ground in your homework assignments, create and maintain a formula-sheet where you record any complex integrals you have personally calculated from first principles. By the end of the class, if your trophy case contains 50 integrals you have personally calculated all by yourself, then you will earn 100% on your final. Another thing to try: review the integral formulas in the back of the book and see how many of them you can derive.

Links

[More examples of integration techniques]
`http://en.wikibooks.org/wiki/Calculus/Integration_techniques/`

5.16 Applications of integration

Applications to mechanics

Calculus was essentially invented *for* mechanics, so it's not surprising there are many links between the two subjects.

Kinematics

Suppose a constant force F_{net} is applied to an object of mass m. Newton's second law tells us the acceleration of the object will be constant and equal to $a = \frac{F_{\text{net}}}{m}$.

We can find the equation of motion for the object $x(t)$ by integrating $a(t)$ twice, since $a(t) = x''(t)$. We start with the acceleration function $a(t) = a$ and integrate once to obtain

$$v(\tau) = \int_0^\tau a(t)\, dt = at + v_i,$$

where $v_i = v(0)$ is the object's initial velocity at $t = 0$. We obtain the position function by integrating the velocity function and adding the initial position $x_i = x(0)$:

$$x(\tau) = \int v(t)\, dt = \int (at + v_i)\, dt = \frac{1}{2}a\tau^2 + v_i\tau + x_i.$$

Non-constant acceleration

If the net force acting on the object is not constant, the acceleration will not be constant either. In general, both force and mass can change over time, and if they do, acceleration will also change over time $a(t) = \frac{F_{\text{net}}(t)}{m(t)}$. This sort of problem is usually not covered in a first mechanics course because the establishment assumes it is too complicated for you to handle.

Now that you know more about integrals, you can learn how to predict the motion of an object for an arbitrary acceleration function $a(t)$. To find the velocity at time $t = \tau$, we must sum all acceleration felt by the object between $t = 0$ and $t = \tau$:

$$v(\tau) = v_i + \int_0^\tau a(t)\, dt.$$

The equation of motion $x(t)$ is obtained by integrating the velocity $v(t)$:

$$x(s) = x_i + \int_0^s v(\tau)\, d\tau = \int_0^s \left[v_i + \int_0^\tau a(t)\, dt \right] d\tau.$$

The above expression looks quite intense, but in fact it is no more complicated than the simple integrals used in UAM. The expression *looks* complicated because it contains three different variables representing time, as well as two consecutive integration steps.

Gravitational potential energy

The work done by a force $\vec{F}$ during a displacement $\vec{d}$ is computed using the integral $W = \int_0^d \vec{F} \cdot d\vec{x}$, which simplifies to $W = \vec{F} \cdot \vec{d}$ for a constant force. The negative of the work done by a conservative force defines the *potential energy* function associated with that force.

Since gravity $\vec{F}_g$ is a conservative force, we can integrate it to obtain the gravitational potential energy U_g. On the surface of the Earth, $\vec{F}_g = -gm\hat{\jmath}$. The negative sign means the force of gravity acts in the direction opposite to "upward," as represented by the $\hat{\jmath}$ unit vector pointing in the positive y-direction (toward the sky). In particular, gravitational force as a function of height $\vec{F}_g(y)$ is a constant $\vec{F}_g(y) = \vec{F}_g$. By definition, gravitational potential energy is the negative of the integral of the force over some distance, say from height $y_i = 0$ to height $y_f = h$:

$$\Delta U_g = U_g(h) - U_g(0) = -\int_{y_i}^{y_f} \vec{F}_g \cdot d\vec{y} = -\int_0^h -mg\, dy = \Big[mgy \Big]_0^h = mgh.$$

The general form of the gravitational force acting on an object of mass m due to another object of mass M is given by Newton's famous one-over-r-squared law,

$$\vec{F}_g = \frac{GMm}{r^2} \hat{r}.$$

In this law, r is the distance between the objects and $\hat{r}$ points toward the other object.

The general formula for gravitational potential energy is obtained by taking the integral of the gravitational force over some distance. Imagine a planet of mass m and another planet of mass M. The two masses start infinitely far away from each other and slowly move closer until they are a distance $r = R$ apart. The change in gravitational potential from $r = \infty$ to $r = R$ is

$$\begin{aligned}
\Delta U_g(R) &= \int_{r=\infty}^{r=R} \frac{GMm}{r^2}\, dr \\
&= GMm \int_{\infty}^{R} \frac{1}{r^2}\, dr \\
&= GMm \left[\frac{-1}{r}\right]_{\infty}^{R} \\
&= GMm \left[\frac{-1}{R} - \frac{-1}{\infty}\right] \\
&= -\frac{GMm}{R}.
\end{aligned}$$

The gravitational potential energy of two planets separated by distance R is negative since work is *required* to pull the planets apart once they have come together.

There is an important physics lesson to learn here. For each conservative force $\vec{F}_?(x)$, there is an associated potential energy function $U_?(x)$ that is defined as the negative of the work done when moving an object against the force $\vec{F}_?(x)$:

$$\text{Given } \vec{F}_?(x) \qquad \Rightarrow \qquad U_?(x) \equiv -\int_0^x \vec{F}_?(u) \cdot d\vec{u}.$$

We can use this relationship in the other direction too. Given a potential energy function $U_?(x)$, we can find the force $F_?(x)$ associated with that potential energy function by taking the derivative:

$$\text{Given } U_?(x) \qquad \Rightarrow \qquad F_?(x) \equiv -\frac{d}{dx}\Big[U_?(x)\Big].$$

The negative of the derivative of the gravitational potential energy $U_g(y) = mgy$ gives $F_g(y) = -mg$. The negative of the derivative of the spring potential energy $U_s(x) = \frac{1}{2}kx^2$ gives $F_s(x) = -kx$.

Integrals over circular objects

We can use integration to obtain area and volume formulas of objects with circular symmetries.

Consider the disk-shaped region described by the equation $D = \{x, y \in \mathbb{R} \mid x^2 + y^2 \leqslant R^2\}$. In polar coordinates we describe this region as $r \leqslant R$, where it is implicit that the angle θ varies between 0 and 2π. Because this region is two-dimensional, computing an integral over this region requires a *double integral*, which is the subject of multivariable calculus. Even before you learn about double integrals, you still know enough to integrate over a circular region by breaking the region into thin circle-shaped slices of disk dD.

Similar to the way a horizontal slice through an onion consists of many thin onion rings, we can break the disk into a number of thin, circular strips of width dr as shown in Figure 5.26. The circular strip with radius r has an area of

$$dD = 2\pi r\, dr,$$

since $2\pi r$ is the circumference of a circle with radius r, and since the width of the strip is dr.

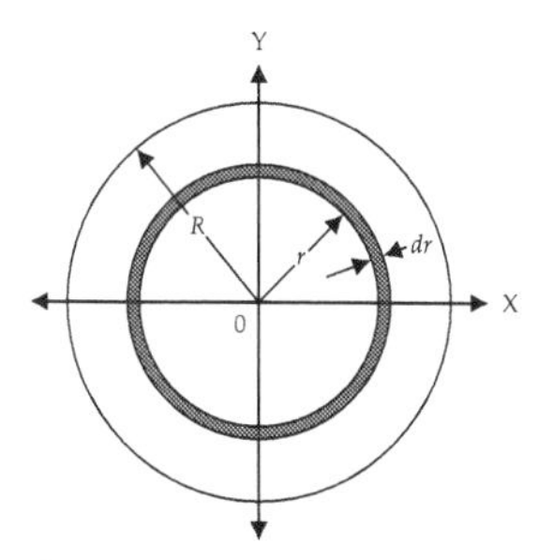

Figure 5.26: We can break up the area of a disk of radius R into many thin, circular strips of width dr and radius r varying from $r = 0$ to $r = R$.

Using this method to break apart the disk, we can check that adding the areas of all the "pieces of disk" dD gives a total area of πR^2:

$$A_{\text{disk}} = \int_D dD = \int_{r=0}^{r=R} 2\pi r\, dr = 2\pi \int_0^R r\, dr = 2\pi \left[\frac{r^2}{2}\right]_0^R = \pi R^2.$$

The following sections discuss different variations of this breaking-an-onion-slice-into-onion-rings idea. We can use the circular symmetry of various objects to compute their area, volume, and moment of inertia.

Total mass of a disk

Suppose you have a disk of total mass m and radius R. You can think of the disk as being made of parts, each of mass dm, such that adding all the parts gives the disk's total mass:

$$\int_{\text{disk}} dm = m.$$

The mass density is defined as the total mass divided by the area of the disk: $\sigma = \frac{m}{A_{\text{disk}}} = \frac{m}{\pi R^2}[\text{kg/m}^2]$. Mass density corresponds to the amount of mass per unit area. We can split the disk into concentric circular strips of width dr. The mass contribution of each strip is equal to σ times the area of that strip. The strip at radius r has circumference $2\pi r$ and width dr, so its mass contribution is $dm = \sigma 2\pi r\, dr$.

Let's check that we obtain the total mass by adding the pieces:

$$\int_{\text{disk}} dm = \int_0^R \sigma 2\pi r\, dr = 2\pi\sigma \left[\frac{r^2}{2}\right]_0^R = 2\pi \frac{m}{\pi R^2} \frac{R^2 - 0}{2} = m.$$

Moment of inertia of a disk

An object's moment of inertia is a measure of how difficult it is to make the object turn. The moment of inertia appears in the rotational version of $F = ma$, in place of the mass m: $\mathcal{T} = I\alpha$. The moment of inertia I also appears in the formula for angular momentum $L = I\omega$ and the formula for rotational kinetic energy $K_r = \frac{1}{2}I\omega^2$.

To compute an object's moment of inertia, we must add all the mass contributions dm, multiplying each by r^2, where r is the distance of the piece dm from the disk's centre:

$$I = \int_{\text{disk}} r^2\, dm.$$

We can perform the integral over the whole disk by adding the contributions of all the strips:

$$I_{\text{disk}} = \int_0^R r^2\, dm = \int_0^R r^2 \sigma 2\pi r\, dr = \int_0^R r^2 \frac{m}{\pi R^2} 2\pi r\, dr =$$

$$= \frac{2m}{R^2} \int_0^R r^3\, dr = \frac{2m}{R^2} \left[\frac{r^4}{4}\right]_0^R = \frac{2m}{R^2} \frac{R^4}{4} = \frac{1}{2} m R^2.$$

Arc length of a curve

Given a function $y = f(x)$, how can you calculate the total *arc length* of the graph of $f(x)$ between $x = a$ and $x = b$?

If $f(x)$ is the equation of a line, the length of its graph can be calculated as the hypotenuse of the change-in-x and the change-in-y triangle: $\ell = \sqrt{\text{run}^2 + \text{rise}^2} = \sqrt{(b-a)^2 + (f(b) - f(a))^2}$.

However, if the function is *not* a straight line, we need to apply this hypotenuse calculation to each piece of the curve $d\ell = \sqrt{dx^2 + dy^2}$, then sum all the contributions using integration $\ell = \int d\ell$.

The arc length ℓ of the function $f(x)$ between $x = a$ and $x = b$ is

$$\ell = \int d\ell = \int \sqrt{dx^2 + dy^2} = \int \sqrt{\left(1 + \frac{dy^2}{dx^2}\right) dx^2} = \int_a^b \sqrt{1 + (f'(x))^2} dx.$$

Example Use the arc length formula to compute the length of the curve $f(x) = \frac{2}{3}\sqrt{x^3}$ between the points $(1, \frac{2}{3})$ and $(6, 4\sqrt{6})$.

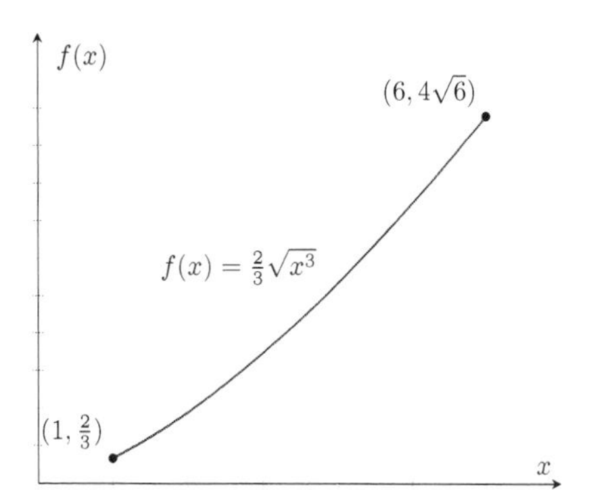

Figure 5.27: Graph of the function $f(x) = \frac{2}{3}x^{\frac{3}{2}}$ between $x = 1$ and $x = 6$.

The formula for the length of a curve is $\ell = \int d\ell = \int_1^6 \sqrt{1 + (f'(x))^2}\, dx$. Applying this formula to the function $f(x)$, we obtain $f'(x) = \sqrt{x}$ and then find $\sqrt{1 + (f'(x))^2} = \sqrt{1 + x}$. The length of the curve between $x = 1$ and $x = 6$ is

$$\ell = \int_1^6 \sqrt{1 + x}\, dx = \frac{2}{3}(x + 1)^{\frac{3}{2}}\Big|_1^6 = \frac{14}{3}\sqrt{7} - \frac{4}{3}\sqrt{2}.$$

Area of a surface of revolution

We can modify the arc length formula to calculate the surface area A of a *surface of revolution*. A surface with circular symmetry can be generated by a revolution of a curve $f(x)$ around the x-axis. Imagine a potter's wheel with an axis of rotation that corresponds to the x-axis. If the potter's fingers trace out the curve $f(x)$ in space, the result will be a circular vase with sides in the shape of $f(x)$.

We can split the surface area into circular strips by cutting the surface at regular intervals dx along the x-axis. The radius of each strip varies according to $f(x)$, and the width of each strip is given by the arc length $d\ell = \sqrt{dx^2 + dy^2} = \sqrt{1 + (f'(x))^2}dx$. We can approximate the area of each circular strip as $2\pi f(x)d\ell$.

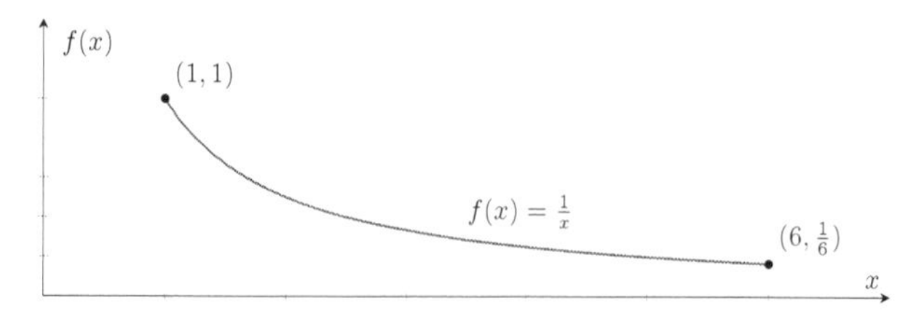

Figure 5.28: Graph of $f(x) = \frac{1}{x}$ between $x = 1$ and $x = 6$. What surface will be produced if we rotate this curve around the x-axis?

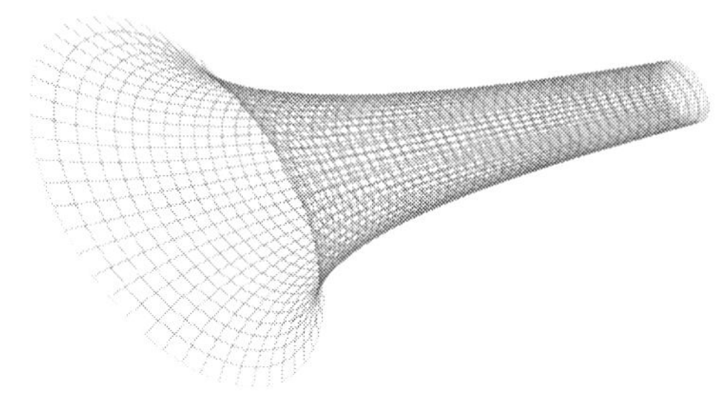

Figure 5.29: The surface of revolution generated by the section of the curve $f(x) = \frac{1}{x}$ between $x = 1$ and $x = 6$ when rotated around the x-axis.

The area of the surface of revolution traced by the graph of $f(x)$ between $x = a$ and $x = b$ as it rotates around the x-axis is given by the formula

$$A = \int_a^b 2\pi f(x) d\ell = \int_a^b 2\pi f(x) \sqrt{1 + (f'(x))^2}\, dx.$$

Volumes of revolution

Let's move on to three-dimensional integrals, or integrals over volumes. Again, we'll use the circular symmetry of the object's volume to split the object into little "pieces of volume" and then compute an integral to find the total volume.

Disk method

We can describe the volume of an object with circular symmetry as the sum of a number of disks. Each disk will have thickness dx and a radius proportional to the function $f(x)$. In other words, the function $f(x)$ describes the object's outer boundary. The area of each disk is $\pi(f(x))^2$ and its thickness is dx.

The volume of a solid of revolution with boundary $f(x)$ rotated around the x-axis is given by the formula

$$V = \int A_{\text{disk}}(x)\,dx$$
$$= \int \pi(f(x))^2\,dx.$$

Example Use the disk method to calculate the volume of a sphere with radius R. The volume we want to calculate is bounded by the curve $f(x) = \sqrt{R^2 - x^2}$ and the horizontal line $y = 0$. Our limits of integration are the x-values where the curve intersects the line $y = 0$, namely, $x = \pm R$. We have

$$\begin{aligned} V_{\text{sphere}} &= \int_{-R}^{R} \pi(R^2 - x^2)dx \\ &= \pi\left(\int_{-R}^{R} R^2\,dx - \int_{-R}^{R} x^2\,dx\right) \\ &= \pi\left(R^2x\Big|_{-R}^{R} - \frac{x^3}{3}\Big|_{-R}^{R}\right) \\ &= \pi\left(2R^3 - \frac{2R^3}{3}\right) \\ &= \frac{4}{3}\pi R^3\,. \end{aligned}$$

Indeed, this is the formula for the volume of a sphere that we first encountered in Chapter 1 (see page 81).

Washer method

The washer method is a generalization of the disk method for computing volumes. Consider a volume of revolution with an inner radius described by the function $g(x)$ and an outer radius described by the function $f(x)$. Figure 5.30 shows such a volume of revolution. Instead of using thin disks, we can represent this volume as the sum of thin washers, which are disks of radius $f(x)$ with a middle section of radius $g(x)$ removed.

The volume dV of each washer is equal to the outer area $\pi(f(x))^2$ minus the removed inner area $\pi(g(x))^2$, times the thickness dx. The

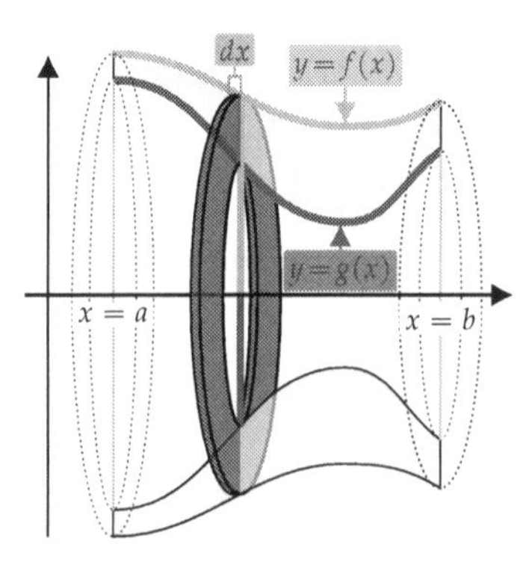

Figure 5.30: We can break the volume of a thee-dimensional shape into thin, washers-shaped slices of thickness dx. The inner radius of each washer is described by the function $g(x)$ and its outer radius by $f(x)$.

total volume is given by

$$\begin{aligned} V &= \int dV = \int A_{\text{washer}}(x)\, dx \\ &= \int (A_{\text{outer}}(x) - A_{\text{inner}}(x))\, dx = \int \pi \left[(f(x))^2 - (g(x))^2 \right] dx. \end{aligned}$$

Cylindrical shell method

We can split any circularly symmetric volume into thin, cylindrical shells of thickness dr as illustrated in Figure 5.31. If the volume has a circular symmetry and is bounded from above by $F(r)$ and from below by $G(r)$, then the integral over the volume will be

$$\begin{aligned} V &= \int C_{\text{shell}}(r)\, h_{\text{shell}}(r)\, dr \\ &= \int 2\pi r |F(r) - G(r)|\, dr. \end{aligned}$$

The cylindrical shell with radius r has circumference $2\pi r$, thickness dr, and its height is described by the expression $|F(r) - G(r)|$.

Example Calculate the volume of a sphere of radius R using the cylindrical shell method. We are talking about the region enclosed by the surface $x^2 + y^2 + z^2 = R^2$.

At radius $r = \sqrt{x^2 + y^2}$, the cylindrical shell will be bounded from above by $z = F(r) = \sqrt{R^2 - r^2}$, and bounded from below by $z = G(r) = -\sqrt{R^2 - r^2}$. The height of the cylindrical shell is given by

$|F(r) - G(r)| = 2\sqrt{R^2 - r^2}$. The circumference of the shell is $2\pi r$ and its width is dr. The integral proceeds like this:

$$\begin{aligned}
V &= \int_0^R 2\pi r|F(r) - G(r)|\, dr \\
&= \int_0^R 2\pi r 2\sqrt{R^2 - r^2}\, dr \\
&= -2\pi \int_{R^2}^0 \sqrt{u}\, du \qquad (\text{using } u = R^2 - r^2, du = -2rdr) \\
&= -2\pi \left[\tfrac{2}{3}u^{3/2}\right]_{R^2}^0 \\
&= -2\pi[0 - \tfrac{2}{3}R^3] \\
&= \frac{4}{3}\pi R^3.
\end{aligned}$$

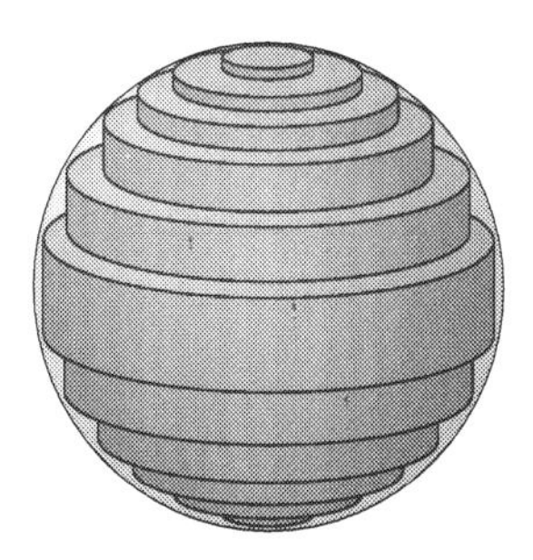

Figure 5.31: We can break up the volume of a sphere into thin, cylindrical shells of thickness dr and height determined by the enclosing surface.

Discussion

The formulas for calculating the surface areas and volumes of revolutions can be adapted for computing other quantities that have circular symmetry. For example, the formula for the surface area of a revolution can be used to compute the moment of inertia of a thin, spherical shell. The formula for the surface are of a spherical shell of radius R can be obtained as the area of revolution for the curve $f(x) = \sqrt{R^2 - x^2}$ around the x-axis:

$$A_{\text{sph.shell}} = \int_{-R}^R dA = \int_{-R}^R 2\pi f(x)\sqrt{1 + (f'(x))^2}\, dx = 4\pi R^2.$$

We can adapt this formula to calculate the moment of inertia of a spherical shell of mass m. The general formula for the moment of inertia is $I = \int r^2\, dm$, which tells us that the contribution of each "piece of mass" dm must be multiplied by its squared distance from the axis of rotation. For a spherical shell, each "piece of mass" can be written as $dm = \sigma dA$, where $\sigma = \frac{m}{4\pi R^2}$ is the mass density. The distance of the pieces from the rotation axis varies according to $f(x)$. The moment of inertia of a thin, spherical shell is therefore given by the integral

$$I_{\text{sph.shell}} = \int_{-R}^{R} (f(x))^2 \sigma dA = \int_{-R}^{R} (f(x))^2\, \sigma 2\pi f(x) \sqrt{1 + (f'(x))^2}\, dx.$$

In problem **P5.126** you'll be asked to complete this calculation and verify the formula $I_{\text{sph.shell}} = \frac{2}{3}mR^2$, which was stated in Section 4.8 without proof.

We can use a similar approach to calculate the moment of inertia of a solid sphere $I_{\text{sphere}} = \frac{2}{5}mR^2$. We can use either the disk method or the cylindrical shell method, adapting the volume of revolution formula to transform each piece of volume dV into a piece of mass dm, multiplied by its squared distance from the axis of rotation. See **P5.127** and **P5.128** for the calculations.

Exercises

E5.5 Calculate the volume of a cone with radius R and height h that is generated by the revolution around the x-axis of the region bounded by the curve $y = R - \frac{R}{h}x$ and the lines $y = 0$ and $x = 0$.

E5.6 Find the volume of a vertical cone with radius R and height h formed by the revolution of the region bounded by the curves $y = 0$, $y = h - \frac{h}{R}x$, and $x = 0$ around the y-axis. Use cylindrical shells.

Links

[An animation showing how a volume of revolution is constructed]
`http://mathforum.org/mathimages/index.php/Volume_of_Revolution`

5.17 Improper integrals

Imagine you want to find the area under the function $f(x) = \frac{1}{x^2}$ from $x = 1$ all the way to $x = \infty$. This kind of calculation is known as an *improper integral* since one of the endpoints of the integration is not a regular number, but infinity.

We can compute this integral as the following limit:

$$\int_1^\infty \frac{1}{x^2}\,dx \equiv \lim_{b\to\infty}\int_1^b \frac{1}{x^2}\,dx = \lim_{b\to\infty}\left[\frac{-1}{x}\right]_1^b = \lim_{b\to\infty}\left[-\frac{1}{b}+\frac{1}{1}\right] = 1.$$

This calculation describes an integration over a region with infinite width. Because the height of the region ($f(x)=\frac{1}{x^2}$) becomes smaller and smaller, the region still has finite area.

Definition

An *improper integral* is an integral in which one of the limits of integration goes to infinity. Improper integrals are evaluated as regular integrals, where infinity is replaced by a dummy variable, after which a limit calculation is applied to take the dummy variable to infinity:

$$\int_a^\infty f(x)\,dx \equiv \lim_{b\to\infty}\int_a^b f(x)\,dx = \lim_{b\to\infty}\left[F(b)-F(a)\right],$$

where $F(x)$ is the antiderivative function of $f(x)$.

Applications Later in this chapter, we'll learn about the "integral test" for the convergence of series, which requires the evaluation of an improper integral.

5.18 Sequences

A *sequence* is an ordered list of numbers that follows some pattern, much like "find the pattern" questions on IQ tests. We can study the properties of sequences as mathematical objects. For example, by checking whether the sequence *converges* to some limit.

Understanding sequences is a prerequisite for understanding series, which is an important topic we will discuss in the next section.

Definitions

- $\mathbb{N}$: the set of *natural* numbers $\mathbb{N}\equiv\{0,1,2,3,\ldots\}$
- $\mathbb{N}_+ = \mathbb{N}\backslash\{0\}$: the set of *strictly positive* natural numbers $\{1,2,3,\ldots\}$. The set $\mathbb{N}_+$ is the same as $\mathbb{N}$, except $\mathbb{N}_+$ starts from 1 instead of 0.

- a_n: a sequence of numbers $(a_0, a_1, a_2, a_3, a_4, \ldots)$. You can also think of each sequence as a function

$$a : \mathbb{N} \to \mathbb{R},$$

where the input n is an integer (the *index* into the sequence) and the output is some number $a_n \in \mathbb{R}$.

Examples of sequences

Consider the following common sequences.

Arithmetic progression

A sequence is an arithmetic progression if the terms of the sequence differ by a constant amount. The terms in the simplest arithmetic progression differ by one:

$$(0,\ 1,\ 2,\ 3,\ 4,\ 5,\ 6,\ \ldots).$$

This sequence is described by the formula

$$a_n = n, \qquad n \in \mathbb{N}.$$

More generally, an arithmetic sequence can start at any value a_0 and make jumps of size d at each step:

$$a_n = a_0 + nd, \qquad n \in \mathbb{N}.$$

Harmonic sequence

In a *harmonic* sequence, each element of the sequence is inversely proportional to its index n:

$$\left(1,\ \frac{1}{2},\ \frac{1}{3},\ \frac{1}{4},\ \frac{1}{5},\ \frac{1}{6},\ \ldots\right)$$

$$a_n = \frac{1}{n}, \qquad n \in \mathbb{N}_+.$$

More generally, we can define a p-sequence in which the index n appears in the denominator raised to the power p:

$$a_n = \frac{1}{n^p}, \qquad n \in \mathbb{N}_+.$$

For example, when $p = 2$, the result is a sequence of inverse squares of the integers:

$$\left(1,\ \frac{1}{4},\ \frac{1}{9},\ \frac{1}{16},\ \frac{1}{25},\ \frac{1}{36},\ \ldots\right).$$

Geometric sequence

By using the index as the exponent of a fixed number r, we obtain the geometric series

$$a_n = r^n, \quad n \in \mathbb{N},$$

which is a sequence of the form

$$\left(1, r, r^2, r^3, r^4, r^5, r^6, \ldots\right).$$

If we choose $r = \frac{1}{2}$, then the geometric series with this ratio will be

$$\left(1, \frac{1}{2}, \frac{1}{4}, \frac{1}{8}, \frac{1}{16}, \frac{1}{32}, \frac{1}{64}, \frac{1}{128}, \ldots\right).$$

Fibonacci

The Fibonacci numbers are constructed according to the following pattern. The first Fibonacci number is 0, the second Fibonacci number is 1, and each subsequent number is the sum of the two preceding it:

$$a_0 = 0, \; a_1 = 1, \qquad a_n = a_{n-1} + a_{n-2}, \; n \geqslant 2.$$

$$(0, 1, 1, 2, 3, 5, 8, 13, 21, 34, 55, 89, 144, 233, 377, \ldots).$$

Convergence

We say a sequence a_n *converges* to a limit L, written mathematically as

$$\lim_{n \to \infty} a_n = L,$$

if for large values of n the terms in the sequence become arbitrarily close to the value L.

More precisely, the limit expression $\lim\limits_{n \to \infty} a_n = L$ means that for *any* precisions $\epsilon > 0$, we can pick a number N_ϵ such that

$$|a_n - L| < \epsilon, \qquad \forall n \geqslant N_\epsilon.$$

The notion of a limit of a sequence is the same as the notion of a limit of a function. Just as we learned how to calculate which number the function $f(x)$ tends to for large x values (see page 293), we can study which number the sequence a_n tends to for large n values.

Ratio convergence

The numbers in the Fibonacci sequence grow indefinitely large ($\lim_{n\to\infty} a_n = \infty$), while the ratio of $\frac{a_{n+1}}{a_n}$ converges to a constant:

$$\lim_{n\to\infty} \frac{a_{n+1}}{a_n} = \varphi = \frac{1+\sqrt{5}}{2} \approx 1.618033\ldots$$

This constant is known as the *golden ratio.*

Calculus on sequences

If a sequence a_n is like a function $f(x)$, we should be able to perform calculus on it. We already saw how we can take limits of sequences, but can we also compute derivatives and integrals of sequences? Derivatives are a no-go, because they depend on the function $f(x)$ being *continuous*, and sequences are only defined for integer values. We *can* take integrals of sequences, however, and this is the subject of the next section.

5.19 Series

Can you compute ln(2) using only a basic calculator with four operations, $\boxed{+}$, $\boxed{-}$, $\boxed{\times}$, and $\boxed{\div}$? I can tell you one way to do this; compute the following infinite sum:

$$\ln(2) = 1 - \frac{1}{2} + \frac{1}{3} - \frac{1}{4} + \frac{1}{5} - \frac{1}{6} + \frac{1}{7} - \frac{1}{8} + \cdots.$$

Since the sum is infinite, it will take a while to obtain the value of $\ln(2)$, but if you keep adding more terms in the sum, you will eventually obtain the answer $\ln(2) = 0.693147\ldots$.

Let's make the computer carry out the summation for us. First we define the formula for the nth term in the series $a_n = \frac{(-1)^{n+1}}{n}$, then we compute the sum of the first 100, 1000, and 1000000 terms:

```
>>> def an_ln2(n): return (-1.0)**(n+1)/n
>>> sum([ an_ln2(n)  for n in range(1,100) ])
0.69...
>>> sum([ an_ln2(n)  for n in range(1,1000) ])
0.693...
>>> sum([ an_ln2(n)  for n in range(1,1000000) ])
0.693147...
```

Observe how the approximation becomes more accurate as more terms are added in the sum. A lot of practical mathematical computations are performed in this *iterative* fashion. In this section we'll learn about a powerful technique for calculating quantities to arbitrary precision by summing together more and more terms of a series.

Definitions

- $\mathbb{N} \equiv \{0,1,2,3,4,5,6,\ldots\}$: the set of natural numbers
- $\mathbb{N}_+ \equiv \mathbb{N}\backslash\{0\} \equiv \{1,2,3,4,5,6,\ldots\}$: the set of positive natural numbers
- a_n: a sequence of numbers $(a_0, a_1, a_2, a_3, a_4, \ldots)$
- $\sum$: sum. This symbol indicates taking the sum of several objects grouped together. The summation sign is the short way to express certain long expressions:

$$a_3 + a_4 + a_5 + a_6 + a_7 = \sum_{3 \leqslant n \leqslant 7} a_n = \sum_{n=3}^{7} a_n.$$

- $\sum a_n$: the *series* a_n is the sum of all terms in the sequence a_n:

$$S_\infty = \sum_{n=1}^{\infty} a_n = a_1 + a_2 + a_3 + a_4 + a_5 + a_6 + \cdots.$$

- $n!$: the *factorial* function $n! = n(n-1)(n-2)\cdots 3\cdot 2\cdot 1$, if $n \geqslant 1$. We define $0! = 1$.
- $f(x) = \sum_{n=0}^{\infty} c_n x^n$: the *Taylor series* approximation of the function $f(x)$. It has the form of an infinitely long polynomial $c_0 + c_1x^1 + c_2x^2 + c_3x^3 + \ldots$ where the coefficients c_n are chosen so as to encode the properties of the function $f(x)$.

Exact sums

Formulas exist for calculating the exact sum of certain series.

The sum of the geometric series of length N is

$$S_N = \sum_{n=0}^{N} r^n = 1 + r + r^2 + \cdots + r^N = \frac{1 - r^{N+1}}{1 - r}.$$

If $|r| < 1$, taking the limit $N \to \infty$ in the above expression leads to

$$S_\infty = \lim_{N\to\infty} S_N = \sum_{n=0}^{\infty} r^n = 1 + r + r^2 + r^3 + \cdots = \frac{1}{1-r}.$$

Example Consider the geometric series with $r = \frac{1}{2}$. Applying the above formula, we obtain

$$S_\infty = \sum_{n=0}^{\infty} \left(\frac{1}{2}\right)^n = 1 + \frac{1}{2} + \frac{1}{4} + \frac{1}{8} + \frac{1}{16} + \frac{1}{32} + \cdots = \frac{1}{1 - \frac{1}{2}} = 2.$$

You can visualize this infinite summation graphically. Imagine starting with a piece of paper of size one-by-one, then adding next to it a second piece of paper with half the size of the first, and a third piece with half the size of the second, and so on. The total area occupied by these pieces of papers is shown in Figure 5.32.

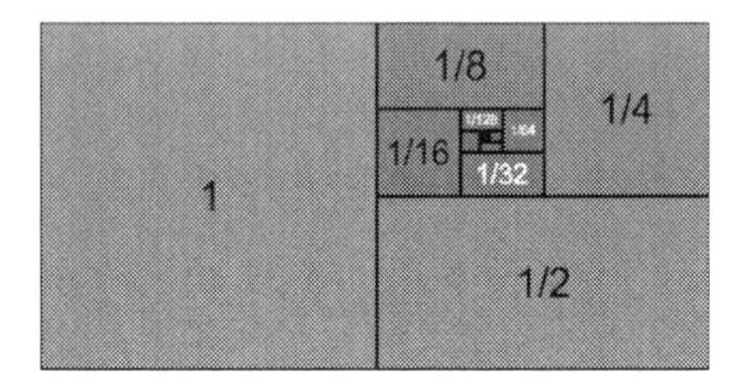

Figure 5.32: A graphical representation of the infinite sum of the geometric series with $r = \frac{1}{2}$. The area of each region corresponds to one of the terms in the series. The total area is equal to $\sum_{n=0}^{\infty} \left(\frac{1}{2}\right)^n = \frac{1}{1-\frac{1}{2}} = 2$.

We'll now state without proof a number of other formulas where the sum of a series can be obtained as a closed-form expression.

The formulas for the sum of the first N positive integers and the sum of the squares of the first N positive integers are

$$\sum_{n=1}^{N} n = \frac{N(N+1)}{2}, \qquad \sum_{n=1}^{N} n^2 = \frac{N(N+1)(2N+1)}{6}.$$

See problem **P5.119** for the derivations of these formulas. The sum of the first N terms in an arithmetic sequence is

$$\sum_{n=1}^{N} (a_0 + nd) = a_0 N + \frac{N(N+1)}{2} d.$$

It will be important to remember these formulas because they can occur in calculus problems. For example, computing the integral of the function $f(x) = ax^2 + bx + c$ using an infinite Riemann sum requires these formulas.

There are many other series whose infinite sum is described by an exact formula. Below, you'll find some known formulas for the sums of certain infinite series. The p-series involving even values of p can be computed:

$$\sum_{n=1}^{\infty} \frac{1}{n^2} = \frac{\pi^2}{6}, \qquad \sum_{n=1}^{\infty} \frac{1}{n^4} = \frac{\pi^4}{90}, \qquad \sum_{n=1}^{\infty} \frac{1}{n^6} = \frac{\pi^6}{945}.$$

Note you're not required to memorize these formulas. They are given here as examples of what is possible. Other closed-form expressions for infinite series include:

$$\sum_{n=1}^{\infty} \frac{(-1)^{n+1}}{n^2} = \frac{\pi^2}{12}, \qquad \sum_{n=1}^{\infty} \frac{(-1)^{n+1}}{n} = \ln(2), \qquad \sum_{n=1}^{\infty} \frac{1}{4n^2-1} = \frac{1}{2},$$

$$\sum_{n=0}^{\infty} \frac{(-1)^{n}}{2n+1} = \frac{\pi}{4}, \qquad \sum_{n=0}^{\infty} \frac{1}{(2n+1)^2} = \frac{\pi^2}{8}, \qquad \sum_{n=0}^{\infty} \frac{(-1)^{n}}{(2n+1)^3} = \frac{\pi^3}{32}.$$

Again, don't worry about memorizing all these formulas; just think of them as prizes in a trophy case—a representation of some mathematical success stories. Mathematicians experience great pride whenever they manage to make sense of some complicated, infinite sum expression by finding a simple formula to describe its value. In general most infinite series do not have such closed-form expressions, so you can understand mathematicians' excitement and why they'd want to build a trophy case of known formulas. The series formulas shown above are analogous to the "trophy case" of integral formulas on page 481.

Exercises

E5.7 Compute the values of the following summations using the formulas given above.

(a) $\sum_{n=1}^{N} c(a+bn)$ (b) $\sum_{n=1}^{N} c(a+bn)^2$ (c) $\sum_{n=1}^{\infty} \frac{6}{n^2}$

Convergence and divergence of series

Even when we can't compute an exact expression for the infinite sum of a series, it's important to distinguish series that converge from series that do not converge.

We say a series $\sum a_n$ *converges* if the infinite sum $S_\infty \equiv \sum_{n\in\mathbb{N}} a_n$ equals some finite number $L \in \mathbb{R}$.

$$S_\infty = \sum_{n=0}^{\infty} a_n = L \quad \Rightarrow \quad \text{the series } \sum a_n \text{ converges.}$$

If the infinite sum $S_\infty \equiv \sum_{n\in\mathbb{N}} a_n$ grows to infinity, we say the series $\sum a_n$ *diverges*.

$$S_\infty = \sum_{n=0}^{\infty} a_n = \pm\infty \quad \Rightarrow \quad \text{the series } \sum a_n \text{ diverges.}$$

Convergence of a series is not the same as convergence of the underlying sequence a_n. Consider the sequence of partial sums $S_N = \sum_{n=0}^{N} a_n$:

$$S_0, S_1, S_2, S_3, \ldots,$$

where each of the terms in the sequence corresponds to

$$a_0, \;\; a_0 + a_1, \;\; a_0 + a_1 + a_2, \;\; a_0 + a_1 + a_2 + a_3, \;\; \ldots.$$

We say the series $\sum a_n$ converges if the sequence of partial sums S_N converges to a limit L:

$$\lim_{N\to\infty} S_N = L.$$

This limit statement indicates that the partial sums S_N approach the number L as we include more terms in the series.

The precise meaning of the limit statement is as follows. For any precision $\epsilon > 0$, there exists a starting point N_ϵ such that, for all $N > N_\epsilon$, it will be true that

$$|S_N - L| < \epsilon.$$

The number N_ϵ corresponds to how many terms of the series you need for the partial sum S_N to become ϵ-close to the limit L.

Convergence tests

The main thing you need to know about series are the different *tests* you can perform to check whether a series converges or diverges.

Divergence test

The only way the infinite sum $\sum_{n=0}^{\infty} a_n$ will converge is if the elements of the sequence a_n tend to zero for large n. This observation gives us a simple series *divergence test*. If $\lim_{n\to\infty} a_n \neq 0$ then $\sum_{n=0}^{\infty} a_n$ diverges. How could an infinite sum of non-zero quantities add to a finite number?

Absolute convergence

If $\sum_n |a_n|$ converges, $\sum_n a_n$ also converges. The opposite is not necessarily true, since the convergence of a_n might be due to negative terms *cancelling* with positive terms.

A sequence a_n for which $\sum_n |a_n|$ converges is called *absolutely convergent*. A sequence b_n for which $\sum_n b_n$ converges but $\sum_n |b_n|$ diverges is called *conditionally convergent*.

Decreasing alternating sequences

An alternating series a_n in which the absolute values of the terms is decreasing ($|a_n| > |a_{n+1}|$), and tend to zero ($\lim a_n = 0$) converges. For example, we know the series $\sum_{n=1}^{\infty} \frac{(-1)^{n+1}}{n} = 1 - \frac{1}{2} + \frac{1}{3} - \frac{1}{4} + \frac{1}{5} - \frac{1}{6} + \cdots$ converges because it is a decreasing alternating series and $\lim_{n\to\infty} \frac{1}{n} = 0$.

Integral test

If the integral $\int_a^{\infty} f(x)\,dx$ is finite, then the series $\sum_n f(n)$ converges. If the integral $\int_a^{\infty} f(x)\,dx$ diverges, then the series $\sum_n f(n)$ also diverges.

The improper integral is defined as a limit expression:

$$\int_a^{\infty} f(x)\,dx \equiv \lim_{b\to\infty} \int_a^{b} f(x)\,dx.$$

The p-series converges if p $>$ 1

The convergence conditions for p-series, $a_n = \frac{1}{n^p}$, can be obtained using the integral test.

The series $\sum_{n=1}^{\infty} \frac{1}{n^p}$ converges if $p > 1$, and diverges if $p \leqslant 1$. Note that $p = 1$ corresponds to the harmonic series $\sum_{n=1}^{\infty} \frac{1}{n}$ which diverges.

Direct comparison test

Often times we can understand the convergence properties of a series $\sum_n a_n$ by comparing it to another series $\sum_n b_n$ whose convergence properties are known. One approach is to directly compare the values of each term. In particular, we can draw the following conclusions:

- If $a_n \leqslant b_n$ for all n, and $\sum_n b_n$ converges, then $\sum_n a_n$ converges.
- If $a_n \geqslant b_n$ for all n, and $\sum_n b_n$ diverges, then $\sum_n a_n$ diverges.

The first conclusion follows from the squeezing principle: since b_n is always above a_n, and $\sum_n b_n$ converges, then so must $\sum_n a_n$. The second conclusion uses this reasoning in reverse: since $\sum_n b_n = \infty$ and $a_n \geqslant b_n$, then we must also have $\sum_n a_n = \infty$.

Limit comparison test

We can also compare series by comparing the relative size of their n^{th} terms. Suppose $\lim_{n\to\infty} \frac{a_n}{b_n} = L$. We can draw the following conclusions:

- If $0 < L < \infty$, then $\sum_n a_n$ and $\sum_n b_n$ either both converge or both diverge.
- If $L = 0$ and $\sum_n b_n$ converges, then $\sum_n a_n$ also converges.
- If $L = \infty$ and $\sum_n b_n$ diverges, then $\sum_n a_n$ also diverges.

The nth root test

If r is defined by $r = \lim_{n\to\infty} \sqrt[n]{|a_n|}$, then $\sum_n a_n$ diverges if $r > 1$ and converges if $r < 1$. If $r = 1$, the test is inconclusive.

The ratio test

The most useful convergence test is the ratio test. To use the ratio test, compute the limit of the ratio of successive terms in the sequence:

$$R = \lim_{n\to\infty} \left| \frac{a_{n+1}}{a_n} \right|.$$

The series $\sum_n^\infty a_n$ converges if $R < 1$, and $\sum_n^\infty a_n$ diverges if $R > 1$. If $R = 1$, the test is inconclusive.

Taylor series

The *Taylor series* of a function $f(x)$ approximates the function by an infinitely long polynomial:

$$f(x) = \sum_{n=0}^{\infty} c_n x^n = c_0 + c_1 x + c_2 x^2 + c_3 x^3 + c_4 x^4 + \cdots.$$

Each term in the series is of the form $a_n = c_n x^n$, where the coefficient c_n depends on the properties of the function $f(x)$. For example, the Taylor series of the function $\sin(x)$ is

$$\sin(x) = \sum_{n=0}^{\infty} \frac{(-1)^n}{(2n+1)!} x^{2n+1} = x - \frac{x^3}{3!} + \frac{x^5}{5!} - \frac{x^7}{7!} + \frac{x^9}{9!} - \frac{x^{11}}{11!} + \cdots.$$

How do the coefficients c_n depend on the function $f(x)$? How can we compute the Taylor series for other functions?

The general procedure for computing the coefficients c_n in the Taylor series of a function $f(x)$ is to choose c_n equal to the nth derivative of $f(x)$ divided by $n!$:

$$\begin{aligned} f(x) &= f(0) + f'(0)x + \frac{f''(0)}{2!}x^2 + \frac{f'''(0)}{3!}x^3 + \frac{f^{(4)}(0)}{4!}x^4 + \cdots \\ &= \sum_{n=0}^{\infty} \frac{f^{(n)}(0)}{n!}x^n. \end{aligned}$$

Using this formula and your knowledge of derivatives, you can compute the Taylor series of any function $f(x)$.

Example Find the Taylor series of $f(x) = e^x$. The formula for the nth coefficient in the Taylor series of the function $f(x)$ is $c_n = \frac{f^{(n)}(0)}{n!}$. The first derivative of $f(x) = e^x$ is $f'(x) = e^x$. The second derivative of $f(x) = e^x$ is $f''(x) = e^x$. In fact, all the derivatives of $f(x)$ will be e^x because the e^x is a special function that is equal to its derivative! The nth coefficient in the power series of $f(x) = e^x$ at the point $x = 0$ is equal to the value of the nth derivative of $f(x)$ evaluated at $x = 0$. In the case of $f(x) = e^x$ we have $f^{(n)}(0) = e^0 = 1$, so the coefficient of the nth term is $c_n = \frac{f^{(n)}(0)}{n!} = \frac{1}{n!}$. The Taylor series of $f(x) = e^x$ is

$$e^x = \sum_{n=0}^{\infty} \frac{1}{n!}x^n = 1 + x + \frac{x^2}{2} + \frac{x^3}{3!} + \frac{x^4}{4!} + \frac{x^5}{5!} + \cdots$$

Here are the Taylor series of some other commonly used functions:

$$\cos(x) = 1 - \frac{x^2}{2} + \frac{x^4}{4!} - \frac{x^6}{6!} + \frac{x^8}{8!} - \frac{x^{10}}{10!} + \cdots = \sum_{n=0}^{\infty} \frac{(-1)^n}{(2n)!}x^{2n}$$

$$\ln(x+1) = x - \frac{x^2}{2} + \frac{x^3}{3} - \frac{x^4}{4} + \frac{x^5}{5} - \frac{x^6}{6} + \cdots = \sum_{n=1}^{\infty} \frac{(-1)^{n+1}}{n}x^n$$

$$\cosh(x) = 1 + \frac{x^2}{2} + \frac{x^4}{4!} + \frac{x^6}{6!} + \frac{x^8}{8!} + \frac{x^{10}}{10!} + \cdots = \sum_{n=0}^{\infty} \frac{1}{(2n)!}x^{2n}$$

$$\sinh(x) = x + \frac{x^3}{3!} + \frac{x^5}{5!} + \frac{x^7}{7!} + \frac{x^9}{9!} + \frac{x^{11}}{11!} + \cdots = \sum_{n=0}^{\infty} \frac{1}{(2n+1)!}x^{2n+1}$$

Note the similarities between the power series of cos and cosh. The formulas are the same, but the hyperbolic version does not alternate.

When the formula for the nth coefficient c_n contains the factor $(-1)^n$, the terms in the series will alternate between positive and negative.

Both cos and cosh are *even* functions, meaning $f(x) = f(-x)$. The "evenness" of cos and cosh can also be confirmed by comparing their power series, which contain only even powers of x. Note how the index $n \in \mathbb{N} = \{0, 1, 2, 3, 4, \ldots\}$ is transformed to an even index $2n \in \{0, 2, 4, 6, 8, \ldots\}$. Similarly, we use the index $(2n + 1)$ to obtain only odd numbers $(2n + 1) \in \{1, 3, 5, 7, \ldots\}$.

Terminology

A more specific mathematical term for the series we discussed above is *Maclaurin series*, which is a specific case of a Taylor series.

The coefficients c_n in the *Taylor series* of $f(x)$ are obtained by computing the value of the nth derivative of $f(x)$. The Taylor series of a function $f(x)$ at the point $x = a$ is given by

$$\begin{aligned} f(x) &= f(a) + f'(a)(x-a) + \frac{f''(a)}{2!}(x-a)^2 + \frac{f'''(a)}{3!}(x-a)^3 + \cdots \\ &= \sum_{n=0}^{\infty} \frac{f^{(n)}(a)}{n!}(x-a)^n. \end{aligned}$$

The *Maclaurin series* of $f(x)$ is the Taylor series of $f(x)$ with $a = 0$:

$$\begin{aligned} f(x) &= f(0) + f'(0)x + \frac{f''(0)}{2!}x^2 + \frac{f'''(0)}{3!}x^3 + \cdots \\ &= \sum_{n=0}^{\infty} \frac{f^{(n)}(0)}{n!}x^n. \end{aligned}$$

The term *power series* is also used to describe Taylor series, since each term in the series contains x raised to a certain power.

Radius of convergence for power series

Consider the power series $f(x) = \sum c_n x^n$. The nth term in the series contains the nth power of x. The convergence or divergence of the series depends on the choice of the input variable x.

The *radius of convergence* of the series $\sum_{n=0}^{\infty} c_n x^n$ is denoted ρ (the Greek letter *rho*) and can be obtained either by using the nth root test or the ratio test:

$$\frac{1}{\rho} = \lim_{n\to\infty} \sqrt[n]{|c_n|} = \lim_{n\to\infty} \left| \frac{c_{n+1}}{c_n} \right|.$$

The power series $f(x) = \sum_{n=0}^{\infty} c_n x^n$ converges for all $-\rho < x < \rho$.

Explanations

Taylor series

Do you remember your derivative formulas? You can calculate the Taylor series $c_0 + c_1(x-a) + c_2(x-a)^2 + \ldots$ of any function $f(x)$, by choosing c_n equal to the value of the nth derivative of $f(x)$ divided by the appropriate factorial. The more terms you compute in the series, the more accurate your approximation will become.

The zeroth-order approximation to a function $f(x)$ at $x = a$ is

$$f(x) \approx f(a).$$

This approximation is not very accurate in general, but at least it is correct when $x = a$.

The best *linear* approximation to $f(x)$ at $x = a$ is the tangent line $T_1(x)$, which is a line that passes through the point $(a, f(a))$ and has a slope equal to $f'(a)$. Indeed, this is exactly what the first-order Taylor series formula tells us to compute. The coefficient in front of x in the Taylor series is obtained by first calculating $f'(x)$, then evaluating the result at $x = a$:

$$f(x) \approx f(a) + f'(a)(x-a) = T_1(x).$$

To find the best quadratic approximation to $f(x)$, we must compute the second derivative $f''(x)$. The coefficient in front of the x^2 term will be $f''(a)$ divided by $2! = 2$:

$$f(x) \approx f(a) + f'(a)(x-a) + \frac{f''(a)}{2!}(x-a)^2 = T_2(x).$$

If we continue like this, we'll obtain the whole Taylor series of the function $f(x)$. At step n, the coefficient c_n will be proportional to the nth derivative of $f(x)$ and the resulting n^{th}-degree polynomial will **imitate the function** in its behaviour up to the nth derivative.

Proof of the sum of the geometric series

We are looking for the sum S_n given by

$$S_n = \sum_{k=0}^{n} r^k = 1 + r + r^2 + r^3 + \cdots + r^n.$$

Observe there is a self-similar pattern in the expanded summation S_n, where subsequent terms gain an additional power of r. Suppose we multiply the above equation by r. This has the effect of "shifting" all the terms to the right:

$$rS_n = r\sum_{k=0}^{n} r^k = r + r^2 + r^3 + \cdots + r^n + r^{n+1}.$$

We can add 1 to both sides of the equation to obtain

$$1 + rS_n = \underbrace{1 + r + r^2 + r^3 + \cdots + r^n}_{S_n} + r^{n+1} = S_n + r^{n+1}.$$

Note how the sum S_n appears as the first part of the expression on the right-hand side. The resulting equation is $1 + rS_n = S_n + r^{n+1}$. Since we want to find S_n, we can isolate all the S_n terms on one side,

$$1 - r^{n+1} = S_n - rS_n = S_n(1 - r),$$

and solve for S_n to obtain $S_n = \frac{1-r^{n+1}}{1-r}$. Neat, huh? This is what math is all about—mathematicians spend their time looking for some *structure* in the equations they're solving and then use this structure to solve the problem with just a few lines of arithmetic.

Examples

An infinite series Compute the sum of the infinite series

$$\sum_{n=0}^{\infty} \frac{1}{N+1}\left(\frac{N}{N+1}\right)^n.$$

This may appear complicated, but only until we recognize this is a type of geometric series $\sum ar^n$, where $a = \frac{1}{N+1}$ and $r = \frac{N}{N+1}$:

$$\sum_{n=0}^{\infty} \frac{1}{N+1}\left(\frac{N}{N+1}\right)^n = \sum_{n=0}^{\infty} ar^n = \frac{a}{1-r} = \frac{\frac{1}{N+1}}{1 - \frac{N}{N+1}} = 1.$$

Computational example Compute $\sin(40^\circ)$ to 15 decimal places. The Maclaurin series of $\sin(x)$ is

$$\sin(x) = x - \frac{x^3}{3!} + \frac{x^5}{5!} - \frac{x^7}{7!} + \frac{x^9}{9!} + \ldots = \sum_{n=0}^{\infty} \frac{(-1)^n x^{2n+1}}{(2n+1)!}.$$

To calculate the sine of 40 degrees, we compute the sum of the series with x replaced by 40 degrees (expressed in radians). In theory, we need to sum *infinitely* many terms in the series, but in practice we only need to sum the first 8 terms in the series to obtain an accuracy of 15 digits after the decimal. In other words, the series converges very quickly.

Let's use the computer algebra system at `live.sympy.org` to compute the first few terms in the series to see what is going on.

First, we define the nth term:

$$a_n(x) = \frac{(-1)^n x^{2n+1}}{(2n+1)!}.$$

```
>>> def axn_sin(x,n):
        return (-1.0)**n * x**(2*n+1) / factorial(2*n+1)
```

Next we convert 40° to radians:

```
>>> forty = (40*pi/180).evalf()
0.698131700797732                  # 40 degrees in radians
```

Let's look at the list of the first 10 coefficients in the series:

```
>>> [ axn_sin(forty,n) for n in range(0,10) ]
[ 0.69813170079773179,             # a_0
 -0.056710153964883062,            # a_1
  0.0013819920621191727,           # a_2
 -1.6037289757274478e-05,          # a_3
  1.0856084058295026e-07,          # a_4
 -4.8101124579279279e-10,          # a_5
  1.5028144059670851e-12,          # a_6
 -3.4878738801065803e-15,          # a_7
  6.2498067170560129e-18,          # a_8
 -8.9066666494280343e-21 ]         # a_9
```

To compute $\sin(40^\circ)$, we sum together all the terms:

```
>>> sum( [ axn_sin(forty,n) for n in range(0,10) ] )
0.642787609686539        # the Taylor series approximation

>>> sin(forty).evalf()
0.642787609686539        # the true value of sin(40)
```

Note the first 8 terms of the series would have been sufficient to obtain an approximation to 15 decimals since the terms a_8 and a_9 are much smaller than 10^{-15}.

Discussion

You can think of the Taylor series as containing the "similarity coefficients" between $f(x)$ and the different powers of x. We choose the terms in the Taylor series of $f(x)$ to ensure the series approximation has the same n^{th} derivative as the function $f(x)$. For a Maclaurin series, the similarity between $f(x)$ and its power series representation is measured at $x = 0$, so the coefficients are chosen as $c_n = \frac{f^{(n)}(0)}{n!}$. The more general Taylor series allows us to build an approximation to $f(x)$ at any point $x = a$, and its similarity coefficients are calculated to match the derivatives at that point: $c_n = \frac{f^{(n)}(a)}{n!}$.

Another way of looking at the Maclaurin series is to imagine it is a kind of X-ray picture for each function $f(x)$. The zeroth coefficient c_0 in the Maclaurin series tells you how much of the constant function is in $f(x)$. The first coefficient, c_1, tells you how much of the linear function x is in f; the coefficient c_2 tells you about the x^2 contents of f, and so on.

Now get ready for some crazy shit. I want you to go back to page 397 and take a careful look at the Maclaurin series of e^x, $\sin(x)$, and $\cos(x)$. As you will observe, it's as if e^x *contains* both $\sin(x)$ and $\cos(x)$, the only difference being the presence of the alternating negative signs. How about that? Do you remember Euler's formula $e^{ix} = \cos x + i \sin x$? Verify Euler's formula (page 181) by substituting ix into the power series for e^x.

Another interesting equation to think about in terms of series is $e^x = \cosh x + \sinh x$.

Links

[Animation showing Taylor series approximations to $\sin(x)$]
`http://mathforum.org/mathimages/index.php/Taylor_Series`

[Good summary with many interesting examples]
`http://en.wikipedia.org/wiki/Series_(mathematics)`

[A comprehensive list of important math series]
`http://en.wikipedia.org/wiki/List_of_mathematical_series`

5.20 Conclusion

Now you know how to take derivatives, calculate integrals, and find sums of infinite series. These practical skills will come in handy in the future, especially if you choose to pursue a career in science. The exposure you had to formal math definitions prepared you for more advanced math classes. In particular, you learned how to deal with limits involving infinitely small quantities like ϵ and δ. Recall that both the derivative and the integral are defined as limit expressions.

The derivative is defined as a rise-over-run calculation for an infinitely short run. The integral is defined as a Riemann sum with infinitely narrow rectangles. We also learned important facts about sequences and series. Series teach us how to think about computations with an infinite number of steps. Particularly, the notion of a Taylor series is a foundational idea for understanding functions.

Let's close the chapter by comparing the new procedures we learned in calculus with the type of math procedures used in high school math. Most tricks for solving high school algebra problems involve a finite number of steps: we start from a description of a problem, model it using an equation, and then solve this equation to obtain the answer using a couple of algebra steps. For example, we can solve the equation $x^2 - 2 = 0$ by rewriting it as $x^2 = 2$ and computing the square root of both sides of the equation to obtain $x = \pm\sqrt{2}$. Note it took us two steps of algebra to find the answer. A more complicated equation might require more steps, but in general, a finite number of steps are sufficient to solve most high school math problems.

In calculus we learn to solve a much broader class of problems. Using limits allows us to obtain answers computed by mathematical procedures with an infinite number of steps! For example, the answer to the question "What is the effective interest rate for a loan with a nominal interest rate of 100%, compounded infinitely often," is equal to the number $e = \lim_{n\to\infty}(1 + \frac{1}{n})^n$. If you borrow N dollars today, you'll owe Ne dollars after one year. Note the number e cannot be computed by any mathematical procedure with a finite number of steps. A limit is required to model the "infinitely frequent" compounding.

Above all, the purpose of calculus is to solve problems. Speaking of problems, you should flip the page and dig in. The only way to test if you understand the theory is to apply it in practice.

5.21 Calculus problems

In this chapter we learned about derivatives and integrals, which are mathematical operations relating to the slope of a function and the area under the graph of a function. We also learned about limits, sequences, and series. It's now time to see how much you've really learned by trying to solve some calculus problems.

Calculus hasn't changed much in the last hundred years. It is testament to this fact that many of the problems presented here were adapted from the book "Calculus Made Easy" by Silvanus Thompson, originally published[1] in 1910. These problems remain as pertinent and interesting today as they were 100 years ago.

As much as calculus is about understanding things conceptually and seeing the big picture (abstraction), calculus is also about practice. There are more than 120 problems to solve in this section. The goal is to turn differentiation and integration into routine operations that you can carry out without stressing out. You should vanquish as many problems as you need to feel comfortable with the procedures of calculus.

Okay, enough prep talk. Let's get to the problems!

Limits problems

P5.1 Use the graph of the function $f(x)$ shown in Figure 5.33 to calculate the following limit expressions:

(1) $\lim_{x\to -5^-} f(x)$ (2) $\lim_{x\to -5^+} f(x)$ (3) $\lim_{x\to -5} f(x)$

(4) $\lim_{x\to 2^-} f(x)$ (5) $\lim_{x\to 2^+} f(x)$ (6) $\lim_{x\to 2} f(x)$

(7) $\lim_{x\to 5^-} f(x)$ (8) $\lim_{x\to 5^+} f(x)$ (9) $\lim_{x\to 5} f(x)$

(10) Is the function $f(x)$ continuous at $x = 5$?

(11) What are the intervals where the function $f(x)$ is continuous?

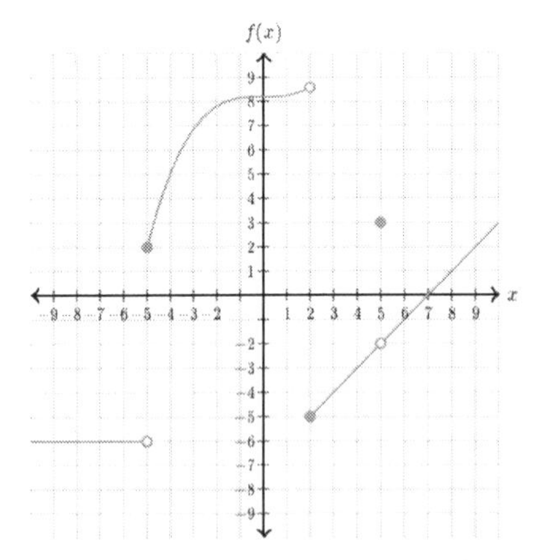

Figure 5.33: The graph of a piecewise-continuous function $f(x)$. The function $f(x)$ has two jump discontinuities at $x = -5$ and $x = 2$ and one removable discontinuity at $x = 5$.

P5.2 Find the value of the following limit expressions:

(a) $\lim_{x\to 3} 4$ (b) $\lim_{x\to 3} 2x$ (c) $\lim_{x\to 3} x^2 - 2x + 2$

[1] Full text is available at `http:/gutenberg.org/ebooks/33283` (public domain).

P5.3 Prove the following limit statement by constructing an ϵ, δ-proof:

$$\lim_{x \to 5} 3x = 15.$$

Recall the ϵ,δ-game: one player (the sceptic) specifies the required precision $\epsilon > 0$, and the other player (the prover) must find a value $\delta > 0$ such that $|3x - 15| \leqslant \epsilon$ for all x in the interval $(5 - \delta, 5 + \delta)$.
Hint: Choose δ to be a multiple of ϵ.

P5.4 Calculate the limit if it exists, or explain why it doesn't.

(1) $\lim_{x \to -\infty} \sin(x)$ (2) $\lim_{x \to 0^+} \sin(x)$ (3) $\lim_{x \to \infty} \sin(x)$

(4) $\lim_{x \to -\infty} \sin(\frac{1}{x})$ (5) $\lim_{x \to 0^+} \sin(\frac{1}{x})$ (6) $\lim_{x \to \infty} \sin(\frac{1}{x})$

(7) $\lim_{x \to -\infty} x\sin(\frac{1}{x})$ (8) $\lim_{x \to 0^+} x\sin(\frac{1}{x})$ (9) $\lim_{x \to \infty} x\sin(\frac{1}{x})$

Hint: Use the substitution $y = \frac{1}{x}$ to rewrite $\lim_{x \to 0^+} \sin(\frac{1}{x})$ as $\lim_{y \to \infty} \sin(y)$.

P5.5 Calculate the following limit expressions:

(1) $\lim_{x \to 1} \frac{x^2 + 5x + 6}{x - 1}$ (2) $\lim_{x \to 1} \frac{x^2 + x - 2}{x - 1}$ (3) $\lim_{x \to a} \frac{x^2 - a^2}{x - a}$

Hint: L'Hopital's rule might come in handy.

P5.6 Use a calculator to verify numerically the limits (1) through (6):

(1) $\lim_{n \to \infty} \left(1 + \frac{1}{n}\right)^n = e$ (2) $\lim_{x \to 0} \frac{x}{e^x} = 0$ (3) $\lim_{x \to 0} \frac{\ln x}{x} = 0$

(4) $\lim_{\epsilon \to 0} (1 + \epsilon)^{1/\epsilon} = e$ (5) $\lim_{x \to 0} \frac{\sin x}{x} = 1$ (6) $\lim_{x \to 0} \cos x = 1$

(7) Prove (5) and (6) by expanding sin and cos as Maclaurin series.

Stage 1 cleared! I hope working through these problems helped you feel more confident about limits. If you liked the ϵ,δ-argument used in **P5.3**, you should look into learning analysis. Analysis is like calculus but with proper proofs from first principles.

Derivatives problems

P5.7 Find the derivative with respect to x of the functions:

(1) $y = x^{13}$ (2) $y = x^{-\frac{3}{2}}$ (3) $y = x^{2a}$

(4) $u = x^{2.4}$ (5) $z = \sqrt[3]{x}$ (6) $y = \sqrt[3]{x^{-5}}$

(7) $u = \sqrt[5]{\frac{1}{x^8}}$ (8) $y = 2x^a$ (9) $y = \sqrt[q]{x^3}$

P5.8 Differentiate the following:

(1) $y = ax^3 + 6$ (2) $y = 13x^{\frac{3}{2}} - c$ (3) $y = 12x^{\frac{1}{2}} + c^{\frac{1}{2}}$

(4) $y = c^{\frac{1}{2}}x^{\frac{1}{2}}$ (5) $u = \frac{az^n - 1}{c}$ (6) $y = 1.18t^2 + 22.4$

P5.9 Take the derivative with respect to x of the following expressions:

(a) $u = 1 + x + \frac{x^2}{1\cdot 2} + \frac{x^3}{1\cdot 2\cdot 3} + \frac{x^4}{1\cdot 2\cdot 3\cdot 4} + \frac{x^5}{1\cdot 2\cdot 3\cdot 4\cdot 5} + \cdots$

(b) $y = ax^2 + bx + c$ (c) $y = (x+a)^3$

P5.10 Use the product rule to find the following derivatives:

(1) If $w = t(a - \frac{1}{2}bt)$, find $\frac{dw}{dt}$.
(2) Find the derivative of $y = (x + \sqrt{-1})(x - \sqrt{-1})$.
(3) Differentiate $y = (197x - 34x^2)(7 + 22x - 83x^3)$.
(4) If $x = (y+3)(y+5)$, what is $\frac{dx}{dy}$?
(5) Differentiate $y = 1.3709x(112.6 + 45.202x^2)$.

P5.11 Find the derivative of the following rational functions:

(1) $p(x) = \dfrac{2x+3}{3x+2}$ (2) $q(x) = \dfrac{1 + x + 2x^2 + 3x^3}{1 + x + 2x^2}$

(3) $r(x) = \dfrac{ax+b}{cx+d}$ (4) $s(x) = \dfrac{x^n + a}{x^{-n} + b}$

Hint: Use the quotient rule.

P5.12 Differentiate the following functions:

(1) $y = \sqrt{x^2+1}$ (2) $y = \sqrt{x^2+a^2}$ (3) $y = \dfrac{1}{\sqrt{a+x}}$

(4) $y = \dfrac{a}{\sqrt{a-x^2}}$ (5) $y = \dfrac{\sqrt{x^2-a^2}}{x^2}$ (6) $y = \dfrac{\sqrt[3]{x^4+a}}{\sqrt[2]{x^3+a}}$

(7) $y = \dfrac{a^2+x^2}{(a+x)^2}$ (8) $y = \sqrt[n]{\frac{1}{x^m}}$ (9) $y = \dfrac{\sqrt{1-x^2}}{1-x}$

P5.13 Use the chain rule to solve the following problems:

(1) Find $\frac{dw}{dx}$ if $u = \frac{1}{2}x^3$, $v = 3(u+u^2)$, and $w = \frac{1}{v^2}$.
(2) Find $\frac{dv}{dx}$ if $y = 3x^2 + \sqrt{2}$, $z = \sqrt{1+y}$, and $v = \frac{1}{\sqrt{3}+4z}$.
(3) Find $\frac{du}{dx}$ if $y = \frac{x^3}{\sqrt{3}}$, $z = (1+y)^2$, and $u = \frac{1}{\sqrt{1+z}}$.

P5.14 Differentiate $f(x) = b(e^{ax} - e^{-ax})$.

P5.15 Find the derivative with respect to t of $u(t) = at^2 + 2\ln t$.

P5.16 If $y = n^t$, find $\dfrac{d(\ln y)}{dt}$.

P5.17 Find the derivative of $f(x) = \dfrac{1}{b}\dfrac{a^{bx}}{\ln a}$.

P5.18 Differentiate the functions:

(1) $y = \ln x^n$ (2) $y = 3e^{-\frac{x}{x-1}}$

(3) $y = (3x^2+1)e^{-5x}$ (4) $y = (3x^2-1)(\sqrt{x}+1)$

(5) $y = \ln(x^a + a)$ (6) $y = \frac{\ln(x+3)}{x+3}$ (7) $y = a^x x^a$

(8) $y = \ln(axe^x)$ (9) $y = (\ln ax)^3$

P5.19 Find the derivative of y with respect to x for

(a) $y = x^x$ (b) $y = (e^x)^x$ (c) $y = e^{x^x}$

Hint: Recall that $\ln(a^b) = b\ln(a)$ and $a = e^{\ln a}$, for $a > 0$.

P5.20 Differentiate the following functions with respect to θ

(1) $y = A\sin(\theta - \frac{\pi}{2})$ (2) $y = \sin^2\theta$ (3) $y = \sin 5\theta$

(4) $y = \sin^3\theta$ (5) $y = 18\cos(\theta + 6)$ (6) $y = \ln\cos\theta$

P5.21 Differentiate $y = \frac{1}{2\pi}\cos(2\pi n t)$.

P5.22 Take the derivative with respect to x of the following functions:

(i) $y = \sin(a^x)$ (ii) $y = \sec x$ (iii) $y = \cos^{-1}(x)$

(iv) $y = \tan^{-1}(x)$ (v) $y = \sec^{-1}(x)$ (vi) $y = \tan(x)\sqrt{3\sec x}$

P5.23 Find the derivatives of the following functions:

(1) $y = \sin\theta\sin(2\theta)$ (2) $y = a\tan^m(\theta^n)$ (3) $y = e^x\sin^2 x$

(4) $y = \sin\left((2\theta+3)^{2.3}\right)$ (5) $y = \theta^3 + 3\sin(\theta+3) - 3^{\sin\theta} - 3^\theta$

P5.24 The length of an iron rod varies with temperature. Let $\ell(t)$ denote the length of the iron rod (in metres) at temperature t[°C]. We measure the length of the rod at different temperatures and determine its length is described by the function $\ell(t) = \ell_o(1 + 0.000012t)$[m], where ℓ_o is the length of the rod at 0[°C]. Find the change of length of the rod per degree Celsius.

P5.25 The power P[W] consumed by an incandescent light bulb when connected is given by the equation $P = aV^b$, where a and b are constants, and V is the voltage drop across the bulb's terminals.

Find the rate of change of the power with respect to the voltage. Calculate the change in power per volt at the operating voltages $V_1 = 100$[V], $V_2 = 110$[V], and $V_3 = 120$[V], in the case of a light bulb for which $a = 0.008264$ and $b = 2$.

P5.26 The frequency f of vibration of a string of diameter D, length L and mass density σ, stretched with a tension T is given by the formula

$$f = \frac{1}{DL}\sqrt{\frac{gT}{\pi\sigma}}.$$

Find the rate of change of the frequency f with respect to each of the variables: D, L, σ, and T.

P5.27 Find the rate at which the following geometric quantities vary as a function of the radius:

(a) the circumference of a circle of radius r
(b) the area of a circle of radius r
(c) the area of a sphere of radius r
(d) the volume of a sphere of radius r

Hint: The surface area and volume formulas for a sphere are on page 81.

P5.28 The temperature T of the filament of an incandescent electric lamp is connected to the current I passing through the lamp by the relation

$$I = a + bT + cT^2.$$

Find an expression giving the variation of the current with respect to a variation in temperature.

P5.29 The following formulae have been proposed to express the relation between the electric resistance $R[\Omega]$ of a wire at the temperature $t[°\mathrm{C}]$. The resistance R_o corresponds to the resistance of the wire at $0[°\mathrm{C}]$, and a, b, c are constants.

$$\begin{aligned} R_1(t) &= R_o(1 + at + bt^2), \\ R_2(t) &= R_o(1 + at + b\sqrt{t}), \\ R_3(t) &= R_o(1 + at + bt^2)^{-1}. \end{aligned}$$

Find the rate of variation of the resistance with regard to temperature as given by each of these formulae.

P5.30 The voltage V of a certain type of standard cell varies with temperature $t[°\mathrm{C}]$ according to the relation

$$V(t) = 1.4340\left[1 - 0.000814(t - 15) + 0.000007(t - 15)^2\right]. \quad [\mathrm{V}]$$

Find the change of voltage per degree at 15°C, 20°C, and 25°C.

P5.31 The voltage necessary to maintain an electric arc of length ℓ with a current of intensity I was found by Mrs. Ayrton to be

$$V = a + b\ell + \frac{c + k\ell}{I},$$

where a, b, c, k are constants. Find an expression for the variation of the voltage (a) with regard to the length of the arc ℓ; and (b) with regard to the strength of the current I.

P5.32 Find $\frac{dy}{dx}$ and $\frac{d^2y}{dx^2}$ for the following functions:

(1) $y = 17x + 12x^2$ $\quad cx^4$
(2) $y = a + bx^2 +$ $\quad$ (3) $y = \frac{x^2+a}{x+a}$

P5.33 Calculate $\frac{d^2y}{dx^2}$ and $\frac{d^3y}{dx^3}$ for the functions in **P5.9**.

P5.34 Calculate second and third derivatives of the functions in **P5.10**.

P5.35 The distance travelled by a body falling freely in space is described by the equation $d = 16t^2$, where d is in feet, and t is in seconds. Draw a curve showing the relation between d and t. Determine the velocity of the body at the following times: $t = 2[\mathrm{s}]$, $t = 4.6[\mathrm{s}]$, and $t = 0.01[\mathrm{s}]$.

P5.36 Given $x(t) = v_i t - \frac{1}{2}gt^2$, find $\dot{x}$ and $\ddot{x}$.
Hint: Physicists sometimes use $\dot{x}$ and $\ddot{x}$ to denote $x'(t)$ and $x''(t)$.

P5.37 If a body moves according to the law $x(t) = 12 - 4.5t + 6.2t^2$[m], find its velocity and its acceleration when $t = 4$[s].

P5.38 The angle of rotation θ[rad] of a revolving wheel as a function of time t[s] is described by the equation $\theta(t) = 2.1 - 3.2t + 4.8t^2$. Find the angular velocity of the wheel when $t = 1\frac{1}{2}$[s]. Find also its angular acceleration.

P5.39 A slider moves so that its position x in inches from its starting point is given by the expression $x(t) = 6.8t^3 - 10.8t$. Find the expression for its velocity and its acceleration at all times. Find its velocity and its acceleration at $t = 3$[s].

P5.40 The height of a rising balloon (in [km]) is given at any instant by the expression $h(t) = 0.5 + \frac{1}{10}\sqrt[3]{t - 125}$, where t is in seconds. Find the velocity and the acceleration at any time.

P5.41 A stone is thrown downward into water and its depth p (from the French *profondeur*) in metres after t seconds is given by the expression $p(t) = \frac{4}{4+t^2} + 0.8t - 1$. Find its velocity and its acceleration functions. Find the velocity and the acceleration at $t = 10$[s].

P5.42 A body's position as a function of time t is described by $x(t) = t^n$, where n is a constant. Find the value of n when the velocity is doubled from the 5th to the 10th second. Find also the value of n when the velocity is numerically equal to the acceleration at the end of the 10th second.

P5.43 Draw a graph of the function $f(x) = \frac{3}{4}x^2 - 5$ by hand using a scale of millimetres. Measure the slope of the function approximately from the graph at three different values of x.

Next, find the derivative of the function and evaluate it at the same values of x. See whether the slopes obtained from the derivative agree with the slopes measured graphically.

P5.44 Find the slope of the function $f(x) = 0.12x^3 - 2$ at $x = 2$.

P5.45 Given the function $f(x) = (x - a)(x - b)$, find the x where $f'(x) = 0$.

P5.46 Find $\frac{dy}{dx}$ for the function $y = x^3 + 3x$ and calculate the numerical values of $\frac{dy}{dx}$ for the points $x = 0$, $x = \frac{1}{2}$, $x = 1$, and $x = 2$.

P5.47 Draw the graph the function $f(x) = be^{-\frac{t}{T}}$, with $b = 12$ and $T = 8$. Evaluate the function at various values of t from 0 to 20.

P5.48 Differentiate the three functions from **P5.50**.

P5.49 Plot the curve $y(\theta) = 100\sin(\theta - 15^\circ)$ and show that the slope of the curve at $\theta = 75^\circ$ is half the maximum slope.

P5.50 The following equations give very similar graphs:

(i) $y = \frac{ax}{x+b}$ (ii) $y = a(1 - e^{-\frac{x}{b}})$ (iii) $y = \frac{2a}{\pi}\tan^{-1}\left(\frac{x}{b}\right)$

Obtain the graphs of these functions, taking $a = 100$[mm] and $b = 30$[mm].

P5.51 Consider the curve described by the equation $x^2 + y^2 = 4$. Find the values of x where the slope of the curve is 1. What are the (x, y) coordinates of the points on the curve where the slope is 1?

P5.52 Find the slope of the curve with equation $\frac{x^2}{3^2} + \frac{y^2}{2^2} = 1$ and give the numerical value of the slope at $x = 0$ and $x = 1$.

P5.53 Differentiate the expression $z = \frac{x^3}{3} - 2x^3y - 2y^2x + \frac{y}{3}$ with respect to x, then differentiate with respect to y.

P5.54 Find the derivatives with respect to x, y, and z of the expression $x^2yz + xy^2z + xyz^2 + x^2y^2z^2$.

P5.55 Let $r^2 = (x - a)^2 + (y - b)^2 + (z - c)^2$. Find the value of $\frac{dr}{dx} + \frac{dr}{dy} + \frac{dr}{dz}$. Also find $\frac{d^2r}{dx^2} + \frac{d^2r}{dy^2} + \frac{d^2r}{dz^2}$.

P5.56 Find the total differential of $y = u^v$.

P5.57 Find the total differential of the following expressions:

(1) $y = u^3 \sin v$ (2) $y = (\sin x)^u$ (3) $y = \frac{\ln u}{v}$

P5.58 The equation of a tangent to the curve $y = 5 - 2x + 0.5x^3$ is of the form $y = mx + b$, where m and b are constants. Find the value of m and b for the tangent to the curve at $x = 2$.

P5.59 Consider the line ℓ_1 defined by the equation $y = x$ and the line ℓ_2 defined by $y = 3x$. Use the equation $\theta = \tan^{-1}\left(\frac{\Delta y}{\Delta x}\right)$ to find the angle each line makes with the x-axis. Find the angle of intersection between the lines.

P5.60 What is the *intersection angle* between the curve $f(x) = 3.5x^2 + 2$ and the curve $g(x) = x^2 - 5x + 9.5$ at the point(s) where they meet?

P5.61 Two tangent lines to the curve $y = \sqrt{25 - x^2}$ are drawn at points $x = 3$ and $x = 4$. Find the coordinates of the point where the tangent lines intersect and their angle of intersection.

P5.62 The line $y = 2x - b$ touches the curve $y = 3x^2 + 2$ at one point. Where is this point of contact and what is the value of b?

P5.63 Find the value(s) of x that make y maximum or minimum:

(1) $y = \dfrac{x^2}{x + 1}$ (2) $y = \dfrac{x}{a^2 + x^2}$ (3) $y = x^5 - 5x$

P5.64 Find the maxima and minima of $f(x) = x^3 + x^2 - 10x + 8$.

P5.65 Given $y = \frac{b}{a}x - cx^2$, find expressions for $\frac{dy}{dx}$ and $\frac{d^2y}{dx^2}$. Find the value of x that makes y a maximum or a minimum. Assume $c > 0$.

P5.66 Find how many maxima and minima there are in the curves:

(a) $y = 1 - \frac{x^2}{2} + \frac{x^4}{24}$ (b) $y = 1 - \frac{x^2}{2} + \frac{x^4}{24} - \frac{x^6}{720}$

P5.67 Find the maxima and minima of

(1) $y = 2x + 1 + \frac{5}{x^2}$ (2) $y = \frac{3}{x^2+x+1}$ (3) $y = \frac{5x}{2+x^2}$

P5.68 Divide a number N into two parts in such a way that three times the square of one part plus twice the square of the other part will be a minimum.

P5.69 The efficiency u of an electric generator at different values of output power x[W] is expressed by the general equation

$$u = \frac{x}{a + bx + cx^2},$$

where a is a constant depending on the energy losses in the iron core and c is a constant depending on the resistance of the copper wires. Find the value of the power x at which the efficiency is maximum.

P5.70 Suppose the consumption of coal by a certain steamer is represented by the formula $y = 0.3 + 0.001v^3$, where y is the number of tons of coal burned per hour and v is the speed expressed in nautical miles per hour. The cost of wages, financing, and depreciation of that ship are together equal, per hour, to the cost of 1 ton of coal. What speed will make the total cost of a voyage of 1000 nautical miles a minimum? And, if coal costs \$100 per ton, what will that minimum cost of the voyage amount to?

P5.71 Find the maxima and minima of

(1) $f(x) = \pm\frac{x}{6}\sqrt{x(10-x)}$ (2) $g(x) = 4x^3 - x^2 - 2x + 1$

P5.72 Find the minimum or maximum of

(1) $y = x^x$ (2) $y = x^{\frac{1}{x}}$ (3) $y = xa^{\frac{1}{x}}$

P5.73 Find the value of $\theta \in [0, \pi]$ for which $\sin\theta\cos\theta$ is a maximum.

P5.74 Find the local maximum and minimum of $y = \theta\cos\theta$ that are closest to the origin.

P5.75 One day you get tired of eating vegetables from the store and you decide to register for a spot in a local community garden to grow some yourself. When you sign up, you're given p metres of fencing to enclose a rectangle of land for your use. Show that the area of the rectangle will be a maximum if each of its sides is equal to $\frac{1}{4}p$.

P5.76 A 30[in]-long piece of string is joined in a loop and is stretched by three pegs so as to form a triangle. What is the largest triangular area the string can enclose?

P5.77 Plot the curve corresponding to the equation $y = \frac{10}{x} + \frac{10}{8-x}$. Find $\frac{dy}{dx}$ and deduce the value of x that will make y minimum. What is the value of y at the minimum?

P5.78 What is the smallest square that fits inside another square, such that all the corners of the inner square touch the sides of the outer square?

P5.79 Suppose you have a sphere of radius R and you want to draw a cylinder with radius r that fits inside the sphere. What is the cylinder whose (a) volume is maximum, (b) whose lateral area is maximum, and (c) whose total area is a maximum?

P5.80 A spherical balloon is increasing in volume. When its radius is r feet, its volume is increasing at the rate of 4 cubic feet per second. At what rate is its surface area increasing?

P5.81 It was shown by Lord Kelvin that the speed of signalling through a submarine cable depends on the value of the ratio of the external diameter of the cable's core to the diameter of the enclosed copper wire. If this ratio is called y, the number of signals s that can be sent per minute can be expressed by the formula

$$s(y) = ay^2 \ln \frac{1}{y},$$

where a is a constant depending on the length and the quality of the materials. Find the value of y that makes s maximum.

Congratulations, you just cleared the second stage of calculus problems!

Integrals problems

We're now starting the third part of the problem set. Get ready to integrate!

I must give you a heads up to caffeinate properly and see that you're well-rested when you begin these problems. Unlike the "recipe" approach we use to solve derivative problems, integral problems require a lot more thinking and a trial-and-error approach. Instead of following a predefined procedure like the optimization algorithm, you'll need to mentally browse through the integration techniques that you know and see which one applies to the problem you're solving.

I'm not going to lie and tell you calculating integrals is easy. It's hard work. The good news is that you'll get a little mental buzz every time you solve a problem.

P5.82 Explain the equation $\frac{d}{dx}\int_a^x f(s)\,ds = f(x)$ in your own words.

P5.83 Calculate the integrals of these two polynomials:

(a) $\displaystyle\int (4x^3 + 3x^2 + 2x + 1)\,dx$ (b) $\displaystyle\int \left(\frac{ax}{2} + \frac{bx^2}{3} + \frac{cx^3}{4}\right) dx$

P5.84 Calculate the following integrals:

(1) $\displaystyle\int \sqrt{4ax}\,dx$ (2) $\displaystyle\int \frac{3}{x^4}\,dx$ (3) $\displaystyle\int \frac{1}{a}x^3\,dx$

(4) $\displaystyle\int (x^2 + a)\,dx$ (5) $\displaystyle\int 5x^{-\frac{7}{2}}\,dx$ (6) $\displaystyle\int \left(\frac{x^2 + a}{x + a}\right) dx$

(7) $\displaystyle\int (x + 3)^3\,dx$ (8) $\displaystyle\int (x + 2)(x - a)\,dx$ (9) $\displaystyle\int (\sqrt{x} + \sqrt[3]{x})3a^2\,dx$

(10) $\displaystyle\int (\sin\theta - \tfrac{1}{2})\,\frac{d\theta}{3}$ (11) $\displaystyle\int \cos^2(a\theta)\,d\theta$ (12) $\displaystyle\int \sin^2\theta\,d\theta$

(13) $\displaystyle\int \sin^2 a\theta\,d\theta$ (14) $\displaystyle\int e^{3x}\,dx$ (15) $\displaystyle\int \frac{1}{1 + x}\,dx$

P5.85 Calculate the integrals:

(1) $\int \sqrt{a^2 - x^2}\, dx$ (2) $\int x \ln x\, dx$ (3) $\int x^a \ln x\, dx$

(4) $\int e^x \cos e^x\, dx$ (5) $\int \frac{1}{x} \cos(\ln x)\, dx$ (6) $\int x^2 e^x\, dx$

(7) $\int \frac{(\ln x)^a}{x}\, dx$ (8) $\int \frac{1}{x \ln x}\, dx$ (9) $\int \frac{1}{x\sqrt{a - bx^2}}\, dx$

P5.86 Split into partial fractions:

(1) $\frac{3x+5}{x^2+x-12}$ (2) $\frac{x+1}{x^2-7x+12}$

(3) $\frac{x-8}{(2x+3)(3x-2)}$ (4) $\frac{x^2-13x+26}{(x-2)(x-3)(x-4)}$

(5) $\frac{x^2-3x+1}{(x-1)(x+2)(x-3)}$ (6) $\frac{5x^2+7x+1}{(2x+1)(3x-2)(3x+1)}$

(7) $\frac{x^2}{x^3-1}$ (8) $\frac{x^4+1}{x^3+1}$

(9) $\frac{5x^2+6x+4}{(x+1)(x^2+x+1)}$ (10) $\frac{x}{(x-1)(x-2)^2}$

P5.87 Calculate these integrals:

(1) $\int \frac{5x+1}{x^2+x-2}\, dx$ (2) $\int \frac{(x^2-3)}{x^3-7x+6}\, dx$ (3) $\int \frac{b}{x^2-a^2}\, dx$

(4) $\int \frac{4x}{x^4-1}\, dx$ (5) $\int \frac{1}{1-x^4}\, dx$

P5.88 Find the area under $f(x) = x^2 + x - 5$ between $x = 0$ and $x = 6$.

P5.89 Find the area under the parabola $y = 2a\sqrt{x}$ from $x = 0$ to $x = a$.

P5.90 Find the area under the sine curve from $x = 0$ to $x = \pi$.

P5.91 Find the area under the curve $y = \sin^2 x$ from $x = 0$ to $x = \pi$.

P5.92 Find the area between the curves $f(x) = x^2 + x^{\frac{5}{2}}$ and $g(x) = x^2 - x^{\frac{5}{2}}$ from $x = 0$ to $x = 1$.

P5.93 What is the area under the graph of $f(x) = x^3 - \ln x$ between $x = 0$ and $x = 1$?

P5.94 Find the area of the portion of the curve $xy = a$ included between $x = 1$ and $x = a$.

P5.95 A certain curve has the equation $y = 3.42e^{0.21x}$. Find the area included between the curve and the x-axis, from $x = 2$ to $x = 8$.

P5.96 Find the general solution to the following differential equations:

(a) $\frac{dy}{dx} = \frac{1}{4}x$ (b) $\frac{dy}{dx} = \cos x$ (c) $\frac{dy}{dx} = 2x + 3$

Choose the additive constant of the general solution to obtain a specific solution $y(x)$ that satisfies $y(0) = 1$.
Hint: The solution to a differential equation is a function $y : \mathbb{R} \to \mathbb{R}$.

P5.97 Solve the differential equation $f''(x) + 2f'(x) + f(x) = 0$ for the unknown function $f : \mathbb{R} \to \mathbb{R}$ and choose the coefficients in the general solution to obtain a specific solution that satisfies the initial conditions $f(0) = 1$ and $f'(0) = 1$.
Hint: The solutions has two independent parts of the form $e^{-\lambda x}$ and $xe^{-\lambda x}$.

P5.98 Calculate the length of the curve $f(x) = \frac{1}{2}x^2$ between $x = 0$ and $x = 1$.
Hint: This problem requires a long integral calculation. Start by rewriting $\sqrt{1+x^2} = \frac{1+x^2}{\sqrt{1+x^2}}$. Lookup the derivative formula for $\sinh^{-1}(x)$. Use integration by parts and the self-referential trick from page 373.

P5.99 The voltage coming out of a North American electric wall outlet is described by the equation $V(t) = 155.57\cos(\omega t)[\text{V}]$. The average squared voltage is calculated using the integral $V_{\text{avg}}^2 = \frac{1}{T}\int_0^T V(t)^2\, dt$. Calculate the root-mean-squared voltage $V_{\text{rms}} \equiv \sqrt{V_{\text{avg}}^2}$.
Hint: Make the substitution $\tau = \omega t$ and recall $\frac{1}{\omega} = \frac{T}{2\pi}$.

P5.100 Find the volume generated by the curve $y = \sqrt{1+x^2}$ between $x = 0$ and $x = 4$ as it revolves about the x-axis.

P5.101 Find the volume generated by $\sin(x)$ revolving about the x-axis from $x = 0$ to $x = \pi$. Find also the surface area of this solid of revolution.

P5.102 Find the volume generated by the curve $y = \frac{x}{6}\sqrt{x(10-x)}$ between $x = 0$ and $x = 10$ as it rotates about the x-axis.

Stage 4 complete. Good job getting this far! Your progress is impressive!

Sequences and series problems

We're now entering the home stretch of the calculus problem set. You might want to revisit the definitions of convergence for sequences and series, and review the various convergence tests.

P5.103 Determine whether the following sequences converge or diverge. If a sequence converges, state its limit.

(a) $a_n = \dfrac{2n+3}{n+1}$ (b) $b_n = \dfrac{n+20}{\sqrt{n^2-10n}}$ (c) $c_n = \sqrt[n]{n} \equiv n^{\frac{1}{n}}$

(d) $d_n = (-1)^n$

Hint: For (c), recall $e^{\ln(y)} = y$ for all $y > 0$.

P5.104 Prove that the series $\sum_n \frac{1}{2^n+n}$ converges.
Hint: Use the direct comparison test with $b_n = \frac{1}{2^n}$.

P5.105 Prove the series $\sum_n \frac{n^2}{2n^2+1}$ diverges using the divergence test.

P5.106 State whether the following series converge or diverge:

(1) $\sum\limits_{n=1}^{\infty} \frac{\ln n}{n}$ (2) $\sum\limits_{n=1}^{\infty} \frac{0.7}{n^2}$ (3) $\sum\limits_{n=1}^{\infty} \frac{3}{3^{1/n}+3}$

(4) $\sum\limits_{n=1}^{\infty} \frac{1}{n^{1.1}}$ (5) $\sum\limits_{n=1}^{\infty} \frac{1}{1+n^2}$ (6) $\sum\limits_{n=1}^{\infty} \frac{2n}{n^2+2}$

(7) $\sum\limits_{n=1}^{\infty} \frac{\ln n}{n^2}$ (8) $\sum\limits_{n=1}^{\infty} e^{-n}$ (9) $\sum\limits_{n=1}^{\infty} ne^{-n}$

Hint: For (1) and (2), use direct comparison with $\frac{1}{n}$ and $\frac{1}{n^2}$.

P5.107 State whether the following series converge or diverge:

(1) $\sum\limits_{n=1}^{\infty} \frac{(-1)^n n}{n^2+n}$ (2) $\sum\limits_{n=1}^{\infty} \frac{(-1)^n 2n}{3n-2n}$ (3) $\sum\limits_{n=1}^{\infty} \frac{(-1)^n \ln n}{n}$

Hint: Use the alternating series test.

P5.108 Check whether the following series converge or diverge:

(1) $\sum\limits_{n=1}^{\infty} \frac{1}{2n^2-3n-5}$ (2) $\sum\limits_{n=1}^{\infty} \frac{\ln n}{n^3}$ (3) $\sum\limits_{n=1}^{\infty} \frac{2^n}{3^n+4^n}$

Hint: Use the alternating series test.

P5.109 Calculate the values of the following infinite series:

(1) $\sum\limits_{n=0}^{\infty} \frac{2^n}{3^{n+1}}$ (2) $\sum\limits_{n=0}^{\infty} \left(\frac{2}{3^n}+\frac{4}{5^n}\right)$ (3) $\sum\limits_{n=1}^{\infty} \left(\frac{2}{3}\right)^n$

P5.110 State whether the series converge absolutely, converge conditionally, or diverge.

(1) $\sum\limits_{n=1}^{\infty} \frac{(-1)^{n-1}}{2n^2+2}$ (2) $\sum\limits_{n=1}^{\infty} \frac{(-1)^n \ln n}{n}$ (3) $\sum\limits_{n=2}^{\infty} \frac{(-1)^n}{\ln n}$

P5.111 Use the nth root test or the ratio test to see whether the following series converge:

(a) $\sum\limits_{n=1}^{\infty} \frac{n!}{n^n}$ (b) $\sum\limits_{n=1}^{\infty} \frac{n^2}{n^n}$ (c) $\sum\limits_{n=1}^{\infty} \frac{(n!)^2}{n^n}$

P5.112 Find the sum of $\frac{2}{3}+\frac{1}{3}+\frac{1}{6}+\frac{1}{12}+\frac{1}{24}+\cdots$.

P5.113 Calculate the Maclaurin series of the function $f(x)=\frac{1}{1-x}$.

P5.114 Find the Maclaurin series for the following functions:

(a) $f(x)=\frac{1}{(1-x)^2}$ (b) $g(x)=e^{-x}$ (c) $h(x)=x^2\cos(x^2)$

Hint: For (b) and (c), you don't need to compute all the derivatives; use algebraic manipulations starting from a Maclaurin series that you know.

P5.115 Find the Taylor series expansions at the point $x=a$ specified.

(a) $f(x)=e^x$, around $a=5$. (b) $g(x)=\sin(x)$, at $a=10$.

P5.116 Find the radius of convergence for the following power series:

(1) $\sum_{n=0}^{\infty} nx^n$ (2) $\sum_{n=0}^{\infty} \frac{x^n}{n!}$ (3) $\sum_{n=1}^{\infty} \frac{x^n}{n(n+1)}$

(4) $\sum_{n=0}^{\infty} \frac{2^n}{n!}x^n$ (5) $\sum_{n=0}^{\infty} \frac{x^n}{1+3^n}$ (6) $\sum_{n=1}^{\infty} \frac{(-1)^n}{n^2 3^n}x^{2n}$

P5.117 Find a series for each function, using the formula for Maclaurin series and algebraic manipulation as appropriate.

(1) 2^x (2) $\ln(1+x)$ (3) $\ln\left(\frac{1+x}{1-x}\right)$

(4) $\sqrt{1+x}$ (5) $\frac{1}{1+x^2}$ (6) $\tan^{-1}(x)$

P5.118 Figure out which test you need to use and determine if the following series converge or diverge:

(1) $\sum_{n=0}^{\infty} \frac{n}{n^2+4}$ (2) $\sum_{n=0}^{\infty} \frac{n}{(n^2+4)^2}$ (3) $\sum_{n=0}^{\infty} \frac{n!}{8^n}$

(4) $\sum_{n=0}^{\infty} \frac{1}{\sqrt{n^2+4}}$ (5) $\sum_{n=0}^{\infty} \frac{\sin^3(n)}{n^2}$ (6) $\sum_{n=0}^{\infty} \frac{n}{e^n}$

(7) $\sum_{n=1}^{\infty} \frac{1}{n\sqrt{n}}$ (8) $\sum_{n=1}^{\infty} \frac{1\cdot 3\cdot 5\cdots(2n-1)}{(2n)!}$ (9) $\sum_{n=0}^{\infty} \frac{6^n}{n!}$

(10) $\sum_{n=1}^{\infty} \frac{(-1)^{n-1}}{\sqrt{n}}$ (11) $\sum_{n=1}^{\infty} \frac{2^n 3^{n-1}}{n!}$ (12) $\sum_{n=1}^{\infty} \sin(1/n)$

P5.119 Prove the formulas for the infinite sum of the first N positive integers, and the sum of the squares of the first N positive integers:

$$\sum_{n=1}^{N} n = \frac{N(N+1)}{2}, \qquad \sum_{n=1}^{N} n^2 = \frac{N(N+1)(2N+1)}{6}.$$

Hint: For the first part, try writing the terms of the summation in increasing order, as well as in decreasing order on separate lines. For the second part, you might be interested in computing the sum $\sum_{n=1}^{N}(n+1)^3 - n^3$ using two different approaches, and equating the results.

P5.120 Compute the definite integral $\int_{\alpha}^{\beta} mx + b$ using the Riemann sum approach, taking the limit $n \to \infty$ for the number of vertical rectangles.

P5.121 Find the area under the curve for the function $f(x) = ax^2 + bx + c$ between $x = 0$ and $x = d$ using the infinite Riemann sum approach.

P5.122 Calculate the surface area of a sphere of radius R using the surface of revolution formula given on page 381.
Hint: Split the surface area into narrow strips of width $d\ell$. Imagine you're peeling an orange. You start from the top and peel around the orange in circles. Each circle produces a ring of peel of area $dA = 2\pi r d\ell$. Since the surface area of an orange is equal to the area of its peel, we have $A = \int dA$.

P5.123 Calculate the volume of the solid of revolution generated by revolving the region bounded by the curve $y = x^2$ and the lines $x = 0$, $x = 1$, and $y = 0$ around the x-axis.

P5.124 Calculate the volume of the solid of revolution generated by revolving the region bounded by the curves $y = x^2$ and $y = x^3$ and the lines $x = 0$ and $x = 1$ around the x-axis.

P5.125 *Torricelli's trumpet* is the surface of revolution generated by rotating the curve $f(x) = \frac{1}{x}$ around the x-axis. Figure 5.29 on page 382 shows part of its surface. Calculate the total volume enclosed by Torricelli's trumpet between $x = 1$ and $x = \infty$.
Hint: Use the disk method to compute the volume of revolution between $x = 1$ and $x = a$; then take the limit as $a \to \infty$.

P5.126 Calculate the moment of inertia of a thin, spherical shell with mass m and radius R by adapting the formula for the surface area of a revolution from page 381.
Hint: See page 385 for a reminder of how to setup the integral.

P5.127 Calculate the moment of inertia of a solid sphere with mass m and radius R using the cylindrical shell method.
Hint: Adapt the formula for computing the volume of a sphere, taking into account the total mass and the squared distance of each spherical shell.

P5.128 Calculate the moment of inertia of a solid sphere with mass m and radius R by splitting it into thin disks. The moment of inertia of a disk of thickness dx, radius $r(x)$, and mass $m(x)$ is given by $I_{\text{disk}}(x) = \frac{1}{2}m(x)[r(x)]^2$, where the mass of the disk is proportional to the mass density $\rho = \frac{m}{\frac{4}{3}\pi R^3}$ and its area $A(x)$: $m(x) = \rho A(x) = \rho\pi[r(x)]^2$.
Hint: The radius of each disk as a function of x is described by $r(x) = \sqrt{R^2 - x^2}$. The integral you want to set up looks like $\int_{-R}^{R} I_{\text{disk}}(x)\, dx$.

Links

Here are some links to more calculus problems with solutions:

[Lots of solved calculus examples by Larry Perez]
`http://saddleback.edu/faculty/lperez/algebra2go/calculus/calc3A.pdf`

[Try the odd-numbered problems in Gilbert Strang's calculus book]
`http://bit.ly/1mnheSD`

End matter

Conclusion

We managed to cover a lot of ground, explaining many topics and concepts in a relatively small textbook. We reviewed high school math and learned about mechanics and calculus. Above all, we examined math and physics material in an integrated manner.

If you liked or hated this book, be sure to send me feedback. Feedback is crucial so I know how to adjust the writing, the content, and the attitude of the book for future learners of math. Please take the time to drop me a line if you find a mistake or to let me know what you thought. You can reach me by email at `ivan@minireference.com`.

If you want to learn about other books in the NO BULLSHIT GUIDE series and hear about the technology we're using at `Minireference Publishing` to take over the textbook industry, check out the company blog at `minireference.com/blog/`. You can also find us on the twitter `@minireference` and on the facebook `fb.me/noBSguide`.

Acknowledgments

This book would not have been possible without the support and encouragement of the people around me. I am fortunate to have grown up surrounded by good people who knew the value of math and encouraged me in my studies and with this project. In this section, I want to *big up* all the people who deserve it.

First and foremost in this list are my parents from whom I have learned everything, and who have supported me throughout my life.

Next in line are all my teachers. I thank my CEGEP teachers: Karnig Bedrossian from whom I learned calculus, Paul Kenton from whom I learned how to think about physics in a chill manner, and Benoit Larose who taught me that more dimensions does not mean things get more complicated. I thank Kohur Gowrisankaran, Frank

Ferrie, Mourad El-Gamal, and Ioannis Psaromiligkos for their teaching during my engineering days, and Guy Moore and Zaven Altounian for teaching me advanced physics topics. Among all my teachers, I owe the most to Patrick Hayden whose teaching methods have always inspired me. From him, I learned that by defining things clearly, you can *trick* students into learning advanced topics, and even make it seem that the results are obvious! Thanks go out to all my research collaborators and friends: David Avis, Arlo Breault, Juan Pablo Di Lelle, Omar Fawzi, Adriano Ferrari, Igor Khavkine, Felix Kwok, Doina Precup, Andie Sigler, and Mark M. Wilde. Thank you all for teaching me a great many things!

Preparing this book took many years and the combined efforts of many people. I want to thank Afton Lewis, Oleg Zhoglo, and Alexandra Foty for helping me proofread v2 of the book, and all the readers who reported typos and suggested clarifications. Thank you all for your comments and feedback! Georger Araujo and Tomasz Święcicki deserve particular mention as their meticulous reading of the text led to the correction of many technical mistakes. I also want to thank Mohamad Nizar Kezzo for helping me prepare the problems and exercises for the book. Above all, I want to thank my editor Sandy Gordon, who helped me substantially improve the writing in the book. Her expertise with the English language and her advice on style and content have been absolutely invaluable.

Last but not least, I want to thank all my students for their endless questions and demands for explanations. If I have developed any skill for explaining things, I owe it to them.

Further reading

You have reached the end of this book, but you're only at the beginning of the journey of scientific discovery. There are a lot of cool things left for you to learn about. Below are some recommendation of subjects you might find interesting.

Electricity and Magnetism

Electrostatics is the study of the electric force $\vec{F}_e$ and the associated electric potential U_e. Here, you will also learn about the electric field $\vec{E}$ and electric potential V.

Magnetism is the study of the magnetic force $\vec{F}_b$ and the magnetic field $\vec{B}$, which are caused by electric currents flowing through wires. The current I is the total number of electrons passing through a cross-section of the wire in one second. By virtue of its motion through space, each electron contributes to the strength of the magnetic field surrounding the wire.

The beauty of electromagnetism is that the entire theory can be described in just four equations:

$$\nabla \cdot \vec{E} = \frac{\rho}{\varepsilon_0} \qquad \text{Gauss's law}$$

$$\nabla \cdot \vec{B} = 0 \qquad \text{Gauss's law for magnetism}$$

$$\nabla \times \vec{E} = -\frac{\partial \vec{B}}{\partial t} \qquad \text{Faraday's law of induction}$$

$$\nabla \times \vec{B} = \mu_0 \vec{J} + \mu_0 \varepsilon_0 \frac{\partial \vec{E}}{\partial t} \qquad \text{Ampère's circuital law}$$

Together, these are known as Maxwell's equations.

Vector calculus

You may be wondering what the triangle thing is. The symbol ∇ (called *nabla*) is the vector derivative operation: $\nabla \equiv \left(\frac{\partial}{\partial x}, \frac{\partial}{\partial y}, \frac{\partial}{\partial z} \right)$. Guess what—you can also do calculus with vectors.

If you take a vector calculus course, you'll learn about path integrals, surface integrals, and volume integrals of vector functions. You will also learn about vector-derivatives, as well as two vector equivalents of the fundamental theorem of calculus:

- Stokes' Theorem:

$$\iint_{\Sigma} \nabla \times \vec{F} \cdot d\vec{S} = \int_{\partial \Sigma} \vec{F} \cdot d\vec{r},$$

  which states that the integral of the curl, $\text{curl}(\vec{F}) \equiv \nabla \times \vec{F}$, of the field $\vec{F}$ over the surface Σ is equal to the circulation of $\vec{F}$ along the boundary of the surface $\partial\Sigma$.
- Gauss' Divergence Theorem:

$$\iiint_{V} \nabla \cdot \vec{F}\, dV = \iint_{\partial V} \vec{F} \cdot d\vec{S},$$

  which states the integral of the divergence, $\text{div}(\vec{F}) \equiv \nabla \cdot \vec{F}$, of the field $\vec{F}$ over the volume V is equal to the flux of $\vec{F}$ through the volume's boundary ∂V.

Both theorems relate the total of the derivative of a quantity over some region R to the value of that quantity on the boundary of the region, which we denote ∂R. The fundamental theorem of calculus can also be interpreted in this manner:

$$\int_a^b F'(x)\,dx = \int_I F'(x)\,dx = F_{\partial I} = F(b) - F(a),$$

where $I = [a, b]$ is the *interval* from a to b on the real line and the two points a and b form its boundary ∂I.

Vector calculus is of interest mainly for physicists and engineers.

Multivariable calculus

Of wider interest is the study of calculus with functions that have more than one input variable. Consider as an example a function $f(x, y)$ that has two input variables, x and y. You can plot a function $f : \mathbb{R} \times \mathbb{R} \to \mathbb{R}$ as a *surface*, where the height z of the surface above the point (x, y) is given by the function value $z = f(x, y)$.

There is no new math to learn in multivariable calculus: it's the same stuff as differential calculus and integral calculus but with more variables. For a function (x, y), there is an "x-derivative" $\frac{\partial}{\partial x}$ and a "y-derivative" $\frac{\partial}{\partial y}$. The operation $\frac{\partial}{\partial x} f(x, y)$ describes taking the derivative of $f(x, y)$ with respect to the variable x, while keeping the variable y constant.

The discussion in Section 5.11 (page 329) about the total derivative of a function is a topic from multivariable calculus. Taking the derivative of a multivariable function with respect to one of the input variables is known as a *partial derivative* and denoted ∂. In Section 5.11, we didn't introduce the notation $\frac{\partial g}{\partial x}$ and $\frac{\partial g}{\partial y}$ in order to keep things simple, but it's really not that complicated. I'll show you.

The partial-derivative notation is necessary to distinguish the partial derivative with respect to x from the total derivative with respect to x. For example, consider a function $g(x, y)$ in which y is a function of x. The total derivative of $g(x, y)$ captures the dependence between g and x on both branches of the function: the direct dependence $g(x, .)$ and the dependence passing through y as intermediary $g(., y(x))$:

$$\frac{dg}{dx} = \frac{\partial g}{\partial x} + \frac{\partial g}{\partial y}\frac{dy}{dx}.$$

The notation $\frac{\partial g}{\partial x}$ describes "differentiate $g(x, y)$ keeping y constant," whereas $\frac{dg}{dx}$ says "differentiate $g(x, y)$ by all possible paths." Without the new ∂-notation, we wouldn't be able to distinguish between these two different notions of derivative.

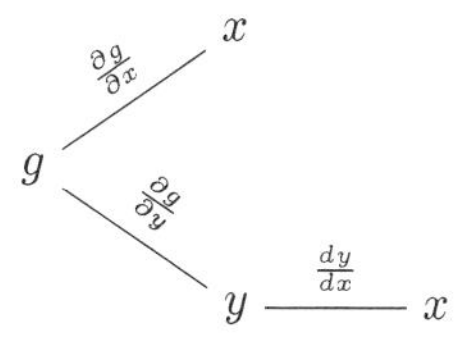

Figure 5.34: The total derivative of the function $g(x, y(x))$ with respect to x.

The operator ∇ is a combination of both the x and y derivatives: $\nabla f(x,y) = [\frac{\partial f}{\partial x}, \frac{\partial f}{\partial x}]$. Note that ∇ acts on a function $f(x,y)$ to produce a vector. This is known as the *gradient* vector, which tells you the "slope" of the surface. More specifically, the gradient vector tells you the direction of the function's maximum increase. If you think of $z = f(x,y)$ as the height of a mountain at particular (x,y) coordinates on a map, then the gradient vector $\nabla f(x,y)$ always points uphill.

In the second part of multivariable calculus you'll learn how to do double integrals, which are integrals over two variables:

$$\int_{y=0}^{y=1}\int_{x=0}^{x=1} yx\,dxdy = \int_{y=0}^{y=1}\left[y\frac{x^2}{2}\right]_{x=0}^{x=1} dy = \int_{y=0}^{y=1}\frac{y}{2}\,dy = \left[\frac{1}{4}y^2\right]_0^1 = \frac{1}{4}.$$

Once you get over the initial shock of seeing two integral signs, you should be able to understand the above integral calculation. Proceeding from inside-out, a double integral is nothing more than two integral operators applied in succession. Instead of an interval of integration split into tiny integration steps dx, we have a *region of integration* split into tiny integration boxes with area $dxdy$. In the above example, the region of integration is a unit square in the xy-plane.

If you understand derivatives and integrals, you will find multivariable calculus easy: it's just the multivariable upgrade of the concepts from Chapter 5.

Linear algebra

Learning linear algebra will open many doors for you. You need linear algebra to understand statistics, computer graphics, machine learning, quantum mechanics, and many other areas of science and business.

Here's a little preview. Linear algebra is the study of vectors $\vec{v} \in \mathbb{R}^n$ and linear transformations $T : \mathbb{R}^n \to \mathbb{R}^m$. Linear transformations are *vector functions* that obey the linear property $T(\alpha\vec{v}_1 + \beta\vec{v}_2) = \alpha T(\vec{v}_1) + \beta T(\vec{v}_2)$. Using the standard notation for functions, we write $T(\vec{x}) = \vec{y}$ to show the linear transformation T acting on an input vector $\vec{x} \in \mathbb{R}^n$ to produce the output vector $\vec{y} \in \mathbb{R}^m$. Every linear transformation T can be *represented* as a matrix $A_T \in \mathbb{R}^{m \times n}$, which is an array of numbers with m rows and n columns. Computing $T(\vec{x})$ is equivalent to computing the matrix-vector product $A_T\vec{x}$. Because of the equivalence between linear transformations and matrices, we can also say that linear algebra is the study of vectors and matrices.

Vectors and matrices are used all over the place! If your knowledge of high-school math gave you modelling superpowers, then linear algebra is the vector-upgrade that teaches you how to build models in multiple dimensions.

[VIDEO LECTURES] Gilbert Strang. *Linear Algebra,* MIT OpenCourseWare, 2010, online: `http://bit.ly/StrangLAlectures`.

[BOOK] Ivan Savov. *No bullshit guide to linear algebra,* Minireference Publishing, Second edition, 2017, ISBN 978-0-9920010-2-5.

General mathematics

Mathematics is a hugely broad field. There are all kinds of topics to learn about; some of them are fun, some of them are useful, and some of them are totally mind expanding.

The following books cover math topics of general interest and serve as a great overview of all areas of mathematics. I highly recommend you take a look at both books for some easy and enlightening reading.

[BOOK] Richard Elwes. *Mathematics 1001: Absolutely Everything,* Firefly Books, 2010, ISBN 1554077192.

[BOOK] Alfred North Whitehead. *An Introduction to Mathematics,* Williams & Norgate, 1911, `www.gutenberg.org/ebooks/41568`.

Probability

Probability distributions are a fundamental tool for modelling non-deterministic behaviour. A discrete random variable X is associated with a probability mass function $p_X(x) \equiv \Pr(\{X = x\})$, which assigns a "probability mass" to each of the possible outcomes of the random variable X. For example, if X represents the outcome of the throw of a fair die, then the possible outcomes are $\mathcal{X} = \{1,2,3,4,5,6\}$ and the probability mass function has the values $p_X(x) = \frac{1}{6}, \forall x \in \mathcal{X}$.

Probability distributions and random variables allow us to model random processes like the roll of a die. We can't predict the exact outcome when two dice X_1 and X_2 are rolled, but we can predict the probability of different outcomes. For example, the "pair of sixes" outcome is described by the event $\{X_1 + X_2 = 12\}$. Assuming the dice are fair, this outcome has probability $\Pr(\{X_1 + X_2 = 12\}) = \frac{1}{36}$.

Probability theory is used all over the place, including in statistics, machine learning, quantum mechanics, gambling, and risk analysis.

General physics

If you want to learn more about physics, I highly recommend the Feynman lectures on physics. This three-tome collection covers all of undergraduate physics and explains many more advanced topics.

[BOOK] Richard P. Feynman. *The Feynman Lectures on Physics, The Definitive and Extended Edition*, Addison Wesley, 2005, ISBN 0805390456. Read online at: `http://feynmanlectures.caltech.edu`

Lagrangian mechanics

In this book we learned about *Newtonian mechanics*, that is, mechanics starting from Newton's laws. There is a much more general framework known as Lagrangian mechanics that can be used to analyze more complex mechanical systems. The following is an excellent book on the subject.

[BOOK] Herbert Goldstein, Charles P. Poole Jr., John L. Safko. *Classical Mechanics*, Addison-Wesley, Third edition, 2001, ISBN 0201657023.

Quantum mechanics

Quantum mechanics describes the physics of all things is small: photons, electrons and atoms. An absolutely approachable and readable introduction to the subject is Richard Feynman's QED book.

For a deeper understanding of quantum mechanics, I recommend the book by Sakurai. If you understand linear algebra, then you can understand quantum mechanics.

[BOOK] Richard P. Feynman. *QED: The strange theory of light and matter*. Princeton University Press, 2006, ISBN 0691125759.

[BOOK] Jun John Sakurai. *Modern Quantum Mechanics*, Second Edition, Addison-Wesley, 2010, ISBN 0805382917.

Information theory

Claude Shannon developed a mathematical framework for studying the problems of information storage and information transmission. Using statistical notions such as entropy, we can quantify the information content of data sources and the information transmitting abilities of noisy communication channels.

We can arrive at an *operational* interpretation of the information carrying capacity of a noisy communication channel in terms of our ability to convert it into a noiseless channel. Channels with more noise have a smaller capacity for carrying information. Consider a channel that allows us to send data at the rate of 1[MB/sec], on which half of the packets sent get lost due to the effects of noise on the channel. It is not true that the capacity of such a channel is 1[MB/sec], because we must also account for the need to retransmit lost packets. To correctly characterize a channel's information carrying capacity, we must consider the rate of the end-to-end *code*, which converts many uses of the noisy channel into an effectively noiseless communication channel.

Channel coding is one of the fundamental problems studied in information theory. I highly recommend the excellent textbook on the subject by Cover and Thomas.

[BOOK] Thomas M. Cover, Joy A. Thomas. *Elements of Information Theory*, Wiley, 2006, ISBN 0471241954.

Final words

Throughout this book, I strived to equip you with the tools you'll need to make your future science studies enjoyable and pain free. Remember to always take it easy. Play with math and never take things too seriously. Grades don't matter. Big paycheques don't matter. Never settle for a boring job just because it pays well. Try to work only on projects you care about.

I want you to be confident in your ability to handle math, physics, and the other complicated stuff life will throw at you. You have the tools to do anything you want; choose your own adventure. And if the big banks come-a-knocking one day with a big paycheque trying to bribe you into applying your analytical skills to their avaricious schemes, send them-a-walking.

Appendix A

Answers and solutions

Chapter 1 solutions

Answers to exercises

E1.1 a) $x = 3$; **b)** $x = 30$; **c)** $x = 2$; **d)** $x = -3$. **E1.2 a)** $\mathbb{Z}, \mathbb{Q}, \mathbb{R}, \mathbb{C}$; **b)** $\mathbb{C}$; **c)** $\mathbb{N}, \mathbb{Z}, \mathbb{Q}, \mathbb{R}, \mathbb{C}$; **d)** $\mathbb{Q}, \mathbb{R}, \mathbb{C}$; **e)** $\mathbb{R}, \mathbb{C}$. **E1.3 a)** 21; **b)** 0; **c)** $\frac{2}{27}$. **E1.4 a)** $\frac{5}{6}$; **b)** $\frac{13}{12} = 1\frac{1}{12}$; **c)** $\frac{31}{6} = 5\frac{1}{6}$. **E1.5 a)** $x = 2$; **b)** $x = 25$; **c)** $x = 100$. **E1.6 a)** $f^{-1}(x) = x^2$, $x = 16$. **b)** $g^{-1}(x) = -\frac{1}{2}\ln(x)$, $x = 0$. **E1.7 a)** $(x-1)(x-7)$; **b)** $(x+2)^2$. **E1.8 a)** $a^2 + 2ab + b^2$; **b)** $a^3 + 3a^2b + 3ab^2 + b^3$; **c)** $a^4 + 4a^3b + 6a^2b^2 + 4ab^3 + b^4$; **d)** $a^5 + 5a^4b + 10a^3b^2 + 10a^2b^3 + 5ab^4 + b^5$. **E1.9** $x_1 = \frac{3}{2}$ and $x_2 = -1$. **E1.10** $x = \pm\sqrt{2}$. **E1.11 a)** 8; **b)** $a^{-1}b^{-2}c^{-3} = \frac{1}{ab^2c^3}$; **c)** $8\alpha^2$; **d)** a^6b^{-2}. **E1.12 a)** 3; **b)** 12; **c)** $\sqrt{3}$; **d)** $|a|$. **E1.13 a)** 2π; **b)** $4 + \frac{1}{4} = 4.25$; **c)** 1; **d)** x^2. **E1.14 a)** $x = \sqrt{a}$ and $x = -\sqrt{a}$; **b)** $x = \sqrt[3]{b}$; **c)** $x = \sqrt[4]{c}$ and $x = -\sqrt[4]{c}$; **d)** $x = \sqrt[5]{d}$. Bonus points if you can also solve $x^2 = -1$. We'll get to that in Section 3.5. **E1.15** $k_e = 8.988 \times 10^9$. **E1.16 a)** $\log(2xy)$. **b)** $-\log(z)$. **c)** $\log(y)$. **d)** 3. **e)** -3. **f)** 4. **E1.17** Domain: $x \in \mathbb{R}$. Image: $f(x) \in [-2, 2]$. Roots: $[\ldots, -\frac{\pi}{2}, \frac{\pi}{2}, \frac{3\pi}{2}, \frac{5\pi}{2}, \ldots]$. **E1.18 a)** $p(x)$ is even and has degree 4. **b)** $q(x)$ is odd and has degree 7. **E1.19 a)** $x = 5$ and $x = -3$; **b)** $x = 1 + \sqrt{3}$ and $x = 1 - \sqrt{3}$. **E1.20 a)** $(q \circ f)(x) \equiv q(f(x)) = (x+5)^2$; $q(x)$ shifted five units to the left. **b)** $(f \circ q)(x) = x^2 + 5$; $q(x)$ shifted upward by five units. **c)** $(q \circ g)(x) = (x-6)^2$; $q(x)$ shifted six units to the right. **d)** $(q \circ h)(x) = 49x^2$; $q(x)$ horizontally compressed by a factor of seven. **E1.21** $A = 5$, $\lambda = 0.1$, and $\phi = \frac{\pi}{8}$. **E1.22** $f(x) = x^2 - 2x + 5$. **E1.23** $g(x) = 2\sqrt{x-3} - 2$. **E1.24** $x = \sqrt{21}$. **E1.25** $V = 33.51$ and $A = 50.26$. **E1.26** $x = 5\cos(45°) = 3.54$, $y = 5\sin(45°) = 3.54$; $C = 10\pi$. **E1.27 a)** $\frac{\pi}{6}$[rad]; **b)** $\frac{\pi}{4}$[rad]; **c)** $\frac{\pi}{3}$[rad]; **d)** $\frac{3\pi}{2}$[rad]. **E1.28 a)** -1; **b)** 1; **c)** 0. **E1.29 a)** 0; **b)** 1; **c)** $\frac{1}{2}$; **d)** 1. **E1.30** Length of track $= 5C = 5\pi d = 11.47$[m]. **E1.31** $(x-1)^2 + (y-4)^2 = 9$ or $\{(x,y) \in \mathbb{R}^2 \mid x = 1 + 3\cos\theta, y = 4 + 3\sin\theta, \theta \in [0, 2\pi)\}$. **E1.32** $x = 2$, $y = 3$. **E1.33** $x = 5$, $y = 6$, and $z = -3$. **E1.34** $p = 7$ and $q = 3$. **E1.35 a)** \$53 974.14; **b)** \$59 209.77; **c)** \$65 948.79. **E1.36** \$32 563.11. **E1.37 a)** $\{2,4,6,7\}$; **b)** $\{1,2,3,4,5,6\}$; **c)** $\{1,3,5\}$; **d)** $\varnothing$; **e)** $\{1,2,3,4,5,6,7\}$; **f)** $\{7\}$; **g)** $\{2,4,6,7\}$; **h)** $\varnothing$. **E1.38 a)** $x \in (-\infty, \frac{3}{2})$; **b)** $x \in (-\infty, -5]$; **c)** $x \in (-1, 4)$; **d)** $x \in (4, \infty)$; **e)** $x \in [\frac{14}{3}, \infty)$; **f)** $(-\infty, -4] \cup [2, \infty)$.

Solutions to selected exercises

E1.4 **a)** To compute $\frac{1}{2} + \frac{1}{3}$, we rewrite both fractions using the common denominator 6, then compute the sum: $\frac{1}{2} + \frac{1}{3} = \frac{3}{6} + \frac{2}{6} = \frac{5}{6}$. **b)** You can use the answer from part (a), or compute the triple sum directly by setting all three fractions to a common denominator: $\frac{1}{2}+\frac{1}{3}+\frac{1}{4}=\frac{6}{12}+\frac{4}{12}+\frac{3}{12}=\frac{13}{12}$. **c)** Here we first rewrite $3\frac{1}{2}$ as $\frac{7}{2}$, then use the common denominator 6 for the computation: $\frac{7}{2}+2-\frac{1}{3}=\frac{21}{6}+\frac{12}{6}-\frac{2}{6}=\frac{31}{6}$.

E1.8 The coefficients of the expression of $(a+b)^n$ for different values of n correspond to the rows in *Pascal's triangle*. Check out the Wikipedia page for Pascal's triangle to learn the general formula and see an interesting animation of how it can be constructed.

E1.15 If you're using a very basic calculator, you should first compute the expression in the denominator, and then invert the fraction. Calculators that support scientific notation have an "`exp`" or "`E`" button, which allows you to enter ε_0 as `8.854e-12`. If your calculator supports expressions, you can type in the whole expression `1/(4*pi*8.854e-12)`. We report an answer with four significant digits because we started from a value of ε_0 with four significant digits of precision.

E1.19 **a)** Rewrite the equation putting all terms on the right-hand side: $0=x^2-2x-15$. We can factor this quadratic by inspection. Are there numbers a and b such that $a+b=-2$ and $ab=-15$? Yes, $a=-5$ and $b=3$, so $0=(x-5)(x+3)$. **b)** Rewrite the equation so all terms are on the left-hand side: $3x^2-6x-6=0$. Nice, the cubic terms cancel! We'll use the quadratic formula to solve this equation $x=\frac{6\pm\sqrt{(-6)^2-4(3)(-6)}}{6}=\frac{6\pm 6\sqrt{3}}{6}=1\pm\sqrt{3}$.

E1.24 The cosine rule tells us $x^2=4^2+5^2-2(4)(5)\cos(60°)=16+25-40\frac{1}{2}=21$. Therefore $x=\sqrt{21}$.

E1.25 The volume of the sphere with radius $r=2$ is $V=\frac{4}{3}\pi 2^3=33.51$. Its surface area is $A=4\pi 2^2=50.26$.

E1.27 To convert an angle measure from degrees to radians we must multiply it by the conversion ratio $\frac{\pi}{180}[\text{rad}/°]$.

E1.35 **a)** Since the compounding is performed monthly, we first calculate the monthly interest rate: $r=\frac{3\%}{12}=0.25\%=0.0025$. The sum Jack owes after 10 years is $\$40\,000(1.0025)^{120}=\$53\,974.14$. **b)** The calculation that uses the effective annual interest rate is more direct: $\$40\,000(1.04)^{10}=\$59\,209.77$. **c)** When compounding infinitely often at a nominal annual interest rate of 5%, the amount owed will grow by $\exp\left(\frac{5}{100}\right)=1.051271$ each year. After 10 years Jack will owe $\$40\,000(1.051271)^{10}=\$65\,948.79$.

E1.36 Since there are two different interest rates in effect, we must perform two separate calculations. At the end of the first five years, Kate owes $\$20\,000(1.06)^5=\$26\,764.51$. For the remaining five years, the interest changes to 4%, so the sum Kate owes after 10 years is $\$26\,764.51(1.04)^5=\$32\,563.11$.

E1.38 **a)** Dividing both sides of the inequality by two gives $x<\frac{3}{2}$. **b)** Divide both sides by negative four to obtain $x\leqslant-5$. Note the "$\geqslant$" changed to "$\leqslant$" since we divided by a negative number. **c)** If the absolute value of $(2x-3)$ is less than five, then $(2x-3)$ must lie in the interval $(-5,5)$. We can therefore rewrite the inequality as $-5<2x-3<5$, then add three to both sides to obtain $-2<2x<8$, and divide by two to obtain the final answer $-1<x<4$. **d)** Let's collect all the x-terms on the right and all the constants on the left: $8<2x$, which leads to $4<x$. **e)** To simplify, add two to both sides of the inequality to obtain $\frac{1}{2}x\geqslant\frac{1}{3}+2$. You remember how to add fractions right? We have $\frac{1}{3}+2=\frac{1}{3}+\frac{6}{3}=\frac{7}{3}$, and therefore $\frac{1}{2}x\geqslant\frac{7}{3}$. Multiply both sides by two to obtain $x\geqslant\frac{14}{3}$. **f)** The first step is to get rid of the square by taking the square root operation on both sides: $\sqrt{(x+1)^2}\geqslant\sqrt{9}$. Recall that $\sqrt{x^2}=|x|$, so we have $|x+1|\geqslant 3$. There are two ways for the absolute value of $(x+1)$ to be greater than three. Either $x+1\geqslant 3$ or $x+1\leqslant-3$. We subtract one in each of these inequalities to find $x\geqslant 2$ or $x\leqslant-4$. The solution to this inequality is the union of these two intervals.

Answers to problems

P1.1 $x = \pm 4$. **P1.2** $x = A\cos(\omega t + \phi)$. **P1.3** $x = \frac{ab}{a+b}$. **P1.4 a)** 2.2795. **b)** 1024. **c)** -8.373. **d)** 11. **P1.5 a)** $\frac{3}{4}$. **b)** $\frac{-141}{35}$. **c)** $3\frac{23}{32}$. **P1.6 a)** c. **b)** 1. **c)** $\frac{9|a|}{|b|}$. **d)** a. **e)** $\frac{b}{ac}$. **f)** $x^2 + ab$. **P1.7 a)** $x^2 + (a-b)x - ab$. **b)** $2x^2 - 7x - 15$. **c)** $10x^2 + 31x - 14$. **P1.8 a)** $(x-4)(x+2)$. **b)** $3x(x-3)(x+3)$. **c)** $(x+3)(6x-7)$. **P1.9 a)** $(x-2)^2 + 3$. **b)** $2(x+3)^2 + 4$. **c)** $6\left(x + \frac{11}{12}\right)^2 - \frac{625}{24}$. **P1.10** \$0.05. **P1.11** 13 people, 30 animals. **P1.12** 5 years later. **P1.13** girl = 80 nuts, boy = 40 nuts. **P1.14** Alice is 15. **P1.15** 18 days. **P1.16** After 2 hours. **P1.18** $\varphi = \frac{1+\sqrt{5}}{2}$. **P1.19** $x = \frac{-5\pm\sqrt{41}}{2}$. **P1.20 a)** $x = \sqrt[3]{2}$. **b)** $x = (\frac{\pi}{2} + 2\pi n)$ for $n \in \mathbb{Z}$. **P1.21** No real solutions if $0 < m < 8$. **P1.22 a)** e^z. **b)** $\frac{x^3y^{15}}{z^3}$. **c)** $\frac{1}{4x^4}$. **d)** $\frac{1}{4}$. **e)** -3. **f)** $\ln(x+1)$. **P1.23** $\epsilon = 1.110 \times 10^{-16}$; $n = 15.95$ in decimal. **P1.24 a)** $x \in (4, \infty)$. **b)** $x \in [3, 6]$. **c)** $x \in (-\infty, -1] \cup [\frac{1}{2}, \infty)$. **P1.25** For $n > 250$, Algorithm Q is faster. **P1.26** 10 cm. **P1.27** 22.52 in. **P1.28** $h = \sqrt{3.33^2 - 1.44^2} = 3\,\text{m}$. **P1.29** The opposite side has length 1. **P1.30** $x = \sqrt{3}$, $y = 1$, and $z = 2$. **P1.31** $d = \frac{1800\tan 20° - 800\tan 25°}{\tan 25° - \tan 20°}$, $h = 1658.46\,\text{m}$. **P1.32** $x = \frac{2000}{\tan 24°}$. **P1.33** $x = \tan\theta\sqrt{a^2+b^2+c^2}$. **P1.34** $a = \sqrt{3}$, $A_\triangle = \frac{3\sqrt{3}}{4}$. **P1.35** $\sin^2\theta\cos^2\theta = \frac{1-\cos 4\theta}{8}$. **P1.36** $P_\circ = 16\tan(22.5°)$, $A_\circ = 8\tan(22.5°)$. **P1.37** $c = \frac{a\sin 75°}{\sin 41°} \approx 14.7$. **P1.38 a)** $h = a\sin\theta$. **b)** $A = \frac{1}{2}ba\sin\theta$. **c)** $c = \sqrt{a^2 + b^2 - 2ab\cos(180° - \theta)}$. **P1.39** $B = 44.8°$, $C = 110.2°$. $c = \frac{a\sin 110.2°}{\sin 25°} \approx 39.97$. **P1.40** $v = 742.92$ km/h. **P1.41** 1.06 cm. **P1.42** $x = 9.55$. **P1.43** $\frac{1}{2}(\pi 4^2 - \pi 2^2) = 18.85\ \text{cm}^2$. **P1.44** $\ell_\text{rope} = 8.42\,\text{m}$. **P1.45** $A_\text{rect} = 5c + 10$. **P1.46** $V_\text{box} = 1.639\,\text{L}$. **P1.47** $\theta = 140°$. **P1.48** $\frac{R}{r} = \frac{1-\sin 15°}{\sin 15°} = 2.8637$. **P1.49** 7 cm. **P1.50** $V = 300\,000\,\text{L}$. **P1.51** 315 000 L. **P1.52** 4000 L. **P1.53** $d = \frac{1}{2}(35 - 5\sqrt{21})$. **P1.54** A rope of length $\sqrt{2}\ell$. **P1.55** 20 L of water. **P1.56** $h = 7.84$ inches. **P1.57** $1 + 2 + \cdots + 100 = 50 \times 101 = 5050$. **P1.58** $x = -2$ and $y = 2$. **P1.59** $x = 1$, $y = 2$, and $z = 3$. **P1.60** \$112. **P1.61** 20%. **P1.62** \$16501.93. **P1.64** 0.14 s. **P1.65** $\tau = 34.625$ min, 159.45 min. **P1.66** $V(0.01) = 15.58$ volts. $V(0.1) = 1.642$ volts. **P1.70** $A_1(x) = 3x$ and $A_2(x) = \frac{1}{2}x^2$.

Solutions to selected problems

P1.5 For **c)**, $1\frac{3}{4} + 1\frac{31}{32} = \frac{7}{4} + \frac{63}{32} = \frac{56}{32} + \frac{63}{32} = \frac{119}{32} = 3\frac{23}{32}$.

P1.9 The solutions for **a)** and **b)** are fairly straightforward. To solve **c)**, we first factor out 6 from the first two terms to obtain $6(x^2 + \frac{11}{6}x) - 21$. Next we choose half of the coefficient of the linear term to go inside the square and add the appropriate correction to maintain equality: $6[x^2 + \frac{11}{6}x] - 21 = 6[(x + \frac{11}{12})^2 - \left(\frac{11}{12}\right)^2] - 21$. After expanding the rectangular brackets and simplifying, we obtain the final expression: $6\left(x + \frac{11}{12}\right)^2 - \frac{625}{24}$.

P1.11 Let p denote the number of people and a denote the number of animals. We are told $p + a = 43$ and $a = p + 17$. Substituting the second equation into the first, we find $p + (p + 17) = 43$, which is equivalent to $2p = 26$ or $p = 13$. There are 13 figures of people and 30 figures of animals.

P1.12 We must solve for x in $35 + x = 4(5 + x)$. We obtain $35 + x = 20 + 4x$, then $15 = 3x$, so $x = 5$.

P1.14 Let A be Alice's age and B be Bob's age. We're told $A = B + 5$ and $A + B = 25$. Substituting the first equation into the second we find $(B + 5) + B = 25$, which is the same as $2B = 20$, so Bob is 10 years old. Alice is 15 years old.

P1.15 The first shop can bind $4500/30 = 150$ books per day. The second shop can bind $4500/45 = 100$ books per day. The combined production capacity rate is $150 + 100 =$

250 books per day. It will take $4500/250 = 18$ days to bind the books when the two shops work in parallel.

P1.16 Let t_m denote the time when the two planes meet, as measured from the moment the second plane departs. Since it left one hour earlier, the slower plane will have travelled a distance $600(t_\text{m}+1)$ km when they meet. The faster plane will have travelled the distance $900t_\text{m}$ km when they meet. Combining the two expressions we find $600(t_\text{m}+1) = 900t_\text{m}$. The time when the planes meet is $t_\text{m} = 2$ hours after the departure of the second plane.

P1.17 This is a funny nonsensical problem that showed up on a school exam. I'm just checking to make sure you're still here.

P1.21 Using the quadratic formula, we find $x = \frac{m\pm\sqrt{m^2-8m}}{4}$. If $m^2 - 8m \geqslant 0$, the solutions are real. If $m^2 - 8m < 0$, the solutions will be complex numbers. Factoring the expressions and plugging in some numbers, we observe that $m^2 - 8m = m(m-8) < 0$ for all $m \in (0, 8)$.

P1.23 See `bit.ly/float64prec` for the calculations.

P1.24 For **c)**, complete the square on the left side: $2x^2 + x = 2(x+\frac{1}{4})^2 - \frac{1}{8}$. The inequality $2x^2 + x \geqslant 1$ can be rewritten as $2(x+\frac{1}{4})^2 \geqslant 1 + \frac{1}{8} = \frac{9}{8}$. Dividing by 2 on both sides gives $(x+\frac{1}{4})^2 \geqslant \frac{9}{16}$. Taking the square root produces $|x+\frac{1}{4}| \geqslant \frac{3}{4}$, which is satisfied if $x \geqslant \frac{1}{2}$ or if $x \leqslant -1$. Use the union operation to combine the two parts of the solution interval.

P1.25 The running time of Algorithm Q grows linearly with the size of the problem, whereas Algorithm P's running time grows quadratically. To find the size of the problem when the algorithms take the same time, we solve $P(n) = Q(n)$, which is $0.002n^2 = 0.5n$. The solution is $n = 250$. For $n > 250$, the linear-time algorithm (Algorithm Q) will take less time.

P1.29 Solve for b in Pythagoras' formula $c^2 = a^2 + b^2$ with $c = \varphi$, and $a = \sqrt{\varphi}$. The triangle with sides 1, $\sqrt{\varphi}$, and φ is called Kepler's triangle.

P1.30 Use Pythagoras' theorem to find x. Then use $\cos(30°) = \frac{\sqrt{3}}{2} = \frac{x}{z}$ to find z. Finally use $\sin(30°) = \frac{1}{2} = \frac{y}{z}$ to find y.

P1.31 Observe the two right-angle triangles drawn in Figure 1.65. From the triangle with angle 25° we know $\tan 25° = \frac{h}{800+d}$. From the triangle with angle 20° we know $\tan 20° = \frac{h}{1800+d}$. We isolate h in both equations and eliminate h by equating $(1800 + d)\tan 25° = \tan 20°(800+d)$. Solving for d we find $d = \frac{1800\tan 20° - 800\tan 25°}{\tan 25° - \tan 20°} = 2756.57\,\text{m}$. Finally we use $\tan 25° = \frac{h}{800+d}$ again to obtain $h = \tan 25°(800+d) = 1658.46\,\text{m}$.

P1.32 Consider the right-angle triangle with base x and opposite side 2000. Looking at the diagram we see that $\theta = 24°$. We can then use the relation $\tan 24° = \frac{2000}{x}$ and solve for x.

P1.34 The internal angles of an equilateral triangle are all 60°. Draw three radial lines that connect the centre of the circle to each vertex of the triangle. The equilateral triangle is split into three obtuse triangles with angle measures 30°, 30°, and 120°. Split each of these obtuse sub-triangles down the middle to obtain six right-angle triangles with hypotenuse 1. The side of the equilateral triangle is equal to two times the base of the right-angle triangles $a = 2\cos(30°) = \sqrt{3}$. To find the area, we use $A_\triangle = \frac{1}{2}ah$, where $h = 1 + \sin(30°)$.

P1.35 We know $\sin^2(\theta) = \frac{1}{2}(1-\cos(2\theta))$ and $\cos^2(\theta) = \frac{1}{2}(1+\cos(2\theta))$, so their product is $\frac{1}{4}(1-\cos(2\theta)\cos(2\theta))$, and $\cos(2\theta)\cos(2\theta) = \cos^2(2\theta)$. Using the power-reduction formula on the term $\cos^2(2\theta)$ gives $\sin^2\theta\cos^2\theta = \frac{1}{4}\left(1 - \frac{1}{2}(1+\cos(4\theta))\right)$.

P1.36 Split the octagon into eight isosceles triangles. The height of each triangle will be 1, and its angle measure at the centre will be $\frac{360°}{8} = 45°$. Split each of these triangles into two halves down the middle. The octagon is now split into 16 similar right-angle triangles with angle measure 22.5° at the centre. In a right-angle triangle with angle 22.5° and adjacent side 1, what is the length of the opposite side? The opposite side of each of the 16 triangles is $\frac{b}{2} = \tan(22.5°)$, so the perimeter of the octagon is $P_{\circ} = 16\tan(22.5°)$. In general, if a unit circle is inscribed inside an n-sided regular polygon, the perimeter of the polygon is $P_n = 2n\tan\left(\frac{360°}{2n}\right)$. To find the area of the octagon, we use the formula $A_{\triangle} = \frac{1}{2}bh$, with $b = 2\tan(22.5°)$ and $h = 1$ to find the area of each isosceles triangle. The area of the octagon is $A_{\circ} = 8 \cdot \frac{1}{2}(2\tan(22.5°))(1) = 8\tan(22.5°)$. For an n-sided regular polygon the area formula is $A_n = n\tan\left(\frac{360°}{2n}\right)$. Bonus points if you can tell me what happens to the formulas for P_n and A_n as n goes to infinity (see `bit.ly/1jGU1Kz`).

P1.40 Initially the horizontal distance between the observer and the plane is $d_1 = \frac{2000}{\tan 30°}$ m. After 10 seconds, the distance is $d_2 = \frac{2000}{\tan 55°}$ m. Velocity is change in distance divided by the time $v = \frac{d_1 - d_2}{10} = 206.36$ m/s. To convert m/s into km/h, we must multiply by the appropriate conversion factors: $206.36\,\text{m/s} \times \frac{1\,\text{km}}{1000\,\text{m}} \times \frac{3600\,\text{s}}{1\,\text{h}} = 742.92$ km/h.

P1.41 The volume of the water stays constant and is equal to $1000\,\text{cm}^3$. Initially the height of the water h_1 can be obtained from the formula for the volume of a cylinder $1000\,\text{cm}^3 = h_1\pi(8.5\,\text{cm})^2$, so $h_1 = 4.41\,\text{cm}$. After the bottle is inserted, the water has the shape of a cylinder with a cylindrical part missing. The volume of water is $1000\,\text{cm}^3 = h_2\left(\pi(8.5\,\text{cm})^2 - \pi(3.75\,\text{cm})^2\right)$. We find $h_2 = 5.47\,\text{cm}$. The change in height is $h_2 - h_1 = 5.47 - 4.41 = 1.06\,\text{cm}$.

P1.42 Using the law of cosines for the angles α_1 and α_2, we obtain the equations $7^2 = 8^2 + 12^2 - 2(8)(12)\cos\alpha_1$ and $11^2 = 4^2 + 12^2 - 2(4)(12)\cos\alpha_2$ from which we find $\alpha_1 = 34.09°$ and $\alpha_2 = 66.03°$. In the last step we use the law of cosines again to obtain $x^2 = 8^2 + 4^2 - 2(8)(4)\cos(34.09° + 66.03°)$.

P1.44 The length of the horizontal part of the rope is $\ell_h = 4\sin 40$. The circular portion of the rope that hugs the pulley has length $\frac{1}{4}$ of the circumference of a circle with radius $r = 50\,\text{cm} = 0.5\,\text{m}$. Using the formula $C = 2\pi r$, we find $\ell_c = \frac{1}{4}(2\pi(0.5)) = \frac{\pi}{4}$. The vertical part of the rope has length $\ell_v = 4\cos 40 + 2$. The total length of rope is $\ell_h + \ell_c + \ell_v = 8.42\,\text{m}$.

P1.45 The rectangle's area is equal to its length times its height $A_{\text{rect}} = \ell h$.

P1.46 The box's volume is $V = w \times h \times \ell = 10.5 \times 7 \times 22.3 = 1639\,\text{cm}^3$=1.639 L.

P1.47 We didn't really cover these concepts in the book, but since we're on the topic let's define some vocabulary. The *complement* of an acute angle is its defect from a right angle; that is, the angle by which it falls short of a right angle. (i) Two angles are complementary when their sum is 90°. The *supplement* of an angle is its defect from two right angles, that is, the angle by which it falls short of 180°. (ii) Two angles are supplementary when their sum is 180°. Angles that are complementary or supplementary to the same angle are equal to one another.

We'll now use these facts and the diagram below to find the angle θ.

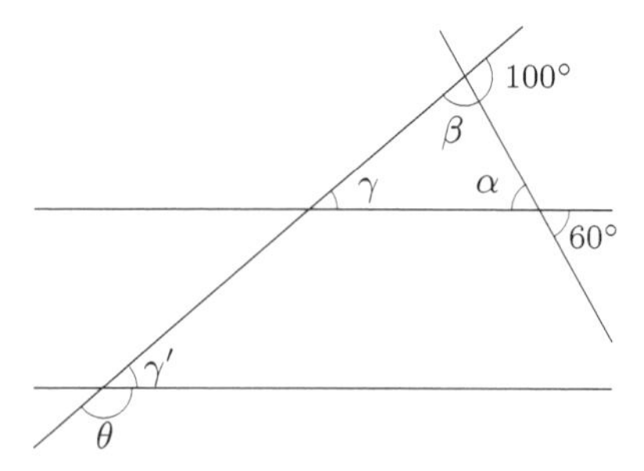

The angle α is vertically opposite to the angle $60°$ so $\alpha = 60°$. The angle β is supplementary to the angle $100°$ so $\beta = 180 - 100 = 80°$. The sum of the angles in a triangle is $180°$ so $\gamma = 180° - \alpha - \beta = 40°$. The two horizontal lines are parallel so the diagonally cutting line makes the same angle with them: $\gamma' = \gamma = 40°$. The angle θ is supplementary to the angle γ' so $\theta = 180 - 40 = 140°$.

P1.48 The base of this triangle has length $2r$ and each side has length $R + r$. If you split this triangle through the middle, each half is a right triangle with an angle at the centre $\frac{360°}{24} = 15°$, hypotenuse $R + r$, and opposite side r. We therefore have $\sin 15° = \frac{r}{R+r}$. After rearranging this equation, we find $\frac{R}{r} = \frac{1-\sin 15°}{\sin 15°} = 2.8637$.

P1.51 The tank's total capacity is $15 \times 6 \times 5 = 450\,\text{m}^3$. If 30% of its capacity is spent, then 70% of the capacity remains: $315\,\text{m}^3$. Knowing that $1\,\text{m}^3 = 1000\,\text{L}$, we find there are 315 000 L in the tank.

P1.52 The first tank contains $\frac{1}{4} \times 4000 = 1000\,\text{L}$. The second tank contains three times more water, so 3000 L. The total is 4000 L.

P1.53 Let's define w and h to be the width and the height of the hole. Define d to be the distance from the hole to the sides of the lid. The statement of the problem dictates the following three equations must be satisfied: $w + 2d = 40$, $h + 2d = 30$, and $wh = 500$. After some manipulations, we find $w = 5(1 + \sqrt{21})$, $h = 5(\sqrt{21} - 1)$ and $d = \frac{1}{2}(35 - 5\sqrt{21})$.

P1.54 The amount of wood in a pack of wood is proportional to the area of a circle $A = \pi r^2$. The circumference of this circle is equal to the length of the rope $C = \ell$. Note the circumference is proportional to the radius $C = 2\pi r$. If we want double the area, we need the circle to have radius $\sqrt{2}r$, which means the circumference needs to be $\sqrt{2}$ times larger. If we want a pack with double the wood, we need to use a rope of length $\sqrt{2}\ell$.

P1.55 In 10 L of a 60% acid solution there are 6 L of acid and 4 L of water. A 20% acid solution will contain four times as much water as it contains acid, so 6 L acid and 24 L water. Since the 10 L we start from already contains 4 L of water, we must add 20 L.

P1.56 The document must have a 768/1004 aspect ratio, so its height must be $6 \times \frac{1004}{768} = 7.84375$ inches.

P1.57 If we rewrite $1 + 2 + 3 + \cdots + 98 + 99 + 100$ by pairing numbers, we obtain the sum $(1 + 100) + (2 + 99) + (3 + 98) + \cdots$. This list has 50 terms and each term has the value 101. Therefore $1 + 2 + 3 + \cdots + 100 = 50 \times 101 = 5050$.

P1.62 An nAPR of 12% means the monthly interest rate is $\frac{12\%}{12} = 1\%$. After 10 years you'll owe $\$5000(1.01)^{120} = \$16501.93$. Yikes!

P1.63 The graphs of the functions are shown in Figure A.1. Observe that $f(x)$ decreases to 37% of its initial value when $x = 2$. The increasing exponential $g(x)$ reaches 63% of its maximum value at $x = 2$.

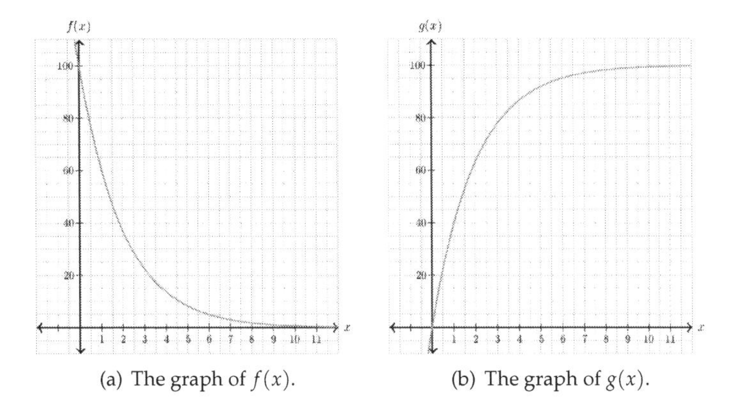

(a) The graph of $f(x)$. (b) The graph of $g(x)$.

Figure A.1: The graphs of the two functions from **P1.63**.

P1.64 We're looking for the time t such that $Q(t)/Q_o = \frac{1}{2}$, which is the same as $e^{-5t} = 0.5$. Taking logarithms of both sides we find $-5t = \ln(0.5)$, and solving for t we find $t = 0.14\,\text{s}$.

P1.65 We're told $T(24)/T_o = \frac{1}{2} = e^{-24/\tau}$, which we can rewrite as $\ln(\frac{1}{2}) = -24/\tau$. Solving for τ, we find $\tau = \frac{24}{\ln 2} = 34.625\,\text{min}$. To find the time the body takes to reach 1% of its initial temperature, we must solve for t in $T(t)/T_o = 0.01 = e^{-t/34.625}$. We find $t = 159.45\,\text{min}$.

P1.67 There exists at least one banker who is not a crook. Another way of saying the same thing is "not all bankers are crooks"—just *most* of them.

P1.68 Everyone steering the ship at Monsanto ought to burn in hell, forever.

P1.69 **a)** Investors with money but without connections. **b)** Investors with connections but no money. **c)** Investors with both money and connections.

Chapter 2 solutions

Answers to problems

P2.1 The particle is gaining speed and its motion is a UAM. **P2.2** You're not running with UVM. **P2.3** (1) Speed is decreasing. (2) Speed is increasing. **P2.4** UAM before $t = t_0$ and UVM after $t = t_0$. **P2.5** $v_A = 6[\text{m/s}]$, $v_B = 6[\text{m/s}]$, $v_C = 8[\text{m/s}]$, $v_D = 8[\text{m/s}]$, and $v_E = 4[\text{m/s}]$. **P2.6** $v(t) = 9t^2 + 10t - 3$, $a(t) = 18t + 10$. **P2.7** (1) $g_{\text{jupiter}} = 24.5[\text{m/s}^2]$. (2) $y(t) = 4 - 12.25t^2$. **P2.8** (1) $v(t) = 12t + 2[\text{m/s}]$, $a(t) = 12[\text{m/s}^2]$. (2) $F = 60[\text{N}]$. **P2.9** (1) $a(t) = 2[\text{m/s}^2]$, $v(t) = 2t[\text{m/s}]$, and $x(t) = t^2[\text{m}]$. (2) $v(4) = 8[\text{m/s}]$. (3) $v = 6[\text{m/s}]$ when $x = 9[\text{m}]$. **P2.10** (1) $v(2) = 6[\text{m/s}]$, $x(2) = 4[\text{m}]$. (2) For $t > 2[\text{s}]$: $v(t) = 6 + 6(t-2)[\text{m/s}]$, $x(t) = 4 + 6(t-2) + 3(t-2)^2[\text{m}]$. (3) When $x = 49[\text{m}]$, $t = 5[\text{s}]$. (4) $v = 12[\text{m/s}]$ when $x = 13[\text{m}]$. **P2.11** (1) $v_{A\to B} = 0[\text{m/s}]$, $v_{C\to D} = 2[\text{m/s}]$, and $v_{E\to F} = -1.5[\text{m/s}]$. (2) From 0[s] to 2[s] the squirrel is not running, from 2[s] to 6[s] it's running forward, and from 6[s] to 9[s] it's running backward. The squirrel changes direction at $t = 6[\text{s}]$. **P2.12** (1) $v_i = 6[\text{m/s}]$. (2) $x(t) = 6t - t^2\ [\text{m}]$. **P2.13** (1) $x_1(t) = \frac{3}{2}t^2[\text{m}]$ and $x_2(t) = \frac{1}{2}t^2 + 3t + 4[\text{m}]$. (2) $x_1 = x_2 = 24[\text{m}]$ when $t = 4[\text{s}]$. **P2.14** (1) $x_i = 7[\text{m}]$ and $v_i = 5[\text{m/s}]$. (2) $v(t) = 4t + 5\ [\text{m/s}]$ and $a(t) = 4[\text{m/s}^2]$. (3) $x(5) = 82[\text{m}]$ and $v(5) = 25[\text{m/s}]$. **P2.15** $v_i = 4\sqrt{2}[\text{m/s}]$ and $t_{\text{stop}} = \sqrt{2}[\text{s}]$.

Solutions to problems

P2.1 The relation between velocity and time is linear and v increases with time. The rate at which the velocity increases is constant so the acceleration is constant.

P2.2 Your velocity during the first time interval (from $t = 0$[s] to $t = 2$[s]) is 1.5[m/s]. During the second time interval your velocity is 2.5[m/s], and during the third it is 3[m/s]. Your run is not a UVM.

P2.3 When the velocity and the acceleration are in opposite directions, the car's speed will decrease. When the velocity and the acceleration are in the same direction, the car's speed will increase.

P2.4 Use $F = ma$. When F is constant, a is constant and the motion is UAM. When $F = 0$, $a = 0$ and the motion is UVM.

P2.5 To find the velocity, calculate the area under the graph and add the areas for each step. Note the area is negative from D to E.

P2.6 Differentiate the function $x(t)$ to find the velocity $v(t)$. Differentiate $v(t)$ to find the acceleration $a(t)$.

P2.7 Use $v_f^2 - v_i^2 = 2a(y_f - y_i)$ to find the acceleration. Use the general equation $y(t) = y_i + v_i t + \frac{1}{2}at^2$ and plug in $y_i = 4$[m], $v_i = 0$[m/s], and $a = -24.5$[m/s^2] to find the height as a function of time.

P2.8 Differentiate the position with respect to t to find $v(t)$, then differentiate $v(t)$ to find $a(t)$. Use $F = ma$ to find the force.

P2.9 (1) Calculate $a(t)$ from Newton's 2nd law to obtain $a(t) = 2$[m/s^2]. Integrate with respect to time to obtain the velocity and then integrate again to find the position. (2) Plug $t = 4$[s] into $v(t)$. (3) Use the fourth equation to find the speed after the car has travelled 9[m].

P2.10 (1) Use integration to find $v(t) = \frac{3}{2}t^2$[m/s] and $x(t) = \frac{1}{2}t^3$[m], then plug in $t = 2$[s]. (2) To describe UAM starting at $t = 2$[s], use the general equation $x(t) = x_2 + v_2(t-2) + \frac{1}{2}a(t-2)^2$, where $x_2 = 4$[m] and $v_2 = 6$[m/s] are the initial conditions at $t = 2$[s]. (3) Solve for t in $x(t) = 49$[m]. (4) Use $v_f^2 - v_i^2 = 2a(x - x_2)$ with $v_i = 6$[m/s], $v_f = 12$[m/s], and $x_2 = 4$[m] to find the displacement during the UAM.

P2.11 (1) In each time interval, divide Δx by Δt to find the velocity. (2) Increasing x means the squirrel is running forward. Decreasing x means the squirrel is running backward.

P2.12 Use the fourth equation of motion to find $v_i = 6$[m/s], then construct the position function $x(t) = x_i + v_i t + \frac{1}{2}at^2$ using $x_i = 0$[m], $v_i = 6$[m/s], and $a = -2$[m/s^2].

P2.13 Find the position functions of both dogs, then equate them to obtain an equation with t unknown. Solve $x_1(t) = x_2(t)$ for t to find the time when the dogs meet.

P2.14 Recall that the coefficient in front of t in the general form of the position function is the initial velocity v_i and the constant term is x_i. Use differentiation to find the velocity and acceleration functions and then evaluate them at $t = 5$[s].

P2.15 Use the fourth equation of motion twice. First between $x = 2$[m] and $x = 4$[m] to find the acceleration $a = -4$[m/s^2], then between $x = 0$[m] and $x = 4$[m] to find v_i. Construct the position as a function of time and find the time needed to reach $x = 4$[m].

Chapter 3 solutions

Answers to problems

P3.1 a) $\vec{u}_1 = 5\angle 90°$. **b)** $\vec{u}_2 = \sqrt{5}\angle 63.4°$. **c)** $\vec{u}_3 = \sqrt{5}\angle 243.4°$ or $\sqrt{5}\angle -116.6°$. **P3.2 a)** $\vec{v}_1 = (17.32, 10)$. **b)** $\vec{v}_2 = (0, -10)$. **c)** $\vec{v}_3 = (-4.33, 2.5)$. **P3.3 a)** $\vec{w}_1 = 9.06\hat{\imath} + 4.23\hat{\jmath}$. **b)** $\vec{w}_2 = -7\hat{\jmath}$. **c)** $\vec{w}_3 = 3\hat{\imath} - 2\hat{\jmath} + 3\hat{k}$. **P3.4 a)** $(3,4)$. **b)** $(0,1)$. **c)** $(7.33, 6.5)$. **P3.5** $Q = (5.73, 4)$. **P3.6 a)** 6. **b)** 0. **c)** -3. **d)** $(-2,1,1)$. **e)** $(3,-3,0)$. **f)** $(7,-5,1)$. **P3.7 a)** $(2,3,3,7,8)$. **b)** $(0,-1,-3,-1,-2)$. **c)** 30. **P3.8** $(-\frac{2}{3}, \frac{1}{3}, \frac{2}{3})$ or $(\frac{2}{3}, -\frac{1}{3}, -\frac{2}{3})$. **P3.9** $(12,-4,-12)$. **P3.10 a)** $2i$. **b)** $\frac{1}{4}(5+i)$. **c)** $2+i$. **P3.11 a)** $x = \pm 2i$. **b)** $x = -16$. **c)** $x = -1-i$ and $x = -1+i$. **d)** $x = i$, $x = -i$, $x = \sqrt{3}i$, and $x = -\sqrt{3}i$. **P3.12 a)** $\sqrt{5}$. **b)** $\frac{1}{2}(-3+i)$. **c)** $-5-5i$. **P3.13** $t = 52$ weeks. **P3.14** The tractor's trajectory is a half-circle. The total distance travelled is 3.14[km].

Solutions to selected problems

P3.8 See `bit.ly/1cOa8yo` for calculations.

P3.9 Any multiple of the vector $\vec{u}_1 \times \vec{u}_2 = (-3,1,3)$ is perpendicular to both $\vec{u}_1$ and $\vec{u}_2$. We must find a multiplier $t \in \mathbb{R}$ such that $t(-3,1,3)\cdot(1,1,0) = 8$. Computing the dot product we find $-3t + t = 8$, so $t = -4$. The vector we're looking for is $(12,-4,-12)$. See `bit.ly/1nmYH8T` for calculations.

P3.13 We want the final state of the project to be 100% real: $p_f = 100$. Since we start from $p_o = 100i$, the rotation required is $e^{-i\alpha h(t)} = e^{-i\frac{\pi}{2}}$, which means $\alpha h(t) = \frac{\pi}{2}$. We can rewrite this equation as $h(t) = 0.2t^2 = \frac{\pi}{2\alpha}$ and solving for t we find $t = \sqrt{\frac{\pi}{2(0.002904)(0.2)}} = 52$ weeks.

P3.14 The direction of the tractor changes constantly throughout the day, and the overall trajectory has the shape of a half-circle. The total distance travelled by the tractor is equal to half the circumference of a circle of radius R. Since it took the tractor six hours of movement at $v = 0.524$[km/h] to travel half the circumference of the circle, we have $\frac{1}{2}C = \pi R = v(t_f - t_i) = 0.524(6)$, from which we find $R = 1$[km]. The total distance travelled by the tractor is $\pi R = 3.14$[km].

Chapter 4 solutions

Answers to exercises

E4.1 7.5[m/s]. **E4.2** $E_{\text{lost}} = K_i - K_f = 19.7$[J].

Solutions to exercises

E4.1 Assume the initial velocity is in the x-direction. The initial momentum of the incoming ball is $\vec{p}_{1,\text{in}} = m\vec{v} = 3 \times 20\hat{\imath} = 60\hat{\imath}$. The initial momentum of the stationary ball is zero. The momentum after the collision is $\vec{p}_{\text{out}} = \vec{p}_{1,\text{in}} + \vec{p}_{2,\text{in}} = 60\hat{\imath} + 0 = 60\hat{\imath}$. The two balls stick together so the total mass of the system after the collision is $M = 3 + 5 = 8$[g]. The final velocity is $\vec{v}_{\text{out}} = \vec{p}_{\text{out}}/M = \frac{1}{8}(60,0) = (7.5,0)$[m/s].

E4.2 The energy that is lost is the kinetic energy. Before you catch the frisbee it has $K_i = \frac{1}{2}mv^2 = 19.7$[J] of kinetic energy. After you stop it with your hand, the frisbee has $K_f = 0$. The change in K before and after the frisbee is caught is $K_f - K_i = -19.7$[J] so $E_{\text{lost}} = 19.7$[J].

Answers to problems

P4.1 (1) With y pointing up $v_y(t) = v_{iy}t - \frac{1}{2}gt^2$, with y pointing down $v_y(t) = -v_{iy}t + \frac{1}{2}gt^2$, where $v_{iy} = \|\vec{v}_i\| \sin\theta$. (2) The cat gets splashed! **P4.2** See solution. **P4.3** The particles have the same momentum. The first particle has twice the kinetic energy of the second. **P4.4** (1) $\vec{v}_B = \vec{v}$, (2) $\vec{v}_B = 3\vec{v}$, and (3) $\vec{v}_B = 2\vec{v}$. **P4.5** In position 1, there is only K. In position 2 there is K, U_s, and U_g. **P4.6** The ball will have the same speed on Earth and on the Moon. **P4.7** The ball will have a higher speed on Earth. **P4.8** The torque on M is zero. The rod's angular velocity will remain ω. **P4.9** $\|\vec{N}_{\text{bottom}}\| > \|\vec{N}_{\text{top}}\|$. **P4.10** The balls will have the same speed when they hit the ground. **P4.11** Since the three pendulums' strings have the same length ℓ, they have the same period $T_1 = T_2 = T_3$. **P4.12** $T_1 = 1.42$[s], $T_2 = 1.74$[s], and $T_3 = 2.01$[s]. **P4.13** The pendulum swings through its centre position with greater speed on Earth. **P4.14** Energies present: K, K_r, and U_g. Momenta present: $\vec{p}$ and L. **P4.15** The period will decrease. **P4.16** $F_{\text{push}} = 4.71$[N]. **P4.17** The pulley with the larger radius R will spin faster and have more K_r. **P4.18** (1) $v_2 = -5.4$[m/s]. (2) Not elastic. **P4.19** (1) See solution. (2) $a_1 = 1$[m/s^2], $a_2 = 0$[m/s^2], and $a_3 = -1$[m/s^2]. (3) $F = 40$[N]. **P4.20** $v_{\text{obj}} = \sqrt{2}\,v$ [m/s]. **P4.21** (1) $\mathcal{T} = 4.9$[N m]. (2) $W = 9.6$[J]. **P4.22** $m = 1.46$[kg]. **P4.23** $\|\vec{F}\| = 3$[N]. **P4.24** (1) $h = d$. (2) $v_i = 19.8$[m/s] and $t_{\text{hit}} = 1.43$[s]. **P4.25** (1) $\mu_s \geqslant \frac{M}{m_1+m_2}$. (2) $\mu_s \geqslant 0.421$. (3) $a = \frac{Mg}{m_1+m_2+M}$. **P4.26** (1) $d = 4.41$[m]. (2) $\vec{v}_{2i} = 5\angle 90°$[m/s]. **P4.27** (1) $F_{\text{lift}} = 158 \times 10^3$[N]. (2) The vertical acceleration is zero so the plane will maintain a horizontal trajectory. **P4.28** $v = 10.2$[m/s]. **P4.29** (1) $v_i = \left(\frac{\sin 30}{\tan 60} + \cos 30\right)\sqrt{2dg\mu_k}$. (2) $v_i = 2.24$[m/s], $v_1 = 1.12$[m/s] and $v_2 = 1.94$[m/s]. (3) 0.233[m]. (4) The collision is elastic. **P4.30** (1) $\mathcal{T} = 3.6$[N m]. (2) 18.9 revolutions. **P4.31** The solid cylinder will reach the bottom first. **P4.32** $t_{\text{flight}} = 2t_{\text{top}} = 4.1$[s]. **P4.33** $\mu_k = \frac{M^2}{m^2}\frac{L}{d}$. **P4.34** Range is 0.65[m] greater on the summit than on the North Pole. **P4.35** $x(t) = 2t^2 + 10t + 20$ in metres. **P4.36** The slug loses contact at $R = \frac{0.4g}{\omega^2}$. **P4.37** upward $F_{fs} >$ stationary $F_{fs} >$ downward F_{fs}. **P4.38** The coin farthest from the centre will fly off first. **P4.39** (1) $F_f = 3000$[N] per wheel. (2) $\mathcal{T} = 180$[N m]. (3) 2.21 turns. (4) $2.\overline{7}$[m]. **P4.40** $x_f = 2.09$[m]. **P4.41** $y(x) = \ell \sin(\theta_{\max}) \cos((\omega/v)x)$.

Solutions to problems

P4.1 When the y-axis points up, $a_y = -g$ and v_{iy} is positive. The opposite applies when the y-axis is directed downward. The balloon moves at the same horizontal speed as the cat; the balloon is always directly above the cat, and splashes the cat when it comes back down. The cat is not happy about that.

P4.2 (1) $\vec{F}_4$ points right and is perpendicular to the left face of the block, (2) $\vec{F}_4$ points up and is perpendicular to the bottom face of the block, and (3) $\vec{F}_4$ points left and is perpendicular to the right face of the block. In each case, the sum of the forces produces an $\vec{a}_{\text{block}}$ in the desired direction.

P4.3 Calculate the momentum and energy using the formulas $\|\vec{p}\| = m\|\vec{v}\|$ and $K = \frac{1}{2}mv^2$. Observe that two objects moving with equal momentum can carry different amounts of kinetic energy; this problem shows momentum and energy are different quantities.

P4.4 In each case, the sum $\vec{p}_A + \vec{p}_B$ after the separation equals the momentum of the station before the compartments split apart: $2m\vec{v} = m\vec{v}_A + m\vec{v}_B$.

P4.5 When there is a velocity, there is kinetic energy K. When the spring is stretched, there is spring potential energy U_s. When the position of the mass is above or below $y = 0$, there is gravitational potential energy U_g.

P4.6 The ball's initial kinetic energy is the same on Earth and on the Moon. Because of conservation of energy, when the ball returns to ground level, it will have the same kinetic energy it had initially, regardless of the value of g.

P4.7 Define the zero potential-energy level to be at ground level. The bottom of the 10[m] pit has a lower potential energy on Earth because $g_{\text{Earth}} > g_{\text{Moon}}$. The ball will therefore gain more kinetic energy on Earth when it reaches the bottom of the pit and thus have a higher speed.

P4.8 The rotation of the mass M is at a constant angular velocity so the net torque on the mass is zero. Let us denote by L_{rod}, L_{mass}, and L_{sys} the angular momenta of the rod, the mass M, and the total angular momentum of the mass-on-a-rod system. Initially, $L_{\text{sys}} = L_{\text{rod}} + L_{\text{mass}}$. When the mass M detaches, its velocity $\vec{v}$ will remain the same as before the moment it detached. This means its angular momentum L_{mass} will remain the same after it detaches. This in turn implies the rod will also maintain its angular momentum, so its angular velocity will remain ω.

P4.9 At the top of the loop, the car's weight contributes to the centripetal force. At the bottom, the loop must exert a force that counteracts the car's weight in addition to the centripetal force. Therefore, the normal force of the loop on the car is larger at the bottom of the loop.

P4.10 The two balls have the same initial kinetic and initial potential energy. They also have the same final potential energy so they must have the same final kinetic energy. They will hit the ground at the same speed.

P4.11 The period T is not related to the maximum angle of oscillation $\theta_{\max}$. The clocks will have the same T if their strings have the same length.

P4.12 Using the formula $T = 2\pi\sqrt{\frac{\ell}{g}}$ and $g = 9.81[\text{m/s}^2]$ on Earth, we find $T_1 = 1.42[\text{s}]$, $T_2 = 1.74[\text{s}]$, and $T_3 = 2.01[\text{s}]$.

P4.13 The gravitational acceleration on Earth is stronger than on the Moon so the pendulum has a greater potential energy when deviated by an angle $\theta_{\max}$ on Earth. Specifically, $U_{gi} = mg\ell(1 - \cos\theta_{\max})$. When it swings to $\theta = 0$, the pendulum will gain more kinetic energy and hence have higher speed on Earth.

P4.14 The diver is rotating, so we must consider the rotational kinetic energy K_r and the angular momentum L associated with this rotation. The kinetic energy K and linear momentum $\vec{p}$ exist every time there is linear motion. Finally, we must also consider the potential energy U_g since it is part of the physics model for objects moving in a gravitational field.

P4.15 Because $T = 2\pi\sqrt{\frac{\ell}{g}}$, the period will decrease as the string shortens.

P4.16 First calculate the normal force N between the floor on the box. Next calculate the force of friction $F_{fk} = \mu_k N$. For the box to move at constant velocity, you must counteract the kinetic force of friction and make the net force on the box zero. Therefore, $F_{\text{push}} = F_{fk} = 4.71[\text{N}]$.

P4.17 The two pulleys have the same moment of inertia I. The string wound around the larger radius R will produce the larger torque. Higher torque will produce more angular acceleration and therefore a bigger angular velocity and angular kinetic energy.

P4.18 (1) The momentum of the players after the collision is zero, therefore the sum of their momenta before the collision must also be zero: $m_1v_1 + m_2v_2 = 0$. We can find v_2 since m_1, m_2, and v_1 are known. (2) Since the players come to a stop after the collision, they lose all their kinetic energy, thus the collision is not elastic. In fact, the collision is completely inelastic.

P4.19 (1) Build a force diagram and include the weights, tension forces, and the force exerted by the professor. The total mass of the system is $2m = 40[\text{kg}]$. (2) Use the 4th equation of motion to calculate the acceleration. (3) Apply Newton's 2nd law $F = ma$ for the system.

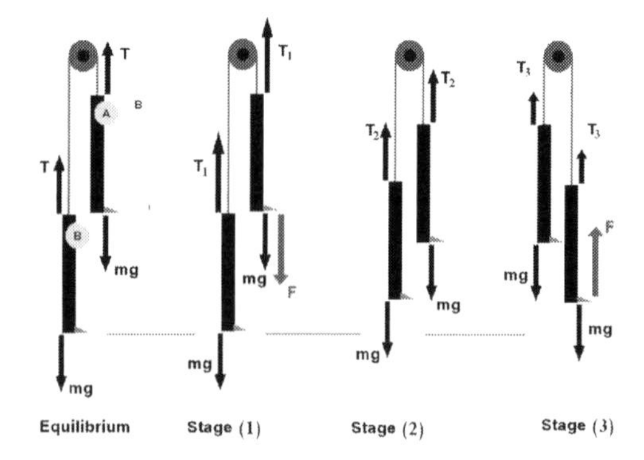

P4.20 The work done to compress the spring transforms into kinetic energy. Equate the kinetic energy with the work stored in the spring, then compare it to the initial kinetic energy given to the mass: W_a[J] turns into speed v[m/s], while $2W_a$[J] turns into speed $\sqrt{2}\,v$ [m/s], because $K = \frac{1}{2}mv^2$[J].

P4.21 Use the initial and final angular velocities and the equation $\omega(t) = \omega_i + \alpha t$ to calculate acceleration. Find the torque using $\mathcal{T} = I\alpha$. The work done is equal to the rotational kinetic energy gained by the door $K_r = \frac{1}{2}I(\omega_f)^2$.

P4.22 The spring's potential energy is equal to the sum of the linear and rotational kinetic energies of the ball: $\frac{1}{2}k(\Delta x)^2 = \frac{1}{2}mv^2 + \frac{1}{2}I_{\text{ball}}\omega^2$. Because the ball is rolling without skidding, we can calculate the linear velocity from the angular velocity and the radius $v = \omega R = 3$[m/s]. Substituting all knowns into the energy equation, we can solve for the mass m.

P4.23 In the case where the static friction between the blocks is strong enough for them to remain stuck together without slipping, the two blocks will act as a single block of mass $m_1 + m_2 = 1.25$[kg] pushed by an external force $\vec{F}$[N]. We can also analyze the contact forces (normal force and friction force) between the two blocks. The upper block feels a normal force of $N = 2.45$[N], and the maximum static friction that can exist between it and the bottom block is $\max F_{fs} = \mu_s N = 0.6$[N]. The upper block also feels the static friction force F_{fs} in the positive x-direction—this is the force that causes the block to accelerate in tandem with the block below it. Using $F = m_1 a_1$ for the upper block, we find that the friction force can cause a maximum acceleration of $a_1 = \frac{\max F_{fs}}{m_1} = 2.4$[m/s^2]. We can now find the amount of the external force F required to accelerate both blocks at 2.4[m/s^2] by using the equation $F = (m_1 + m_2)a = (0.25 + 1)2.4 = 3$[N].

P4.24 Find the time $t = t_{\text{hit}}$ when the ball reaches height $\frac{h}{2}$, then plug that time into the position equations of the shell so that $x_{\text{shell}}(t_{\text{hit}}) = 0 + v_i\cos(45°)t_{\text{hit}} = d$ and $y_{\text{shell}}(t_{\text{hit}}) = 0 + v_i\sin(45°)t_{\text{hit}} - \frac{1}{2}gt_{\text{hit}}^2 = \frac{h}{2}$.

P4.25 Draw a force diagram for each block considering acceleration is zero, then construct three equations for the three blocks and calculate μ_s. For part (3), you can reuse the force diagram but this time the acceleration is not zero. The three blocks have the same acceleration.

P4.26 To answer (1), find the maximum range of the first ball. Half of this range is the distance d where you should fire the second ball. To answer (2), find the maximum height reached by the first ball, then use conservation of energy to find the initial velocity needed for the second ball.

P4.27 We must calculate the lift force F_{lift} whose horizontal (radial) component provides the required centripetal acceleration: $F_{\text{lift}}\sin 30° = F_r = m\frac{v^2}{R} = 14000\frac{(605.5/3.6)^2}{5000}$, so $F_{\text{lift}} = 158 \times 10^3$[N]. The vertical component of the lift force is $F_{\text{lift}} \cos 30° = 137.2 \times 10^3$[N], which equals the weight of the plane mg, thus the plane has no acceleration in the vertical direction.

P4.28 The bottle has linear kinetic energy $K_i = \frac{1}{2}m(12.5)^2$[J] before the subway starts braking. This energy transforms into both linear kinetic and rotational kinetic energy of the rolling bottle. Equating the energy before and after stopping, we obtain $\frac{1}{2}m(12.5)^2 = \frac{1}{2}mv^2 + \frac{1}{2}(\frac{1}{2}mr^2)\omega^2$. Cancelling the mass m and replacing the angular velocity ω using $\omega = \frac{v}{r}$, we can solve for v. We find $v = 10.2$[m/s].

P4.29 (1) Use conservation of momentum $\vec{p}_i = \vec{p}_f$ to construct two equations relating v_i, v_1, and v_2. Calculate the minimum v_2 that gets puck 2 to the pocket (such that puck 2 stops when it reaches the pocket) using the relation between work done by the force of friction and the kinetic energy of the puck $\Delta K = W$, then find v_i and v_1 using the previous equations. (2) Plug in the provided values. (3) Use $K_i = K_f + W_{\text{lost}}$ with $K_f = 0$. (4) Calculate $K_{1,i}$, then compare it to $K_{1,f} + K_{2,f}$ after the collision.

P4.30 Use $a = r\alpha$ to find α, then use $\mathcal{T} = I\alpha$ to find the torque. Use the angular equations of motion to find $\theta(4)$. The number of revolutions is $\frac{\theta(4)}{2\pi}$.

P4.32 This is a kinematics question. Start from the equation $v(t) = at + v_i$ and $a = -9.81$. We know $v(t_{\text{top}}) = 0$, so we can solve to find t_{top}.

P4.33 First we use $U_i = K_f$ for the pendulum, obtaining $MgL = \frac{1}{2}Mv_{\text{in}}^2$ and thus $v_{\text{in}} = \sqrt{2gL}$. Next we use a momentum reasoning $\vec{p}_{\text{in}} = \vec{p}_{\text{out}}$ where the incoming momentum is that of the mass M and the outgoing momentum is that of the mass m. The conservation of momentum equation becomes $Mv_{\text{in}} + 0 = 0 + mv_{\text{out}}$, where v_{out} is the velocity of the mass m after the collision, and the momentum of the pendulum is zero after the collision since it doesn't bounce back. Solving for v_{out} we find $v_{\text{out}} = \frac{M}{m}\sqrt{2gL}$. Finally, we use an energy calculation $K_i = W_{\text{lost}}$, which becomes $\frac{1}{2}m\left(\frac{M}{m}\sqrt{2gL}\right)^2 = mg\mu_k d$. After some simplifications, we find $\mu_k = \frac{M^2}{m^2}\frac{L}{d}$.

P4.34 We want to find the range—how far the ball will reach after being kicked—in both situations. The first thing to calculate is the total time of flight by solving for t in $0 = 0 + v_{iy}t + \frac{1}{2}(-g)t^2$. The time of flight will be 4.347[s] on the Nevado Huascarán summit, and 4.316[s] on the North Pole. The range in each case corresponds to $d = v_{ix}4.347 = 92.21$[m] and $d = v_{ix}4.316 = 91.56$[m]. The difference in range is $92.21 - 91.56 = 0.65$[m].

P4.36 The normal force between the slug and the turntable is $N = mg$. With the slug located at radius R, the centripetal acceleration required to keep the slug on the disk is $F_r = ma_r = m\frac{(R\omega)^2}{R}$. The friction force available is $F_f = 0.4mg$. The slug will fly off when the friction force becomes insufficient, which happens at a distance of $R = \frac{0.4g}{\omega^2}$ from the centre.

P4.37 The equation for F_{fs} is $F_{fs} = \mu_s N$, where N is the normal force (the contact force between the fridge and the elevator floor). The force diagram on the elevator reads $\sum F_y = N - mg = ma_y$. When the elevator is static, $a_y = 0$ so $N = mg$. If $a_y > 0$ (upward acceleration), then we must have $N > mg$; hence the friction force will be larger than when the elevator is static. When $a_y < 0$ (downward acceleration), N must be smaller than mg, and consequently there will be less F_{fs}.

P4.38 The coin farthest from the centre will be the first to fly off the spinning turntable because the centripetal force required to keep this coin turning is the largest. Recall that $F_r = ma_r$, $a_r = v^2/R$, and $v = \omega R$. If the turntable turns with angular velocity ω, the centripetal acceleration required to keep a coin turning in a radius R is $F_r = m\omega^2 R$. This centripetal force must be supplied by the static force of friction F_{fs} between the coin and the turntable. Larger Rs require more F_{fs}.

P4.39 (1) The friction force is proportional to the normal force. The friction on each side of each disk is $F_f = 0.3 \times 5000 = 1500$[N] for a total friction force of $F_f = 3000$[N] per wheel. (2) The friction force of the brakes acts with a leverage of 0.06[m], so the torque produced by each brake is $\mathcal{T} = 0.06 \times 3000 = 180$[N m]. (3) The kinetic energy of a 100[kg] object moving at 10[m/s] is equal to $K_i = \frac{1}{2}100(10)^2 = 5000$[J]. We'll use $K_i - W = 0$, where W is the work done by the brakes. Let θ_{stop} be the angle of rotation of the wheels when the bike stops. The work done by each brake is $180\theta_{\text{stop}}$. It will take a total of $\theta_{\text{stop}} = \frac{5000}{360} = 13.\overline{8}$[rad] to stop the bike. This angle corresponds to 2.21 turns of the wheels. (4) Your stopping distance will be $13.\overline{8} \times 0.20 = 2.\overline{7}$[m]. Yay for disk brakes!

P4.40 The energy equation $\sum E_i = \sum E_f$ in this case is $U_i = U_f + K_f$, or $mg(6 - 6\cos 50°) = mg(6 - 6\cos 10°) + \frac{1}{2}mv^2$, which can be simplified to $v^2 = 12g(\cos 10° - \cos 50°)$. Solving for v we find $v = 4.48$[m/s]. Now for the projectile motion part. The initial velocity is 4.48[m/s] at an angle of 10° with respect to the horizontal, so $\vec{v}_i = (4.42, 0.778)$[m/s]. Tarzan's initial position is $(x_i, y_i) = (6\sin(10), 6[1 - \cos(10)]) = (1.04, 0.0911)$[m]. To find the total time of flight, we solve for t in $0 = -4.9t^2 + 0.778t + 0.0911$ and find $t = 0.237$[s]. Tarzan will land at $x_f = 6\sin(10) + 4.42t = 2.09$[m].

P4.41 We begin by writing the general equation of motion for a pendulum: $\theta(t) = \theta_{\max}\cos(\omega t)$, where $\omega = \sqrt{g/\ell}$. Enter the walkway, which is moving to the left at velocity v. If we choose the $x = 0$ coordinate at a time when $\theta(t) = \theta_{\max}$, the pattern on the walkway can be described by the equation $y(x) = \ell\sin(\theta_{\max})\cos(kx)$, where $k = 2\pi/\lambda$, and λ tells us how long (measured as a distance in the x-direction) it takes for the pendulum to complete one cycle. One full swing of the bucket takes $T = 2\pi/\omega$[s]. In that time, the moving walkway will have moved a distance of vT metres. So one cycle in space (one wavelength) is $\lambda = vT = v2\pi/\omega$. We conclude that the equation of the paint on the moving sidewalk is $y(x) = \ell\sin(\theta_{\max})\cos((\omega/v)x)$.

Chapter 5 solutions

Answers to exercises

E5.1 (a) 0. (b) 2. (c) ∞. Each limit expression describes what happens to the ratio of two functions for large values of the input variable. **E5.2** (a) 2. (b) ∞. (c) $-\infty$. (d) $\frac{3}{4}$. (e) 0. (f) 0. **E5.3** Max at $x = \frac{1}{3}$; $f\left(\frac{1}{3}\right) = \frac{4}{27}$. **E5.4** (a) $\frac{2}{x-3} + \frac{1}{x+4}$, $\int(\text{a})\,dx = 2\ln(x-3) + \ln(x+4)$. (b) $\frac{1}{x-1} + \frac{2}{x-2}$, $\int(\text{b})\,dx = \ln(x-1) + 2\ln(x-2)$. (c) $\frac{1}{4(x-1)} - \frac{1}{4(x+1)} + \frac{1}{2(x+1)^2}$, $\int(\text{c})\,dx = \frac{1}{4}\ln(x-1) - \frac{1}{4}\ln(x+1) - \frac{1}{2}\frac{1}{x+1}$. **E5.5** $\frac{\pi R^2 h}{3}$. **E5.6** $\frac{\pi R^2 h}{3}$. **E5.7** (a) $caN + cb\frac{N(N+1)}{2}$. (b) $ca^2N + cabN(N+1) + cb^2\frac{N(N+1)(2N+1)}{6}$. (c) π^2.

Answers to problems

P5.1 (1) -6. (2) 2. (3) Doesn't exist. (4) 8.6 (eyeballing it). (5) -5. (6) Doesn't exist. (7) -2. (8) -2. (9) -2. (10) No. (11)$[-10,-5)$, $[-5,2)$, $[2,5)$, $(5,10]$. **P5.2** (a) 4. (b) 6. (c) 5. **P5.4** (1) Doesn't exist. (2) 0. (3) Doesn't exist. (4) 0. (5) Doesn't exist. (6) 0. (7) 1. (8) 0. (9) 1. **P5.5** (1) Doesn't exist. (2) 3. (3) $2a$. **P5.7** (1) $\frac{dy}{dx} = 13x^{12}$. (2) $\frac{dy}{dx} = -\frac{3}{2}x^{-\frac{5}{2}}$. (3) $\frac{dy}{dx} = 2ax^{(2a-1)}$. (4) $\frac{du}{dx} = 2.4x^{1.4}$. (5) $\frac{dz}{dx} = \frac{1}{3}x^{-\frac{2}{3}}$. (6) $\frac{dy}{dx} = -\frac{5}{3}x^{-\frac{8}{3}}$. (7) $\frac{du}{dx} = -\frac{8}{5}x^{-\frac{13}{5}}$. (8) $\frac{dy}{dx} = 2ax^{a-1}$. (9) $\frac{dy}{dx} = \frac{3}{q}x^{\frac{3-q}{q}}$. **P5.8** (1) $\frac{dy}{dx} = 3ax^2$. (2) $\frac{dy}{dx} = 13 \times \frac{3}{2}x^{\frac{1}{2}}$. (3) $\frac{dy}{dx} = 6x^{-\frac{1}{2}}$. (4) $\frac{dy}{dx} = \frac{1}{2}c^{\frac{1}{2}}x^{-\frac{1}{2}}$. (5) $\frac{du}{dz} = \frac{an}{c}z^{n-1}$. (6) $\frac{dy}{dt} = 2.36t$. **P5.9** (a) $1 + x + \frac{x^2}{2} + \frac{x^3}{6} + \frac{x^4}{24} + \ldots$; (b) $2ax + b$; (c) $3x^2 + 6ax + 3a^2$. **P5.10** (1) $\frac{dw}{dt} = a - bt$. (2) $\frac{dy}{dx} = 2x$. (3) $14110x^4 - 65404x^3 - 2244x^2 + 8192x + 1379$.

(4) $\frac{dx}{dy} = 2y+8$. (5) $185.9022654x^2 + 154.36334$. **P5.11** (1) $p'(x) = \frac{-5}{(3x+2)^2}$. (2) $q'(x) = \frac{6x^4+6x^3+9x^2}{(1+x+2x^2)^2}$. (3) $r'(x) = \frac{ad-bc}{(cx+d)^2}$. (4) $s'(x) = \frac{anx^{-n-1}+bnx^{n-1}+2nx^{-1}}{(x^{-n}+b)^2}$. **P5.12** (1) $\frac{x}{\sqrt{x^2+1}}$. (2) $\frac{x}{\sqrt{x^2+a^2}}$. (3) $-\frac{1}{2\sqrt{(a+x)^3}}$. (4) $\frac{ax}{\sqrt{(a-x^2)^3}}$. (5) $\frac{2a^2-x^2}{x^3\sqrt{x^2-a^2}}$. (6) $\frac{\frac{3}{2}x^2\left[\frac{8}{9}x(x^3+a)-(x^4+a)\right]}{(x^4+a)^{\frac{2}{3}}(x^3+a)^{\frac{3}{2}}}$. (7) $\frac{2a(x-a)}{(x+a)^3}$. (8) $-\frac{m}{n}x^{-\frac{m+n}{n}}$. (9) $\frac{1}{(1-x)\sqrt{1-x^2}}$. **P5.13** (1) $\frac{dw}{dx} = \frac{3x^2(3+3x^3)}{27\left(\frac{1}{2}x^3+\frac{1}{4}x^6\right)^3}$. (2) $\frac{dv}{dx} = -\frac{12x}{\sqrt{1+\sqrt{2}+3x^2}\left(\sqrt{3}+4\sqrt{1+\sqrt{2}+3x^2}\right)^2}$. (3) $\frac{du}{dx} = -\frac{x^2(\sqrt{3}+x^3)}{\sqrt{\left[1+\left(1+\frac{x^3}{\sqrt{3}}\right)^2\right]^3}}$. **P5.14** $f'(x) = ab(e^{ax}+e^{-ax})$. **P5.15** $u'(t) = 2at + \frac{2}{t}$. **P5.16** $\ln n$. **P5.17** $f'(x) = a^{bx}$. **P5.18** (1) $\frac{n}{x}$. (2) $\frac{3e^{-\frac{x}{x-1}}}{(x-1)^2}$. (3) $6xe^{-5x} - 5(3x^2+1)e^{-5x}$. (4) $6x(\sqrt{x}+1) + \frac{3x^2-1}{2\sqrt{x}}$. (5) $\frac{ax^{a-1}}{x^a+a}$. (6) $\frac{1-\ln(x+3)}{(x+3)^2}$. (7) $a^x\left(ax^{a-1}+x^a\ln a\right)$. (8) $\frac{1+x}{x}$. (9) $\frac{3}{x}(\ln ax)^2$. **P5.19** (a) $x^x(1+\ln x)$; (b) $2x(e^x)^x$; (c) $e^{x^x}x^x(1+\ln x)$. **P5.20** (1) $A\cos\left(\theta-\frac{\pi}{2}\right)$. (2) $2\sin\theta\cos\theta = \sin 2\theta$. (3) $5\cos 5\theta$. (4) $3\sin^2\theta\cos\theta$. (5) $-18\sin(\theta+6)$. (6) $\frac{-\sin\theta}{\cos\theta} = -\tan\theta$. **P5.21** $\frac{dy}{dt} = -n\sin(2\pi nt)$. **P5.22** (i) $a^x\ln a\cos a^x$. (ii) $\frac{dy}{dx} = \tan x\sec x$. (iii) $\frac{dy}{dx} = -\frac{1}{\sqrt{1-x^2}}$. (iv) $\frac{dy}{dx} = \frac{1}{1+x^2}$. (v) $\frac{dy}{dx} = \frac{1}{x\sqrt{x^2-1}}$. (vi) $\frac{dy}{dx} = \frac{\sqrt{3}\sec x(3\sec^2 x-1)}{2}$. **P5.23** (1) $2\sin\theta\left(3\cos^2\theta-1\right)$. (2) $amn\theta^{n-1}\times\tan^{m-1}(\theta^n)\sec^2\theta^n$. (3) $e^x\left(\sin^2 x+\sin 2x\right)$. (4) $4.6(2\theta+3)^{1.3}\cos\left((2\theta+3)^{2.3}\right)$. (5) $3\theta^2+3\cos(\theta+3)-\ln(3)\left(3^{\sin\theta}\cos\theta+3^{\theta}\right)$. **P5.24** $\frac{d\ell}{dt} = 0.000012\ell_0$[m/°C]. **P5.25** $\frac{dP}{dV} = abV^{b-1}$[W/V], $\frac{dP}{dV}(100) = 1.65$[W/V], $\frac{dP}{dV}(110) = 1.82$[W/V], and $\frac{dP}{dV}(120) = 1.98$[W/V]. **P5.26** $\frac{df}{dD} = -\frac{1}{LD^2}\sqrt{\frac{gT}{\pi\sigma}}$, $\frac{df}{dL} = -\frac{1}{DL^2}\sqrt{\frac{gT}{\pi\sigma}}$, $\frac{df}{d\sigma} = -\frac{1}{2DL}\sqrt{\frac{gT}{\pi\sigma^3}}$, and $\frac{df}{dT} = \frac{1}{2DL}\sqrt{\frac{g}{\pi\sigma T}}$. **P5.27** (a) $\frac{dC}{dr} = 2\pi$; (b) $\frac{dA}{dr} = 2\pi r$; (c) $\frac{dA}{dr} = 8\pi r$; (d) $\frac{dV}{dr} = 4\pi r^2$. **P5.28** $\frac{dI}{dT} = b+2cT$. **P5.29** $R_1'(t) = R_0(a+2bt)$, $R_2'(t) = R_0\left(a+\frac{b}{2\sqrt{t}}\right)$, $R_3'(t) = -\frac{R_0(a+2bt)}{(1+at+bt^2)^2}$. **P5.30** $V'(t) = 1.4340(0.000014t-0.001024)$, $V'(15) = -0.00117$, $V'(20) = -0.00107$, $V'(25) = -0.00097$. **P5.31** (a) $\frac{dV}{d\ell} = b+\frac{k}{I}$; (b) $\frac{dE}{dI} = -\frac{c+k\ell}{I^2}$. **P5.32** (1) $17+24x$; 24. (2) $2bx+4cx^3$; $2b+12cx^2$. (3) $\frac{x^2+2ax-a}{(x+a)^2}$; $\frac{2a(a+1)}{(x+a)^3}$. **P5.33** (a) $\frac{d^2y}{dx^2} = \frac{d^3y}{dx^3} = 1+x+\frac{1}{2}x^2+\frac{1}{6}x^3+\ldots$. (b) $\frac{d^2y}{dx^2} = 2a$; $\frac{d^3y}{dx^3} = 0$. (c) $\frac{d^2y}{dx^2} = 6x+6a$; $\frac{d^3y}{dx^3} = 6$. **P5.34** (1) $-b$; 0. (2) 2; 0. (3) $56440x^3-196212x^2-4488x+8192$; $169320x^2-392424x-4488$. (4) 2; 0. (5) $371.80453x$; 371.80453. **P5.35** $v(2) = 64$[ft/s], $v(4.6) = 147.2$[ft/s], $v(0.01) = 0.32$[ft/s]. **P5.36** $\dot{x} = v_i - gt$, $\ddot{x} = -g$. **P5.37** $v(4) = 45.1$[m/s], $a(4) = 12.4$[m/s^2]. **P5.38** $\omega(1.5) = 11.2$[rad/s], $\alpha = 9.6$[rad/s^2]. **P5.39** $v(t) = 20.4t^2-10.8$[in/s], $a(t) = 40.8t$[in/s^2]. $v(3) = 172.8$[in/s], $a(3) = 122.4$[in/s^2]. **P5.40** $v(t) = \frac{1}{30\sqrt[3]{(t-125)^2}}$[km/s], $a(t) = -\frac{1}{45\sqrt[3]{(t-125)^5}}$[km/s^2]. **P5.41** $v(t) = 0.8-\frac{8t}{(4+t^2)^2}$, $a(t) = \frac{24t^2-32}{(4+t^2)^3}$. $v(10) = 0.7926$[m/s], $a(10) = 0.00211$[m/s^2]. **P5.42** $n = 2$, $n = 11$. **P5.44** $f'(2) = 1.44$. **P5.45** $x = \frac{1}{2}(a+b)$. **P5.46** $\frac{dy}{dx}(x) = 3x^2+3$, $\frac{dy}{dx}(0) = 3$, $\frac{dy}{dx}\left(\frac{1}{2}\right) = 3\frac{3}{4}$, $\frac{dy}{dx}(1) = 6$, and $\frac{dy}{dx}(2) = 15$. **P5.48** (i) $\frac{dy}{dx} = \frac{ab}{(x+b)^2}$; (ii) $\frac{dy}{dx} = \frac{a}{b}e^{-\frac{x}{b}}$; (iii) $\frac{dy}{dx} = \frac{2a}{\pi}\frac{b}{b^2+x^2}$. **P5.51** $x = \pm\sqrt{2}$; $(-\sqrt{2},\sqrt{2})$, $(\sqrt{2},-\sqrt{2})$. **P5.52** $\frac{dy}{dx} = -\frac{4}{9}\frac{x}{y}$. $\frac{dy}{dx} = 0$ when $x = 0$; $\frac{dy}{dx} = \frac{\pm 1}{3\sqrt{2}}$ when $x = 1$. **P5.53** $\frac{dz}{dx} = x^2-6x^2y-2y^2$ and $\frac{dz}{dy} = -2x^3-4xy+\frac{1}{3}$. **P5.54** $2xyz+y^2z+z^2y+2xy^2z^2$; $2xyz+x^2z+xz^2+2x^2yz^2$; $2xyz+x^2y+xy^2+2x^2y^2z$. **P5.55** $\frac{1}{r}\{(x-a)+(y-b)+(z-c)\} = \frac{(x+y+z)-(a+b+c)}{r}$; $\frac{3}{r}$. **P5.56** $dy = vu^{v-1}\,du + u^v\ln(u)\,dv$. **P5.57** (1) $dy = 3u^2\sin v\,du + u^3\cos v\,dv$. (2) $dy = u(\sin x)^{u-1}\cos x\,dx + (\sin x)^u\ln(\sin x)du$. (3) $dy = \frac{1}{v}\frac{1}{u}\,du - \ln u\frac{1}{v^2}\,dv$. **P5.58** $m = 4$, $b = -3$. **P5.59** $\angle\ell_1$ is 45°, $\angle\ell_2$ is 71.56°. Lines ℓ_1 and ℓ_2 intersect at an

angle 26.56°. **P5.60** Intersections at $x = 1$ and $x = -3$. Angles 153°26′ and 2°28′. **P5.61** The tangents intersect at $(x, y) = (3.57, 3.50)$ at an angle of 16°16′. **P5.62** $x = \frac{1}{3}, y = 2\frac{1}{3}, b = -\frac{5}{3}$. **P5.63** (1) Max at $x = -2, y = -4$. Min at $x = 0, y = 0$. (2) Max at $x = a, y = \frac{1}{2a}$. Min at $x = -a, y = \frac{-1}{2a}$. (3) Max at $x = -1$. Min at $x = 1$. **P5.64** Max: $x = -2.19$, $f(-2.19) = 24.19$; min: $x = 1.52$, $f(1.52) = -1.38$. **P5.65** $\frac{dy}{dx} = \frac{b}{a} - 2cx$; $\frac{d^2y}{dx^2} = -2c$. Max at $x = \frac{b}{2ac}$. **P5.66** (a) One maximum and two minima. (b) One maximum at $x = 0$. **P5.67** (1) Min: $x = 1.71, y = 6.14$. (2) Max: $x = -0.5, y = 4$. (3) Max: $x = 1.414, y = 1.7675$; min: $x = -1.414, y = 1.7675$. **P5.68** $0.4N, 0.6N$. **P5.69** $x = \sqrt{\frac{a}{c}}$. **P5.70** Speed: 8.66 nautical miles per hour. Time taken: 115.47 hours. Minimum cost: \$22.5k. **P5.71** (1) Max and min for $x = 7.5$, $f(7.5) = \pm 5.414$. (2) Min: $x = \frac{1}{2}, g(\frac{1}{2}) = 0.25$; max: $x = -\frac{1}{3}, g(-\frac{1}{3}) = 1.408$. **P5.72** (1) Min at $x = \frac{1}{e}$. (2) Max at $x = e$. (3) Min at $x = \ln a$. **P5.73** $\theta = \frac{\pi}{4}$ (45°). **P5.74** Max at $\theta = 0.86$[rad], min at $\theta = -0.86$[rad]. **P5.76** $25\sqrt{3}$[in^2] (equilateral triangle). **P5.77** $\frac{dy}{dx} = -\frac{10}{x^2} + \frac{10}{(8-x)^2}$. Min at $x = 4, y = 5$. **P5.78** Join the middle points of the four sides. **P5.79** (a) $r = R\sqrt{\frac{2}{3}}$. (b) $r = \frac{R}{\sqrt{2}}$. (c) $r = 0.8506R$. **P5.80** The surface area increases at $\frac{8}{r}$ square feet per second. **P5.81** $y = \frac{1}{\sqrt{e}}$. **P5.83** (a) $x^4 + x^3 + x^2 + x + C$. (b) $\frac{ax^2}{4} + \frac{bx^3}{9} + \frac{cx^4}{16} + C$. **P5.84** (1) $\frac{4\sqrt{a}x^{\frac{3}{2}}}{3} + C$. (2) $-\frac{1}{x^3} + C$. (3) $\frac{x^4}{4a} + C$. (4) $\frac{1}{3}x^3 + ax + C$. (5) $-2x^{-\frac{5}{2}} + C$. (6) $\frac{x^2}{2} - ax + (a^2 + a)\ln(x + a) + C$. (7) $\frac{x^4}{4} + 3x^3 + \frac{27}{2}x^2 + 27x + C$. (8) $\frac{x^3}{3} + \frac{2-a}{2}x^2 - 2ax + C$. (9) $a^2(2x^{\frac{3}{2}} + \frac{9}{4}x^{\frac{4}{3}}) + C$. (10) $-\frac{1}{3}\cos\theta - \frac{1}{6}\theta + C$. (11) $\frac{\theta}{2} + \frac{\sin(2a\theta)}{4a} + C$. (12) $\frac{\theta}{2} - \frac{\sin 2\theta}{4} + C$. (13) $\frac{\theta}{2} - \frac{\sin 2a\theta}{4a} + C$. (14) $\frac{1}{3}e^{3x} + C$. (15) $\ln(1 + x) + C$. **P5.85** (1) $\frac{x\sqrt{a^2-x^2}}{2} + \frac{a^2}{2}\sin^{-1}\frac{x}{a} + C$. (2) $\frac{x^2}{2}(\ln x - \frac{1}{2}) + C$. (3) $\frac{x^{a+1}}{a+1}\left(\ln x - \frac{1}{a+1}\right) + C$. (4) $\sin(e^x) + C$. (5) $\sin(\ln x) + C$. (6) $e^x(x^2 - 2x + 2) + C$. (7) $\frac{1}{a+1}(\ln x)^{a+1} + C$. (8) $\ln(\ln x) + C$. (9) $\frac{1}{\sqrt{a}}\log\frac{\sqrt{a}-\sqrt{a-bx^2}}{x\sqrt{a}}$. **P5.86** (1) $\frac{2}{x-3} + \frac{1}{x+4}$. (2) $\frac{5}{x-4} - \frac{4}{x-3}$. (3) $\frac{19}{13(2x+3)} - \frac{22}{13(3x-2)}$. (4) $\frac{2}{x-2} + \frac{4}{x-3} - \frac{5}{x-4}$. (5) $\frac{1}{6(x-1)} + \frac{11}{15(x+2)} + \frac{1}{10(x-3)}$. (5) $\frac{7}{9(3x+1)} + \frac{71}{63(3x-2)} - \frac{5}{7(2x+1)}$. (7) $\frac{1}{3(x-1)} + \frac{2x+1}{3(x^2+x+1)}$. (8) $x + \frac{2}{3(x+1)} + \frac{1-2x}{3(x^2-x+1)}$. (9) $\frac{3}{(x+1)} + \frac{2x+1}{x^2+x+1}$. (10) $\frac{1}{x-1} - \frac{1}{x-2} + \frac{2}{(x-2)^2}$. **P5.87** (1) $2\ln(x-1) + 3\ln(x+2) + C$. (2) $\frac{1}{2}\ln(x-1) + \frac{1}{5}\ln(x-2) + \frac{3}{10}\ln(x+3) + C$. (3) $\frac{b}{2a}\ln\frac{x-a}{x+a} + C$. (4) $\ln\frac{x^2-1}{x^2+1} + C$. (5) $\frac{1}{4}\ln\frac{1+x}{1-x} + \frac{1}{2}\tan^{-1}(x) + C$. **P5.88** $A(0, 6) = 60$. **P5.89** $A(0, a) = \frac{4a^2\sqrt{a}}{3}$. **P5.90** $A(0, \pi) = 2$. **P5.91** $A(0, \pi) = \frac{\pi}{2} \approx 1.57$. **P5.92** 0.572. **P5.93** $A(0, 1) = 1.25$. **P5.94** $A(1, a) = a\ln a$. **P5.95** $A(2, 8) = 62.6$. **P5.96** (a) $y = \frac{1}{8}x^2 + C$; (b) $y = \sin x + C$; (c) $y = x^2 + 3x + C$. To satisfy $y(0) = 1$, we must set $C = 1$ in each case. **P5.97** General solution: $f(x) = C_1e^{-x} + C_2xe^{-x}$. Specific solution: $f(x) = e^{-x} + 2xe^{-x}$ to satisfy initial conditions $f(0) = 1$ and $f'(0) = 1$. **P5.98** $\ell = \frac{1}{2}\sinh^{-1}(1) + \frac{1}{2}\sqrt{2}$. **P5.99** $V_{\text{rms}} = 110$[V]. **P5.100** 79.4. **P5.101** Volume = 4.9348. Surface area = 12.57. **P5.102** 436.3. **P5.103** (a) Converges to 2. (b) Converges to 1. (c) Converges to 1. (d) Doesn't converge. **P5.106** (1) Diverges. (2) Converges. (3) Diverges. (4) Converges. (5) Converges. (6) Diverges. (7) Converges. (8) Converges. (9) Converges. **P5.107** (1) Converges. (2) Diverges. (3) Converges. **P5.108** (1) Converges. (2) Converges. (3) Converges. **P5.109** (1) 1. (2) 8. (3) 2. **P5.110** (1) Converges absolutely. (2) Converges conditionally. (3) Converges conditionally. **P5.111** (a) Converges. (b) Converges. (c) Diverges. **P5.112** $\frac{4}{3}$. **P5.113** $f(x) = \sum_{n=0}^{\infty} x^n$. **P5.114** (a) $\sum_{n=0}^{\infty}(n+1)x^n$. (b) $\sum_{n=0}^{\infty}(-1)^n\frac{x^n}{n!}$. (c) $\sum_{n=0}^{\infty}(-1)^n\frac{x^{4n+2}}{(2n)!}$. **P5.115** (a) $f(x) = \sum_{n=0}^{\infty}\frac{e^5(x-5)^n}{n!}$. (b) $g(x) = \sin(10) + \cos(10)(x - 10) - \frac{\sin(10)}{2!}(x - 10)^2 - \frac{\cos(10)}{3!}(x - 10)^3 + \cdots$. **P5.116** (1) $\rho = 1$. (2) $\rho = \infty$. (3) $\rho = 1$. (4) $\rho = \infty$. (5) $\rho = 3$. (6) $\rho = \sqrt{3}$. **P5.117** (1) $\sum_{n=0}^{\infty}\frac{(\ln(2))^n}{n!}x^n$. (2) $\sum_{n=0}^{\infty}\frac{(-1)^n}{n+1}x^{n+1}$. (3) $\sum_{n=0}^{\infty}\frac{2}{2n+1}x^{2n+1}$.

(4) $1 + \frac{x}{2} + \sum_{n=2}^{\infty}(-1)^{n+1}\frac{1\cdot3\cdot5\cdots(2n-3)}{2^n n!}x^n$. (5) $\sum_{n=0}^{\infty}(-1)^n x^{2n}$. (6) $\sum_{n=0}^{\infty}\frac{(-1)^n}{2n+1}x^{2n+1}$.
P5.118 (1) Diverges. (2) Converges. (3) Diverges. (4) Diverges. (5) Converges. (6) Converges. (7) Converges. (8) Converges. (9) Converges. (10) Converges. (11) Converges. (12) Diverges. **P5.120** $\int_{\alpha}^{\beta}(mx+b)\,dx = \frac{m}{2}(\beta^2-\alpha^2)+b(\beta-\alpha)$. **P5.121** $\int_0^d (ax^2+bx+c)\,dx = \frac{1}{3}ad^3+\frac{1}{2}bd^2+cd$. **P5.122** $A_{\text{sphere}} = 4\pi R^2$. **P5.123** $\frac{\pi}{5}$. **P5.124** $\frac{2\pi}{35}$. **P5.125** $V=\pi$. **P5.126** $I_{\text{sph.shell}} = \frac{2}{3}mR^2$. **P5.127** $I_{\text{sphere}} = \frac{2}{5}mR^2$. **P5.128** $I_{\text{sphere}} = \frac{2}{5}mR^2$.

Solutions to selected problems

P5.1 (10) For $x=5$, we have $\lim_{x\to5} f(x) \neq f(5)$ so the $f(x)$ is discontinuous at $x=5$. This is called a removable discontinuity. (11) The function is continuous everywhere except for the discontinuities. The function $f(x)$ is continuous from the right at $x=-5$ and $x=2$, so these endpoints are included in the intervals to the right.

P5.3 We can choose the value δ (how close we must be to $x=5$) as a function of the precision ϵ specified by the sceptic. One possible choice is $\delta(\epsilon) = \frac{\epsilon}{3}$ although $\frac{\epsilon}{4}$ or $\frac{\epsilon}{5}$ would also work. First we prove $\lim_{x\to5^+} 2x = 15$ using the following chain of inequalities. Starting from the assumption $x \in [5, 5+\delta)$, we have

$$\begin{aligned}5 &\leqslant x < 5+\delta\\ 0 &\leqslant x-5 < 5+\delta-5 = \delta\\ 0 &\leqslant 3x-15 < 3\delta = 3\tfrac{\epsilon}{3} = \epsilon\end{aligned}$$

Thus we have shown that $|3x-15| < \epsilon$ for all possible ϵ, which is a proof of $\lim_{x\to5^+} 3x = 15$. The procedure is similar for the limit from the left: starting from the assumption $x \in (5-\delta, 5]$ and choosing $\delta = \frac{\epsilon}{3}$ again, we show that $|3x-15| < \epsilon$ for all ϵ. Because the limits from both sides exist and are equal to 15, we have proved $\lim\limits_{x\to5} 3x = 15$.

P5.4 (8) We can prove $\lim_{x\to0^+} x\sin(\frac{1}{x}) = 0$ using the squeezing principle. Observe that $-1 \leqslant \sin(\frac{1}{x}) \leqslant 1$, then $-x \leqslant x\sin(\frac{1}{x}) \leqslant x$. Since the limits of both the lower bound $\ell(x) = -x$ and the upper bound $u(x) = x$ are 0 as $x \to 0^+$, so is the limit of $x\sin(\frac{1}{x})$, which is squeezed between them.

P5.25 See `bit.ly/0iAjIN` for calculations.

P5.49 The derivative is $\frac{dy}{d\theta} = 100\cos(\theta - 15^\circ)$. The maximum slope is when $\theta = 15^\circ$ and is equal to $y'(15^\circ) = 100$. When $\theta = 75^\circ$ the slope is $100\cos(75^\circ - 15^\circ) = 100\cos(60^\circ) = 50$, which is half of the maximum.

P5.51 First take the derivative with respect to x of the entire equation: $\frac{d}{dx}[x^2+y^2] = \frac{d}{dx}[4]$. We obtain the equation $2x + 2y\frac{dy}{dx} = 0$, from which we conclude $\frac{dy}{dx} = \frac{-x}{y}$. The condition $\frac{-x}{y} = 1$ is equivalent to the line $y = -x$, which intersects the circle $x^2+y^2=4$ at points $(-\sqrt{2},\sqrt{2})$ and $(\sqrt{2},-\sqrt{2})$.

P5.52 Taking the implicit derivative of the equation (which is an ellipse), we find $\frac{2x}{9} + \frac{2y}{4}\frac{dy}{dx} = 0$. Isolating the derivative, we find $\frac{dy}{dx} = -\frac{4}{9}\frac{x}{y}$. Note the similarity with the slope equation of a circle. When $x=0$, $\frac{dy}{dx} = 0$. The vertical line $x=1$ intersects the curve in two places: the slope is positive $\frac{dy}{dx} = \frac{+1}{3\sqrt{2}}$ on the bottom half of the ellipse, and the slope is negative $\frac{dy}{dx} = \frac{-1}{3\sqrt{2}}$ on the top half.

P5.75 The area of a rectangle is width times height: $A = w\ell$. Assuming you use all the fence, the rectangle constructed will have a perimeter equal to $p = 2w + 2\ell$. We can rewrite the width as a function of the (fixed) perimeter and the length: $w = \frac{p}{2} - \ell$. To find the maximum area, we maximize the function $A(\ell) = w\ell = \left(\frac{p}{2} - \ell\right)\ell$. $A'(\ell) = -\ell + \left(\frac{p}{2} - \ell\right)$. Solving for ℓ in $A'(\ell) = 0$ we find $\ell = \frac{p}{4}$. The largest-area rectangle with perimeter p is a square with side length $\frac{1}{4}p$.

P5.82 This is the fundamental theorem of calculus, which states that the derivative of the integral function of a function is the function itself.

P5.96 (a) We're looking for a function $y(x)$ whose derivative is equal to $\frac{1}{4}x$. Integrating we find $y(x) = \frac{1}{8}x^2$, but there could also have been an additive constant C so the general solution is $y(x) = \frac{1}{8}x^2 + C$. (b) Taking the indefinite integral on both sides of the equation $\frac{dy}{dx} = \cos x$ we find $y = \sin x + C$. (c) Integrating $\frac{dy}{dx} = 2x + 3$ we find $y = x^2 + 3x + C$.

P5.97 For a second-order differential equation (a differential equation involving second derivatives) there will be two independent solutions. The hint tells us these solutions are $e^{-\lambda x}$ and $xe^{-\lambda x}$ and we choose $\lambda = 1$ to satisfy the differential equation. The general solution is any linear combination of these solutions $f(x) = C_1e^{-x} + C_2xe^{-x}$, where C_1 and C_2 are arbitrary constants. By computing $f(0)$ and $f'(0)$, we find that the choice $C_1 = 1$ and $C_2 = 2$ satisfies the initial conditions $f(0) = 1$ and $f'(0) = 1$. See `bit.ly/1kNxhvo`.

P5.98 The arc length of a curve $f(x)$ is $\ell = \int_a^b d\ell = \int_a^b \sqrt{1 + (f'(x))^2}\,dx$. In the current problem $f'(x) = x$ so the integral we want to find is $I = \int \sqrt{1 + x^2}\,dx$. Note $\sqrt{1 + x^2} = \frac{1+x^2}{\sqrt{1+x^2}} = \frac{1}{\sqrt{1+x^2}} + \frac{x^2}{\sqrt{1+x^2}}$. The first term is the derivative of $\sinh^{-1}(x)$. For the second term, use integration by parts with $u = x$, $dv = \frac{x}{\sqrt{1+x^2}}\,dx$. You'll obtain the equation $I = \sinh^{-1}(x) + x\sqrt{1 + x^2} - I$, where I is the integral we want to find.

Evaluating I at the endpoints, we find $\ell = I\big|_0^1 = \frac{1}{2}\sinh^{-1}(1) + \frac{1}{2}\sqrt{2}$. The answer $\frac{1}{2}\ln(1 + \sqrt{2}) + \frac{1}{2}\sqrt{2}$ is also correct because $\sinh^{-1}(x) \equiv \ln(x + \sqrt{1 + x^2})$.

P5.99 We want to calculate the square of the voltage during one period T: $V_{\text{avg}}^2 = \frac{1}{T}\int_0^T 155.57^2\cos^2(\omega t)\,dt$. Making the substitution $\tau = \omega t$, we obtain an equivalent expression $V_{\text{avg}}^2 = \frac{1}{2\pi}\int_0^{2\pi} 155.57^2\cos^2(\tau)\,d\tau$, which is $\frac{155.57^2}{2\pi}\int_0^{2\pi}\cos^2(\tau)\,d\tau = \frac{155.57^2}{2\pi}\left[\frac{t}{2} + \frac{\sin(t)\cos(t)}{2}\right]_0^{2\pi} = \frac{155.57^2}{2\pi}\left[\frac{2\pi}{2}\right] = \frac{155.57^2}{2}$. The root-mean-squared voltage is $V_{\text{rms}} = \sqrt{\frac{155.57^2}{2}} = \frac{155.57}{\sqrt{2}} = 110[\text{V}]$.

P5.104 Observe that $\frac{1}{2^n+n} < \frac{1}{2^n}$ for all $n \geqslant 1$. We know $\sum_n \frac{1}{2^n}$ converges since it is a geometric series with $r = \frac{1}{2}$ and $|r| < 1$. By the direct comparison test, $\sum_n \frac{1}{2^n+n}$ also converges.

P5.105 The limit of the nth term in the series is $\lim_{n\to\infty} \dfrac{n^2}{2n^2+1} = \dfrac{1}{2} \neq 0$. The series $\sum_n \frac{n^2}{2n^2+1}$ involves a limit of an infinite number of nonzero terms; therefore it must be divergent.

P5.109 In each case we use the formula for the geometric series $\sum_{n=0}^{\infty} ar^n = \frac{a}{1-r}$. See `bit.ly/1e9F52v` for the calculations.

P5.110 Use the geometric series formula $\sum_{n=0}^{\infty} ar^n = \frac{a}{1-r}$.

P5.112 This is a geometric series with $r = \frac{1}{2}$ and $a = \frac{2}{3}$, so $\frac{a}{1-r} = \frac{\frac{2}{3}}{1-\frac{1}{2}} = \frac{4}{3}$.

P5.119 Taking the approach suggested in the hint, we write the summation $\sum_{n=1}^{N} n$ by grouping 1 with N, 2 with $N-1$, 3 with $N-2$, and so on to obtain $\frac{N}{2}$ terms, each with value $N+1$. We thus find $\sum_{n=1}^{N} n = \frac{N}{2}(N+1) = \frac{N(N+1)}{2}$.

For the second part, we can use the "telescopic" nature of this series. Except for the first and last terms in this series, the negative part of each term $(n+1)^3 - n^3$ cancels the positive part of the next term. Thus only the negative part of the first term and the positive part of the last term remain: $\sum_{n=1}^{N}(n+1)^3 - n^3 = (N+1)^3 - 1$. Using basic algebra operations, we find:

$$(n+1)^3 - n^3 = n^3 + 3n^2 + 3n + 1 - n^3 = 3n^2 + 3n + 1.$$

Since we know $\sum_{n=1}^{N}(n+1)^3 - n^3 = (N+1)^3 - 1$ from the telescopic approach, we obtain the equation

$$(N+1)^3 - 1 = \sum_{n=1}^{N} 3n^2 + 3n + 1 = 3\sum_{n=1}^{N} n^2 + 3\sum_{n=1}^{N} n + \sum_{n=1}^{N} 1.$$

Using the formulas $\sum_{n=1}^{N} n = \frac{N(N+1)}{2}$ and $\sum_{n=1}^{N} 1 = N$, we rewrite the equation as

$$(N+1)^3 - 1 = 3\sum_{n=1}^{N} n^2 + 3\frac{N(N+1)}{2} + N.$$

Isolating $\sum_{n=1}^{N} n^2$ and simplifying leads us to the desired result.

P5.120 Using the definition of the integral as a the limit of a Riemann sum from page 347, we can write the following formula for the integral of $f(x)$ between $x = \alpha$ and $x = \beta$:

$$\int_{\alpha}^{\beta} f(x)\, dx \equiv \lim_{n\to\infty} \sum_{k=1}^{n} f(a + k\Delta x)\Delta x,$$

where $\Delta x = \frac{\beta - \alpha}{n}$ denotes the width of the rectangles used to approximate the area under the curve. For the integral of the function $f(x) = mx + b$, the formula becomes

$$\begin{aligned}
\int_{\alpha}^{\beta} mx + b\, dx &= \lim_{n\to\infty} \sum_{k=1}^{n} (m(\alpha + k\Delta x) + b)\,\Delta x \\
&= \lim_{n\to\infty} \Delta x \left((m\alpha + b)\sum_{k=1}^{n} 1 + m(\Delta x)\sum_{k=1}^{n} k \right) \\
&= \lim_{n\to\infty} \Delta x \left((m\alpha + b)n + m(\Delta x)\frac{n(n+1)}{2} \right).
\end{aligned}$$

After taking the limit $n \to \infty$, and after several steps of simplification, we obtain the final answer, $\int_{\alpha}^{\beta}(mx + b)\, dx = b(\beta - \alpha) + \frac{m}{2}(\beta^2 - \alpha^2)$.

P5.121 Using the definition of the integral as an infinite Riemann sum and taking $x_k = 0 + \Delta x k$ and $\Delta x = \frac{d-0}{n}$, we obtain the following formula for the area under the curve of $f(x) = ax^2 + bx + c$ between $x = 0$ and $x = d$:

$$\begin{aligned}
\int_{0}^{d} ax^2 + bx + c\, dx &= \lim_{n\to\infty} \sum_{k=1}^{n} \left(a(\Delta x)^2 k^2 + b(\Delta x)k + c \right) \Delta x \\
&= \lim_{n\to\infty} \Delta x \left(a(\Delta x)^2 \sum_{k=1}^{n} k^2 + b(\Delta x)\sum_{k=1}^{n} k + c\sum_{k=1}^{n} 1 \right) \\
&= \lim_{n\to\infty} \Delta x \left(a(\Delta x)^2 \sum_{k=1}^{n} \frac{n(n+1)(2n+1)}{6} + b(\Delta x)\frac{n(n+1)}{2} + cn \right),
\end{aligned}$$

which becomes $\frac{1}{3}ad^3 + \frac{1}{2}bd^2 + cd$ after using $\Delta x = \frac{d}{n}$ and taking the limit.

P5.122 The surface area of a sphere of radius R can be computed by splitting it into narrow, circular strips of area dA, with a radius varying according to $f(x) = \sqrt{R^2 - x^2}$. The width of each strip is given by the arc length formula, $d\ell = \sqrt{1 + (f'(x))^2}\,dx$. To compute $A_{\text{sphere}} = \int_{-R}^{R} 2\pi f(x)\sqrt{1 + (f'(x))^2}\,dx$, we first find $f'(x) = \frac{-x}{\sqrt{R^2-x^2}}$, then obtain $\sqrt{1 + (f'(x))^2} = \frac{R}{\sqrt{R^2-x^2}}$. Substituting into the formula, we find $A_{\text{sphere}} = \int_{-R}^{R} 2\pi\sqrt{R^2 - x^2}\frac{R}{\sqrt{R^2-x^2}}\,dx$, which simplifies to $2\pi R\int_{-R}^{R} 1\,dx$, which gives $4\pi R^2$ as expected.

P5.125 Using the disk method, we find the volume of Torricelli's trumpet between $x = 1$ and $x = a$ is $\int_1^a \pi(f(x))^2\,dx = \pi\int_1^a \frac{1}{x^2}\,dx = \pi\left(1 - \frac{1}{a}\right)$. To find the total volume, we compute the limit $\lim_{a\to\infty} \pi\left(1 - \frac{1}{a}\right) = \pi$.

P5.126 To evaluate $I_{\text{sph.shell}} = \int_{-R}^{R}(f(x))^2\,\sigma 2\pi f(x)\sqrt{1 + (f'(x))^2}\,dx$, we first compute $f'(x) = \frac{-x}{\sqrt{R^2-x^2}}$ then obtain $\sqrt{1 + (f'(x))^2} = \frac{R}{\sqrt{R^2-x^2}}$. Substituting these calculations into the integral, we find $I_{\text{sph.shell}} = 2\pi\sigma R\int_{-R}^{R}(R^2 - x^2)\,dx$, which is the integral of a polynomial.

P5.127 The formula for computing the volume of a sphere using the spherical shell method is $V_{\text{sphere}} = \int_0^R 2\pi r h(r) dr$, where $h(r) = 2\sqrt{R^2 - r^2}$ is the height of the thin cylindrical shell at radius r, and $2\pi r$ is its circumference. To evaluate the integral $I_{\text{sphere}} = \int r^2 dm$, we define $dm = \rho A(r) dr = \rho 2\pi r h(r)\,dr$ and scale the contributions of each dm by an extra factor r^2. We thus obtain $I_{\text{sphere}} = \int_0^R r^2\rho 2\pi r 2\sqrt{R^2 - r^2}\,dr$. Computing the integral $\int_0^R r^3\sqrt{R^2 - r^2}\,dr$ requires several steps, and I encourage you to perform the calculation on your own. The substitutions $r = R\sin\theta$ and later $u = \cos\theta$ might come in handy.

P5.128 The integral to calculate, $\int_{-R}^{R} I_{\text{disk}}(x)\,dx = \int_{-R}^{R} \frac{1}{2}m(x)[r(x)]^2\,dx$, becomes $\frac{1}{2}\pi\rho\int_{-R}^{R}(f(x))^4\,dx$ after substituting all the known values. After expanding $(f(x))^4$, we find $I_{\text{sphere}} = \frac{1}{2}\pi\rho\int_{-R}^{R}(R^4 - 2R^2x^2 + x^4)\,dx$, which is straightforward to compute.

Appendix B

Notation

This appendix contains a summary of the notation used in this book.

Math notation

Expression	Read as	Used to denote
a, b, x, y		variables
$=$	is equal to	expressions that have the same value
$\equiv$	is defined as	a new variable definition
$a + b$	a plus b	the combined lengths of a and b
$a - b$	a minus b	the difference in lengths between a and b
$a \times b \equiv ab$	a times b	the area of a rectangle
$a^2 \equiv aa$	a squared	the area of a square of side length a
$a^3 \equiv aaa$	a cubed	the volume of a cube of side length a
a^n	a exponent n	a multiplied by itself n times
$\sqrt{a} \equiv a^{\frac{1}{2}}$	square root of a	the side length of a square of area a
$\sqrt[3]{a} \equiv a^{\frac{1}{3}}$	cube root of a	the side length of a cube with volume a
$a/b \equiv \frac{a}{b}$	a divided by b	a parts of a whole split into b parts
$a^{-1} \equiv \frac{1}{a}$	one over a	division by a
$f(x)$	f of x	the function f applied to input x
f^{-1}	f inverse	the inverse function of $f(x)$
$f \circ g$	f compose g	function composition; $f \circ g(x) \equiv f(g(x))$
e^x	e to the x	the exponential function base e
$\ln(x)$	natural log of x	the logarithm base e
a^x	a to the x	the exponential function base a
$\log_a(x)$	log base a of x	the logarithm base a
θ, ϕ	*theta, phi*	angles
sin, cos, tan	sin, cos, tan	trigonometric ratios
%	percent	proportions of a total; $a\% \equiv \frac{a}{100}$

Set notation

You don't need a lot of fancy notation to understand mathematics. It really helps, though, if you know a little bit of set notation.

Symbol	Read as	Denotes
$\{\ldots\}$	the set ...	define a sets
$\mid$	such that	describe or restrict the elements of a set
$\mathbb{N}$	the naturals	the set $\mathbb{N} \equiv \{0, 1, 2, \ldots\}$. Note $\mathbb{N}_{+} \equiv \mathbb{N}\{0\}$.
$\mathbb{Z}$	the integers	the set $\mathbb{Z} \equiv \{\ldots, -2, -1, 0, 1, 2, 3, \ldots\}$
$\mathbb{Q}$	the rationals	the set of fractions of integers
$\mathbb{A}$		the set of algebraic numbers
$\mathbb{R}$	the reals	the set of real numbers
$\mathbb{C}$		the set of complex numbers
$\subset$	subset	one set strictly contained in another
$\subseteq$	subset or equal	containment or equality
$\cup$	union	the combined elements from two sets
$\cap$	intersection	the elements two sets have in common
$S \backslash T$	S set minus T	the elements of S that are not in T
$a \in S$	a in S	a is an element of set S
$a \notin S$	a not in S	a is not an element of set S
$\forall x$	for all x	a statement that holds for all x
$\exists x$	there exists x	an existence statement
$\nexists x$	there doesn't exist x	a non-existence statement

An example of a condensed math statement that uses set notation is "$\nexists m, n \in \mathbb{Z}$ such that $\frac{m}{n} = \sqrt{2}$," which reads "there don't exist integers m and n whose fraction equals $\sqrt{2}$." Since we identify the set of fractions of integers with the rationals, this statement is equivalent to the shorter "$\sqrt{2} \notin \mathbb{Q}$," which reads "$\sqrt{2}$ is irrational."

Complex numbers notation

Expression	Denotes
$\mathbb{C}$	the set of complex numbers $\mathbb{C} \equiv \{a + bi \mid a, b \in \mathbb{R}\}$
i	the unit imaginary number $i \equiv \sqrt{-1}$ or $i^2 = -1$
$\text{Re}\{z\} = a$	real part of $z = a + bi$
$\text{Im}\{z\} = b$	imaginary part of $z = a + bi$
$\lvert z \rvert \angle \varphi_z$	polar representation of $z = \lvert z \rvert \cos \varphi_z + i \lvert z \rvert \sin \varphi_z$
$\lvert z \rvert = \sqrt{a^2 + b^2}$	magnitude of $z = a + bi$
$\varphi_z = \tan^{-1}(b/a)$	phase or argument of $z = a + bi$
$\bar{z} = a - bi$	complex conjugate of $z = a + bi$

Vectors notation

Expression	Denotes
$\mathbb{R}^n$	the set of n-dimensional vectors
$\vec{v}$	a vector
(v_x, v_y)	vector in component notation
$v_x\hat{\imath} + v_y\hat{\jmath}$	vector in unit vector notation
$\\|\vec{v}\\|\angle\theta$	vector in length-and-direction notation
$\\|\vec{v}\\|$	length of the vector $\vec{v}$
θ	angle the vector $\vec{v}$ makes with the x-axis
$\hat{v} \equiv \frac{\vec{v}}{\\|\vec{v}\\|}$	unit vector in the same direction as $\vec{v}$
$\vec{u} \cdot \vec{v}$	dot product of the vectors $\vec{u}$ and $\vec{v}$
$\vec{u} \times \vec{v}$	cross product of the vectors $\vec{u}$ and $\vec{v}$

Mechanics notation

Expression	Denotes
$x(t)$	position of an object as a function of time
$v(t)$	velocity of an object as a function of time
$a(t)$	acceleration of an object as a function of time
m	mass of an object
$\vec{F}$	a force
$\vec{N}$	normal force
$\vec{F}_{fs}$	static force of friction
$\vec{F}_{fk}$	kinetic force of friction
$\vec{F}_g \equiv \vec{W}$	gravitational force; the weight of an object
U_g	gravitational potential energy
$\vec{F}_s$	force of a spring
U_s	spring potential energy
$\vec{p}$	momentum of a moving object
K	kinetic energy
$\theta(t)$	angular position of a rotating object over time
$\omega(t)$	angular velocity of an object as a function of time
$\alpha(t)$	angular acceleration of an object as a function of time
I_{obj}	moment of inertia of an object
$\mathcal{T}$	torque
L	angular momentum of a spinning object
K_r	rotational kinetic energy of a spinning object

Calculus notation

Expression	Denotes
∞	infinity
ϵ, δ	the Greek letters *epsilon* and *delta*
$f(x)$	a function of the form $f : \mathbb{R} \to \mathbb{R}$
$\lim_{x\to\infty} f(x)$	limit of $f(x)$ as x goes to infinity
$\lim_{x\to a^+} f(x)$	limit of $f(x)$ as x approaches a from the right
$\lim_{x\to a^-} f(x)$	limit of $f(x)$ as x approaches a from the left
$\lim_{x\to a} f(x)$	limit of $f(x)$ as x goes to a
$f'(x)$	derivative of $f(x)$
$f''(x)$	second derivative of $f(x)$
$\frac{d}{dx}$	derivative operator
$F(x)$	antiderivative function of $f(x)$
$\int f(x)\,dx$	indefinite integral of $f(x)$ (spoiler: $\int f(x)\,dx \equiv F(x) + C$)
$\int_a^b f(x)\,dx$	definite integral of $f(x)$ between $x = a$ and $x = b$
$F(x)\vert_\alpha^\beta$	change in $F(x)$ between α and β: $F(x)\vert_\alpha^\beta = F(\beta) - F(\alpha)$
$\sum_{k=1}^{N} s_k$	summation of N terms $s_1 + s_2 + \cdots + s_N$
a_n	sequence $a_n : \mathbb{N} \to \mathbb{R}$, also denoted $(a_0, a_1, a_2, a_3, \ldots)$
$\sum_{n=0}^{\infty} a_n$	series $\sum a_n$, which is the infinite sum of the sequence a_n

Appendix C

Constants, units, and conversion ratios

In this appendix you will find a number of tables of useful information that you might need when solving math and physics problems.

Fundamental constants of Nature

Many of the equations of physics include constants as parameters of the equation. For example, Newton's law of gravitation says that the force of gravity between two objects of mass M and m separated by a distance r is $F_g = \frac{GMm}{r^2}$, where G is Newton's gravitational constant.

Symbol	Value	Units	Name
G	$6.673\,84 \times 10^{-11}$	$\text{m}^3\,\text{kg}^{-1}\text{s}^{-2}$	gravitational constant
g	$9.806\,65 \approx 9.81$	m s^{-2}	Earth free-fall acceleration
m_p	$1.672\,621 \times 10^{-27}$	kg	proton mass
m_e	$9.109\,382 \times 10^{-31}$	kg	electron mass
N_A	$6.022\,141 \times 10^{23}$	mol^{-1}	Avogadro's number
k_B	$1.380\,648 \times 10^{-23}$	J K^{-1}	Boltzmann's constant
R	$8.314\,462\,1$	$\text{J K}^{-1}\,\text{mol}^{-1}$	gas constant $R = N_\text{A}k_\text{B}$
μ_0	$1.256\,637 \times 10^{-6}$	N A^{-2}	permeability of free space
ε_0	$8.854\,187 \times 10^{-12}$	F m^{-1}	permittivity of free space
c	$299\,792\,458$	m s^{-1}	speed of light $c = \frac{1}{\sqrt{\mu_0\varepsilon_0}}$
e	$1.602\,176 \times 10^{-19}$	C	elementary charge
h	$6.626\,069 \times 10^{-34}$	J s	Planck's constant

Units

The International System of Units (*Système International*) defines seven base units for measuring physical quantities.

Name	Sym.	Measures	Definition
metre	m	length	The distance travelled by light in vacuum during $\frac{1}{299792458^{\text{th}}}$ of a second.
kilogram	kg	mass	The mass of the *international prototype kilogram* (a cylinder of platinum-iridium kept at Sèvres near Paris).
second	s	time	The time for 9192631770 transitions in the ground state of the caesium-133 atom.
Ampere	A	electric current	One ampere is the current that has to flow in two infinitely long wires placed a distance 1[m] apart, to produce a force between them of 2×10^{-7}[N/m].
Kelvin	K	temperature	The Kelvin is $\frac{1}{273.16}$ of the thermodynamic temperature of the triple point of water.
mole	mol	# of atoms	One mole is how many carbon atoms are in 0.012[kg] of carbon-12.
candela	cd	light intensity	One candela is defined as the luminous intensity of a monochromatic source with a particular frequency and radiant intensity.

Derived units

The base SI units cover most of the fundamental quantities. Other physical units are defined as combinations of the basic units.

Name	Sym.	Measures	Definition	SI equivalent
Hertz	Hz	frequency		s^{-1}
Newton	N	force		$\text{kg}\,\text{m}\,\text{s}^{-2}$
Pascal	Pa	pressure	N/m^2	$\text{kg}\,\text{m}^{-1}\,\text{s}^{-2}$
Joule	J	energy, work, heat	N m	$\text{kg}\,\text{m}^2\,\text{s}^{-2}$
Watt	W	power	J/s	$\text{kg}\,\text{m}^2\,\text{s}^{-3}$
Coulomb	C	electric charge		s A
Volt	V	voltage, electric potential		$\text{kg}\,\text{m}^2\,\text{s}^{-3}\,\text{A}^{-1}$
Ohm	Ω	resistance, reactance	V/A	$\text{kg}\,\text{m}^2\,\text{s}^{-3}\,\text{A}^{-2}$
Siemens	S	electrical conductance	A/V	$\text{kg}^{-1}\,\text{m}^{-2}\,\text{s}^3\,\text{A}^2$
Farad	F	capacitance	C/V	$\text{kg}^{-1}\,\text{m}^{-2}\,\text{s}^4\,\text{A}^2$
Tesla	T	magnetic field strength		$\text{kg}\,\text{s}^{-2}\,\text{A}^{-1}$
Henry	H	inductance	Ω s	$\text{kg}\,\text{m}^2\,\text{s}^{-2}\,\text{A}^{-2}$
Weber	Wb	magnetic flux	$\text{T}\,\text{m}^2$	$\text{kg}\,\text{m}^2\,\text{s}^{-2}\,\text{A}^{-1}$

Other units and conversions

We often measure physical quantities like length, weight, and velocity in nonstandard units like feet, pounds, and miles per hour. The following table lists the conversion ratios which are required to covert these nonstandard measurement units to SI units.

Dimension	Symb.	Name	Conversion
length	Å	Angstrom	$1[\text{Å}] = 10^{-10}[\text{m}] = 0.1[\text{nm}]$
	in, "	inch	$1[\text{in}] = 2.54[\text{cm}]$
	ft, '	foot	$1[\text{ft}] = 12[\text{in}] = 0.3048[\text{m}]$
	yd	yard	$1[\text{yd}]= 3[\text{ft}] = 0.9144[\text{m}]$
	mi	mile	$1[\text{mi}] = 5280[\text{ft}] = 1609.344[\text{m}]$
	nmi	nautical mile	$1[\text{nmi}] = 1852[\text{m}]$
	ly	light-year	$1[\text{ly}] = 9.460\,730\,472 \times 10^{15}[\text{m}]$
area	in^2	square inch	$1[\text{in}^2] = 6.452 \times 10^{-4}[\text{m}^2]$
	ft^2	square foot	$1[\text{ft}^2] = 9.290 \times 10^{-2}[\text{m}^2]$
			$1[\text{m}^2] = 110.764[\text{ft}^2]$
	ac	acre	$1[\text{ac}] = 4840[\text{yd}^2] = 4046.856[\text{m}^2]$
	ha	hectare	$1[\text{ha}] = 10\,000[\text{m}^2]$
	mi^2	square mile	$1[\text{mi}^2] = 2.589\,988 \times 10^6[\text{m}^2]$
volume	L	litre	$1[\text{L}] = 1[\text{dm}^3] = \frac{1}{1000}[\text{m}^3]$
	gal(US)	gallon (fluid)	$1[\text{gal}] = 3.785[\text{L}]$
weight	lb	pound	$1[\text{lb}] = 0.454[\text{kg}] = 453.592[\text{g}]$
	t	tonne	$1[\text{t}] = 1000[\text{kg}]$
angle	rad	radian	$1[\text{turn}] = 2\pi[\text{rad}]$
	°	degree	$360[^\circ] = 2\pi[\text{rad}]$
	rev	revolution	$1[\text{rev}] = 360[^\circ] = 2\pi[\text{rad}]$
	grad	gradian	$1[\text{grad}]=\frac{1}{400}[\text{rev}] = 0.9[^\circ]$
time	min	minute	$1[\text{min}] = 60[\text{s}]$
	h	hour	$1[\text{h}] = 60[\text{min}] = 3600[\text{s}]$
velocity	km/h	km per hour	$1[\text{km/h}] = \frac{1}{3.6}[\text{m/s}] = 0.2\overline{7}[\text{m/s}]$
	mph	mile per hour	$1[\text{mph}] = 0.447[\text{m/s}] = 1.61[\text{km/h}]$
temperature	°C	Celsius	$x[^\circ\text{C}] = (x + 273.15)[^\circ\text{K}]$
	°F	Fahrenheit	$x[^\circ\text{F}] = \frac{5}{9}(x + 459.67)[^\circ\text{K}]$
			$x[^\circ\text{F}] = \frac{5}{9}(x - 32)[^\circ\text{C}]$
pressure	atm	atmosphere	$1[\text{atm}] = 101\,325[\text{Pa}]$
	bar	bar	$1[\text{bar}] =10^5[\text{Pa}]$

Appendix D

SymPy tutorial

Computers can be very useful for dealing with complicated math expressions or when slogging through tedious calculations. Throughout this book we used SymPy to illustrate several concepts from math and physics. We'll now review all the math and physics tools available through the SymPy command line. Don't worry if you're not a computer person; we'll only discuss concepts we covered in the book, and the computer commands we'll learn are very similar to the math operations you're already familiar with. This section also serves as a final review of the material covered in the book.

Introduction

You can use a computer algebra system (CAS) to compute complicated math expressions, solve equations, perform calculus procedures, and simulate physics systems.

All computer algebra systems offer essentially the same functionality, so it doesn't matter which system you use: there are free systems like SymPy, Magma, or Octave, and commercial systems like Maple, MATLAB, and Mathematica. This tutorial is an introduction to SymPy, which is a *symbolic* computer algebra system written in the programming language Python. In a symbolic CAS, numbers and operations are represented symbolically, so the answers obtained are exact. For example, the number $\sqrt{2}$ is represented in SymPy as the object `Pow(2,1/2)`, whereas in *numerical* computer algebra systems like Octave, the number $\sqrt{2}$ is represented as the approximation 1.41421356237310 (a `float`). For most purposes the approximation is okay, but sometimes approximations can lead to problems: `float(sqrt(2))*float(sqrt(2)) = 2.00000000000000044` $\neq$ 2. Because SymPy uses exact representations, you'll never run into such problems: `Pow(2,1/2)*Pow(2,1/2)`$=$ 2.

This tutorial presents many explanations as blocks of code. Be sure to try the code examples on your own by typing the commands into SymPy. It's always important to verify for yourself!

Using SymPy

The easiest way to use SymPy, provided you're connected to the internet, is to visit http://live.sympy.org. You'll be presented with an interactive prompt into which you can enter your commands—right in your browser.

If you want to use SymPy on your own computer, you must install Python and the python package sympy. You can then open a command prompt and start a SymPy session using:

```
you@host$ python
Python X.Y.Z
[GCC a.b.c (Build Info)] on platform
Type "help", "copyright", or "license" for more information.
>>> from sympy import *
>>>
```

The >>> prompt indicates you're in the Python shell which accepts Python commands. The command `from sympy import *` imports all the SymPy functions into the current namespace. All SymPy functions are now available to you. To exit the python shell press CTRL+D.

I highly recommend you also install ipython, which is an improved interactive python shell. If you have ipython and SymPy installed, you can start an ipython shell with SymPy pre-imported using the command isympy. For an even better experience, you can try jupyter notebook, which is a web frontend for the ipython shell.

Each section in this appendix begins with a python import statement for the functions used in that section. If you use the statement `from sympy import *` in the beginning of your code, you don't need to run these individual import statements, but I've included them so you'll know which SymPy vocabulary is covered in each section.

Fundamentals of mathematics

Let's begin by learning about the basic SymPy objects and the operations we can carry out on them. We'll learn the SymPy equivalents of the math verbs we used in Chapter 1: "to solve" (an equation), "to expand" (an expression), "to factor" (a polynomial).

Numbers

```
>>> from sympy import  sympify, S,  evalf, N
```

In Python, there are two types of number objects: ints and floats.

```
>>> 3
3                             # an int
>>> 3.0
3.0                           # a float
```

Integer objects in Python are a faithful representation of the set of integers $\mathbb{Z} = \{\ldots, -2, -1, 0, 1, 2, \ldots\}$. Floating point numbers are approximate representations of the reals $\mathbb{R}$. Regardless of its absolute size, a floating point number is only accurate to 16 decimals.

Special care is required when specifying rational numbers, because integer division might not produce the answer you want. In other words, Python will not automatically convert the answer to a floating point number, but instead round the answer to the closest integer:

```
>>> 1/7
0                             # int/int gives int
```

To avoid this problem, you can force float division by using the number 1.0 instead of 1:

```
>>> 1.0/7
0.14285714285714285           # float/int gives float
```

This result is better, but it's still only an approximation of the exact number $\frac{1}{7} \in \mathbb{Q}$, since a float has 16 decimals while the decimal expansion of $\frac{1}{7}$ is infinitely long. To obtain an *exact* representation of $\frac{1}{7}$ you need to create a SymPy expression. You can sympify any expression using the shortcut function S():

```
S('1/7')
1/7                           # = Rational(1,7)
```

Note the input to S() is specified as a text string delimited by quotes. We could have achieved the same result using S('1')/7 since a SymPy object divided by an int is a SymPy object.

Except for the tricky Python division operator, other math operators like addition +, subtraction -, and multiplication * work as you would expect. The syntax ** is used in Python to denote exponentiation:

```
>>> 2**10                    # same as S('2^10')
1024
```

When solving math problems, it's best to work with SymPy objects, and wait to compute the numeric answer in the end. To obtain a numeric approximation of a SymPy object as a float, call its .evalf() method:

```
>>> pi
pi
>>> pi.evalf()
3.14159265358979
```

The method `.n()` is equivalent to `.evalf()`. The global SymPy function `N()` can also be used to to compute numerical values. You can easily change the number of digits of precision of the approximation. Enter `pi.n(400)` to obtain an approximation of π to 400 decimals.

Symbols

```
>>> from sympy import Symbol, symbols
```

Python is a civilized language so there's no need to define variables before assigning values to them. When you write `a = 3`, you define a new name `a` and set it to the value 3. You can now use the name `a` in subsequent calculations.

Most interesting SymPy calculations require us to define `symbols`, which are the SymPy objects for representing variables and unknowns. For your convenience, when `live.sympy.org` starts, it runs the following commands automatically:

```
>>> from __future__ import division
>>> from sympy import *
>>> x, y, z, t = symbols('x y z t')
>>> k, m, n = symbols('k m n', integer=True)
>>> f, g, h = symbols('f g h', cls=Function)
```

The first statement instructs python to convert `1/7` to `1.0/7` when dividing, potentially saving you from any `int` division confusion. The second statement imports all the SymPy functions. The remaining statements define some generic symbols `x`, `y`, `z`, and `t`, and several other symbols with special properties.

Note the difference between the following two statements:

```
>>> x + 2
x + 2                    # an Add expression
>>> p + 2
NameError: name 'p' is not defined
```

The name `x` is defined as a symbol, so SymPy knows that `x + 2` is an expression; but the variable `p` is not defined, so SymPy doesn't know what to make of `p + 2`. To use `p` in expressions, you must first define it as a symbol:

```
>>> p = Symbol('p')    # the same as p = symbols('p')
>>> p + 2
p + 2                    # = Add(Symbol('p'), Integer(2))
```

You can define a sequence of variables using the following notation:

```
>>> a0, a1, a2, a3 = symbols('a0:4')
```

You can use any name you want for a variable, but it's best if you avoid the letters `Q,C,O,S,I,N` and `E` because they have special uses in `SymPy`: `I` is the unit imaginary number $i \equiv \sqrt{-1}$, `E` is the base of the natural logarithm, `S()` is the `sympify` function, `N()` is used to obtain numeric approximations, and `O` is used for big-`O` notation.

The underscore symbol `_` is a special variable that contains the result of the last printed value. The variable `_` is analogous to the `ans` button on certain calculators, and is useful in multi-step calculations:

```
>>> 3+3
6
>>> _*2
12
```

Expressions

```
>>> from sympy import simplify, factor, expand, collect
```

You define `SymPy` expressions by combining symbols with basic math operations and other functions:

```
>>> expr = 2*x + 3*x - sin(x) - 3*x + 42
>>> simplify(expr)
2*x - sin(x) + 42
```

The function `simplify` can be used on any expression to simplify it. The examples below illustrate other useful `SymPy` functions that correspond to common mathematical operations on expressions:

```
>>> factor( x**2-2*x-8 )
(x - 4)*(x + 2)
>>> expand( (x-4)*(x+2) )
x**2 - 2*x - 8
>>> collect(x**2 + x*b + a*x + a*b, x)
x**2 + (a+b)*x + a*b      # collect terms for diff. pows of x
```

To substitute a given value into an expression, call the `.subs()` method, passing in a python dictionary object `{ key:val, ... }` with the symbol–value substitutions you want to make:

```
>>> expr  = sin(x) + cos(y)
>>> expr
sin(x) + cos(y)
>>> expr.subs({x:1, y:2})
sin(1) + cos(2)
>>> expr.subs({x:1, y:2}).n()
0.425324148260754
```

Note how we used `.n()` to obtain the expression's numeric value.

Solving equations

```
>>> from sympy import solve
```

The function `solve` is the main workhorse in `SymPy`. This incredibly powerful function knows how to solve all kinds of equations. In fact `solve` can solve pretty much *any* equation! When high school students learn about this function, they get really angry—why did they spend five years of their life learning to solve various equations by hand, when all along there was this `solve` thing that could do all the math for them? Don't worry, learning math is *never* a waste of time.

The function `solve` takes two arguments. Use `solve(expr,var)` to solve the equation `expr==0` for the variable `var`. You can rewrite any equation in the form `expr==0` by moving all the terms to one side of the equation; the solutions to $A(x) = B(x)$ are the same as the solutions to $A(x) - B(x) = 0$.

For example, to solve the quadratic equation $x^2 + 2x - 8 = 0$, use

```
>>> solve( x**2 + 2*x - 8, x)
[2, -4]
```

In this case the equation has two solutions so `solve` returns a list. Check that $x = 2$ and $x = -4$ satisfy the equation $x^2 + 2x - 8 = 0$.

The best part about `solve` and `SymPy` is that you can obtain symbolic answers when solving equations. Instead of solving one specific quadratic equation, we can solve all possible equations of the form $ax^2 + bx + c = 0$ using the following steps:

```
>>> a, b, c = symbols('a b c')
>>> solve( a*x**2 + b*x + c, x)
[(-b + sqrt(b**2 - 4*a*c))/(2*a), (-b-sqrt(b**2-4*a*c))/(2*a)]
```

In this case `solve` calculated the solution in terms of the symbols `a`, `b`, and `c`. You should be able to recognize the expressions in the solution—it's the quadratic formula $x_{1,2} = \frac{-b \pm \sqrt{b^2-4ac}}{2a}$.

To solve a *system of equations*, you can feed `solve` with the list of equations as the first argument, and specify the list of unknowns you want to solve for as the second argument. For example, to solve for x and y in the system of equations $x + y = 3$ and $3x - 2y = 0$, use

```
>>> solve([x + y - 3, 3*x - 2*y], [x, y])
{x: 6/5, y: 9/5}
```

The function `solve` is like a Swiss Army knife you can use to solve all kind of problems. Suppose you want to *complete the square* in the expression $x^2 - 4x + 7$, that is, you want to find constants h and k such that $x^2 - 4x + 7 = (x - h)^2 + k$. There is no special "complete the square" function in `SymPy`, but you can call `solve` on the equation $(x - h)^2 + k - (x^2 - 4x + 7) = 0$ to find the unknowns h and k:

```
>>> h, k = symbols('h k')
>>> solve( (x-h)**2 + k  - (x**2-4*x+7), [h,k] )
[(2, 3)]                                  # so h = 2 and k = 3
>>> ((x-2)**2+3).expand()                 # verify...
x**2 - 4*x + 7
```

Learn the basic SymPy commands and you'll never need to suffer another tedious arithmetic calculation painstakingly performed by hand again!

Rational functions

```
>>> from sympy import together, apart
```

By default, SymPy will not combine or split rational expressions. You need to use together to symbolically calculate the addition of fractions:

```
>>> a, b, c, d = symbols('a b c d')
>>> a/b + c/d
a/b + c/d
>>> together(a/b + c/d)
(a*d + b*c)/(b*d)
```

Alternately, if you have a rational expression and want to divide the numerator by the denominator, use the apart function:

```
>>> apart( (x**2+x+4)/(x+2)  )
x - 1  +  6/(x + 2)
```

Exponentials and logarithms

Euler's number $e = 2.71828\ldots$ is defined one of several ways,

$$e \equiv \lim_{n\to\infty}\left(1+\frac{1}{n}\right)^n \equiv \lim_{\epsilon\to 0}(1+\epsilon)^{1/\epsilon} \equiv \sum_{n=0}^{\infty}\frac{1}{n!},$$

and is denoted E in SymPy. Using exp(x) is equivalent to E**x.

The functions log and ln both compute the logarithm base e:

```
>>> log(E**3)     # same as ln(E**3)
3
```

By default, SymPy assumes the inputs to functions like exp and log are complex numbers, so it will not expand certain logarithmic expressions. However, indicating to SymPy that the inputs are positive real numbers will make the expansions work:

```
>>> x, y = symbols('x y')
>>> log(x*y).expand()
log(x*y)
>>> a, b = symbols('a b', positive=True)
>>> log(a*b).expand()
log(a) + log(b)
```

Polynomials

Let's define a polynomial P with roots at $x = 1$, $x = 2$, and $x = 3$:

```
>>> P = (x-1)*(x-2)*(x-3)
>>> P
(x - 1)*(x - 2)*(x - 3)
```

To see the expanded version of the polynomial, call its `expand` method:

```
>>> P.expand()
x**3 - 6*x**2 + 11*x - 6
```

When the polynomial is expressed in it's expanded form $P(x) = x^3 - 6^2 + 11x - 6$, we can't immediately identify its roots. This is why the factored form $P(x) = (x-1)(x-2)(x-3)$ is preferable. To factor a polynomial, call its `factor` method or `simplify` it:

```
>>> P.factor()
(x - 1)*(x - 2)*(x - 3)
>>> P.simplify()
(x - 1)*(x - 2)*(x - 3)
```

Recall that the roots of the polynomial $P(x)$ are defined as the solutions to the equation $P(x) = 0$. We can use the `solve` function to find the roots of the polynomial:

```
>>> roots = solve(P,x)
>>> roots
[1, 2, 3]
# let's check if P equals (x-1)(x-2)(x-3)
>>> simplify( P  -  (x-roots[0])*(x-roots[1])*(x-roots[2]) )
0
```

Equality checking

In the last example, we used the `simplify` function to check whether two expressions were equal. This way of checking equality works because $P = Q$ if and only if $P - Q = 0$. This is the best way to check if two expressions are equal in SymPy because it attempts all possible simplifications when comparing the expressions. Below is a list of other ways to check whether two quantities are equal with example cases where they fail:

```
>>> p = (x-5)*(x+5)
>>> q = x**2 - 25
>>> p == q                                          # fail
False
>>> p - q == 0                                      # fail
False
>>> simplify(p - q) == 0
```

```
True
>>> sin(x)**2 + cos(x)**2  == 1                     # fail
False
>>> simplify( sin(x)**2 + cos(x)**2 - 1 ) == 0
True
```

Trigonometry

```
from sympy import sin, cos, tan, trigsimp, expand_trig
```

The trigonometric functions `sin` and `cos` take inputs in radians:

```
>>> sin(pi/6)
1/2
>>> cos(pi/6)
sqrt(3)/2
```

For angles in degrees, you need a conversion factor of $\frac{\pi}{180}$[rad/°]:

```
>>> sin(30*pi/180)                   # 30 deg = pi/6 rads
1/2
```

The inverse trigonometric functions $\sin^{-1}(x) \equiv \arcsin(x)$ and $\cos^{-1}(x) \equiv \arccos(x)$ are used as follows:

```
>>> asin(1/2)
pi/6
>>> acos(sqrt(3)/2)
pi/6
```

Recall that $\tan(x) \equiv \frac{\sin(x)}{\cos(x)}$. The inverse function of $\tan(x)$ is $\tan^{-1}(x) \equiv \arctan(x) \equiv$ `atan(x)`

```
>>> tan(pi/6)
1/sqrt(3)                            # = ( 1/2 )/( sqrt(3)/2 )
>>> atan( 1/sqrt(3) )
pi/6
```

The function `acos` returns angles in the range $[0, \pi]$, while `asin` and `atan` return angles in the range $[-\frac{\pi}{2}, \frac{\pi}{2}]$.

Here are some trigonometric identities that SymPy knows:

```
>>> sin(x) == cos(x - pi/2)
True
>>> simplify( sin(x)*cos(y)+cos(x)*sin(y) )
sin(x + y)
>>> e = 2*sin(x)**2 + 2*cos(x)**2
>>> trigsimp(e)
2
>>> trigsimp(log(e))
log(2*sin(x)**2 + 2*cos(x)**2)
>>> trigsimp(log(e), deep=True)
log(2)
```

```
>>> simplify(sin(x)**4 - 2*cos(x)**2*sin(x)**2 + cos(x)**4)
cos(4*x)/2 + 1/2
```

The function `trigsimp` does essentially the same job as `simplify`.

If instead of simplifying you want to expand a trig expression, you should use `expand_trig`, because the default `expand` won't touch trig functions:

```
>>> expand(sin(2*x))          # = (sin(2*x)).expand()
sin(2*x)
>>> expand_trig(sin(2*x))     # = (sin(2*x)).expand(trig=True)
2*sin(x)*cos(x)
```

Complex numbers

```
>>> from sympy import I, re, im, Abs, arg, conjugate
```

Consider the quadratic equation $x^2 = -1$. There are no real solutions to this equation, but we can define an imaginary number $i = \sqrt{-1}$ (denoted `I` in `SymPy`) that satisfies this equation:

```
>>> I*I
-1
>>> solve( x**2 + 1 , x)
[I, -I]
```

The solutions are $x = i$ and $x = -i$, and indeed we can verify that $i^2 + 1 = 0$ and $(-i)^2 + 1 = 0$ since $i^2 = -1$.

The complex numbers $\mathbb{C}$ are defined as $\{a + bi \,|\, a, b \in \mathbb{R}\}$. Complex numbers contain a real part and an imaginary part:

```
>>> z = 4 + 3*I
>>> z
4 + 3*I
>>> re(z)
4
>>> im(z)
3
```

The *polar* representation of a complex number is $z \equiv |z|\angle\theta \equiv |z|e^{i\theta}$. For a complex number $z = a + bi$, the quantity $|z| = \sqrt{a^2 + b^2}$ is known as the *absolute value* of z, and θ is its *phase* or its *argument*:

```
>>> Abs(z)
5
>>> arg(z)
atan(3/4)
```

The complex conjugate of $z = a + bi$ is the number $\bar{z} = a - bi$:

```
>>> conjugate( z )
4 - 3*I
```

Complex conjugation is important for computing the absolute value of z ($|z| \equiv \sqrt{z\bar{z}}$) and for division by z ($\frac{1}{z} \equiv \frac{\bar{z}}{|z|^2}$).

Euler's formula

```
>>> from sympy import expand, rewrite
```

Euler's formula shows an important relation between the exponential function e^x and the trigonometric functions $\sin(x)$ and $\cos(x)$:

$$e^{ix} = \cos x + i \sin x.$$

To obtain this result in SymPy, you must specify that the number x is real and also tell expand that you're interested in complex expansions:

```
>>> x = symbols('x', real=True)
>>> exp(I*x).expand(complex=True)
cos(x) + I*sin(x)
>>> re( exp(I*x) )
cos(x)
>>> im( exp(I*x) )
sin(x)
```

Basically, $\cos(x)$ is the real part of e^{ix}, and $\sin(x)$ is the imaginary part of e^{ix}. Whaaat? I know it's weird, but weird things are bound to happen when you input imaginary numbers to functions.

Euler's formula is often used to rewrite the functions sin and cos in terms of complex exponentials. For example,

```
>>> (cos(x)).rewrite(exp)
exp(I*x)/2 + exp(-I*x)/2
```

Compare this expression with the definition of hyperbolic cosine.

Calculus

Calculus is the study of the properties of functions. The operations of calculus are used to describe the limit behaviour of functions, calculate their rates of change, and calculate the areas under their graphs. In this section we'll learn about the SymPy functions for calculating limits, derivatives, integrals, and summations.

Infinity

```
from sympy import oo
```

The infinity symbol is denoted oo (two lowercase os) in SymPy. Infinity is not a number but a process: the process of counting forever. Thus, $\infty + 1 = \infty$, ∞ is greater than any finite number, and $1/\infty$ is an infinitely small number. Sympy knows how to correctly treat infinity in expressions:

```
>>> oo+1
oo
>>> 5000 < oo
True
>>> 1/oo
0
```

Limits

```
from sympy import limit
```

We use limits to describe, with mathematical precision, infinitely large quantities, infinitely small quantities, and procedures with infinitely many steps.

The number e is defined as the limit $e \equiv \lim_{n\to\infty}\left(1+\frac{1}{n}\right)^n$:

```
>>> limit( (1+1/n)**n, n, oo)
E            # = 2.71828182845905
```

This limit expression describes the annual growth rate of a loan with a nominal interest rate of 100% and infinitely frequent compounding. Borrow $1000 in such a scheme, and you'll owe $2718.28 after one year.

Limits are also useful to describe the behaviour of functions. Consider the function $f(x) = \frac{1}{x}$. The `limit` command shows us what happens to $f(x)$ near $x = 0$ and as x goes to infinity:

```
>>> limit( 1/x, x, 0, dir="+")
oo
>>> limit( 1/x, x, 0, dir="-")
-oo
>>> limit( 1/x, x, oo)
0
```

As x becomes larger and larger, the fraction $\frac{1}{x}$ becomes smaller and smaller. In the limit where x goes to infinity, $\frac{1}{x}$ approaches zero: $\lim_{x\to\infty}\frac{1}{x} = 0$. On the other hand, when x takes on smaller and smaller positive values, the expression $\frac{1}{x}$ becomes infinite: $\lim_{x\to 0^+}\frac{1}{x} = \infty$. When x approaches 0 from the left, we have $\lim_{x\to 0^-}\frac{1}{x} = -\infty$. If these calculations are not clear to you, study the graph of $f(x) = \frac{1}{x}$.

Here are some other examples of limits:

```
>>> limit(sin(x)/x, x, 0)
1
>>> limit(sin(x)**2/x, x, 0)
0
>>> limit(exp(x)/x**100,x,oo) # which is bigger e^x or x^100 ?
oo                            # exp f >> all poly f for big x
```

Derivatives

The derivative function, denoted $f'(x)$, $\frac{d}{dx}f(x)$, $\frac{df}{dx}$, or $\frac{dy}{dx}$, describes the *rate of change* of the function $f(x)$. The SymPy function diff computes the derivative of any expression:

```
>>> diff(x**3, x)
3*x**2
```

The differentiation operation knows about the product rule $[f(x)g(x)]' = f'(x)g(x) + f(x)g'(x)$, the chain rule $f(g(x))' = f'(g(x))g'(x)$, and the quotient rule $\left[\frac{f(x)}{g(x)}\right]' = \frac{f'(x)g(x)-f(x)g'(x)}{g(x)^2}$:

```
>>> diff( x**2*sin(x), x )
2*x*sin(x) + x**2*cos(x)
>>> diff( sin(x**2), x )
cos(x**2)*2*x
>>> diff( x**2/sin(x), x )
(2*x*sin(x) - x**2*cos(x))/sin(x)**2
```

The second derivative of a function f is diff(f,x,2):

```
>>> diff(x**3, x, 2)        # same as diff(diff(x**3, x), x)
6*x
```

Tangent lines

The *tangent line* to the function $f(x)$ at $x = x_0$ is the line that passes through the point $(x_0, f(x_0))$ and has the same slope as the function at that point. The tangent line to the function $f(x)$ at the point $x = x_0$ is described by the equation

$$T_1(x) = f(x_0) \; + \; f'(x_0)(x - x_0).$$

What is the equation of the tangent line to $f(x) = \frac{1}{2}x^2$ at $x_0 = 1$?

```
>>> f = S('1/2')*x**2
>>> f
x**2/2
>>> df = diff(f, x)
>>> df
x
>>> T_1 = f.subs({x:1}) + df.subs({x:1})*(x - 1)
>>> T_1
x - 1/2            # y = x - 1/2
```

The tangent line $T_1(x)$ has the same value and slope as the function $f(x)$ at $x = 1$:

```
>>> T_1.subs({x:1}) == f.subs({x:1})
True
>>> diff(T_1, x).subs({x:1}) == diff(f, x).subs({x:1})
True
```

See Figure 5.10 on page 307.

Optimization

Recall the *second derivative test* for finding the maxima and minima of a function, which we learned on page 325.

Let's find the critical points of the function $f(x) = x^3 - 2x^2 + x$ and use the information from its second derivative to find the maximum of the function on the interval $x \in [0, 1]$.

```
>>> x = Symbol('x')
>>> f = x**3-2*x**2+x
>>> diff(f, x)
3*x**2 - 4*x + 1
>>> sols = solve( diff(f,x),  x)
>>> sols
[1/3, 1]
>>> diff(diff(f,x), x).subs( {x:sols[0]} )
-2
>>> diff(diff(f,x), x).subs( {x:sols[1]} )
2
```

It will help to look at the graph of this function. The point $x = \frac{1}{3}$ is a local maximum because it is a critical point of $f(x)$ where the curvature is negative, meaning $f(x)$ looks like the peak of a mountain at $x = \frac{1}{3}$. The maximum value of $f(x)$ on the interval $x \in [0, 1]$ is $f\left(\frac{1}{3}\right) = \frac{4}{27}$. The point $x = 1$ is a local minimum because it is a critical point with positive curvature, meaning $f(x)$ looks like the bottom of a valley at $x = 1$.

Integrals

In SymPy we use `integrate(f, x)` to obtain the integral function $F(x)$ of any function $f(x)$: $F(x) = \int_0^x f(u)\,du$.

```
>>> integrate(x**3, x)
x**4/4
>>> integrate(sin(x), x)
-cos(x)
>>> integrate(ln(x), x)
x*log(x) - x
```

This is known as an *indefinite integral* since the limits of integration are not defined.

In contrast, a *definite integral* computes the area under $f(x)$ between $x = a$ and $x = b$. Use `integrate(f, (x,a,b))` to compute the definite integrals of the form $A(a, b) = \int_a^b f(x)\,dx$:

```
>>> integrate(x**3, (x,0,1))
1/4                  # the area under x^3 from x=0 to x=1
```

We can obtain the same area by first calculating the indefinite integral $F(c) = \int_0^c f(x)\,dx$, then using $A(a,b) = F(x)\big|_a^b \equiv F(b) - F(a)$:

```
>>> F = integrate(x**3, x)
>>> F.subs({x:1}) - F.subs({x:0})
1/4
```

Integrals correspond to *signed* area calculations:

```
>>> integrate(sin(x), (x,0,pi))
2
>>> integrate(sin(x), (x,pi,2*pi))
-2
>>> integrate(sin(x), (x,0,2*pi))
0
```

During the first half of its 2π-cycle, the graph of $\sin(x)$ is above the x-axis, so it has a positive contribution to the area under the curve. During the second half of its cycle (from $x = \pi$ to $x = 2\pi$), $\sin(x)$ is below the x-axis, so it contributes negative area. Draw a graph of $\sin(x)$ to see what is going on.

Fundamental theorem of calculus

The integral is the "inverse operation" of the derivative. If you perform the integral operation followed by the derivative operation on some function, you'll obtain the same function:

$$\left(\frac{d}{dx} \circ \int dx\right) f(x) \equiv \frac{d}{dx} \int_c^x f(u)\,du = f(x).$$

```
>>> f = x**2
>>> F = integrate(f, x)
>>> F
x**3/3              # + C
>>> diff(F, x)
x**2
```

Alternately, if you compute the derivative of a function followed by the integral, you will obtain the original function $f(x)$ (up to a constant):

$$\left(\int dx \circ \frac{d}{dx}\right) f(x) \equiv \int_c^x f'(u)\,du = f(x) + C.$$

```
>>> f = x**2
>>> df = diff(f, x)
>>> df
2*x
>>> integrate(df, x)
x**2    # + C
```

The fundamental theorem of calculus is important because it tells us how to solve differential equations. If we have to solve for $f(x)$ in the differential equation $\frac{d}{dx}f(x) = g(x)$, we can take the integral on both sides of the equation to obtain the answer $f(x) = \int g(x)\,dx + C$.

Sequences

Sequences are functions that take whole numbers as inputs. Instead of continuous inputs $x \in \mathbb{R}$, sequences take natural numbers $n \in \mathbb{N}$ as inputs. We denote sequences as a_n instead of the usual function notation $a(n)$.

We define a sequence by specifying an expression for its nth term:

```
>>> a_n = 1/n
>>> b_n = 1/factorial(n)
```

Substitute the desired value of n to see the value of the nth term:

```
>>> a_n.subs({n:5})
1/5
```

The Python list comprehension syntax `[item for item in list]` can be used to print the sequence values for some range of indices:

```
>>> [ a_n.subs({n:i}) for i in range(0,8) ]
[oo, 1, 1/2, 1/3, 1/4,  1/5,   1/6,   1/7]
>>> [ b_n.subs({n:i}) for i in range(0,8) ]
[1,  1, 1/2, 1/6, 1/24, 1/120, 1/720, 1/5040]
```

Observe that a_n is not properly defined for $n = 0$ since $\frac{1}{0}$ is a division-by-zero error. To be precise, we should say a_n's domain is the positive naturals $a_n : \mathbb{N}^+ \to \mathbb{R}$. Observe how quickly the `factorial` function $n! = 1 \cdot 2 \cdot 3 \cdots (n-1) \cdot n$ grows: $7! = 5040$, $10! = 3628800$, $20! > 10^{18}$.

We're often interested in calculating the limits of sequences as $n \to \infty$. What happens to the terms in the sequence when n becomes large?

```
>>> limit(a_n, n, oo)
0
>>> limit(b_n, n, oo)
0
```

Both $a_n = \frac{1}{n}$ and $b_n = \frac{1}{n!}$ *converge* to 0 as $n \to \infty$.

Many important math quantities are defined as limit expressions. An interesting example to consider is the number π, which is defined as the area of a circle of radius 1. We can approximate the area of the unit circle by drawing a many-sided regular polygon around the circle. Splitting the n-sided regular polygon into identical triangular splices, we can obtain a formula for its area A_n (see solution to **P1.36**). In the limit as $n \to \infty$, the n-sided-polygon approximation to the area of the unit-circle becomes exact:

```
>>> A_n = n*tan(2*pi/(2*n))
>>> limit(A_n, n, oo)
pi
```

Series

Suppose we're given a sequence a_n and we want to compute the sum of all the values in this sequence $\sum_n^\infty a_n$. Series are sums of sequences. Summing the values of a sequence $a_n : \mathbb{N} \to \mathbb{R}$ is analogous to taking the integral of a function $f : \mathbb{R} \to \mathbb{R}$.

To work with series in SymPy, use the summation function whose syntax is analogous to the integrate function:

```
>>> a_n = 1/n
>>> b_n = 1/factorial(n)
>>> summation(a_n, [n, 1, oo])
oo
>>> summation(b_n, [n, 0, oo])
E
```

We say the series $\sum a_n$ *diverges* to infinity (or *is divergent*) while the series $\sum b_n$ converges (or *is convergent*). As we sum together more and more terms of the sequence b_n, the total becomes closer and closer to some finite number. In this case, the infinite sum $\sum_{n=0}^\infty \frac{1}{n!}$ converges to the number $e = 2.71828\ldots$.

The summation command is useful because it allows us to compute *infinite* sums, but for most practical applications we don't need to take an infinite number of terms in a series to obtain a good approximation. This is why series are so neat: they represent a great way to obtain approximations.

Using standard Python commands, we can obtain an approximation to e that is accurate to six decimals by summing 10 terms in the series:

```
>>> import math
>>> def b_nf(n):
        return 1.0/math.factorial(n)
>>> sum( [b_nf(n) for n in range(0,10)] )
2.718281 52557319
>>> E.evalf()
2.718281 82845905       # true value
```

Taylor series

Wait, there's more! Not only can we use series to approximate numbers, we can also use them to approximate functions.

A *power series* is a series whose terms contain different powers of the variable x. The nth term in a power series is a function of both the sequence index n and the input variable x.

For example, the power series of the function $\exp(x) = e^x$ is

$$\exp(x) \equiv 1 + x + \frac{x^2}{2} + \frac{x^3}{3!} + \frac{x^4}{4!} + \frac{x^5}{5!} + \cdots = \sum_{n=0}^{\infty} \frac{x^n}{n!}.$$

This is, IMHO, one of the most important ideas in calculus: you can compute the value of $\exp(5)$ by taking the infinite sum of the terms in the power series with $x = 5$:

```
>>> exp_xn = x**n/factorial(n)
>>> summation( exp_xn.subs({x:5}), [n, 0, oo] ).evalf()
148.413159102577
>>> exp(5).evalf()
148.413159102577          # the true value
```

Note that `SymPy` is actually smart enough to recognize that the infinite series you're computing corresponds to the closed-form expression e^5:

```
>>> summation( exp_xn.subs({x:5}), [n, 0, oo])
exp(5)
```

Taking as few as 35 terms in the series is sufficient to obtain an approximation to e that is accurate to 16 decimals:

```
>>> import math                        # redo using only python
>>> def exp_xnf(x,n):
        return x**n/math.factorial(n)
>>> sum( [exp_xnf(5.0,i) for i in range(0,35)] )
148.413159102577
```

The coefficients in the power series of a function (also known as the *Taylor series*) depend on the value of the higher derivatives of the function. The formula for the nth term in the Taylor series of $f(x)$ expanded at $x = c$ is $a_n(x) = \frac{f^{(n)}(c)}{n!}(x-c)^n$, where $f^{(n)}(c)$ is the value of the nth derivative of $f(x)$ evaluated at $x = c$. The term *Maclaurin series* refers to Taylor series expansions at $x = 0$.

The `SymPy` function `series` is a convenient way to obtain the series of any function. Calling `series(expr,var,at,nmax)` will show you the series expansion of `expr` near `var=at` up to power `nmax`:

```
>>> series( sin(x), x, 0, 8)
x - x**3/6 + x**5/120 - x**7/5040 + O(x**8)
>>> series( cos(x), x, 0, 8)
1 - x**2/2 + x**4/24 - x**6/720 + O(x**8)
>>> series( sinh(x), x, 0, 8)
x + x**3/6 + x**5/120 + x**7/5040 + O(x**8)
>>> series( cosh(x), x, 0, 8)
1 + x**2/2 + x**4/24 + x**6/720 + O(x**8)
```

Some functions are not defined at $x = 0$, so we expand them at a different value of x. For example, the power series of $\ln(x)$ expanded at $x = 1$ is

```
>>> series(ln(x), x, 1, 6)      # Taylor series of ln(x) at x=1
x - x**2/2 + x**3/3 - x**4/4 + x**5/5  + O(x**6)
```

Here, the result `SymPy` returns is misleading. The Taylor series of $\ln(x)$ expanded at $x = 1$ has terms of the form $(x-1)^n$:

$$\ln(x) = (x-1) - \frac{(x-1)^2}{2} + \frac{(x-1)^3}{3} - \frac{(x-1)^4}{4} + \frac{(x-1)^5}{5} + \cdots.$$

Verify this is the correct formula by substituting $x = 1$. `SymPy` returns an answer in terms of coordinates *relative* to $x = 1$.

Instead of expanding $\ln(x)$ around $x = 1$, we can obtain an equivalent expression if we expand $\ln(x+1)$ around $x = 0$:

```
>>> series(ln(x+1), x, 0, 6)   # Maclaurin series of ln(x+1)
x - x**2/2 + x**3/3 - x**4/4 + x**5/5 + O(x**6)
```

Vectors

A vector $\vec{v} \in \mathbb{R}^n$ is an n-tuple of real numbers. For example, consider a vector that has three components:

$$\vec{v} = (v_1, v_2, v_3) \in (\mathbb{R}, \mathbb{R}, \mathbb{R}) \equiv \mathbb{R}^3.$$

To specify the vector $\vec{v}$, we specify the values for its three components v_1, v_2, and v_3.

A matrix $A \in \mathbb{R}^{m \times n}$ is a rectangular array of real numbers with m rows and n columns. A vector is a special type of matrix; we can think of a vector $\vec{v} \in \mathbb{R}^n$ either as a row vector ($1 \times n$ matrix) or a column vector ($n \times 1$ matrix). Because of this equivalence between vectors and matrices, there is no need for a special vector object in `SymPy`, and `Matrix` objects are used for vectors as well.

This is how we define vectors and compute their properties:

```
>>> u = Matrix([[4,5,6]]) # a row vector = 1x3 matrix
>>> v = Matrix([[7],
                [8],      # a col vector = 3x1 matrix
                [9]])
>>> v.T                   # use the transpose operation to
Matrix([[7, 8, 9]])       # convert a col vec to a row vec

>>> u[0]                  # 0-based indexing for entries
4
>>> u.norm()              # length of u
sqrt(77)
```

```
>>> uhat = u/u.norm()      # unit vector in same dir as u
>>> uhat
[4/sqrt(77), 5/sqrt(77), 6/sqrt(77)]
>>> uhat.norm()
1
```

Dot product

The dot product of the 3-vectors $\vec{u}$ and $\vec{v}$ can be defined two ways:

$$\vec{u}\cdot\vec{v} \equiv \underbrace{u_xv_x + u_yv_y + u_zv_z}_{\text{algebraic def.}} \equiv \underbrace{\|\vec{u}\|\|\vec{v}\|\cos(\varphi)}_{\text{geometric def.}} \quad \in \mathbb{R},$$

where φ is the angle between the vectors $\vec{u}$ and $\vec{v}$. In SymPy,

```
>>> u = Matrix([ 4,5,6])
>>> v = Matrix([-1,1,2])
>>> u.dot(v)
13
```

We can combine the algebraic and geometric formulas for the dot product to obtain the cosine of the angle between the vectors

$$\cos(\varphi) = \frac{\vec{u}\cdot\vec{v}}{\|\vec{u}\|\|\vec{v}\|} = \frac{u_xv_x + u_yv_y + u_zv_z}{\|\vec{u}\|\|\vec{v}\|},$$

and use the acos function to find the angle measure:

```
>>> acos(u.dot(v)/(u.norm()*v.norm())).evalf()
0.921263115666387      # in radians  =  52.76 degrees
```

Just by looking at the coordinates of the vectors $\vec{u}$ and $\vec{v}$, it's difficult to determine their relative direction. Thanks to the dot product, however, we know the angle between the vectors is 52.76°, which means they *kind of* point in the same direction. Vectors that are at an angle $\varphi = 90^\circ$ are called *orthogonal*, meaning at right angles with each other. The dot product of vectors for which $\varphi > 90^\circ$ is negative because they point *mostly* in opposite directions.

The notion of the "angle between vectors" applies more generally to vectors with any number of dimensions. The dot product for n-dimensional vectors is $\vec{u}\cdot\vec{v} = \sum_{i=1}^{n} u_iv_i$. This means we can talk about "the angle between" 1000-dimensional vectors. That's pretty crazy if you think about it—there is no way we could possibly "visualize" 1000-dimensional vectors, yet given two such vectors we can tell if they point mostly in the same direction, in perpendicular directions, or mostly in opposite directions.

The dot product is a commutative operation $\vec{u}\cdot\vec{v} = \vec{v}\cdot\vec{u}$:

```
>>> u.dot(v) == v.dot(u)
True
```

Cross product

The *cross product*, denoted $\times$, takes two vectors as inputs and produces a vector as output. The cross products of individual basis elements are defined as follows:

$$\hat{\imath} \times \hat{\jmath} = \hat{k}, \qquad \hat{\jmath} \times \hat{k} = \hat{\imath}, \qquad \hat{k} \times \hat{\imath} = \hat{\jmath}.$$

Here is how to compute the cross product of two vectors in SymPy:

```
>>> u = Matrix([ 4,5,6])
>>> v = Matrix([-1,1,2])
>>> u.cross(v)
[4, -14, 9]
```

The vector $\vec{u} \times \vec{v}$ is orthogonal to both $\vec{u}$ and $\vec{v}$. The norm of the cross product $\|\vec{u} \times \vec{v}\|$ is proportional to the lengths of the vectors and the sine of the angle between them:

```
(u.cross(v).norm()/(u.norm()*v.norm())).n()
0.796366206088088     # = sin(0.921..)
```

The name "cross product" is well-suited for this operation since it is calculated by "cross-multiplying" the coefficients of the vectors:

$$\vec{u} \times \vec{v} = \left(u_y v_z - u_z v_y,\ u_z v_x - u_x v_z,\ u_x v_y - u_y v_x\right).$$

By defining individual symbols for the entries of two vectors, we can make SymPy show us the cross-product formula:

```
>>> u1,u2,u3 = symbols('u1:4')
>>> v1,v2,v3 = symbols('v1:4')
>>> Matrix([u1,u2,u3]).cross(Matrix([v1,v2,v3]))
[ (u2*v3 - u3*v2), (-u1*v3 + u3*v1), (u1*v2 - u2*v1) ]
```

The cross product is anticommutative, $\vec{u} \times \vec{v} = -\vec{v} \times \vec{u}$:

```
>>> u.cross(v)
[4, -14, 9]
>>> v.cross(u)
[-4, 14,-9]
```

The product of two numbers and the dot product of two vectors are commutative operations. The cross product, however, is not commutative: $\vec{u} \times \vec{v} \neq \vec{v} \times \vec{u}$.

Mechanics

The module called `sympy.physics.mechanics` contains elaborate tools for describing mechanical systems, manipulating reference frames, forces, and torques. These specialized functions are not necessary for a first-year mechanics course. The basic SymPy functions like solve, and the vector operations you learned in the previous sections are powerful enough for basic Newtonian mechanics.

Dynamics

The net force acting on an object is the sum of all the external forces acting on it $\vec{F}_{\text{net}} = \sum \vec{F}$. Since forces are vectors, we need to use vector addition to compute the net force.

Compute $\vec{F}_{\text{net}} = \vec{F}_1 + \vec{F}_2$, where $\vec{F}_1 = 4\hat{\imath}[\text{N}]$ and $\vec{F}_2 = 5\angle 30°[\text{N}]$:

```
>>> F_1 =  Matrix( [4,0] )
>>> F_2 =  Matrix( [5*cos(30*pi/180), 5*sin(30*pi/180) ] )
>>> F_net = F_1 + F_2
>>> F_net
[4 + 5*sqrt(3)/2,   5/2]              # in Newtons
>>> F_net.evalf()
[8.33012701892219,  2.5]              # in Newtons
```

To express the answer in length-and-direction notation, use norm to find the length of $\vec{F}_{\text{net}}$ and atan2[1] to find its direction:

```
>>> F_net.norm().evalf()
8.69718438067042                      # |F_net| in [N]
>>> (atan2( F_net[1],F_net[0] )*180/pi).n()
16.7053138060100                      # angle in degrees
```

The net force on the object is $\vec{F}_{\text{net}} = 8.697\angle 16.7°[\text{N}]$.

Kinematics

Let $x(t)$ denote the position of an object, $v(t)$ denote its velocity, and $a(t)$ denote its acceleration. Together $x(t)$, $v(t)$, and $a(t)$ are known as the *equations of motion* of the object.

Starting from the knowledge of $\vec{F}_{\text{net}}$, we can compute $a(t) = \frac{\vec{F}_{\text{net}}}{m}$, then obtain $v(t)$ by integrating $a(t)$, and finally obtain $x(t)$ by integrating $v(t)$:

$$\underbrace{\frac{\vec{F}_{\text{net}}}{m} = a(t)}_{\text{Newton's 2nd law}} \underbrace{\overset{v_i+\int dt}{\longrightarrow} \quad v(t) \quad \overset{x_i+\int dt}{\longrightarrow} \quad x(t).}_{\text{kinematics}}$$

[1]The function atan2(y,x) computes the correct direction for all vectors (x,y), unlike atan(y/x) which requires corrections for angles in the range $[\frac{\pi}{2}, \frac{3\pi}{2}]$.

Uniform acceleration motion (UAM)

Let's analyze the case where the net force on the object is constant. A constant force causes a constant acceleration $a = \frac{F}{m} =$ constant. If the acceleration function is constant over time $a(t) = a$. We find $v(t)$ and $x(t)$ as follows:

```
>>> t, a, v_i, x_i = symbols('t a v_i x_i')
>>> v = v_i + integrate(a, (t, 0,t) )
>>> v
a*t + v_i
>>> x = x_i + integrate(v, (t, 0,t) )
>>> x
a*t**2/2 + v_i*t + x_i
```

You may remember these equations from Section 2.4 (page 148). They are the *uniform accelerated motion* (UAM) equations:

$$\begin{aligned} a(t) &= a, \\ v(t) &= v_i + at, \\ x(t) &= x_i + v_i t + \frac{1}{2}at^2. \end{aligned}$$

In high school, you probably had to memorize these equations. Now you know how to derive them yourself starting from first principles.

For the sake of completeness, we'll now derive the fourth UAM equation, which relates the object's final velocity to the initial velocity, the displacement, and the acceleration, without reference to time:

```
>>> (v*v).expand()
a**2*t**2 + 2*a*t*v_i + v_i**2
>>> ((v*v).expand() - 2*a*x).simplify()
-2*a*x_i + v_i**2
```

The above calculation shows $v_f^2 - 2ax_f = -2ax_i + v_i^2$. After moving the term $2ax_f$ to the other side of the equation, we obtain

$$(v(t))^2 \;=\; v_f^2 = v_i^2 + 2a\Delta x \;=\; v_i^2 + 2a(x_f - x_i).$$

The fourth equation is important for practical purposes because it allows us to solve physics problems without using the time variable.

Example

Find the position function of an object at time $t = 3$[s], if it starts from $x_i = 20$[m] with $v_i = 10$[m/s] and undergoes a constant acceleration of $a = 5$[m/s^2]. What is the object's velocity at $t = 3$[s]?

```
>>> x_i = 20    # initial position
>>> v_i = 10    # initial velocity
>>> a   = 5     # acceleration (constant during motion)
>>> x = x_i + integrate(  v_i+integrate(a,(t,0,t)),  (t,0,t) )
>>> x
5*t**2/2 + 10*t + 20
>>> x.subs({t:3}).n()                 # x(3) in [m]
72.5
>>> diff(x,t).subs({t:3}).n()         # v(3) in [m/s]
25                                    # = sqrt( v_i**2 + 2*a*52.5 )
```

If you think about it, physics knowledge combined with computer skills is like a superpower!

General equations of motion

The procedure $a(t) \xrightarrow{v_i+\int dt} v(t) \xrightarrow{x_i+\int dt} x(t)$ can be used to obtain the position function $x(t)$ even when the acceleration is not constant. Suppose the acceleration of an object is $a(t) = \sqrt{kt}$; what is its $x(t)$?

```
>>> t, v_i, x_i, k = symbols('t v_i x_i k')
>>> a = sqrt(k*t)
>>> x = x_i + integrate( v_i+integrate(a,(t,0,t)), (t, 0,t) )
>>> x
x_i + v_i*t + (4/15)*(k*t)**(5/2)/k**2
```

Potential energy

For each force $\vec{F}(x)$ there is a corresponding potential energy $U_F(x)$. The change in potential energy associated with the force $\vec{F}(x)$ and displacement $\vec{d}$ is defined as the negative of the work done by the force during the displacement: $U_F(x) = -W = -\int_{\vec{d}} \vec{F}(x) \cdot d\vec{x}$.

The potential energies associated with gravity $\vec{F}_g = -mg\hat{\jmath}$ and the force of a spring $\vec{F}_s = -k\vec{x}$ are calculated as follows:

```
>>> x, y = symbols('x y')
>>> m, g, k, h = symbols('m g k h')
>>> F_g = -m*g                  # Force of gravity on mass m
>>> U_g = - integrate( F_g, (y,0,h) )
>>> U_g
m*g*h                           # Grav. potential energy
>>> F_s = -k*x                  # Spring force for displacement x
>>> U_s = - integrate( F_s, (x,0,x) )
>>> U_s
k*x**2/2                        # Spring potential energy
```

Note the negative sign in the formula defining the potential energy. This negative is canceled by the negative sign of the dot product $\vec{F} \cdot$

$d\vec{x}$: when the force acts in the direction opposite to the displacement, the work done by the force is negative.

Simple harmonic motion

```
from sympy import Function, dsolve
```

The force exerted by a spring is given by the formula $F = -kx$. If the only force acting on a mass m is the force of a spring, we can use Newton's second law to obtain the following equation:

$$F = ma \quad \Rightarrow \quad -kx = ma \quad \Rightarrow \quad -kx(t) = m\frac{d^2}{dt^2}\Big[x(t)\Big].$$

The motion of a mass-spring system is described by the *differential equation* $\frac{d^2}{dt^2}x(t) + \omega^2 x(t) = 0$, where the constant $\omega = \sqrt{\frac{k}{m}}$ is called the angular frequency. We can find the position function $x(t)$ using the `dsolve` method:

```
>>> t = Symbol('t')                    # time            t
>>> x = Function('x')                  # position function x(t)
>>> w = Symbol('w', positive=True)     # angular frequency w
>>> sol = dsolve( diff(x(t),t,t) + w**2*x(t), x(t) )
>>> sol
x(t) == C1*sin(w*t) + C2*cos(w*t)
>>> x = sol.rhs
>>> x
C1*sin(w*t) + C2*cos(w*t)
```

Note the solution $x(t) = C_1\sin(\omega t) + C_2\cos(\omega t)$ is equivalent to $x(t) = A\cos(\omega t + \phi)$, which is more commonly used to describe simple harmonic motion. We can use the `expand` function with the argument `trig=True` to convince ourselves of this equivalence:

```
>>> A, phi = symbols("A phi")
>>> (A*cos(w*t - phi)).expand(trig=True)
A*sin(phi)*sin(w*t) + A*cos(phi)*cos(w*t)
```

If we define $C_1 = A\sin(\phi)$ and $C_2 = A\cos(\phi)$, we obtain the form $x(t) = C_1\sin(\omega t) + C_2\cos(\omega t)$ that SymPy found.

Conservation of energy

We can verify that the total energy of the mass-spring system is conserved by showing $E_T(t) = U_s(t) + K(t) = \text{constant}$:

```
>>> x = sol.rhs.subs({"C1":0,"C2":A})
>>> x
A*cos(t*w)
>>> v = diff(x, t)
```

```
-A*w*sin(t*w)
>>> E_T = (0.5*k*x**2 + 0.5*m*v**2).simplify()
>>> E_T
0.5*A**2*(k*cos(w*t)**2 + m*w**2*sin(w*t)**2)
>>> E_T.subs({k:m*w**2}).simplify()
0.5*m*(w*A)**2                                  # = K_max
>>> E_T.subs({w:sqrt(k/m)}).simplify()
0.5*k*A**2                                      # = U_max
```

Conclusion

I'll conclude with some words of caution about computer overuse. Computer technology is very powerful and is everywhere around us, but we must not forget that computers are actually very dumb. Computers are merely calculators, and they depend on your knowledge to direct them. It's important you learn how to perform complicated math by hand in order to be able to instruct computers to execute math for you, and so you can check the results of your computer calculations. I don't want you to use the tricks you learned in this tutorial to avoid math problems and blindly rely on `SymPy` for all your math needs. That won't work! The idea is for both you and the computer to be math powerhouses.

Most math discoveries were made using pen and paper. When solving a math problem, if you clearly define each variable, draw a diagram, and clearly set up the problem's equations in terms of the variables you defined, then half the work of solving the problem is done. Computers can't help with these important, initial modelling and problem-specific tasks—only humans are good at this stuff. Once you *set up* the problem, `SymPy` can help you breeze through tedious calculations. The combination of pen and paper for thinking and `SymPy` for calculating is indeed quite powerful. Go out there and do some science!

Links

[Installation instructions for `jupyter notebook`]
`https://jupyter.readthedocs.io/en/latest/install.html`

[The official `SymPy` tutorial]
`http://docs.sympy.org/latest/tutorial/intro.html`

[A list of `SymPy` gotchas]
`http://docs.sympy.org/dev/gotchas.html`

Appendix E

Formulas

Calculus formulas

$\frac{dy}{dx}$	$\longleftarrow \; y \; \longrightarrow$	$\int y\,dx$
Algebraic		
1	x	$\frac{1}{2}x^2 + C$
0	a	$ax + C$
nx^{n-1}	x^n	$\frac{1}{n+1}x^{n+1} + C$
$-x^{-2}$	x^{-1}	$\ln x + C$
$\frac{du}{dx} \pm \frac{dv}{dx} \pm \frac{dw}{dx}$	$u \pm v \pm w$	$\int u\,dx \pm \int v\,dx \pm \int w\,dx$
$u\frac{dv}{dx} + v\frac{du}{dx}$	uv	No general form known
$\frac{v\frac{du}{dx} - u\frac{dv}{dx}}{v^2}$	$\frac{u}{v}$	No general form known
	u	$ux - \int x\,du + C$

$\frac{dy}{dx}$	$\longleftarrow \; y \; \longrightarrow$	$\int y\,dx$
Exponential and Logarithmic		
e^x	e^x	$e^x + C$
x^{-1}	$\ln x$	$x(\ln x - 1) + C$
$\frac{1}{\ln 10}\, x^{-1}$	$\log_{10} x$	$\frac{1}{\ln 10}\, x(\ln x - 1) + C$
$a^x \ln a$	a^x	$\frac{a^x}{\ln a} + C$
Trigonometric		
$\cos x$	$\sin x$	$-\cos x + C$
$-\sin x$	$\cos x$	$\sin x + C$
$\sec^2 x$	$\tan x$	$-\ln \cos x + C$
Inverse trigonometric		
$\frac{1}{\sqrt{(1-x^2)}}$	$\sin^{-1}(x)$	$x \sin^{-1}(x) + \sqrt{1-x^2} + C$
$-\frac{1}{\sqrt{(1-x^2)}}$	$\cos^{-1}(x)$	$x \cos^{-1}(x) - \sqrt{1-x^2} + C$
$\frac{1}{1+x^2}$	$\tan^{-1}(x)$	$x \tan^{-1}(x) - \frac{1}{2}\ln(1+x^2) + C$
Hyperbolic		
$\cosh x$	$\sinh x$	$\cosh x + C$
$\sinh x$	$\cosh x$	$\sinh x + C$
$\operatorname{sech}^2 x$	$\tanh x$	$\ln \cosh x + C$
Inverse hyperbolic		
$-\frac{x}{(a^2+x^2)^{\frac{3}{2}}}$	$\frac{1}{\sqrt{a^2+x^2}}$	$\sinh^{-1}(\frac{x}{a}) + C \equiv \ln(x + \sqrt{a^2+x^2}) + C$

$\dfrac{dy}{dx}$	$\longleftarrow \quad y \quad \longrightarrow$	$\int y\,dx$
Miscellaneous		
$-\dfrac{1}{(x+a)^2}$	$\dfrac{1}{x+a}$	$\ln(x+a)+C$
$\mp\dfrac{b}{(a\pm bx)^2}$	$\dfrac{1}{a\pm bx}$	$\pm\dfrac{1}{b}\ln(a\pm bx)+C$
$-\dfrac{3a^2x}{(a^2+x^2)^{\frac{5}{2}}}$	$\dfrac{a^2}{(a^2+x^2)^{\frac{3}{2}}}$	$\dfrac{x}{\sqrt{a^2+x^2}}+C$
$a\cos ax$	$\sin ax$	$-\dfrac{1}{a}\cos ax+C$
$-a\sin ax$	$\cos ax$	$\dfrac{1}{a}\sin ax+C$
$a\sec^2 ax$	$\tan ax$	$-\dfrac{1}{a}\ln\cos ax+C$
$\sin 2x$	$\sin^2 x$	$\dfrac{x}{2}-\dfrac{\sin 2x}{4}+C$
$-\sin 2x$	$\cos^2 x$	$\dfrac{x}{2}+\dfrac{\sin 2x}{4}+C$
$n\sin^{n-1}x\cos x$	$\sin^n x$	$-\dfrac{\cos x}{n}\sin^{n-1}x+\dfrac{n-1}{n}\int\sin^{n-2}x\,dx+C$
$-\dfrac{\cos x}{\sin^2 x}$	$\dfrac{1}{\sin x}$	$\ln\tan\dfrac{x}{2}+C$
$-\dfrac{\sin 2x}{\sin^4 x}$	$\dfrac{1}{\sin^2 x}$	$-\operatorname{cotan}x+C$
$\dfrac{\sin^2 x-\cos^2 x}{\sin^2 x\cos^2 x}$	$\dfrac{1}{\sin x\cos x}$	$\ln\tan x+C$
$n\sin mx\cos nx+$ $m\sin nx\cos mx$	$\sin mx\sin nx$	$\frac{1}{2}\cos(m-n)x-\frac{1}{2}\cos(m+n)x+C$
$2a\sin 2ax$	$\sin^2 ax$	$\dfrac{x}{2}-\dfrac{\sin 2ax}{4a}+C$
$-2a\sin 2ax$	$\cos^2 ax$	$\dfrac{x}{2}+\dfrac{\sin 2ax}{4a}+C$

Mechanics formulas

Forces:

$$W = F_g = \frac{GMm}{r^2} = gm, \quad F_s = -kx, \quad F_{fs} \leqslant \mu_s N, \quad F_{fk} = \mu_k N$$

Newton's three laws:

$$\text{if no } \vec{F}_{\text{ext}}, \text{ then } \vec{v}_i = \vec{v}_f \tag{1}$$

$$\vec{F}_{\text{net}} = m\vec{a} \tag{2}$$

$$\text{if } \vec{F}_{12}, \text{ then } \exists \vec{F}_{21} = -\vec{F}_{12} \tag{3}$$

Uniform acceleration motion (UAM):

$$a(t) = a \tag{4}$$

$$v(t) = at + v_i \tag{5}$$

$$x(t) = \tfrac{1}{2}at^2 + v_i t + x_i \tag{6}$$

$$v_f^2 = v_i^2 + 2a\Delta x \tag{7}$$

Momentum:

$$\vec{p} = m\vec{v} \tag{8}$$

Energy and work:

$$K = \tfrac{1}{2}mv^2, \quad U_g = mgh, \quad U_s = \tfrac{1}{2}kx^2, \quad K_r = \tfrac{1}{2}I\omega^2, \quad W = \vec{F}\cdot\vec{d} \tag{9}$$

Conservation laws:

$$\sum \vec{p}_{\text{in}} = \sum \vec{p}_{\text{out}} \tag{10}$$

$$L_{\text{in}} = L_{\text{out}} \tag{11}$$

$$\sum E_{\text{in}} + W_{\text{in}} = \sum E_{\text{out}} + W_{\text{out}} \tag{12}$$

Circular motion (radial acceleration and radial force):

$$a_r = \frac{v_t^2}{R}, \qquad \vec{F}_r = ma_r\hat{r} \tag{13}$$

Angular motion:

$$F = ma \;\Rightarrow\; \mathcal{T} = I\alpha \tag{14}$$

$$a(t), v(t), x(t) \;\Rightarrow\; \alpha(t), \omega(t), \theta(t) \tag{15}$$

$$\vec{p} = m\vec{v} \;\Rightarrow\; L = I\omega \tag{16}$$

$$K = \tfrac{1}{2}mv^2 \;\Rightarrow\; K_r = \tfrac{1}{2}I\omega^2 \tag{17}$$

SHM with $\omega = \sqrt{\frac{k}{m}}$ (mass-spring system) or $\omega = \sqrt{\frac{g}{\ell}}$ (pendulum):

$$x(t) = A\cos(\omega t + \phi) \tag{18}$$

$$v(t) = -A\omega\sin(\omega t + \phi) \tag{19}$$

$$a(t) = -A\omega^2\cos(\omega t + \phi) \tag{20}$$

Index

absolute value, 5, 43, *62*, 137, 177
acceleration, *137*, 190, 202, 230, 252
    centripetal, *see* radial accel.
algorithm, 301, 321, 325
amplitude, *249*, *251*, 253, 256
angular
    acceleration, 239
    force, *see* torque
    kinetic energy, 239, *243*
    momentum, 239, *243*
    motion, 238
    velocity, 239
angular frequency, 252, 255
annual percentage rate, 108
antiderivative, 334, *335*, 341, 349
approximation, 261, 282, 288, 291, 308, 344, 391, 471
APR, *see* annual percentage rate
arc length, 94, *380*
area, 8, 79, 81, 94, 144, 282, 344, 381
associative, 8, *30*
asymptote, *298*
axis, 48, 95, 171, 177, 192, 381

basis, 162, *172*, 192, 202, 205, 230
bijective, *52*

Cartesian plane, *48*, 51, 165
chain rule, 257, *310*, 313
circle, 81, *92*, 103, 229, 327, 378, 470
codomain, *52*
collect, 198, 459
commutative, 8, *30*, 161, 175, 475
completing the square, *33*, 35, 460
complex number, 7, 113, *176*, 464
cone, *82*
conservation of
    angular momentum, *243*, 245
    energy, 188, *222*, 225
    momentum, 188, *216*
conservative force, *223*, 284, 378
continuous function, *297*, 313, 314, 326, 349, 351
convergence, 286, 287, 294, 300, 389, 393, 394, 398, 470, 471
coordinate system, *see* basis
cosine, 27, *69*, 80, 84, 249, 397, 463
critical point, *281*, 325, 468
cross product, 164, *174*, 475
cylinder, *81*
cylindrical shell method, *384*, 417

De Moivre's formula, 181
derivative, 143, 279, *305*, 308, 467
differentiable, 313, *322*, 326
dimension, 50
disk method, *382*
distributive, *30*
divergence, 394, 471
domain, *52*, 122
dot product, 164, *173*, 221, 474
dynamics, *see* force

eccentricity, 96, 102
ellipse, *95*, 103
energy, 220
    conservation, 188, *222*, 225
    kinetic, *see* kinetic energy
    potential, *223*, 284, 378, 478
Euler's
    formula, *181*, 402, 465
    number, 39, 45, *302*, 461
expand, *30*, 36, 459, 462
exponent, 9, *39*, 45, 457

exponential, 27, 39, *71*, 109, 301, 461
extremum, *322*

factor, 9, *30*
factoring, *30*, 38, 459, 462
Fibonacci sequence, 389, 390
force, 187, *199*, 202, 476, 478
  friction, *201*
  gravitational, 152, 191, *199*, 203, 224, 378
  normal, *200*, 203
  radial, *231*, 237
  spring, *200*, 203, 224, 258, 378
  tension, 201, 203
fraction, 7, *15*, 457, 461
  improper, 19
frequency, 233, 249, 251
friction
  kinetic, *see* kinetic friction
  static, *see* static friction
friction force, *201*
FTC, *see* fundamental theorem of calculus
function, *51*, 58
  even, *66*, 101, 398
  odd, *66*, 101
fundamental theorem of calculus, 336, 341, *349*, 421, 469

GCD, 18, *22*
golden ratio, *37*, 390
gravitational force, 152, 191, *199*, 203, 224, 378
gravitational potential energy, *221*, 224, 256, 377, 378, 478

Hertz (unit), 233, 452
hyperbola, *99*, 103

image, *52*, 122
imaginary number, *see* complex number
implicit differentiation, *326*
improper integral, *387*, 395
incline, 202, 208, 211, 226, 228
infinity, 20, 285, *288*, 294, 347, 465
injective, *52*
integral, 144, 282, 308, *333*, 347, 349, 376, 395, 468
interest rate, *108*, 302, 403, 466
interval, *111*, 120, 289, 322
isolate, 26, 36, 104
isolating, *5*

kinematics, *136*, 148, 186, 214, 240, 376, 476
kinetic energy, *221*, 222, 254
  rotational, 239, *243*
kinetic friction, *201*, 203

L'Hopital's rule, *303*
Laws of motion, *see* Newton's laws
LCM, 18, *22*
length, 8, 84, 164, 178, 473
limit, 110, 285, *293*, 299, 466
linearity, 63, 309, 316, 341, 423
logarithm, 27, 44, *72*, 301, 461

Maclaurin series, *398*, 472
maximum, 135, 281, *322*, 325, 468
minimum, 281, 318, *322*, 325, 468
moment of inertia, 239, *242*, 284, 380, 386
momentum, 188, *215*
  conservation, 188, *216*

Newton (unit), 199, 452
Newton's laws, 186, 199, 243
nonnegative, 52, 61, 62, *112*, 122, 137
normal force, *200*, 203
number line, *19*

one-to-one, *see* injective
one-to-one corresp., *see* bijective
onto, *see* surjective
optimization, 281, 306, 318, *321*, 468
origin, *49*, 62, 85, 93, 171

parabola, *60*, 103
parametric equation, 93
pendulum, 255, 260
period, 233, 249, 252, 255
polar coordinates, *93*, 102, 177, 378
polynomial, *63*, 180, 396, 462
potential energy, *223*, *224*, 284, 378, 478
power rule, 151, *306*, 337
power series, *see* Taylor series

precision, 23, 290, 331, 458
product rule, *310*, 312, 375
projectile motion, *189*
pyramid, *82*

quadratic, 27, 32, 34, 49, *60*, 65, 176
  formula, 34, 64, 142, 460
quotient rule, *310*

radial acceleration, *231*, 236
radian, 84, 89, *95*, 463
range, *see* image
reciprocal, *19*
relation, 59, 92, 327, *see also* function
Riemann sum, 300, 343, *347*

saddle point, *322*, 325
scientific notation, *see* precision
sequence, 286, *387*, 470
  alternating, 395, 415
  arithmetic, 388, 392
  Fibonacci, 389, 390
  geometric, 389, 391
  harmonic, 388, 471
series, 287, *390*, 471
set, 6, 51, *110*, 177, 278, 341, 448
  difference, *111*, 448
  intersection, *111*, 448
  subset, 6, *111*, 448
  union, *111*, 111, 448
SHM, *see* simple harmonic motion
simple harmonic motion, *248*, 479
sine, 27, *67*, 80, 84, 362, 396, 463
speed, *137*, 236
sphere, *81*, 242, 383
spring constant, *200*, 204, 222, 252
spring force, *200*, 203, 224, 258, 378
spring potential energy, *221*, 224, 253, 378, 478
static equilibrium, 206, *246*
static friction, *201*, 203
substitution, 25, 66, 105, 356, 459
summation, 286, 345, 391, 471
surface of revolution, *381*, 416
surjective, *52*

tangent, *70*, 84, 236, 364
tangent line, 281, 288, *307*, 399, 467
Taylor series, 261, 288, 318, *396*, 472
tension, 201, 203
term, *29*, 63, 64, 338, 391
torque, 239, *241*, 243, 246
trigonometric identities, *89*, 254, 259, 354, 358, 360, 463

UAM, *see* uniformly accel. motion
uniform velocity motion, *140*, 191, 240
uniformly accelerated motion, *139*, 150, 191, 240, 477
unit circle, *85*
unit vector, *167*, 202, 473
UVM, *see* uniform velocity motion

vector, 49, *159*, 190, 202, 215, 473
velocity, *137*, 190, 230, 252
volume, 81, 382
volume of revolution, *382*, 417

washer method, *383*
work, 221, *223*, 377, 478

Made in the USA
San Bernardino, CA
27 October 2018